WAVE
MECHANICS
ADVANCED GENERAL
THEORY

BY

J. FRENKEL

PROFESSOR AT THE PHYSICO-TECHNICAL
INSTITUTE, LENINGRAD

DOVER PUBLICATIONS, INC.
1950

FIRST AMERICAN PRINTING
BY SPECIAL ARRANGEMENT WITH
OXFORD UNIVERSITY PRESS
First Edition 1934

PRINTED AND BOUND IN THE UNITED STATES
OF AMERICA

PREFACE

THE present volume forming the second Part of my *Wave Mechanics* is devoted (as foreshadowed in the Preface to Part I) to the mathematical development of the general ideas underlying the new mechanics, connecting it with classical mechanics and constituting it a complete self-supporting theory. In building up the mathematical framework of this theory I have limited myself to what I consider its most essential elements, leaving aside a number of questions which have a methodological value only (such as the group theory) or which are met with in the solution of special problems.

It is my intention to consider some of these questions later on in connexion with the special problems which will be discussed in Part III ('Advanced Special Theory'); I have carefully avoided complicating the general scheme of the theory by such special questions—with a few exceptions inserted for illustration (the relativistic theory of the hydrogen-like atom, for example).

To make the general scheme more comprehensible I have not spared space, dealing with especially important general questions (such as the transformation and the perturbation theory, or the relativistic theory of the electron) at much greater length than would be necessary from the point of view of an adequate presentation to a sophisticated reader.

I must cordially thank the editors for their readiness to meet my demands on space, which have resulted in a book larger than was originally contemplated. I must also thank M. L. Urquhart and Miss B. Swirles for help in correcting the English and the proofs.

The present book, like Part I, is complete in itself, and can be read without acquaintance with Part I, provided the reader is familiar with some elementary account of wave mechanics, and is ready to explore its mathematical depths to obtain a profounder insight into the theory and to prepare himself for applying it to various special problems.

The earlier portions of this book were written in 1931 while I was in America; it was completed in Leningrad nearly two years later. Some of the shortcomings of the book are due to this interruption and the impossibility of revising it in 1933 from the very beginning.

A list of the more important references for each section is given at the end of the book; it is followed by a short index which should enable the reader to locate easily all the more important subjects treated.

LENINGRAD   J. F.
Nov. 1933

CONTENTS

CONTENTS

CONTENTS

ADVANCED GENERAL THEORY

I

CLASSICAL MECHANICS AS THE LIMITING FORM OF WAVE MECHANICS

1. Motion in One Dimension; Partial Reflection and Uncertainty in the Sign of the Velocity

In the first part of this book we have given a general outline of the development and present state of wave mechanics, emphasizing the physical meaning of the new conceptions and avoiding, as far as possible, formal questions connected with the mathematical expression of these new conceptions. We have thus been led astray from the old conceptions based on classical corpuscular mechanics, deepening, as it were, the abyss separating the old from the new mechanics.

A systematic study of the formal questions referred to above reveals the wonderful fact that in spite of the fundamental physical difference between the new and the old mechanics, they are extremely similar from the mathematical point of view, i.e. from the point of view of the mathematical expression of the various physical quantities and the mathematical equations connecting them. This formal similarity forms a bridge over the abyss between the old and the new mechanics, enabling one to consider the latter as an extension or rather a refinement of the former and to establish a one-to-one correspondence between the old 'classical' and the new 'quantum' conceptions, quantities, and equations—a correspondence which often looks like an identity.

The existence of such a correspondence is a very instructive example of the fact—many times already illustrated by the development of physics—that a drastic revision of our physical conceptions can be associated with a simple improvement in the underlying mathematical scheme.

We shall start by considering the simplest case of the wave-mechanical equation, i.e. the equation describing the stationary motion of a particle in one dimension:

$$\frac{d^2\psi}{dx^2} + \frac{8\pi^2 m}{h^2}(W-U)\psi = 0, \tag{1}$$

the potential energy U being supposed to depend on x only (and not upon t, otherwise the total energy W would not be constant).

If U were constant, then this equation would have a solution of the form†

$$\psi = Ae^{i\alpha x} \tag{1a}$$

representing a sine wave travelling in the direction of the positive x-axis, α being the positive square root of the expression $8\pi^2 m(W-U)/h^2$ (supposed to be positive). It must be borne in mind, however, that (1a) is only a particular solution of (1), the general solution being

$$\psi = A'e^{i\alpha x} + A''e^{-i\alpha x}, \tag{1b}$$

which represents the superposition of two sine waves of the same length travelling in opposite directions. The fact that (1) has two independent particular solutions, representing, under the condition $U = \text{const.}$, waves travelling in opposite directions, and that its general solution is equal to the sum of these two, is a consequence of the fact that (1) is a *linear* equation of the *second order*.

In the general case, either for a constant or a variable $U(x)$, the function ψ, which is a *complex* quantity, can be written in the form

$$\psi = Ae^{i\phi}, \tag{2}$$

where $A = |\psi|$ is its modulus and ϕ is its argument (both of them of course being real). This representation of ψ suggests that it may be possible to interpret the process described by it in a way similar to that corresponding to expression (1a), namely, as a propagation of a wave with a (variable) amplitude $A(x)$ in a *definite* direction specified by the phase $\phi(x)$ (positive if $d\phi/dx > 0$ and negative if $d\phi/dx < 0$).

Such an interpretation is, however, in general wrong, as is clearly shown by taking for ψ the expression (1b) corresponding to $U = \text{const.}$ Assuming A' and A'' to be real, we get in this case

$$A\cos\phi = (A'+A'')\cos\alpha x, \qquad A\sin\phi = (A'-A'')\sin\alpha x,$$

and consequently

$$A^2 = A'^2 + A''^2 + 2A'A''\cos 2\alpha x, \tag{2a}$$

$$\tan\phi = \frac{A'-A''}{A'+A''}\tan\alpha x. \tag{2b}$$

The functions A and ϕ can, of course, be interpreted as the *resulting* amplitude and phase at the various points, but they will *not* refer to oscillations propagated in one *definite* direction. It will be noticed that A, instead of being constant, may oscillate with x twice as rapidly as the phase of each of the two component waves, and that the resulting phase ϕ may alternately increase and decrease with increase of x.

† We shall drop in future the time factor $e^{-i2\pi Wt/h}$, the oscillatory character of ψ as a function of the time being understood.

in the direction of the velocity as in its magnitude, whereas in the present case there is no need for constructing such a packet, the *fact asserted being not a definite position* of the particle, but the *connexion* between position, which may be arbitrary (that is, specifiable in terms of probability only) and the magnitude of the velocity. As we have just seen, the uncertainty in the direction of this velocity is connected with the possibility of both transmission and reflection of the particle in every region where it is acted on by some force. At the very beginning of this book we came upon this possibility when attempting to interpret, from the corpuscular point of view, the phenomena of partial reflection and partial transmission of light at the boundary between two homogeneous bodies. Later we studied it in more detail when investigating the motion of material particles in a field of force according to wave mechanics. We can sum up the results arrived at by saying that the indeterminateness which constitutes the characteristic distinction between wave mechanics and classical mechanics is due primarily to this ambiguity in the result produced by a force acting on the particle. Whereas in classical mechanics such a force must either accelerate or retard the particle, reversing the direction of its motion only when the increase of potential energy would exceed the total energy, in wave mechanics a force can reverse the direction of motion, leaving the magnitude of the velocity unchanged, even when this force is acting in the direction of the motion, i.e. even when, according to classical mechanics, the particle should be accelerated without change of direction.

So far as the relation between the wave-mechanical and the classical equations of motion is concerned, this uncertainty in the direction or in the 'sign' of the velocity, when its magnitude and the position of the particle are simultaneously fixed, is much more useful than Heisenberg's uncertainty principle (which is another aspect of the fundamental ambiguity inherent in wave mechanics). It leads us to expect that *the results predicted by wave mechanics will approach those predicted by classical mechanics as the reflection coefficient tends to zero,* i.e. when the ambiguity due to the possibility of reflection as well as transmission vanishes. In this case, transmission, i.e. motion in the same direction, is the only issue that comes into consideration.

It is easy to see that a decrease in the reflection coefficient is brought about by a *decrease in the wave-length.* When the wave-length becomes very small compared with the length over which the potential energy changes by an appreciable amount, the reflection produced by this change of potential energy also becomes very small and vanishes in the limiting case $\lambda = 0$.

This result can be illustrated by the fact, pointed out in Part I, § 12, that cathode rays pass without appreciable reflection through an electric condenser whose thickness is very large compared with the wave-length, while they are appreciably reflected if this thickness is reduced to zero, the potential energy change remaining the same. In the latter case the reflection and transmission coefficients are given by the well-known formulae

$$R = \left(\frac{\alpha'-\alpha''}{\alpha'+\alpha''}\right)^2, \qquad D = 1-R = \frac{4\alpha'\alpha''}{(\alpha'+\alpha'')^2},$$

where α' and α'' are the values of the parameter α on both sides of the discontinuity. It may be recalled that this parameter is proportional to the momentum $g = mv$, i.e. to the velocity of the electron. When the velocity of the impinging electrons, that is α', increases, the jump ΔU of the potential energy remaining constant, α'' also increases, while the difference $\alpha'-\alpha''$ decreases. We have in fact, according to (3),

$$\Delta U = U''-U' = \frac{h^2}{8\pi^2 m}(\alpha'^2-\alpha''^2),$$

whence

$$\alpha'-\alpha'' = \frac{8\pi^2 m}{h^2}\frac{\Delta U}{\alpha'+\alpha''},$$

or approximately

$$\frac{\alpha'-\alpha''}{\alpha'+\alpha''} = \frac{8\pi^2 m}{h^2}\frac{\Delta U}{4\alpha^2} = \frac{\Delta U}{4(W-U)},$$

that is,

$$R \cong \frac{1}{16}\left|\frac{\Delta U}{W-U}\right|^2. \tag{5a}$$

Here $W-U$ is the average kinetic energy $\frac{1}{2}mv^2$ of the electron on both sides of the discontinuity, while ΔU is equal to the change of this kinetic energy, i.e. approximately $mv\,\Delta v$.

We thus get

$$R = \frac{1}{4}\left(\frac{\Delta v}{v}\right)^2 = \frac{1}{4}\left(\frac{\Delta\lambda}{\lambda}\right)^2, \tag{5b}$$

where

$$\lambda = \frac{h}{mv}.$$

Formula (5 a) shows that the reflection coefficient tends to zero when the velocity of the electron is increased, i.e. when the wave-length λ tends to zero, the jump of potential energy ΔU remaining constant ($\Delta\lambda$ is an infinitely small quantity of a higher order than λ itself).

This result holds, of course, not only for electrons but also for any other particles: their behaviour conforms more and more to the fundamental principle of classical mechanics, the principle of determinism which can be stated in the form

$$R = 0, \qquad D = 1$$

as their velocity increases.

It should be noted that, for a given value of ΔU, the magnitude of the velocity for which R becomes inappreciable is the smaller *the larger the mass* m, since, according to (5 a), it is not the velocity itself but the kinetic energy $\frac{1}{2}mv^2$ whose ratio to ΔU determines R.

2. Comparison between the Schrödinger and the Classical Equation of Motion in One Dimension; Average Velocity and Current Density

Discontinuities in the potential-energy function $U(x)$ do not, of course, occur in Nature. When $U(x)$ is a continuous function of x, i.e. when the force has a finite value, it is possible to give another important and interesting formulation of the condition under which the fundamental ambiguity of wave mechanics disappears (i.e. the reflection coefficient vanishes), the wave mechanics thus reducing to classical mechanics. According to de Broglie's relation $\lambda = h/mv$, the wave-length of the waves associated with the motion of a particle is, other things being equal, the smaller, the smaller the value of the constant h. In reality, of course, the latter cannot be changed. If, however, it were not a universal constant, but could have any value whatsoever, then it would be possible to say that wave mechanics would reduce to classical mechanics in the limiting case $h = 0$; for this would mean that the wave-length would vanish for all values of the velocity. Consequently the relative change of the potential energy in a distance of the order of magnitude of the wave-length would also vanish, and with it the partial reflection which is the fundamental cause of the ambiguity characteristic of wave mechanics.

This result can be proved in a general way as follows:

Let us put $\alpha = 2\pi g/h$ in equation (3 a), where $g\,(= mv)$ is the magnitude of the momentum of the particle, and also

$$\phi = \frac{2\pi}{h}s. \tag{6}$$

Multiplying (3 a) by $(h/2\pi)^2$, we get

$$\left(\frac{h}{2\pi}\right)^2 \frac{d^2 A}{dx^2} + \left[g^2 - \left(\frac{ds}{dx}\right)^2\right]A = 0, \tag{6a}$$

where
$$g^2 = 2m(W - U). \tag{6b}$$

It follows from this equation that in the limiting case $h = 0$ the function s remains finite and is determined by the differential equation

$$\left(\frac{ds}{dx}\right)^2 = 2m(W-U). \tag{7}$$

The momentum g can be determined by this function unambiguously, i.e. both with respect to magnitude *and sign*, by the equation

$$g = \frac{ds}{dx}, \tag{7a}$$

which is equivalent to equation (5), corresponding to the one-sided wave propagation, i.e. to the motion of a particle in a *definite* direction. This direction remains arbitrary, since (7) has two solutions, namely $ds/dx = +\sqrt{\{2m(W-U)\}}$ and $ds/dx = -\sqrt{\{2m(W-U)\}}$. But once it is chosen for some initial instant it will remain constant so long as s is a continuous function of x without maxima or minima, where, of course, g will change its sign after passing through the value $g = 0$. This change of sign through a continuous variation corresponds to total reflection and has nothing to do with the discontinuous reversal of the sign of g which is allowed by the exact theory embodied in the wave equation (1) (with $h > 0$) and which corresponds to *partial* reflection. The difference between the exact equation (1) and the approximate equation (7), so far as the ambiguity in the sign, i.e. in the direction of the velocity, is concerned, consists in the fact that the former, being a *linear* equation of the *second* order, admits *both signs simultaneously* (superposition of waves travelling in opposite directions), while the latter, being a *quadratic* equation of the *first* order, admits *either* one sign *or* the other. It should be remembered that the exact equation which is satisfied by the function s is much more complicated than (7). This exact equation can be obtained by eliminating A from equations (3a) and (3b) with $\phi = 2\pi s/h$.

It is often convenient to use, instead of the function defined in this way, another function S defined by the equation

$$\psi = e^{i2\pi S/h}, \tag{8}$$

or

$$S = \frac{h}{2\pi i}\log\psi. \tag{8a}$$

This S is connected with s (i.e. the 'phase' ϕ) and the 'amplitude' A by the relation

$$S = s + \frac{h}{2\pi i}\log A.$$

It is a complex quantity which represents both ϕ and A and is equivalent to ψ.

Substituting the expression (8) in Schrödinger's equation (1) and using the relations

$$\frac{d\psi}{dx} = i\frac{2\pi}{h}\frac{dS}{dx}e^{i2\pi S/h}; \qquad \frac{d^2\psi}{dx^2} = \left(\frac{i2\pi}{h}\right)^2\left(\frac{dS}{dx}\right)^2 e^{i2\pi S/h} + i\frac{2\pi}{h}\frac{d^2S}{dx^2}e^{i2\pi S/h},$$

we get
$$\frac{h}{2\pi i}\frac{d^2S}{dx^2} + \left(\frac{dS}{dx}\right)^2 = 2m(W-U). \qquad (8\,b)$$

If we put here $h = 0$, this equation reduces to (7), so that when $h = 0$ the two functions s and S become identical. We must now investigate the meaning of the approximate equation (7) which they both satisfy in this limiting case.

In a certain sense it merely expresses the law of the conservation of energy—since ds/dx is, by definition, the momentum g of the particle and $\frac{1}{2m}\left(\frac{ds}{dx}\right)^2$ is its kinetic energy.

The equation is unusual, however, in that the momentum of the particle, and consequently its velocity, is determined as a function of the coordinate x, whereas in the classical description of motion the velocity, as well as the coordinate itself, usually appear as functions of the time t. Such a description of motion is impossible in wave mechanics because of the uncertainty in the direction of the velocity. If it is true, however, that in the case $h = 0$ the wave-mechanical equation of motion (8 b) must reduce to the classical equation, then equation (7) must be equivalent to Newton's equation of motion

$$m\frac{d^2x}{dt^2} = -\frac{dU}{dx}, \qquad (9)$$

defining x and $v = dx/dt$ as functions of the time. This equivalence is readily recognized as soon as we realize what is meant by defining the velocity (or momentum) of a particle as a function of its coordinate. Let us suppose that equation (9) has been integrated, and that x and v have been determined as functions of the time t. Then, eliminating the time t between them, we can express one of them, e.g. v, as a function $v(x)$ of the other. The acceleration d^2x/dt^2 can then be calculated by means of the formula

$$\frac{d^2x}{dt^2} = \frac{dv}{dt} = \frac{dv}{dx}\frac{dx}{dt} = \frac{dv}{dx}v = \frac{d}{dx}\left(\frac{v^2}{2}\right),$$

so that equation (9) can be written in the form

$$\frac{d}{dx}\frac{mv^2}{(2)} = -\frac{dU}{dx}$$

or
$$\frac{mv^2}{2} + U = \text{const.}$$

If $mv = g$ is replaced by ds/dx and the constant is denoted by W, we get equation (7).

We thus see that this equation expresses not only the law of conservation of energy, but at the same time the classical law of motion. It should be mentioned that both laws are equivalent to one another only in the special case which we are considering here of motion in *one dimension* (see below).

Another way of interpreting equation (7), or rather the fact implied in it that the velocity $v = \frac{1}{m}\frac{ds}{dx}$ of the particle is determined not as a function of the time but as a function of the coordinate x, is to replace the single particle under consideration by an infinite number of copies of this particle, filling space (or the line x) in a continuous way, so that at any instant t a copy is to be found situated at, or rather passing through, any point x. This method is similar to one used in hydrodynamics except that, in the hydrodynamical case, the copies of a particle are replaced by actual particles (supposed to be identical), moving under the combined influence of external forces and forces of mutual action (represented by the hydrostatic pressure). Provided we are not interested in the individuality of the particles, i.e. in the question *which* particle is to be found at a given point, the motion of the particles can be specified by defining the velocity of the particle passing through each fixed point as a function of the coordinates of this point and, in general, of the time. If the velocity does not depend upon the time (it should be remembered that the velocity we are speaking of refers not to a definite particle but to a definite point) the motion is called *stationary* or *steady*.

Thus the picture which can be associated with equation (7) is that of an assembly of copies of the particle under consideration, streaming steadily and filling space in a continuous way. If we select from this assembly a definite copy which at the time t was passing through the point x, then, knowing the dependence of the velocity v upon x, we can follow its motion and determine both the velocity and position of *this particular* copy as functions of the time. For instance, at the moment $t+dt$ the copy in question will be situated at the point $x+v\,dt$, and will have the velocity $v(x+dx) = v(x+v\,dt) = v(x)+\dfrac{dv}{dx}\,v\,dt$, which means that its acceleration is equal to $v\,dv/dx$, as was obtained above.

We have thus shown that the wave-mechanical equation of motion actually reduces to the classical equation in the limiting case when the wave-length associated with the motion of a particle tends to zero, either owing to increase in velocity (which is a thing that can actually happen) or to decrease in the constant h (which is an artifice). The fundamental reason for this lies in the elimination of partial reflection, i.e. of a reversal in the direction of the velocity or, in other words, the elimination of the uncertainty in its sign.

Strictly speaking, however, this uncertainty cannot be eliminated. It is impossible to describe the motion of a particle in the classical way, i.e. as a determinate change of position and velocity with the time. The only way of describing it is to ascertain the *probability* of finding the particle at a given place and the probability that, being at this place, it is moving in the one or the other direction (the magnitude of the velocity being fixed). This intrusion of the probability conception into the description of the motion is necessary because of the ambiguity arising from the alternative: partial reflection or partial transmission. One could say that this ambiguity—wholly alien to classical mechanics —forms the gate through which the concept of probability penetrates into the realm of physics.

The probability of position is measured, as we know, by the product $\psi\psi^*$, so that $\psi(x)\psi^*(x)\,dx$ measures the probability that the particle is situated in the region between x and $x+dx$. Using the picture of an assembly of copies of the particle in question filling space (or the x-axis) in a continuous way, we can interpret $\psi\psi^*\,dx$ as the relative number of copies situated within the interval dx (this number is independent of the time so long as $\psi = \psi^0 e^{-i2\pi\nu t}$, corresponding to a motion with a definite total energy $W = h\nu$). If the integral $\int\limits_{-\infty}^{+\infty} \psi\psi^*\,dx$ converges, ψ can be normalized in such a way that this integral is equal to 1, in agreement with the usual normalization of probability. Otherwise we need not worry about this normalization, since after all only relative values of $\psi\psi^*$ for different points come into account.

It should be noticed that in the classical description of the motion we can also use a continuous assembly of copies instead of an individual particle, as is actually done when the equation of motion is written in the form (7) corresponding to the determination of the velocity as a function of the coordinate and not of the time. From the point of view of this description the difference between the old and the new theory can be summed up as follows. In the old theory it is always possible to 'individualize' a certain copy by following its motion, i.e. by determining its coordinate and velocity as definite functions of time, whereas in the new theory such 'individualization' is impossible, the direction of motion being uncertain. It thus becomes necessary to consider the assembly as a whole without attempting to disentangle it, i.e. to trace the motion of a particular copy in time. This being so, the density of the assembly, i.e. the relative number of copies per unit range, or, in other words, the probability of finding the particle represented by these copies in a given range, becomes the primary thing that can and must be determined—whereas in classical mechanics it remains irrelevant and therefore arbitrary. Of course the determination of $\psi\psi^*$ in wave mechanics is also connected with some arbitrariness, which can only be removed by specifying the boundary conditions or the conditions at infinity for the function ψ.

Knowing the function ψ, one can determine many other things besides the probability of position. Thus by means of it we can determine the probability of the two opposite directions of motion, that is, of the two opposite signs of the velocity, if the magnitude of the velocity is assumed to be fixed for a given position by the classical relation $v = \sqrt{\{2(W-U)/m\}}$ or by de Broglie's relation $v = h/(m\lambda)$. If p' is the probability of the positive direction and p'' that of the negative direction, then the average or probable value of the velocity at a given point is given by the formula

$$\bar{v} = (p'-p'')|v| \tag{10}$$

with the condition $p'+p'' = 1$.

This probable velocity, or the probabilities p, can be determined quite generally with the help of the relation (4), as soon as the physical meaning of this relation is recognized. We shall first see what the expression $A^2\, d\phi/dx$ means in the simple case of a wave travelling in one direction in a force-free space, that is, a wave representing the free motion of a particle in one direction. We have, in this case, according to (1 a), $\phi = \alpha x$ and consequently $A^2 \dfrac{d\phi}{dx} = A^2\alpha = |\psi|^2 \dfrac{2\pi g}{h} = \dfrac{2\pi m}{h}|\psi|^2 v.$

If $|\psi|^2$ is interpreted as the (relative) density of the copies of the particle, then the product $|\psi|^2 v = j$ must obviously be defined as the corresponding *current density*, i.e. the (relative) number of copies passing through the given point or plane $x =$ const. in the direction of v in unit time. If $|\psi|^2$ is interpreted as the probability density, then j can be defined as the probability current density, i.e. the probability that the particle will cross the plane $x =$ const. in unit time. The ratio $j/|\psi|^2$ is nothing else than the actual velocity of motion, which, in view of the fact that the direction of the motion is perfectly definite, coincides with the probable velocity $\bar{v}$ (p' or $p'' = 1$).

It is natural to extend the above interpretation of the expression $A^2 \, d\phi/dx$ as a measure of the current density to any type of wave function ψ, for from this point of view the fact that $A^2 \, d\phi/dx$ is constant (i.e. independent of x) simply means that the number of copies passing through different planes $x = x_1$ and $x = x_2$, say, is the same, just as if they were actual indestructible particles. The law expressed by the relation (4) would thus be the law of conservation of the number of copies or of the *conservation of probability* (see below). If this interpretation is correct, then it must obviously be possible to write j in the form

$$j = \psi\psi^*\bar{v}, \tag{10a}$$

where $\bar{v}$ denotes the probable velocity of the copies at the point in question. Now this is actually the case if j is defined as $\dfrac{h}{2\pi m} A^2 \dfrac{d\phi}{dx}$ (the coefficient $h/2\pi m$ is the same as in the special case considered above), which gives the following expression for the probable velocity

$$\bar{v} = \frac{h}{2\pi m} \frac{d\phi}{dx}. \tag{10b}$$

The 'phase' ϕ can be expressed in terms of the function $\psi = Ae^{i\phi}$ and its conjugate complex $\psi^* = Ae^{-i\phi}$ by means of the formula

$$\phi = \frac{1}{2i} \log(\psi/\psi^*);$$

whence it follows that

$$\bar{v} = \frac{h}{4\pi i m}\left(\frac{1}{\psi}\frac{d\psi}{dx} - \frac{1}{\psi^*}\frac{d\psi^*}{dx}\right) = \frac{h}{2\pi m}\mathrm{R}\left(\frac{1}{i}\frac{d}{dx}\log\psi\right) \tag{10c}$$

or, according to (8a), $\qquad \bar{v} = \dfrac{1}{m}\mathrm{R}\left(\dfrac{dS}{dx}\right),$

$\mathrm{R}(f)$ denoting the real part of f. In the classical theory this equation reduces to $\bar{v} = v$, in accordance with the fact that the motion proceeds in a perfectly definite direction, the probabilities p' and p'' being equal respectively to 1 and 0. In the wave-mechanical theory $|\bar{v}|$ is, in general, different from $|v|$, the values of the probabilities p' and p'' being different from both 1 and 0. They can be determined from v and $\bar{v}$ by means of the formula

$$p = \frac{1}{2}\left(1 \pm \left|\frac{\bar{v}}{v}\right|\right).$$

Substituting (10 c) in (10 a), we get the following expression for the current density:

$$j = \frac{h}{4\pi i m}\left(\psi^* \frac{d\psi}{dx} - \psi \frac{d\psi^*}{dx}\right) = \frac{h}{2\pi m} R\left(\frac{1}{i}\psi^* \frac{d\psi}{dx}\right). \tag{11}$$

We shall now check these results by applying them to two simple cases.

We shall put first

$$\psi = A'e^{i\alpha x} + A''e^{-i\alpha x},$$

which corresponds to the free motion of a particle along the x-axis in an unspecified direction.

Assuming the coefficients A for the sake of simplicity to be real (this condition does not involve any loss of generality, for it can always be satisfied by a suitable choice of the origin $x = 0$), we have

$$\psi^* = A'e^{-i\alpha x} + A''e^{i\alpha x},$$

whence

$$\frac{1}{i}\psi^* \frac{d\psi}{dx} = \alpha(A'^2 - A''^2) + \alpha(A'A''e^{i2\alpha x} - A'A''e^{-i2\alpha x})$$

$$= \alpha(A'^2 - A''^2) + i2\alpha A'A'' \sin 2\alpha x,$$

so that j reduces to the constant value,

$$j = \frac{h\alpha}{2\pi m}(A'^2 - A''^2)$$

or

$$j = |v|(A'^2 - A''^2). \tag{11 a}$$

Unlike j, the probable velocity

$$\bar{v} = \frac{j}{\psi\psi^*} = |v|\frac{A'^2 - A''^2}{A'^2 + A''^2 + 2A'A'' \cos 2\alpha x}$$

is a function of x, varying periodically between the values

$$\bar{v}_{max} = |v|\frac{A' + A''}{A' - A''}$$

and

$$\bar{v}_{min} = |v|\frac{A' - A''}{A' + A''}.$$

The fact that the maximum value of the probable velocity $\bar{v}$ turns out to be *larger* than the magnitude of the classical velocity $|v|$ invalidates the idea considered above of taking the latter over into the wave-mechanical theory as the magnitude of the 'actual' velocity. With

$|\bar{v}/v| > 1$ formula (10) leads to values of the probabilities p which are devoid of physical meaning, one of them being larger than 1 and the other smaller than 0. Although the classical velocity can be determined wave-mechanically from the wave-length λ (by means of the formula $|v| = h/(m\lambda)$), yet it is the probable velocity $\bar{v}$ only which has a direct physical significance.

This is also clearly seen if we take as a second example the case

$$\psi = A'e^{+\beta x} + A''e^{-\beta x}$$

corresponding to a region of *total reflection* where the kinetic energy is negative and the velocity v is imaginary. We have in this case $\psi^* = \psi$, $j = 0$, and $\bar{v} = 0$, as might be expected.

3. Generalization for Non-stationary Motion in Three Dimensions; The Hamilton-Jacobi Equation

We shall now generalize the results of the preceding section to the motion of a particle in three dimensions under the action of forces derived from a potential-energy function U which may depend not only upon the coordinates x, y, z, but also upon the time t.

The wave-mechanical description of such a motion is given by the generalized equation of Schrödinger

$$\nabla^2\psi - \frac{8\pi^2 m}{h^2}\left(\frac{h}{2\pi i}\frac{\partial}{\partial t} + U\right)\psi = 0. \tag{12}$$

Our main object will be to trace the relation of this equation to the corresponding classical equations of motion,

$$m\frac{d^2x}{dt^2} = -\frac{\partial U}{\partial x}, \qquad m\frac{d^2y}{dt^2} = -\frac{\partial U}{\partial y}, \qquad m\frac{d^2z}{dt^2} = -\frac{\partial U}{\partial z}. \tag{12a}$$

The general character of this relation can be described in a way similar to that used for the one-dimensional motion discussed above. The fundamental characteristics of the wave-mechanical theory can thus be partially reduced, as before, to the ambiguity arising from the phenomenon of partial reflection and partial transmission—a phenomenon which implies a sudden change in the direction of the velocity, its magnitude being assumed to be the same function of the coordinates as in the classical theory.

The uncertainty in the direction of the velocity, which in the case of one-dimensional motion was equivalent to an ambiguity of sign, is now—in the case of motion in space—of a still more distressing character. However, we may still expect this uncertainty, as well as partial reflection, to vanish in the limiting case of motion corresponding

to infinitely short wave-lengths (which can be realized by an increase
of velocity or of mass, or by a fictitious decrease of the constant h).
Thus in this limiting case equation (12) must become equivalent to
equations (12 a) in the sense of admitting *particular* solutions corresponding to a perfectly definite type of classical motion.

To demonstrate this equivalence we shall replace the particle under
consideration by an assembly of copies distributed and moving in space
like the particles of some continuous fluid (without interaction of
course!). The velocity vector **v** of each copy can then be defined—
according to the classical theory—as a function of the coordinates
x, y, z of the (fixed) point through which this copy is passing, and of
the time—the motion being not necessarily a steady one. It should be
noticed that the partial derivative $\partial \mathbf{v}/\partial t$ of **v** with regard to the time
does not define the acceleration of a given copy, for it refers to different
copies passing through the same point at different instants of time t
and $t+dt$. This acceleration can be defined by the total derivative
$d\mathbf{v}/dt$, its x-component being thus given by

$$\frac{dv_x}{dt} = \frac{\partial v_x}{\partial t} + \frac{\partial v_x}{\partial x}\frac{dx}{dt} + \frac{\partial v_x}{\partial y}\frac{dy}{dt} + \frac{\partial v_x}{\partial z}\frac{dz}{dt}$$

or
$$\frac{dv_x}{dt} = \frac{\partial v_x}{\partial t} + v_x\frac{\partial v_x}{\partial x} + v_y\frac{\partial v_x}{\partial y} + v_z\frac{\partial v_x}{\partial z}. \tag{13}$$

We shall now assume the motion of the fluid formed by our assembly
of copies to be *irrotational*, which means that the velocity vector can
be represented as the gradient of a scalar function, the so-called 'velocity
potential'. We shall denote this function by s/m and put accordingly

$$m\mathbf{v} = \nabla s, \tag{13 a}$$

that is
$$v_x = \frac{1}{m}\frac{\partial s}{\partial x}, \qquad v_y = \frac{1}{m}\frac{\partial s}{\partial y}, \qquad v_z = \frac{1}{m}\frac{\partial s}{\partial z}.$$

We make this assumption (which is by no means necessary) not only
because we desire to simplify the formulation of the classical theory as
applied to the copy assembly, but also because we wish to establish the
connexion between this theory and the wave-mechanical theory. We
have in fact, for a wave propagated in one definite direction, a relation
exactly similar to (13 a) between the phase ϕ and the vector $\boldsymbol{\alpha}$ whose
direction is the direction of propagation and whose length is $2\pi/\lambda$, where
λ is the value of the wave-length at the corresponding point:

$$\boldsymbol{\alpha} = \nabla \phi. \tag{14}$$

If we put
$$\alpha = 2\pi \frac{m\mathbf{v}}{h},$$ (14 a)

according to de Broglie's relation, we get
$$\phi = \frac{2\pi}{h} s$$ (14 b)

as before [cf. (6), § 1]. Thus, by assuming irrotational motion of the assembly of copies, it becomes possible to establish a connexion between the motion of a particle and the propagation of waves in the limiting case of infinitely short waves, i.e. when partial reflection is excluded and the motion of every copy of the particle proceeds along a perfectly definite path; this path can be considered as the 'ray' passing through the point at which the copy in question was initially situated. If partial reflection does take place the idea of rays loses all meaning, each ray branching into two at every point. Only by neglecting reflection can one speak of rays as lines along which the waves, i.e. the surfaces of constant phase, are propagated.

Returning to the expression (13) for the x-component of the acceleration of the copy passing through the point $x, y, z,$ at the instant t we can, because of (13 a), rewrite it in the form
$$\frac{dv_x}{dt} = \frac{\partial v_x}{\partial t} + v_x \frac{\partial v_x}{\partial x} + v_y \frac{\partial v_y}{\partial x} + v_z \frac{\partial v_z}{\partial x},$$

since $\dfrac{\partial v_x}{\partial y} = \dfrac{1}{m} \dfrac{\partial^2 s}{\partial x \partial y} = \dfrac{\partial v_y}{\partial x}$, etc. Therefore
$$\frac{dv_x}{dt} = \frac{\partial v_x}{\partial t} + \frac{\partial}{\partial x}\left(\frac{v^2}{2}\right)$$

or
$$\frac{dv_x}{dt} = \frac{1}{m} \frac{\partial}{\partial x}\left[\frac{\partial s}{\partial t} + \frac{1}{2m}(\nabla s)^2\right].$$

The equation $m\dfrac{dv_x}{dt} = -\dfrac{\partial U}{\partial x}$, which is the first of the equations (12 a), is thus equivalent to
$$\frac{\partial}{\partial x}\left[\frac{\partial s}{\partial t} + \frac{1}{2m}(\nabla s)^2 + U\right] = 0.$$

Similar results are obtained for the second and the third equations, and so all three of them can be replaced by the single equation
$$\frac{\partial s}{\partial t} + \frac{1}{2m}(\operatorname{grad} s)^2 + U = F(t),$$

where $F(t)$ is an arbitrary function of the time alone. This function, without loss of generality, can be put equal to zero, for it corresponds to an additive term $\int F(t)\,dt$ in s which is irrelevant for the determination of the velocity according to (13 a). The function s can thus be defined by the equation

$$\frac{\partial s}{\partial t}+\frac{1}{2m}\left[\left(\frac{\partial s}{\partial x}\right)^2+\left(\frac{\partial s}{\partial y}\right)^2+\left(\frac{\partial s}{\partial z}\right)^2\right]+U=0. \tag{15}$$

This equation was established by Hamilton and Jacobi and bears their name. In the special case when U does not depend upon the time explicitly (constant field of force), the function s—usually called the (mechanical) 'action'—reduces to

$$s=s_0(x,y,z)-Wt, \tag{15 a}$$

where s_0 is determined by the equation

$$\frac{1}{2m}\left[\left(\frac{\partial s_0}{\partial x}\right)^2+\left(\frac{\partial s_0}{\partial y}\right)^2+\left(\frac{\partial s_0}{\partial z}\right)^2\right]+U=W. \tag{15 b}$$

Here W is a constant which can obviously be defined as the *energy*. Thus, in a sense, equation (15 b), in conjunction with the relation (13 a), expresses the law of the conservation of energy. However, as we have just seen, it expresses much more than that,† since, in conjunction with (13 a), it is equivalent to the three classical equations of motion (12 a) for the special case of an invariable field of force and of a fixed value of the total energy. The equations (12 a) and (15 b)—or more generally (15)—are formally different because the former refer to an individual particle, while the latter refer to a continuous assembly of copies of this particle. If we select a definite copy and follow its motion we come back to equations (12 a).

It can now easily be shown that in the limiting case of infinitely small wave-length the wave equation (12) admits particular solutions of the form $\psi=Ae^{i\phi}$, representing a one-sided propagation of waves which can be associated, by means of the relations (14), (14 a), and (14 b), with the motion of the particle in question according to the classical theory, the different 'rays' coinciding with the paths of the different copies of this particle.

Putting $\psi=Ae^{i\phi}$, we get in the same way as in § 1

$$\frac{\partial^2\psi}{\partial x^2}=\frac{\partial^2 A}{\partial x^2}e^{i\phi}+2ie^{i\phi}\frac{\partial A}{\partial x}\frac{\partial\phi}{\partial x}+iAe^{i\phi}\frac{\partial^2\phi}{\partial x^2}-Ae^{i\phi}\left(\frac{\partial\phi}{\partial x}\right)^2,$$

whence

$$\nabla^2\psi=\frac{\partial^2\psi}{\partial x^2}+\frac{\partial^2\psi}{\partial y^2}+\frac{\partial^2\psi}{\partial z^2}=e^{i\phi}[\nabla^2 A-A(\nabla\phi)^2+i(2\nabla A\cdot\nabla\phi+A\nabla^2\phi)].$$

† Except in the one-dimensional case.

We have further

$$\frac{\partial \psi}{\partial t} = \frac{\partial A}{\partial t} e^{i\phi} + A e^{i\phi} \frac{\partial \phi}{\partial t}.$$

Substituting these expressions in equation (12), cancelling the common factor $e^{i\phi}$, and separating the real and imaginary parts, we obtain the two equations:

$$\nabla^2 A + \left[\frac{8\pi^2 m}{h^2} \left(-\frac{h}{2\pi} \frac{\partial \phi}{\partial t} - U \right) - (\nabla \phi)^2 \right] A = 0$$

and

$$\frac{4\pi m}{h} \frac{\partial A}{\partial t} + 2\nabla A \cdot \nabla \phi + A \nabla^2 \phi = 0.$$

If ϕ is replaced by $\frac{2\pi}{h} s$, these equations become

$$-\frac{h^2}{8\pi^2 m} \nabla^2 A + \frac{\partial s}{\partial t} + \frac{1}{2m} (\nabla s)^2 + U = 0, \qquad (16)$$

$$2m \frac{\partial A}{\partial t} + 2\nabla A \cdot \nabla s + A \nabla^2 s = 0. \qquad (16\,\text{a})$$

Putting $h = 0$ we see that the first of these equations reduces to the Hamilton-Jacobi equation (15). The same result is obtained if $\nabla^2 A = 0$, which must obviously express the general condition for one-sided propagation of waves of finite length. In both cases the wave-mechanical theory becomes completely equivalent to the classical theory. Both cases are, of course, fictitious, h being a constant and the equation $\nabla^2 A = 0$ being satisfied only under very special conditions—in particular for force-free motion. The equation (16) can, however, reduce *approximately* to (15) in the case of a nearly one-sided wave propagation with a very weak partial reflection—so weak that the reflected (or scattered) waves can be neglected. This condition is more nearly approached the larger the mass m of the particle for a given velocity or the larger the velocity for a given mass, i.e. the smaller the wave-length, if we are treating motion corresponding to a constant value of the energy W. In the latter case the wave-length becomes a definite function of the coordinates. In the general case the idea of wave-length has no precise meaning and can be introduced only by representing the wave function ψ as a superposition of waves with different frequencies, corresponding to motions with different energies.

If U does not contain the time explicitly, equations (16) and (16 a) admit particular solutions of the type $s = s_0(x, y, z) - Wt$ and

$A = A(x, y, z)$, i.e. $\partial s/\partial t = -W$ and $\partial A/\partial t = 0$. They therefore reduce to

$$-\frac{h^2}{8\pi^2 m}\nabla^2 A + \frac{1}{2m}(\nabla s_0)^2 + U = W \tag{17}$$

and
$$2\nabla A \cdot \nabla s_0 + A\nabla^2 s_0 = 0. \tag{17a}$$

In the limiting case $h = 0$ the first of these becomes equivalent to the classical equation (15 b).

This equivalence, as well as the approximate equivalence which can be obtained in the case of large values of W or m, must not be misunderstood. It refers to *particular* solutions of equations (17) and (17 a), or of the corresponding Schrödinger equation

$$\nabla^2\psi + \frac{8\pi^2 m}{h^2}(W - U)\psi = 0 \tag{17b}$$

with
$$\psi = Ae^{i2\pi(s_0 - Wt)/h} = \psi^0(x, y, z)e^{-i2\pi Wt/h} \tag{17c}$$

that is, to *solutions which represent—approximately—waves travelling in a definite direction* (the direction may, of course, vary from point to point, being defined by the direction of the 'rays' passing through these points). Now the general solution of (17 b) in the case of short waves can be represented as a superposition of a number of such particular solutions corresponding to waves travelling in different directions, under the limitations imposed by boundary conditions (in the case of long waves this is possible for force-free motion only). The classical equation (15 b), on the other hand, does not admit of such superposition for the function ψ defined as $Ae^{i2\pi s/h}$. This can clearly be seen in the simple case of one-dimensional motion where A is connected with s by the relation $A^2\frac{ds}{dx} = C$ [cf. (4), §1], so that $\psi = \frac{\sqrt{C}}{\sqrt{(ds/dx)}}e^{i2\pi s/h}$. The physical reason for this is that 'superposition' of two different types of motion would mean, according to classical mechanics, their 'simultaneous realization'—an obviously impossible thing if they are alternative. In wave mechanics, on the contrary, it is just this alternative character which is expressed by superposition, the latter corresponding to the addition law of the classical probability theory. Similar results apply to the general equations (12) and (15), the former allowing the superposition of processes with different energies if U does not depend upon the time—while the latter reduces in this case to equation (15 b) corresponding to one definite value of the energy W.

The non-validity of the superposition principle in classical mechanics can easily be demonstrated with the help of the function $S = \frac{h}{2\pi i}\log\psi$

introduced in § 2 [eq. (8)]. This function satisfies the differential equation

$$\frac{h}{4\pi im}\nabla^2 S + \frac{\partial S}{\partial t} - \frac{1}{2m}(\nabla S)^2 + U = 0 \qquad (18)$$

which is obtained from Schrödinger's equation (12) by the substitution $\psi = e^{i2\pi S/h}$ and which reduces to the Hamilton-Jacobi equation (15) if h is put equal to zero. The function S thus coincides in this case with the function s, which means that the amplitude A can be considered as practically constant.

Now if in the Hamilton-Jacobi equation (15) we put $s = S = \dfrac{h}{2\pi i}\log\psi$, we get the following 'approximate' equation for ψ:

$$\frac{h}{2\pi i}\psi\frac{\partial\psi}{\partial t} - \frac{h^2}{8\pi^2 m}(\nabla\psi)^2 + U\psi^2 = 0$$

or

$$(\nabla\psi)^2 - \frac{8\pi^2 m}{h^2}\left(\frac{h}{4\pi i}\frac{\partial}{\partial t} + U\right)\psi^2 = 0, \qquad (18\,\text{a})$$

which is *quadratic* and of the first order (like the equation for S) instead of being *linear* and of the second order like the-exact equation of Schrödinger. If ψ_1 and ψ_2 are two particular solutions of (18a), the function $\psi = \psi_1 + \psi_2$ will not in general represent a solution of this equation.

Returning to the representation of the exact wave function in the form $Ae^{i\phi} = Ae^{i2\pi s/h}$, and considering equation (16a) connecting A and s, which has been disregarded hitherto, we see that this equation can be simplified if multiplied by A. We have in fact $2A\dfrac{\partial A}{\partial t} = \dfrac{\partial A^2}{\partial t}$ and

$$2A\nabla A\cdot\nabla s + A^2\nabla^2 s = \nabla(A^2)\cdot\nabla s + A^2\nabla^2 s = \text{div}(A^2\nabla s);$$

so that

$$\frac{\partial(A^2)}{\partial t} + \text{div}\left(A^2\nabla\frac{s}{m}\right) = 0. \qquad (19)$$

This equation is of the same form as the equation of continuity, i.e. the equation of the conservation of mass in hydrodynamics or of the conservation of electricity in electrodynamics,

$$\frac{\partial\rho}{\partial t} + \text{div}\,\mathbf{j} = 0,$$

where ρ is the density of mass or electrical charge and $\mathbf{j}$ the corresponding current density. In the present case we can interpret the quantity

$$A^2 = \psi\psi^* = \rho$$

as the density of the copy assembly (i.e. the relative number of copies of the given particle in unit volume) or the density of probability. If, further, we define the corresponding *current density* by the formula

$$\mathbf{j} = \frac{1}{m} A^2 \nabla s, \qquad (19\,\text{a})$$

then equation (19) will express the law of the conservation of the copies or of the probability. In the classical theory the vector $\nabla s/m$ reduces to the actual velocity $\mathbf{v}$ of the particle (or more exactly of its copies at the given point), so that $\mathbf{j}$ assumes the usual form of the product of ρ with $\mathbf{v}$. In the exact wave-mechanical theory it can also be written in the form

$$\mathbf{j} = \rho \mathbf{v}$$

where the vector

$$\mathbf{v} = \frac{1}{m} \nabla s \qquad (19\,\text{b})$$

must obviously be interpreted as the *probable* velocity. The classical velocity can be computed as usual by means of the formula

$$v = \sqrt{\left\{ \frac{2}{m}(W - U) \right\}},$$

its direction being, however, uncertain. According to the definition of A and s, we have $\psi = Ae^{i2\pi s/h}$, $\psi^* = Ae^{-i2\pi s/h}$, whence

$$s = \frac{h}{4\pi i} \log \frac{\psi}{\psi^*},$$

and consequently

$$\mathbf{j} = \frac{h}{4\pi i m}(\psi^* \nabla \psi - \psi \nabla \psi^*) = \frac{h}{2\pi m} \mathrm{R}\left(\frac{1}{i} \psi^* \nabla \psi \right). \qquad (20)$$

Introducing the function $S = \frac{h}{2\pi i} \log \psi$, we get $\nabla S = \frac{h}{2\pi i} \frac{1}{\psi} \nabla \psi$ and $\frac{1}{i} \psi^* \nabla \psi = \frac{2\pi}{h} \psi \psi^* \nabla S$, so that

$$\mathbf{j} = \frac{1}{m} \psi \psi^* \mathrm{R}(\nabla S) \qquad (20\,\text{a})$$

and

$$\dot{\mathbf{v}} = \frac{1}{m} \mathrm{R}(\nabla S). \qquad (20\,\text{b})$$

Comparing this with (19 b), we see that the function s is equal to the real part of S, in accordance with the relation $S = s + \frac{h}{2\pi i} \log A$ which results from comparing the two expressions $e^{i2\pi S/h}$ and $Ae^{i2\pi s/h}$ for ψ. The probable velocity (20 b) could be represented in the form

$$\mathbf{v} = |v| \int \mathbf{n} p(\mathbf{n})\, d\omega,$$

where **n** is the unit vector which defines the direction of the classical velocity and $p(\mathbf{n})\,d\omega$ is the probability that this unit vector lies in the infinitely small solid angle $d\omega$. An unambiguous determination of this probability appears, however, to be impossible, except for one-dimensional motion considered in the preceding section. This is quite natural if we remember that the notion of classical velocity, as measured by the time derivative of the coordinates, cannot be taken over into wave mechanics.

It should be mentioned in conclusion that the relation between wave mechanics and classical mechanics is usually compared with the relation between wave optics and the so-called geometrical optics, the latter being defined as the limiting case of wave optics for very small wavelengths. This statement would, however, be misleading unless we add to it that in geometrical optics partial reflection of light (which actually decreases with decrease of wave-length) should be wholly left out of account—even in its simplest form on the boundary surface between two homogeneous media. In this case—and only in this case—is it possible to introduce the idea of rays as lines along which the propagation of light takes place (this is why geometrical optics is often called 'ray optics' in contradistinction to wave optics, where the idea of 'rays' has in general no meaning). It was the merit of Hamilton to show, one hundred years ago, that in this limiting case the wave conception of light can be replaced by the corpuscular conception, and that the rays can be described as the paths of light particles moving, according to Newton's classical law, in a certain field of force. The potential energy of this field of force U is determined by the refractive index μ according to the relation
$$\mu^2 = \gamma^2(W - U),$$
where γ is a constant depending upon the definition of the mass of a light particle.[†] But perhaps the main merit of Hamilton's work was that he applied the same considerations to the motion of particles of ordinary matter, thus *for the first time associating such motion with the propagation of* (infinitely short) *waves* and describing it by equation (15). This association of particles with waves, which in Hamilton's theory was achieved by interpreting the 'mechanical action' s as a measure of the phase function ϕ, was, however, completely forgotten for a hundred years, until de Broglie rediscovered it in the way described

---

† This relation is obtained in the simplest way by comparing de Broglie's formula for the wave-length $1/\lambda = \sqrt{\{2m(W-U)\}}/h$ with the formula $\lambda_0/\lambda = \mu$, which can be considered as the definition of the refractive index, λ_0 being the value of λ *in vacuo*, i.e. for a place where $\mu = 1$.

in Part I, and Schrödinger introduced his wave equation, whose relation
to the Hamilton-Jacobi equation has been discussed above.

This mutual reaction of optics and mechanics must not be misinter-
preted as an indication of a true analogy between them—in the sense
of a wave-corpuscular duality of light. We must not be led by it to
infer the real existence of photons, moving in material bodies according
to the laws of wave mechanics. For we could replace optics by acoustics,
i.e. light vibrations by mechanical vibrations propagated in the form
of waves in elastic media according to an equation of exactly the same
kind as the differential equation for the light waves. In the limiting
case of infinitely short acoustical waves we could therefore obtain
exactly the same results as in optics, i.e. a kind of 'ray acoustics'
instead of a 'wave acoustics'. This would enable one to formulate a
corpuscular theory of sound and describe the propagation of sound as
the motion, according to wave mechanics, of certain particles—e.g.
'phonons'. I do not think, however, that anybody would believe in the
reality of such 'phonons'. This does not mean, of course, that the
photons are equally unreal, for the analogy between acoustics and optics
is just as superficial as that between optics and mechanics (or acoustics
and the mechanics of single particles).—I am inclined, however, to
think that photons have no more reality than 'phonons', and that they
are created by a 'reflection', as it were, of the wave-corpuscular duality
of matter in the phenomena of light (cf. Part I).

4. Comparison of the Approximate Solutions of Schrödinger's Equation; Comparison of Classical and Wave-mechanical Average Values

Although in the case $h = 0$ the functions s and S satisfy the same
equation—namely, that of Hamilton and Jacobi—yet the approximate
expressions for ψ obtained therefrom, according to the formulae
$\psi = Ae^{i2\pi s/h}$ and $\psi = e^{i2\pi S/h}$, turn out to be somewhat different, for the
'amplitude' A obtained by means of equation (16 a) is in general a
certain function of the coordinates (and the time), varying very slowly
compared with the 'phase factor' $2\pi s/h$.

The discrepancy between the two approximate solutions is due to
the fact that the error introduced by putting $h = 0$ is larger in the
case of equation (18), which contains h in the first power, than in
the case of equations (16) and (16 a), where h appears in the second
power. In the latter case we thus drop a small term of the second order,
while in the former case we drop a much larger term of the first order.

In order to remove this discrepancy we must put

$$S = S^0 + \frac{h}{2\pi i}. S', \tag{21}$$

and after substituting this expression in equation (18) drop terms which are quadratic in h but keep those which are linear in h (S^0 and S' being independent of h and therefore of the same order of magnitude). We thus get the approximate equation

$$\frac{h}{4\pi i m} \nabla^2 S^0 + \frac{\partial S^0}{\partial t} + \frac{h}{2\pi i} \frac{\partial S'}{\partial t} + \frac{1}{2m} (\nabla S^0)^2 + \frac{h}{2\pi m i} \nabla S^0 . \nabla S' + U = 0. \tag{21 a}$$

Here S^0 must be regarded as the zero approximation, corresponding to $h = 0$, i.e. as the solution of the Hamilton-Jacobi equation

$$\frac{\partial S^0}{\partial t} + \frac{1}{2m} (\nabla S^0)^2 + U = 0.$$

It can obviously be identified with the (approximate) function s.

The function S' must therefore satisfy the equation

$$\frac{1}{2m} \nabla^2 S^0 + \frac{\partial S'}{\partial t} + \frac{1}{m} \nabla S^0 . \nabla S' = 0, \tag{21 b}$$

whence it follows that S' is a real quantity. Now according to (21) we have $\psi = e^{i2\pi S/h} = e^{S'} e^{i2\pi S^0/h}$, so that, since $S^0 = s$, $e^{S'}$ must be equal to A. Substituting in (21 b)

$$S' = \log A, \tag{21 c}$$

we do indeed get equation (16 a). It may seem that by developing the function S in a series of powers of the parameter $h/(2\pi i)$

$$S = S^0 + \frac{h}{2\pi i} S' + \left(\frac{h}{2\pi i}\right)^2 S'' + \dots$$

and solving the equation (18) by successive approximations, one can obtain as good an approximation for S as may be desired. This assumption is, however, incorrect, for it can be shown that the preceding series is divergent or rather semi-convergent, which explains why one gets a closer approximation by keeping the first-order term, as has been done above. In fact the general solution of a differential equation of the second order cannot be approximated to by starting with the solution of the equation of the first order obtained by dropping the second-order terms, however small the parameter by which they are multiplied may be, just as a quadratic equation cannot be approximated to by the linear one obtained by dropping the quadratic term. If, however, the latter is multiplied by a small parameter, then *one* of the two solutions of the quadratic equation can be approximated to by the solution of the linear one. A similar relationship exists between the function $\psi = e^{i2\pi S^0/h + S'}$ and one of the particular solutions of Schrödinger's equation, representing approximately waves travelling in one direction. It should be mentioned that this direction need not remain constant; it can be changed by *total* reflection, which, in contradistinction to partial reflection, is a phenomenon perfectly compatible with classical mechanics since it does not involve any ambiguity and therefore does not challenge a deterministic description of the motion. The difference between classical mechanics and wave mechanics in the approximate form given above, in so far as total reflection is concerned, consists only in the fact that, according to the latter, the particle can penetrate into those regions of the field of force where its 'classical' velocity becomes imaginary.

According to the relation $\mathbf{v} = \nabla s/m = \nabla S^0/m$, it should follow that the functions s and S^0 must also become imaginary. So far as S^0 is concerned this is perfectly true. The function s, however, according to its definition, must remain real. It will therefore be different from S^0 for those regions where v is imaginary and will satisfy an equation different from that of Hamilton and Jacobi. We must remember that equations (16) and (16 a) were obtained on the assumption that both s and A were real. The assumption that s satisfies approximately the Hamilton-Jacobi equation, even when the latter gives imaginary values for it, would thus imply a contradiction.

This means that, in the case under consideration, $\nabla^2 A$ must be very large and of the order of magnitude of $1/h^2$, so that the first term in equation (16) or (17), which when omitted reduces (16) or (17) to the Hamilton-Jacobi equation, cannot be dropped. We shall not consider the approximate solution of equations (16) or (16 a) [or (17) and (17 a)] for this case. It is simpler to use instead the alternative representation of ψ by means of the function $S = S^0 + S'h/(2\pi i)$ since we do not have to worry about the reality of S^0. An imaginary value of S^0 leads, according to (21 b), to an imaginary value of S'. The role of the functions S^0 and S' as determining the phase and the amplitude respectively will thus be reversed for classically forbidden regions, so that, using the expression $A e^{i2\pi s/h}$ for ψ, we can put

$$A = e^{i2\pi S^0/h} = e^{\pm 2\pi|S^0|/h} \tag{22}$$

and

$$s = \frac{h}{2\pi i}S' = \pm \frac{h}{2\pi}|S'|. \tag{22 a}$$

The sign ($+$ or $-$) is determined by the condition that A (i.e. ψ) must decrease with increased penetration into the forbidden region. It can easily be proved directly that the expressions (22) and (22 a) constitute an approximate solution of the equations (16) and (16 a) for the case in question if the functions S^0 and S' are determined respectively by the Hamilton-Jacobi equation and by equation (21 b).

Returning to the case when S^0 is real (and equal to s), corresponding to the motion in the classically allowed region of the field of force, let us examine the approximate values which are obtained for the amplitude $A = e^{S'}$.

We shall first consider the simplest case of a one-dimensional motion with constant energy. We have in this case, according to (4),

$$A^2 \frac{dx}{ds} = \text{const.},$$

that is, since

$$\frac{ds}{dx} = v,$$

$$A^2 = \frac{C^2}{|v|}, \tag{23}$$

where C^2 denotes a positive number. We thus get approximately

$$\psi = \frac{C}{\sqrt{|v|}} e^{i\frac{2\pi}{h}[s_0(x) - Wt]}, \tag{23 a}$$

$s_0(x)$ being a solution of the equation

$$\frac{1}{2m}\left(\frac{ds_0}{dx}\right)^2 + U = W.$$

Formula (23) has a very simple physical meaning. It shows that the probability of finding the particle within a certain region between x and $x + dx$ is inversely proportional to its velocity in this region. This is just what we should expect if this probability were defined as proportional to the time $dt = dx/v$ which the particle spends in the region in question. We thus see that the interpretation of the quantity $\psi\psi^* \, dx = A^2 \, dx$ as the relative probability of finding the particle in the region dx is in agreement, so far as the approximate expression for ψ is used, with the classical definition of probability in terms of *duration*.

If $f(x)$ is some quantity depending upon the position of the particle, and if the motion of the latter is confined to a limited region of the x-axis, e.g. between x_1 and x_2, then the average value of this quantity in the sense of classical mechanics, i.e. with respect to the time, can be defined by the expression

$$\bar{f} = \frac{1}{T} \int_0^T f(x)\, dt \qquad (24)$$

taken for a 'round trip' of the particle, T representing the duration of this round trip. The round trip can obviously be replaced by a one-way trip, since the motion must proceed in the same manner on the two halves of a round trip, with the sign of the velocity reversed. We can thus put

$$\bar{f} = \frac{1}{t_2 - t_1} \int_{t_1}^{t_2} f(x)\, dt,$$

where t_1 and t_2 denote the time of starting from the point x_1 and arriving at the point x_2 respectively. Replacing dt by dx/v, where v is a function of x determined by the equation $v^2 = \sqrt{\left\{\frac{2}{m}\{W - U(x)\}\right\}}$, we get

$$\bar{f} = \frac{1}{t_2 - t_1} \int_{x_1}^{x_2} \frac{f(x)}{|v|}\, dx, \qquad (24\,a)$$

or, if a 'round trip' is taken instead of a 'one-way' trip,

$$\bar{f} = \frac{1}{T} \oint \frac{f(x)}{v}\, dx,$$

the velocity v being taken with the same sign as dx (i.e. $+$ when x is increasing from x_1 to x_2, and $-$ when it is decreasing from x_2 to x_1).

Now the expression (24 a) for $\bar{f}$ is identical with that obtained by means of the wave-mechanical definition of the average value of $f(x)$ according to the formula

$$\bar{f} = \int_{x_1}^{x_2} f(x)\psi\psi^*\, dx, \qquad (24\,b)$$

if the function ψ is assumed to vanish outside the region (x_1, x_2) and is replaced by its approximate expression (23 a) for this region. The normalization constant C must be determined by the condition $\int_{x_1}^{x_2} \psi\psi^*\, dx = 1$, that is,

$$C^2 \int_{x_1}^{x_2} \frac{dx}{v} = C^2 \int_{t_1}^{t_2} dt = C^2(t_2 - t_1) = 1.$$

This agreement of the classical theory with the wave-mechanical theory must not be overestimated. As a matter of fact the function ψ does not in general vanish outside the classically allowed region, but, as we have just seen, decreases there approximately as $e^{-2\pi|S^0|/h}$. According to the relation $v = \dfrac{1}{m}\dfrac{dS^0}{dx}$, we can put (dropping the term containing the time)

$$S^0 = m \int v\, dx = \int \sqrt{\{2m(W-U)\}}\, dx. \qquad (25)$$

This formula applies just as well, i.e. with the same degree of approximation, to the points inside and outside the region (x_1, x_2). In the latter case, for a point $x > x_2$, we can put

$$|S^0(x)| = \int\limits_{x_2}^{x} \sqrt{\{2m(U-W)\}}\, dx, \qquad (25\,\mathrm{a})$$

and consequently

$$|\psi| = C e^{-\frac{2\pi}{h}\int\limits_{x_2}^{x}\sqrt{[2m(U-W)]}\, dx} \qquad (25\,\mathrm{b})$$

Thus, to the degree of approximation used, we should define the wave-mechanical average of $f(x)$ by the equation

$$\bar{f} = \int\limits_{-\infty}^{+\infty} f(x)|\psi|^2\, dx$$

with

$$|\psi|^2 = \frac{C^2}{|v|} = C^2 \Big/ \sqrt{\left\{\frac{2}{m}(W-U)\right\}}$$

for $W \geqslant U$, i.e. for $x_1 \leqslant x \leqslant x_2$,

and

$$|\psi|^2 = C^2 e^{-\frac{4\pi}{h}\int\limits_{x_2}^{x}\sqrt{[2m(U-W)]}\, dx}$$

for $x > x_2$ and a similar expression for $x < x_1$. The constant C must be determined from the equation $\int\limits_{-\infty}^{+\infty}|\psi|^2\, dx = 1$.

The difference between the classical and the wave-mechanical averages becomes particularly important when there are two or more classically allowed regions separated from one another by regions for which $W < U$. The latter, being permeable to the particle from the wave-mechanical point of view, do not actually separate but, on the contrary, connect the former regions.

The comparison of the classical 'time-average' with the wave-mechanical 'probable value' for the case of a three-dimensional motion is much more complicated than in the one-dimensional case and will be considered in the next section in connexion with the wave-mechanical interpretation of the quantum conditions. It must be remarked here that such averages or probable values have a meaning only when the motion is confined to a classically limited region, and that these limits can be assigned *a priori* only in the case of a conservative motion, i.e. a motion with a given (constant) value of the energy W. Within the allowed region, limited by the surface $W - U = 0$, the amplitude function A must satisfy the equation

$$\operatorname{div}(A^2 \nabla s_0) = 0,$$

which can be solved after the function s_0 has been determined from the Hamilton-Jacobi equation (17). It should be remembered that this equation, which represents another form of equation (17a), expresses the law of the conservation of the copies of the particle, or of the probability of its location [cf. (19)].

Although there is in general no exact equivalence between the classical and the wave-mechanical average values, yet there are special cases when this equivalence turns out to be exact. An interesting case of this sort is provided by the so-called 'virial', i.e. by the quantity

$$V = \frac{\partial U}{\partial x} x + \frac{\partial U}{\partial y} y + \frac{\partial U}{\partial z} z,$$

which was introduced by Clausius in the kinetic theory of gases.

For a motion restricted to a limited region, the time average of this quantity $\overline{V}$ is connected with the time average of the kinetic energy by the relation

$$2\overline{T} = \overline{V}. \tag{26}$$

This is called the 'virial theorem'. It can be derived as follows: We multiply Newton's equations of motion

$$m_k \frac{d^2 x_k}{dt^2} = -\frac{\partial U}{\partial x}, \text{ etc.},$$

by the corresponding coordinates and write

$$x_k \frac{d^2 x_k}{dt^2} = \frac{d}{dt}\left(x_k \frac{dx_k}{dt}\right) - \left(\frac{dx_k}{dt}\right)^2.$$

Adding these transformed equations, we get

$$\frac{d}{dt} \sum_k m_k \left(x_k \frac{dx_k}{dt} + \dots\right) - \sum_k m_k \left[\left(\frac{dx_k}{dt}\right)^2 + \dots\right] = -\sum_k \left(\frac{\partial U}{\partial x_k} x_k + \dots\right).$$

Formula (26) is then obtained by averaging with respect to the time and taking account of the fact that the mean value of

$$\frac{d}{dt} \sum m_k \left(x_k \frac{dx_k}{dt} + \dots\right)$$

vanishes. If we replace the kinetic energy T by the difference $W - U$ and assume that the potential energy is a homogeneous function of the

nth degree in the coordinates, formula (26) reduces to the form $2(\overline{W-U}) = n\overline{U}$ or

$$\overline{U} = \frac{2}{n+2} W. \tag{26 a}$$

It can easily be shown that this relation remains exactly valid in wave mechanics if $\overline{U}$ is defined as the integral $\int U\psi\psi^* \, dV$ and ψ is defined as the exact solution of the corresponding Schrödinger equation. As an example we shall consider the simplest case of a one-dimensional wave-mechanical problem which is described by the equation

$$\frac{d^2\psi}{dx^2} + \frac{8\pi^2 m}{h^2}(W-U)\psi = 0.$$

If we multiply this equation by $x \, d\psi^*/dx$ and the conjugate equation $\dfrac{d^2\psi^*}{dx^2} + \dfrac{8\pi^2 m}{h^2}(W-U)\psi^* = 0$ by $x\dfrac{d\psi}{dx}$ and add, we obtain

$$x\frac{d}{dx}\left(\frac{d\psi}{dx}\frac{d\psi^*}{dx}\right) + \frac{8\pi^2 m}{h^2}Wx\frac{d}{dx}(\psi\psi^*) - \frac{8\pi^2 m}{h^2}Ux\frac{d}{dx}(\psi\psi^*) = 0.$$

By partial integration with respect to x, taking into account the boundary conditions ($\psi = 0$ and $d\psi/dx = 0$ for $x = \pm\infty$), we get

$$-\int_{-\infty}^{+\infty}\frac{d\psi}{dx}\frac{d\psi^*}{dx}\,dx - \frac{8\pi^2 m}{h^2}W\int_{-\infty}^{+\infty}\psi\psi^*\,dx + \frac{8\pi^2 m}{h^2}\int_{-\infty}^{+\infty}\psi\psi^*\frac{d(Ux)}{dx}\,dx = 0,$$

or, since $\int_{-\infty}^{+\infty}\psi\psi^*\,dx = 1$ and $\int_{-\infty}^{+\infty}f\psi\psi^*\,dx = \bar{f}$,

$$\int_{-\infty}^{+\infty}\frac{d\psi}{dx}\frac{d\psi^*}{dx}\,dx + \frac{8\pi^2 m}{h^2}\left[W - \frac{\overline{d(Ux)}}{dx}\right] = 0.$$

Further, by multiplying the Schrödinger equation by ψ^*, we obtain

$$\int_{-\infty}^{+\infty}\psi^*\frac{d^2\psi}{dx^2}\,dx + \frac{8\pi^2 m}{h^2}\int_{-\infty}^{+\infty}(W-U)\psi\psi^*\,dx = 0,$$

i.e.

$$\int_{-\infty}^{+\infty}\psi^*\frac{d^2\psi}{dx^2}\,dx + \frac{8\pi^2 m}{h^2}(W-\overline{U}) = 0,$$

or, transforming the first term by partial integration,

$$-\int_{-\infty}^{+\infty}\frac{d\psi}{dx}\frac{d\psi^*}{dx}\,dx + \frac{8\pi^2 m}{h^2}(W-\overline{U}) = 0.$$

We have therefore $\qquad W - \overline{U} + W - \dfrac{\overline{d(Ux)}}{dx} = 0$

or $\qquad\qquad\qquad\qquad 2(W - \overline{U}) = x\dfrac{\overline{dU}}{dx}.$

This is exactly formula (26) for the special case that we have considered.†

Another illustration of the connexion between the wave-mechanical and the classical theory is given by the similarity of the classical equations of motion,

$$m\frac{d^2x}{dt^2} = -\frac{\partial U}{\partial x},\ \text{etc.,}$$

and the wave-mechanical relations

$$m\frac{d^2\bar{x}}{dt^2} = -\frac{\overline{\partial U}}{\partial x},\ \text{etc.,} \tag{27}$$

between the corresponding average (or probable) values of the quantities involved.

The relations (27) were found by P. Ehrenfest. They are usually referred to, in connexion with the propagation of a *wave packet*, as the equations of motion of the 'centre' or 'centroid' of the latter, that is, of the point with the coordinates

$$\bar{x} = \int x\psi\psi^*\,dV, \qquad \bar{y} = \int y\psi\psi^*\,dV, \qquad \bar{z} = \int z\psi\psi^*\,dV. \quad (27\,a)$$

If the wave function ψ represents a wave packet formed by superposing waves with slightly different frequencies (i.e. motions with slightly different energies), the coordinates $\bar{x}$, $\bar{y}$, $\bar{z}$ are certain functions of the time (in the case of a stationary state where the dependence of ψ upon the time is specified by the factor $e^{-i2\pi\nu t}$ they reduce to constants), so that we can differentiate them with regard to the time. The corresponding quantities can be defined as the average values of the components of the velocity of the particle or its acceleration, etc.

We shall prove the relations (27) for the simplest case of a motion parallel to the x-axis (the proof can easily be extended to the case of three-dimensional motion). We have, by the definition of $\bar{x}$,

$$\frac{d\bar{x}}{dt} = \int\limits_{-\infty}^{+\infty} x\frac{\partial(\psi\psi^*)}{\partial t}\,dx = \int\limits_{-\infty}^{+\infty} x\left(\psi^*\frac{\partial\psi}{\partial t} + \psi\frac{\partial\psi^*}{\partial t}\right)dx,$$

since x and t are independent variables.

† The proof given is due to B. Finkelstein.

Now ψ and ψ^* satisfy the equations

$$\frac{\partial \psi}{\partial t} = \frac{i}{4\pi}\frac{h}{m}\left(\frac{\partial^2 \psi}{\partial x^2} - \mu U \psi\right)$$

$$\frac{\partial \psi^*}{\partial t} = -\frac{i}{4\pi}\frac{h}{m}\left(\frac{\partial^2 \psi^*}{\partial x^2} - \mu U \psi^*\right),$$

where $\mu = \dfrac{8\pi^2 m}{h^2}$. Hence

$$\frac{d\bar{x}}{dt} = \frac{ih}{4\pi m}\int_{-\infty}^{+\infty} x\left(\psi^* \frac{\partial^2 \psi}{\partial x^2} - \psi \frac{\partial^2 \psi^*}{\partial x^2}\right) dx.$$

By partial integration, in conjunction with the fact that

$$\int_{-\infty}^{+\infty} \frac{df}{dx}\, dx = f(+\infty) - f(-\infty)$$

vanishes if the function f contains x or $d\psi/dx$ as a factor (since $\int_{-\infty}^{+\infty} \psi\psi^*\, dx$ must be finite and equal to 1), we obtain

$$\frac{d\bar{x}}{dt} = \frac{h}{4\pi m i}\int_{-\infty}^{+\infty}\left(\psi^* \frac{\partial \psi}{\partial x} - \psi \frac{\partial \psi^*}{\partial x}\right) dx. \tag{27 b}$$

This expression could be obtained directly from the relation $\dfrac{\partial(\psi\psi^*)}{\partial t} + \dfrac{\partial j}{\partial x} = 0$ (which is a special case of (19)) and the formula $j = \dfrac{h}{4\pi i m}\left(\psi^* \dfrac{\partial \psi}{\partial x} - \psi \dfrac{\partial \psi^*}{\partial x}\right)$ for the current density. Putting $j = \psi\psi^*\bar{v}(x)$, where $\bar{v}(x)$ is the average velocity at the point x, we can rewrite the preceding equation in the form

$$\frac{d\bar{x}}{dt} = \int_{-\infty}^{+\infty} \bar{v}(x)\psi\psi^*\, dx,$$

which agrees with the definition of $d\bar{x}/dt$ as the average value of the velocity of the particle irrespective of its position.

By differentiating (27 b) with respect to the time, we obtain

$$\frac{d^2\bar{x}}{dt^2} = -\frac{h^2}{16\pi^2 m^2}\int_{-\infty}^{+\infty} dx \left[\left(\frac{\partial^2 \psi^*}{\partial x^2} - \mu U \psi^*\right)\frac{\partial \psi}{\partial x} - \psi^* \frac{\partial}{\partial x}\left(\frac{\partial^2 \psi}{\partial x^2} - \mu U \psi\right) + \right.$$

$$\left. + \left(\frac{\partial^2 \psi}{\partial x^2} - \mu U \psi\right)\frac{\partial \psi^*}{\partial x} - \psi \frac{\partial}{\partial x}\left(\frac{\partial^2 \psi^*}{\partial x^2} - \mu U \psi^*\right)\right]$$

$$= -\frac{h^2}{8\pi^2 m^2} \int_{-\infty}^{+\infty} \left[\left(\frac{\partial^2 \psi^*}{\partial x^2} - \mu U \psi^* \right) \frac{\partial \psi}{\partial x} + \left(\frac{\partial^2 \psi}{\partial x^2} - \mu U \psi \right) \frac{\partial \psi^*}{\partial x} \right] dx$$

$$= -\frac{h^2}{8\pi^2 m^2} \int_{-\infty}^{+\infty} \left[\frac{\partial}{\partial x} \left(\frac{\partial \psi}{\partial x} \frac{\partial \psi^*}{\partial x} \right) - \mu U \frac{\partial}{\partial x} (\psi \psi^*) \right] dx$$

$$= -\frac{h^2 \mu}{8\pi^2 m^2} \int_{-\infty}^{+\infty} \frac{\partial U}{\partial x} \psi \psi^* \, dx;$$

i.e.
$$m \frac{d^2 \bar{x}}{dt^2} = -\overline{\frac{\partial U}{\partial x}},$$

where
$$\overline{\frac{\partial U}{\partial x}} = \int_{-\infty}^{+\infty} \frac{\partial U}{\partial x} \psi \psi^* \, dx$$

is the average (or probable) value of the force acting on the particle. It must be emphasized that this value refers not to the average (or probable) position of the particle, determined by the centre of the packet (otherwise this centre would move exactly according to the classical mechanics), but to all possible positions.

If the dimensions of the packet are very small (which means that the uncertainty in the estimation of the particle's velocity is very large) the motion of its centre closely follows classical motion. This, however, persists only for a very short time, for the packet will spread, the rate of this spreading being the larger the smaller its original dimensions (i.e. the larger the original uncertainty in the velocity).

5. Motion in a Limited Region; Quantum Conditions and Average Values

We shall now investigate the case of a (three-dimensional) motion restricted classically to a finite region of space (where $W - U > 0$), and derive the 'quantization rules' characteristic of such a motion with the help of the approximate wave-mechanical theory based on the classical determination of the phase or action function $s (= S^0)$ by means of the Hamilton-Jacobi equation. A motion of this kind must obviously have a periodic or quasi-periodic character, so that the path described by the particle may fill up the whole region or pass many times in various directions through the same or nearly the same point (as, for instance, in the simple case of the oscillatory motion of a particle along a straight line). If the particle is replaced by a continuous assembly of its copies, a rather complicated picture results, different copies passing simultaneously through the same point with velocities which are in general different both in regard to direction and (if the field of force varies with the time) in regard to magnitude. The latter must, of course, remain a single-valued function of the coordinates in the case of motion with a given (constant) value of the total energy W. The function $\phi = s/m$, which can be defined as the velocity potential, must, however, in this case (as well as in the general case of non-conservative motion) be a *multiple-valued function* of the coordinates. Considering the copy assembly as a kind of fluid, we can illustrate the case in question by the familiar type of fluid motion with *closed stream-lines*, each stream-line representing the path of all the particles situated on it. In the associated wave picture these closed paths of the separate particles or copies must be interpreted as *closed rays*.

Now a fluid motion of this type can be irrotational if, for instance, the fluid is flowing in a closed tube or around some closed tube. The velocity $\mathbf{v}$ of the particles, as a function of their coordinates, can then be represented as the gradient of a potential ϕ, provided the latter is defined as a multiple-valued function of the coordinates. In fact, taking the integral of the velocity along a line σ connecting two points P_1 and P_2, then, since the projection v_σ of $\mathbf{v}$ on the line element $d\sigma$ is, by definition, equal to $d\phi/d\sigma$, we get

$$\int_{P_1}^{P_2} v_\sigma \, d\sigma = \phi(P_2) - \phi(P_1).$$

If the line is closed, i.e. if the points P_1 and P_2 coincide, this integral should be equal to zero, irrespective of the shape of the line, unless we assume that for closed lines of certain type the potential ϕ may change after a 'round trip' by an amount $\Delta\phi$ equal to the value of the integral $\oint v_\sigma \, d\sigma$ taken along the corresponding closed line. If the latter coincides with a stream-line, the integral will certainly be different from zero, since along this line we must have $v_\sigma = |v|$.

Now it can easily be proved that in the case of irrotational motion the integral $\oint v_\sigma \, d\sigma$, which is called the 'circulation', will have *the same value for all closed lines of the same family*, i.e. of the same general type. In the case of a fluid flowing around a closed tube along closed stream-lines (Fig. 1), we must distinguish closed lines of two families: those which do not surround the tube, and those which do. For the former the circulation will be equal to zero, while for the latter it will have a certain value different from zero. This result follows from the transformation of the line integral $\oint v_\sigma \, d\sigma$, by means of Stokes's formula, into the integral $\oint (\operatorname{curl} \mathbf{v})_n \, dS$ over any surface S limited by the line σ. In the case of the lines of the first family the surface S will be situated entirely within the fluid, so that the integral will vanish, since the motion is supposed to be irrotational ($\operatorname{curl} \mathbf{v} = 0$). In the case of the lines of the second family the surface S will cut the tube around which the fluid is flowing. Since for points inside the tube the idea of velocity has no meaning, we can replace the surface S by another surface S' bounded by two closed lines of the second family. Stokes's formula applied to this surface which lies wholly within the fluid, and for which therefore the integral $\oint (\operatorname{curl} \mathbf{v})_n \, dS$ vanishes, leads to the result that

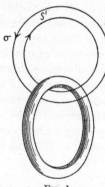

Fig. 1

the integral $\oint v_\sigma \, d\sigma$ taken over the double boundary of S' must vanish if the 'round trip' is made in opposite directions along the two constituent lines, whence it follows that the circulation will have the same value for both lines if the round trip is made in the same direction.

It may be mentioned that exactly similar results are met with in the theory of the magnetic field generated by a linear electric current. This field—outside the wire along which the current is flowing—is also irrotational, so that the magnetic field strength can be defined as the gradient of a certain magnetic potential. With every trip around the wire along any closed line (encircling this wire only once) this potential must change by a definite value, namely $4\pi i$, where i is the strength of the current.

The preceding results can be applied without substantial modification to the flow of the fictitious fluid represented by the copy assembly of a particle moving in a limited region. In the copy assembly, however, we must remember that different copies may be imagined to pass simultaneously through the same point in different directions. This is, of course, impossible in the case of real particles. In particular, closed stream-lines may degenerate into 'double lines', i.e. unclosed lines along which the copies move first in one and then in the opposite direction (oscillatory motion).† The 'circulation' $\oint v_\sigma\, d\sigma$ for such a double line will not be equal to zero, but, on the contrary, will be equal to double the value of the integral $\int v_\sigma\, d\sigma$ for a one-way trip. As a result the velocity potential $\phi = s/m$, in addition to the multiplicity considered above, may acquire a duplicity of an entirely different character, corresponding to the possible presence at each point of two copies moving in opposite or, in general, in different directions.

Leaving aside this duplicity we see that, in the case of a particle confined to a finite region of space, the function s representing the mechanical action or the momentum-potential of the copies of this particle must—so long as the motion of these copies is supposed to be irrotational—be a multiple-valued function of the coordinates, i.e. it must change by a certain amount Δs for all closed lines (including double lines) of a certain family. It should be mentioned that 'round trips' along any of these lines have nothing to do with the actual motion, being performed not by definite copies (the latter need not move in closed lines), but by the process of linear integration referring to a *definite instant of time*. The change Δs of the function s for any such round trip is called a 'periodicity modulus' of s. From the point of view of the wave picture associated with the motion of the copy assembly of the particle these 'periodicity moduli' divided by the constant h represent the number of wave-lengths contained in the corresponding closed lines. In fact $ds/d\sigma = g_\sigma$ is the component of the momentum of the particle along the line-element $d\sigma$ and according to de Broglie's relation $d(s/h)/d\sigma = g_\sigma/h = k_\sigma$ must be equal to the corresponding component of the 'wave-number vector' $\mathbf{k} = \mathbf{g}/h$ of the associated waves. The integral $\oint k_\sigma\, d\sigma = \Delta s/h$ may therefore be defined as the number of wave-lengths contained in the line σ, or, more exactly, as the number of wave-crests cut by this line, or still more exactly, as the difference between the number of waves cut by σ in the positive and in the negative direction (i.e. in the direction of propagation and in the opposite direction).

Now it is clear that in the case of motion corresponding to a definite energy, the wave system associated with it must be such that the number of waves cut by any closed line should be *integral*, corresponding

---

† The tube around which the fluid is supposed to flow degenerating into a ribbon with zero thickness.

to a change of the phase $\phi = 2\pi s/h$ by an integral multiple of 2π, a change which is irrelevant for the value of the wave function $\psi = Ae^{i\phi}$. In the contrary case the latter would also be a multiple-valued function of the coordinates, and would not represent a stationary system of standing waves (each standing wave being produced by the super-position of waves travelling in different directions), determined by the condition that the wave function ψ should vanish at or near the boundary of the region where the particle is supposed to move.

It thus follows from the condition of single-valuedness for the wave function ψ that *the 'periodicity moduli' of the 'action function' s must be integral multiples of h.*

This condition, which—it should be remembered—refers to the case of motion confined to a (classically) limited region, can easily be shown to be equivalent to the quantum conditions of the old quantum theory discovered by Bohr and by Sommerfeld.

For the general formulation of these quantum conditions, it is necessary, instead of the original rectangular coordinates x, y, z, to introduce new variables (generalized coordinates) q_1, q_2, q_3. If we suc-ceed in so choosing these new variables that s assumes the form

$$s = \sum_{\alpha=1}^{f} s_\alpha(q_\alpha) \qquad (28)$$

('separation variables'), then the quantum conditions run as follows:

$$\oint p_\alpha \, dq_\alpha = \oint \frac{ds_\alpha}{dq_\alpha} \, dq_\alpha = (\Delta s)_\alpha = n_\alpha h \quad (n_\alpha \text{ an integer}). \qquad (28\,\text{a})$$

Here the various $p_\alpha \ (= ds_\alpha/dq_\alpha)$ are the 'generalized momenta' and $(\Delta s)_\alpha$ are the 'principal moduli of periodicity' of the function s, i.e. those alterations of this function which correspond to a 'cyclic' change of one of the separation coordinates when the remaining two are kept fixed. By a 'cyclic' change of the coordinate q_α we mean an altera-tion such that the given particle returns to its original position and therefore the rectangular coordinates assume their original values. If the coordinate q_α has the character of an angle so that the rectangular coordinates are periodic functions of it, then the 'cyclic change' of q_α is simply the increase by the corresponding period Δq_α (for example, 2π). Otherwise it is an oscillation of q_α within certain limits determined by the nature of the field of force. The cyclic alterations of the in-dividual separation coordinates in the actual motion of the system take place in periods of time Δt_α which are in general different from one another, so that the motion with regard to the time appears to be non-periodic or *conditionally periodic*. This dependence of the variables q_α on the time plays no part in the 'quantizing' defined by formula (28 a).

The generalized momenta appearing in (28 a) can be defined, and indeed are usually defined, in a different way—namely, as the partial derivatives of the kinetic energy T, expressed as a function of the generalized coordinates and of the corresponding 'velocities' $dq_\alpha/dt = \dot{q}_\alpha$, with respect to the latter. The equivalence of both definitions is obvious in the case of rectangular coordinates, since $T = \frac{1}{2}m(v_x^2 + v_y^2 + v_z^2)$ and $g_x = \partial s/\partial x = \partial T/\partial v_x$, etc. If the coordinates are replaced by new (generalized) coordinates $q_\alpha(x, y, z)$, we have

$$\dot{q}_\alpha = \frac{\partial q_\alpha}{\partial x}v_x + \frac{\partial q_\alpha}{\partial y}v_y + \frac{\partial q_\alpha}{\partial z}v_z,$$

whence $\partial\dot{q}_\alpha/\partial v_x = \partial q_\alpha/\partial x$, etc. We thus get

$$\frac{\partial s}{\partial x} = \sum_{\alpha=1}^{3}\frac{\partial s}{\partial q_\alpha}\frac{\partial q_\alpha}{\partial x}, \qquad \frac{\partial T}{\partial v_x} = \sum_{\alpha=1}^{3}\frac{\partial T}{\partial \dot{q}_\alpha}\frac{\partial \dot{q}_\alpha}{\partial v_x} = \sum_{\alpha=1}^{3}\frac{\partial T}{\partial \dot{q}_\alpha}\frac{\partial q_\alpha}{\partial x},$$

and consequently,
$$\frac{\partial s}{\partial q_\alpha} = \frac{\partial T}{\partial \dot{q}_\alpha} = p_\alpha.$$

The formulation of the quantum conditions in the form (28 a) is sometimes possible in two or more different ways—if there exist several sets of 'separable' coordinates. Theoretically it is possible—in a single way at least—for any type of motion (restricted to a finite region). Practically, however, the 'separation coordinates' can be found only for simple types of motion (i.e. of the field of force). If the separation coordinates cannot be found, then the quantum conditions—in the sense of Bohr's theory—must be stated in the more general form indicated above, namely, that the moduli of periodicity of s with respect to any closed curve should be equal to an integral multiple of h (or to zero).

We shall now turn to the question of the relation between the wave-mechanical average or probable value of any function of the coordinates of the particle for a given quantized state of motion and the corresponding classical 'time average' of this function. The solution of this question depends upon the introduction of new coordinates of a still more general kind than those considered above in connexion with the formulation of the quantum conditions. These still more general coordinates are not directly expressible in terms of the original ones, but in terms of the original coordinates *and* the corresponding momenta, the new momenta being also functions of the old momenta and of the old coordinates.

Coordinate or rather coordinate-momenta transformations of this type were introduced by Hamilton and are called contact or canonical transformations (the transformation considered above being a particular case of these transformations).

The theory of canonical transformations is based upon the preservation of the so-called 'canonical form' of the classical equations of motion. In the case of rectangular coordinates these canonical equations can be obtained directly from the usual equations of motion $m\,d^2x/dt^2 = -\,\partial U/\partial x$, etc., and have the form

$$\frac{dg_x}{dt} = -\frac{\partial H}{\partial x},\dots; \qquad \frac{dx}{dt} = +\frac{\partial H}{\partial g_x},\dots, \tag{29}$$

where
$$H = \frac{1}{2m}(g_x^2+g_y^2+g_z^2)+U \tag{29a}$$

is the total energy expressed as a function of the coordinates and momenta, and is usually denoted as the 'Hamiltonian function'. The equations (29) can be interpreted as referring to a particle moving not in ordinary space with the three coordinates x, y, z but in the six-dimensional *phase-space* (Part I, Chap. V) with the 'coordinates' x, y, z, g_x, g_y, g_z, the time derivatives of these coordinates representing the six components of the 'velocity' in phase-space and H being a function of the 'position' of the particle in the phase-space.†

For the sake of uniformity in notation we shall, in the following, instead of x, y, z write Q_1, Q_2, Q_3, and instead of g_x, g_y, g_z write P_1, P_2, P_3. The equations (29) then become

$$\frac{dP_\alpha}{dt} = -\frac{\partial H}{\partial Q_\alpha}, \qquad \frac{dQ_\alpha}{dt} = \frac{\partial H}{\partial P_\alpha}. \tag{29b}$$

We now introduce new coordinates Q_1', Q_2', Q_3' determined by three equations of the form

$$Q_\beta' = Q_\beta'(Q_1, Q_2, Q_3) \text{ or } Q_\alpha = Q_\alpha(Q_1', Q_2', Q_3') \qquad (\alpha,\beta = 1,2,3). \tag{30}$$

We then define the new momenta P_1', P_2', P_3' by the formulae

$$P_\beta' = \frac{\partial s}{\partial Q_\beta'} = \sum_{\alpha=1}^{3}\frac{\partial s}{\partial Q_\alpha}\frac{\partial Q_\alpha}{\partial Q_\beta'} = \sum_{\alpha=1}^{3} P_\alpha \frac{\partial Q_\alpha}{\partial Q_\beta'} \text{ or } P_\alpha = \sum_{\beta=1}^{3} P_\beta'\frac{\partial Q_\beta'}{\partial Q_\alpha}, \tag{30a}$$

which obviously do not assume a knowledge of the action function s. It can then easily be shown that these new coordinates and momenta satisfy a system of equations of the same form as (29b),

$$\frac{dP_\beta'}{dt} = -\frac{\partial H'}{\partial Q_\beta'}, \qquad \frac{dQ_\beta'}{dt} = \frac{\partial H'}{\partial P_\beta'} \qquad (\beta = 1,2,3), \tag{31}$$

† Instead of one particle one can consider a continuous assembly of its copies, distributed not in the ordinary space as before, but in the phase-space with a density depending in general upon the time.

where H' is the new Hamiltonian function which is obtained by re-placing in the original function $H(Q, P)$ the old coordinates and momenta by the new, according to the formulae (30) and (30 a). The transformation defined by these formulae is called a 'point transforma-tion'. As already mentioned, it is a special case of the *canonical* transformations. A canonical transformation (of the coordinates and momenta) is defined by the formulae

$$P_\alpha = \frac{\partial \Phi}{\partial Q_\alpha}, \qquad Q'_\beta = \frac{\partial \Phi}{\partial P'_\beta}, \tag{31 a}$$

where $\Phi(Q, P')$ is a completely arbitrary function of the *original* co-ordinates and the *new* momentum. If, in particular, we put

$$\Phi = \sum_{\beta=1}^{3} P'_\beta f_\beta(Q_1, Q_2, Q_3)$$

we obtain, by (31 a),

$$Q'_\beta = f_\beta(Q_1, Q_2, Q_3); \qquad P_\alpha = \sum_{\beta=1}^{3} P'_\beta \frac{\partial Q'_\beta}{\partial Q_\alpha},$$

which corresponds to the point transformation (30), (30 a).

The fact that the original canonical equations (29) are transformed by (31 a) into equations of the same canonical form (31) can be shown as follows:

We form the complete differential or rather the variation of the function Φ, corresponding to a virtual variation (completely indepen-dent of the actual motion) of the variables Q, P':

$$\delta\Phi = \sum_\alpha \frac{\partial \Phi}{\partial Q_\alpha} \delta Q_\alpha + \sum_\beta \frac{\partial \Phi}{\partial P'_\beta} \delta P'_\beta = \sum_\alpha P_\alpha \, \delta Q_\alpha + \sum_\beta Q'_\beta \, \delta P'_\beta,$$

and differentiate this expression with regard to the time. We also take the time derivative of Φ

$$\frac{d\Phi}{dt} = \sum_\alpha P_\alpha \frac{dQ_\alpha}{dt} + \sum_\beta Q'_\beta \frac{dP'_\beta}{dt},$$

and form its variation. By subtracting the expressions thus obtained, we get, remembering that δ and dt are commutative,

$$\sum_\alpha \left(\frac{dP_\alpha}{dt} \delta Q_\alpha - \frac{dQ_\alpha}{dt} \delta P_\alpha \right) = \sum_\beta \left(\frac{dP'_\beta}{dt} \delta Q'_\beta - \frac{dQ'_\beta}{dt} \delta P'_\beta \right).$$

Now by (29 b) we have

$$\sum_\alpha \left(\frac{dP_\alpha}{dt} \delta Q_\alpha - \frac{dQ_\alpha}{dt} \delta P_\alpha \right) = - \sum_\alpha \left(\frac{\partial H}{\partial Q_\alpha} \delta Q_\alpha + \frac{\partial H}{\partial P_\alpha} \delta P_\alpha \right) = -\delta H.$$

Hence, in virtue of $H(P, Q) = H'(P', Q')$,
we obtain

$$-\delta H' = -\sum_\beta \left(\frac{\partial H'}{\partial Q'_\beta} \delta Q'_\beta + \frac{\partial H'}{\partial P'_\beta} \delta P'_\beta \right) = \sum_\beta \left(\frac{dP'_\beta}{dt} \delta Q'_\beta - \frac{dQ'_\beta}{dt} \delta P'_\beta \right).$$

Since the variations δQ_β and $\delta P'_\beta$ are arbitrary, we can equate their coefficients. In this way we get equations (31).

Those canonical transformations, in which the transformed Hamiltonian H' depends only on the momenta P' and not on the coordinates Q', play a special role. Such coordinates are usually called *cyclic*. The equations (31) reduce in this case to

$$P'_\beta = \text{const.} \qquad \frac{dQ'_\beta}{dt} = \frac{\partial H'}{\partial P'_\beta} = \omega_\beta = \text{const.},$$

i.e. $Q'_\beta = \omega_\beta t + \phi_\beta.$

If the transformation function Φ leading to cyclic coordinates is known, the mechanical problem can be regarded as solved, for the original coordinates and momenta are then expressed according to the equations (31 a) as functions of the time which, besides t, only contain constants P'_β, ω_β, and ϕ_β.

Now it follows from (31 a) that this special transformation function is just the action function s regarded as a function of Q_1, Q_2, Q_3 and of three arbitrary constants P'_1, P'_2, P'_3 which necessarily appear on solving the Hamilton-Jacobi equation (16) or (17) by which this function is defined. These constants of integration can be expressed in terms of the three principal *moduli* of periodicity of the action function $J_\alpha = (\Delta s)_\alpha$ with regard to a system of separable coordinates q_1, q_2, q_3 (which we need neither actually know nor consider in detail here). Replacing the original constants P'_α by their expressions in terms of J_1, J_2, J_3 we can write the transformation function Φ in the form $s(x, y, z; J_1, J_2, J_3)$ and *define the constants J_α as the new momenta* $(P'_\alpha = J_\alpha)$. Considered from this point of view these constants are called the 'action variables' of the problem. The corresponding cyclic coordinates are called the 'angle variables'. We shall denote them by $w_\beta (= Q'_\beta)$.

We have therefore $w_\beta = \omega_\beta t + \phi_\beta,$ (32)
where according to the transformed canonical equations (31)

$$\omega_\beta = \frac{\partial H'}{\partial J_\beta} = \text{const.} \qquad (H' = W) \tag{32 a}$$

and $$P_\alpha = \frac{\partial s}{\partial Q_\alpha}, \qquad w_\beta = \frac{\partial s}{\partial J_\beta}. \tag{32 b}$$

To ascertain the dependence of the old coordinates Q_α on the new coordinates w_β, we shall introduce for a moment as an intermediate link between them the separation coordinates q_1, q_2, q_3. Expressed as a function of the latter, the function s assumes the form

$$s = \sum_{\alpha=1}^{3} s_\alpha(q_\alpha, J_1, J_2, J_3).$$

To a cyclic alteration of the coordinate q_α there corresponds by (32 b) an alteration of the coordinate w_β by $\Delta_\alpha w_\beta = \Delta_\alpha \partial s_\alpha / \partial J_\beta$. We have therefore, because $\Delta_\alpha s_\beta = J_\alpha$ if $\alpha = \beta$, and $= 0$ if $\alpha \neq \beta$,

$$\Delta_\alpha w_\beta = \frac{\partial J_\alpha}{\partial J_\beta} = \begin{cases} 1 \ (\alpha = \beta), \\ 0 \ (\alpha \neq \beta). \end{cases}$$

These formulae show that when any angle variable w_β is increased by 1 and the remaining w's are maintained constant, which corresponds to the cyclic alteration of the separation coordinate q_β, i.e. to the return of the particle to the original position along a 'β-curve', then the action function s increases exactly by J_β.

From this it follows that the coordinates Q_β, and consequently the momenta P_β, are periodic functions of the angle coordinates with periods equal to 1. Each of them, as well as any function $f(Q_1, Q_2, Q_3)$ (or still more generally $f(Q, P)$), can be expressed in the form of a triple Fourier series

$$f = \sum_{k_1, k_2, k_3} f_{k_1, k_2, k_3} e^{i2\pi(k_1 w_1 + k_2 w_2 + k_3 w_3)}, \qquad (33)$$

where k_1, k_2, k_3 are integers which can assume all values from $-\infty$ to $+\infty$, and f_{k_1, k_2, k_3} are certain expansion coefficients characteristic of the function f. If instead of the w_β we put their values obtained from (32), we get

$$f = \sum_{k_1, k_2, k_3} C_{k_1, k_2, k_3} e^{i2\pi(k_1 \omega_1 + k_2 \omega_2 + k_3 \omega_3)t}, \qquad (33\,a)$$

where the C_k are new expansion coefficients which we can regard as the amplitudes of various harmonic vibrations, while

$$\omega = k_1 \omega_1 + k_2 \omega_2 + k_3 \omega_3 \qquad (33\,b)$$

are the *frequencies* of these vibrations. The quantities ω_β, i.e. the velocities corresponding to the angle coordinates, represent therefore the *fundamental frequencies* of the motion.

We can now return to the problem of determining the time mean value of f. This problem can be solved at once by means of formula (33 a). Indeed, the required time mean value must obviously be equal to that amplitude coefficient in (33 a) for which the vibration frequency ω vanishes—or the sum of such coefficients if the equation $\omega = 0$ is satisfied by several different combinations of the numbers k_1, k_2, k_3.

This mean value can be represented on the one hand by the general

formula $\bar{f} = \lim\limits_{T \to \infty} \dfrac{1}{T} \int\limits_{0}^{T} f \, dt$. On the other hand it can be represented

just as well by the formula

$$\bar{f} = \int\limits_{0}^{1}\int\limits_{0}^{1}\int\limits_{0}^{1} f \, dw_1 \, dw_2 \, dw_3 \tag{34}$$

which does not contain the time explicitly, the triple integration being extended over the 'period cube' in the coordinate space of the angle variables; f is given as a function of the angle variables by formula (33).

The expression (34) has the form of a 'statistical' mean value corresponding to an averaging over the various copies of the given particle distributed with a *constant density in the space of the angle coordinates* w_1, w_2, w_3. Its numerical agreement with the time mean value of f for a definite copy means that the curve described by the motion of such a copy fills up this space uniformly.†

We can now return from the angle coordinates to our original rectangular coordinates $Q_1 = x$, $Q_2 = y$, $Q_3 = z$. In view of the fact that the new momenta are constants, the old coordinates may be considered practically as functions of the new coordinates alone, and vice versa. We can thus transform the volume integral (34) according to the well-known theorem of Jacobi, and put

$$\bar{f} = \int f D \, dV, \tag{34 a}$$

where $dV = dx\,dy\,dz$ and

$$D = \begin{vmatrix} \dfrac{\partial w_1}{\partial x}, & \dfrac{\partial w_1}{\partial y}, & \dfrac{\partial w_1}{\partial z} \\[2mm] \dfrac{\partial w_2}{\partial x}, & \dfrac{\partial w_2}{\partial y}, & \dfrac{\partial w_2}{\partial z} \\[2mm] \dfrac{\partial w_3}{\partial x}, & \dfrac{\partial w_3}{\partial y}, & \dfrac{\partial w_3}{\partial z} \end{vmatrix}.$$

By (32 b) this functional determinant can be written in the form

$$D = \begin{vmatrix} \dfrac{\partial^2 s}{\partial J_1 \, \partial x}, & \dfrac{\partial^2 s}{\partial J_1 \, \partial y}, & \dfrac{\partial^2 s}{\partial J_1 \, \partial z} \\[2mm] \dfrac{\partial^2 s}{\partial J_2 \, \partial x}, & \dfrac{\partial^2 s}{\partial J_2 \, \partial y}, & \dfrac{\partial^2 s}{\partial J_2 \, \partial z} \\[2mm] \dfrac{\partial^2 s}{\partial J_3 \, \partial x}, & \dfrac{\partial^2 s}{\partial J_3 \, \partial y}, & \dfrac{\partial^2 s}{\partial J_3 \, \partial z} \end{vmatrix}. \tag{34 b}$$

† This condition is satisfied for non-degenerate motion, that is, motion for which the three fundamental frequencies ω_1, ω_1, ω_3 are not commensurable with each other.

The volume integration in (34 a) must be extended over the whole region for which $W - U \geqslant 0$. We are thus brought to the conclusion that the relative probability that the particle will be found in the volume-element dV, as measured by the relative *duration* of its presence in this volume-element, is equal to D ($\int D\, dV = 1$). Comparing this result with the wave-mechanical average

$$\bar{f} = \int f \psi \psi^* \, dV,$$

we see that it will agree approximately with (34 a) if $\psi \psi^* = D$. Now in the region $W - U \geqslant 0$ the function $s = S^0$ is real, so that the modulus of the function $\psi = A e^{i2\pi s/h} = e^{i2\pi S^0/h + S'}$ must reduce to $A = e^{S'}$. It follows therefore that

$$A^2 = D.$$

It should be remembered that an *exact* agreement between the classical and the wave-mechanical mean value is out of the question—not only because of the approximative character of the preceding expre sion for ψ (with s determined from the Hamilton-Jacobi equation), out also because in the wave-mechanical case the integration must be extended over *all space* including the classically forbidden region. However, this region, although infinite, contributes in general only a finite and usually a small amount to the integral $\int f \psi \psi^* \, dV$ because of a very rapid decrease of the function $|\psi|^2$.

The relation $A^2 = D$ can of course be derived in a straightforward way by integrating the equation

$$\operatorname{div} A^2 \nabla s = 0$$

[cf. (17 a)], or the equation

$$\nabla^2 S^0 + 2 \nabla S^0 \cdot \nabla S' = 0$$

to which (21 b) is reduced in the case of conservative motion. This integration has been carried out (in the case of the second equation) by Van Vleck, who showed that A^2 must be proportional to the determinant

$$\begin{vmatrix} \dfrac{\partial^2 s}{\partial x \partial \alpha} & \dfrac{\partial^2 s}{\partial y \partial \alpha} & \dfrac{\partial^2 s}{\partial z \partial \alpha} \\[2mm] \dfrac{\partial^2 s}{\partial x \partial \beta} & \dfrac{\partial^2 s}{\partial y \partial \beta} & \dfrac{\partial^2 s}{\partial z \partial \beta} \\[2mm] \dfrac{\partial^2 s}{\partial x \partial \gamma} & \dfrac{\partial^2 s}{\partial y \partial \gamma} & \dfrac{\partial^2 s}{\partial z \partial \gamma} \end{vmatrix},$$

where α, β, γ are any three integration constants occurring in the expression of the function $s(x, y, z; \alpha, \beta, \gamma)$. This determinant is equal to the product of D with the determinant $\dfrac{\partial(\alpha,\beta,\gamma)}{\partial(J_1,J_2,J_3)}$ which is a constant factor playing the role of a normalization constant.

In the special case of uni-dimensional motion the determinant (34 b) reduces to $\partial^2 s/\partial x \partial J$, whereas by direct integration we obtained, in this case, $A^2 = \dfrac{C^2}{v} = mC^2 \Big/ \dfrac{\partial s}{\partial x}$. Thus we must have

$$\frac{\partial^2 s}{\partial x \partial J} = mC^2 \Big/ \frac{\partial s}{\partial x},$$

that is,

$$\frac{\partial s}{\partial x}\frac{\partial}{\partial J}\left(\frac{\partial s}{\partial x}\right) = \frac{\partial}{\partial J}\frac{1}{2}\left(\frac{\partial s}{\partial x}\right)^2 = mC^2,$$

or since $\dfrac{1}{2m}\left(\dfrac{\partial s}{\partial x}\right)^2 = W - U$, we get $\dfrac{\partial}{\partial J}(W-U) = C^2$. This condition is actually fulfilled, for $\partial U/\partial J = 0$ and $\partial W/\partial J = \omega = 1/T$, where T is the period of motion [according to (32 a) with $W = H'$]. Hence we get $C^2 = 1/T$ in accordance with the simple theory developed in the preceding section.

II

OPERATORS

6. Operational Form of Schrödinger's Equation, and Operational Representation of Physical Quantities

The formal relation between classical mechanics and wave mechanics can be presented in another way which not only leads us to a deeper understanding of the theory but also to various important generalizations.

We can arrive at this relation by examining Schrödinger's equation (12) written in the form
$$D\psi = 0,$$
where D denotes the *operator*

$$D \equiv \frac{1}{2m}\left[\left(\frac{h}{2\pi i}\frac{\partial}{\partial x}\right)^2+\left(\frac{h}{2\pi i}\frac{\partial}{\partial y}\right)^2+\left(\frac{h}{2\pi i}\frac{\partial}{\partial z}\right)^2\right]+\frac{h}{2\pi i}\frac{\partial}{\partial t}+U.$$

This can be expressed in terms of the elementary differential operators

$$\frac{h}{2\pi i}\frac{\partial}{\partial x}=p_x, \qquad \frac{h}{2\pi i}\frac{\partial}{\partial y}=p_y, \qquad \frac{h}{2\pi i}\frac{\partial}{\partial z}=p_z, \qquad \frac{h}{2\pi i}\frac{\partial}{\partial t}=p_t \quad (35)$$

by the formula

$$D = \frac{1}{2m}(p_x^2+p_y^2+p_z^2)+p_t+U. \tag{35 a}$$

The equation $D\psi = 0$ thus reduces to the classical equation
$$T+U-W = 0$$
if we replace the operators p_x, p_y, p_z by the components of the momentum, and $-p_t$ by the total energy, i.e. if instead of (35) we put

$$p_x = g_x, \qquad p_y = g_y, \qquad p_z = g_z, \qquad p_t = -W \tag{36}$$

and cancel the function ψ (considering it as a factor). Therefore the transition from classical mechanics to wave mechanics can formally be carried out as follows. In the 'classical' equation

$$\frac{1}{2m}(g_x^2+g_y^2+g_z^2)+U-W = 0, \tag{36 a}$$

which relates the components of the momentum and the total energy of a particle, we must replace these quantities by the elementary operators (35) and then multiply the Schrödinger operator D thus obtained by the wave function ψ on the right, where 'right multiplication' simply means applying the operator to the expression standing on its right.

The replacement of the energy W by the operator $-p_t = -\dfrac{h}{2\pi i}\dfrac{\partial}{\partial t}$ has been made before, although in a somewhat different connexion, namely, in the transition from the wave equation

$$\nabla^2\psi + \frac{8\pi^2 m}{h^2}(W-U)\psi = 0$$

for a conservative motion to the general equation

$$\nabla^2\psi + \frac{8\pi^2 m}{h^2}\left(-\frac{h}{2\pi i}\frac{\partial}{\partial t} - U\right)\psi = 0,$$

which applies to a motion of any kind. In the former case, since $\psi = \psi^0(x,y,z)e^{-i2\pi Wt/h}$, the operator p_t is actually equivalent to the energy in that it satisfies the equation $p_t\psi = -W\psi$, which we could write symbolically (dropping the function operated upon) in the form $p_t = -W$. A similar equivalence exists between the operators p_x, p_y, p_z and the components of the momentum g_x, g_y, g_z with respect to the wave function

$$\psi = \text{const. } e^{i2\pi(g_x x + g_y y + g_z z - Wt)/h},$$

representing the *free* motion of a particle with a velocity of specified magnitude and direction. As we know, the latter can be specified only in this particular case. In the general case the functions $p_x\psi$, $p_y\psi$, $p_z\psi$, $-p_t\psi$ are not equal to the products of the function ψ by constant numbers.

It is natural to associate this result with the fact that, in the general case, the components g_x, g_y, g_z of the momentum, as well as the energy W, cannot be defined as certain numbers since they do not have definite values, and to assume further that the operators p_x, p_y, p_z, $-p_t$ by which they are replaced in the transition from classical to wave mechanics must replace them in all wave-mechanical questions.

This principle is corroborated by the following considerations.

(1) If the wave function ψ can be approximated to by the expression $e^{i2\pi S/h}$ where S is the classical 'action', i.e. the momentum-potential determined by the Hamilton-Jacobi equation, then we have

$$p_x\psi = \frac{h}{2\pi i}\frac{\partial}{\partial x}e^{i2\pi S/h} = e^{i2\pi S/h}\frac{\partial S}{\partial x} = g_x\psi,$$

etc., so that in this approximation the operators p_x, p_y, p_z are actually equivalent to the components of the momentum g_x, g_y, g_z. This result still holds approximately if ψ is represented in the form $Ae^{i2\pi s/h}$ where s is the classical momentum-potential, for the partial derivatives of the amplitude A with regard to x, y, z (so far as the above approximation can be applied) are very small compared with the partial derivatives of s/h, i.e. the components of the wave number (the wave-length being supposed to be very small).

(2) If the function ψ is 'quadratically integrable', i.e. if it can be normalized in such a way that the integral $\int \psi\psi^* \, dV$ is equal to 1, then the integrals

$$\int \psi^* p_x \psi \, dV, \qquad \int \psi^* p_y \psi \, dV, \qquad \int \psi^*_z p\psi \, dV$$

coincide with the average values of the components of the momentum as defined by the integrals

$$m \int j_x \, dV, \qquad m \int j_y \, dV, \qquad m \int j_z \, dV,$$

where $\mathbf{j} = \psi\psi^*\overline{\mathbf{v}}$ is the probability current density and $\overline{\mathbf{v}}$ is the average velocity introduced in the preceding chapter, §§ 2 and 3. We have in fact, according to the definition of j_x,

$$m \int j_x \, dV = \frac{h}{4\pi i} \int \left(\psi^* \frac{\partial \psi}{\partial x} - \psi \frac{\partial \psi^*}{\partial x} \right) dV.$$

Now by partial integration we get

$$\int \psi \frac{\partial \psi^*}{\partial x} \, dV = \int \frac{\partial}{\partial x} (\psi\psi^*) \, dV - \int \psi^* \frac{\partial \psi}{\partial x} \, dV = - \int \psi^* \frac{\partial \psi}{\partial x} dV,$$

since in order that $\int \psi\psi^* \, dV$ should have a finite value the function $\psi\psi^*$ must vanish at infinity rapidly enough to make the integral

$$\int \frac{\partial}{\partial x} (\psi\psi^*) \, dV = \int\int [\psi\psi^*]_{x=-\infty}^{x=+\infty} \, dydz$$

vanish too. Therefore

$$m \int j_x \, dV = \frac{h}{2\pi i} \int \psi^* \frac{\partial \psi}{\partial x} \, dV = \int \psi^* p_x \psi \, dV.$$

The preceding results can be extended to the more complicated operators, by which different classical quantities represented as certain functions of the coordinates and momenta $F(x, y, z; g_x, g_y, g_z)$ must be replaced, when g_x, g_y, g_z are replaced by the operators p_x, p_y, p_z. The simplest example of such a complicated operator is the operator $T = (p_x^2 + p_y^2 + p_z^2)/(2m)$ representing the kinetic energy. If the function ψ describes a motion with a given constant value of the total energy, i.e. if it satisfies the Schrödinger equation $(T + U - W)\psi = 0$, then we have $T\psi = (W - U)\psi$, where the 'operator' $(W - U)$ is a simple factor. The preceding equation expresses the fact that the kinetic energy (i.e. the magnitude of the classical velocity) is a definite function of the coordinates. The sum of the operator T and the potential energy U

represents the total energy of the particle and is usually called the energy operator, or the Hamiltonian operator, or simply the 'Hamiltonian'. Denoting this operator by H, we can write the preceding equation in the form $H\psi = W\psi$. It expresses the fact that the energy of the particle in the motion described by the function ψ has a definite value, namely, W. The general equation referring to a non-conservative motion can be written in the form

$$(H + p_t)\psi = 0. \tag{37}$$

It implies a certain relation between the two operators H and $-p_t$, both of which represent the energy W (when it exists)—the former in a specific way, including the properties of the particle (mass) and the character of the field of force in which it moves, and the latter in a perfectly general way independent of these characteristics.

Independently of the form of the operator $F(x, y, z; p_x, p_y, p_z)$, it can easily be shown that the result of applying it to the function ψ expressed in the approximate form $e^{i2\pi S/h}$ (or $Ae^{i2\pi s/h}$) is equal approximately to the product $F(x, y, z; g_x, g_y, g_z)\psi$. The same is true in the more general case of an operator containing the time t and the time derivative operator p_t. We have namely

$$F(x, y, z, t; p_x, p_y, p_z, p_t)\psi = F(x, y, z, t; g_x, g_y, g_z, -W)\psi,$$

if the energy W is defined as $-\partial S/\partial t$, in accordance with the Hamilton-Jacobi equation which gives $-\partial S/\partial t = (\nabla S)^2/2m + U = T + U$. The function $F\psi$ resulting from the application of the operator F to the *exact* wave function ψ can be represented as the *product* of the latter with a certain function F_C of the coordinates alone (and eventually of the time). The function $F_C = (F\psi)/\psi$ can be defined as the value of the quantity represented by the operator F at the corresponding point (and instant of time). This is precisely the way in which we have defined above the value of the kinetic energy in the case of a conservative motion. If, in particular, the ratio $(F\psi)/\psi$ is equal to a constant C, then the quantity represented by F is said to be a *constant of the motion*, its value C being independent of the position of the particle (and of the time). This case can be illustrated by applying the energy operator H to a function ψ which describes a conservative motion, or by applying any one of the operators p_x, p_y, p_z to the function ψ which describes a uniform rectilinear motion.

If the ratio $F_C = (F\psi)/\psi$ is not equal to a constant, then we can define the average or probable value of the quantity represented by the operator F by means of the formula

$$\bar{F} = \int F_C \psi \psi^* \, dV$$

or
$$\bar{F} = \int \psi^* F \psi \, dV, \tag{38}$$

with the condition that $\int \psi \psi^* \, dV = 1.$ (38 a)

This definition of an average value is a generalization of that already considered in the preceding chapter in connexion with quantities depending on the coordinates alone (such as the potential energy). Its physical significance has been tested above in the case of the fundamental operators p_x, p_y, p_z.

As a further illustration of the operational representation of physical quantities we shall consider the *angular momentum* of a particle, for instance, the angular momentum of an electron moving about a fixed nucleus (cf. Part I, § 14). In classical mechanics this quantity is defined as a vector with the components

$$yg_z - zg_y, \quad zg_x - xg_z, \quad xg_y - yg_x.$$

We shall define it accordingly as a vector-operator **M** with the components

$$M_x = yp_z - zp_y, \qquad M_y = zp_x - xp_z, \qquad M_z = xp_y - yp_x,$$

or
$$\left.\begin{aligned} M_x &= \frac{h}{2\pi i}\left(y\frac{\partial}{\partial z} - z\frac{\partial}{\partial y}\right), \qquad M_y = \frac{h}{2\pi i}\left(z\frac{\partial}{\partial x} - x\frac{\partial}{\partial z}\right) \\ M_z &= \frac{h}{2\pi i}\left(x\frac{\partial}{\partial y} - y\frac{\partial}{\partial x}\right) \end{aligned}\right\} \tag{39}$$

Transforming from rectangular coordinates to spherical coordinates by means of the formulae

$$x = r\sin\theta\cos\phi, \qquad y = r\sin\theta\sin\phi, \qquad z = r\cos\theta,$$

we get
$$\frac{\partial\psi}{\partial r} = \frac{\partial\psi}{\partial x}\frac{\partial x}{\partial r} + \frac{\partial\psi}{\partial y}\frac{\partial y}{\partial r} + \frac{\partial\psi}{\partial z}\frac{\partial z}{\partial r},$$

i.e.
$$r\frac{\partial}{\partial r} = r\sin\theta\cos\phi\frac{\partial}{\partial x} + r\sin\theta\sin\phi\frac{\partial}{\partial y} + r\cos\theta\frac{\partial}{\partial z}$$

$$= x\frac{\partial}{\partial x} + y\frac{\partial}{\partial y} + z\frac{\partial}{\partial z},$$

and likewise
$$\frac{\partial}{\partial\phi} = -r\sin\theta\sin\phi\frac{\partial}{\partial x} + r\sin\theta\cos\phi\frac{\partial}{\partial y} = x\frac{\partial}{\partial y} - y\frac{\partial}{\partial x}.$$

We have therefore $M_z = \frac{h}{2\pi i}\frac{\partial}{\partial\phi}.$ (39 a)

Further, from (39) we get

$$M^2 = M_x^2 + M_y^2 + M_z^2$$

$$= -\frac{h^2}{4\pi^2}\left[y^2\frac{\partial^2}{\partial z^2} + z^2\frac{\partial^2}{\partial y^2} - y\frac{\partial}{\partial z}\left(z\frac{\partial}{\partial y}\right) - z\frac{\partial}{\partial y}\left(y\frac{\partial}{\partial z}\right) + \ldots \right]$$

$$= -\frac{h^2}{4\pi^2}\left[(y^2+z^2)\frac{\partial^2}{\partial x^2} - 2yz\frac{\partial^2}{\partial y\partial z} - 2x\frac{\partial}{\partial x} - \ldots \right]$$

$$= -\frac{h^2}{4\pi^2}\left[(r^2-x^2)\frac{\partial^2}{\partial x^2} - 2yz\frac{\partial^2}{\partial y\partial z} - 2x\frac{\partial}{\partial x} - \ldots \right],$$

where the terms denoted by ... are obtained from the given terms by cyclic permutation of the coordinates x, y, z. Because of the identity

$$\left(x\frac{\partial}{\partial x} + y\frac{\partial}{\partial y} + z\frac{\partial}{\partial z}\right)^2 = x^2\frac{\partial^2}{\partial x^2} + \ldots + x\frac{\partial}{\partial x} + \ldots + 2yz\frac{\partial^2}{\partial y\partial z} + \ldots,$$

or

$$x^2\frac{\partial^2}{\partial x^2} + \ldots + 2yz\frac{\partial^2}{\partial y\partial z} + \ldots = \left(r\frac{\partial}{\partial r}\right)^2 - r\frac{\partial}{\partial r},$$

we can write the previous expression in the form

$$M^2 = -\frac{h^2}{4\pi^2}\left[r^2\left(\frac{\partial^2}{\partial x^2} + \frac{\partial^2}{\partial y^2} + \frac{\partial^2}{\partial z^2}\right) - \left(r\frac{\partial}{\partial r}\right)^2 - r\frac{\partial}{\partial r}\right]$$

$$= -\frac{h^2}{4\pi^2}\left[r^2\nabla^2 - r^2\frac{\partial^2}{\partial r^2} - 2r\frac{\partial}{\partial r}\right].$$

Hence

$$\nabla^2 = -\frac{4\pi^2}{h^2}\frac{1}{r^2}M^2 + \frac{1}{r^2}\left(r\frac{\partial}{\partial r}\right)^2 + \frac{1}{r}\left(\frac{\partial}{\partial r}\right) = -\frac{4\pi^2}{h^2}\frac{M^2}{r^2} + \frac{\partial^2}{\partial r^2} + \frac{2}{r}\frac{\partial}{\partial r},$$

or putting

$$\nabla^2 = \frac{\partial^2}{\partial r^2} + \frac{2}{r}\frac{\partial}{\partial r} + \frac{1}{r^2}\Omega^2,$$

where

$$\Omega^2 = \frac{1}{\sin\theta}\frac{\partial}{\partial\theta}\left(\sin\theta\frac{\partial}{\partial\theta}\right) + \frac{1}{\sin^2\theta}\frac{\partial^2}{\partial\phi^2}$$

denotes the angular part of ∇^2, we get

$$M^2 = -\frac{h^2}{4\pi^2}\Omega^2. \tag{39 b}$$

By applying this operator and the operator (39 a) to the functions $\psi_{nlm} = F_{nl}(r)Y_{lm}(\theta,\phi)$, which specify the stationary states of a hydrogen-like atom, we get

$$M^2\psi_{nlm} = F_{nl}(r)M^2Y_{lm} = -\frac{h^2}{4\pi^2}F_{nl}\Omega^2Y_{lm},$$

and by the equation $\Omega^2Y_{lm} + l(l+1)Y_{lm} = 0$ we get

$$M^2\psi_{nlm} = \frac{h^2}{4\pi^2}l(l+1)\psi_{nlm}. \tag{40}$$

Since, further, the dependence of $Y_{lm}(\theta, \phi)$ upon ϕ is expressed by the factor $e^{im\phi}$,

$$M_z \psi_{nlm} = \frac{hm}{2\pi} \psi_{nlm}. \tag{40a}$$

These relations show that the magnitude of the angular momentum as well as its direction are constants of the motion—just as in the classical theory of a particle moving in a central field of force. It should be mentioned that the character of the central field affects only the radial factor $F_{nl}(r)$ in the wave function ψ_{nlm}, the angular factor $Y_{lm}(\theta, \phi)$ being in all cases a spherical harmonic function. Therefore the above relations hold for the motion of a particle not only in a Coulomb field but in any central field of force. They show further that the quantum numbers l and m which have been introduced in Part I, § 14, as nodal numbers, characterizing the wave function ψ_{nlm} from a purely geometrical point of view, have also a dynamical meaning, one of them (l) determining the total magnitude of the angular momentum according to the relation $M^2 = l(l+1)h^2/4\pi^2$, and the other (m) determining the projection of the angular momentum upon the z-axis according to $M_z = mh/2\pi$. For this reason the numbers l and m will be called respectively the *angular* and the *axial* quantum numbers.† The constancy of the direction of the angular momentum is only proved indirectly by the relation (40a) because the direction of the z-axis can be chosen arbitrarily, the functions ψ_{nlm} being so defined that the z-axis is the axis of the spherical harmonic functions $Y_{lm}(\theta, \phi) = P_{lm}(\theta)e^{im\phi}$. If we apply the operators M_x and M_y to these functions the result will not be similar to that obtained by applying the operator M_z because the functions $M_x \psi_{nlm}$ and $M_y \psi_{nlm}$ are not equal to multiples of ψ_{nlm}. Since we know that M_x and M_y also represent constants of the motion, we see that the condition $F\psi = \text{const.}\,\psi$ cannot be regarded as the general criterion for the constancy of the quantity represented by the operator F. It can easily be shown that the above failure of this equation to express the general condition of dynamical constancy is connected with *degeneracy*, i.e. with the fact that the functions ψ_{nlm} are not determined by the value of the energy W_n which, in fact, depends only on the 'principal' quantum number (n). Any linear combination of the n^2 functions ψ_{nlm}, which differ from one another by the values assigned to the numbers l and m, will also represent a stationary state belonging to the same value of the energy. This linear combination, i.e. the

† This seems preferable to the traditional denomination where l is referred to as the 'azimuthal' quantum number and m as the 'magnetic' quantum number.

coefficients C_{lm} in the sum $\sum_l \sum_m C_{lm}\psi_{nlm}$, can be so chosen that the resulting function ψ_n' will represent the same thing with respect to the x-axis as $\psi_{nl'm'}$ with respect to the z-axis. Applied to *this* function the operator M_x would be equivalent to multiplication by $m'h/2\pi$ according to the equation $M_x\psi_n' = (hm'/2\pi)\psi_n'$ which could be considered as a direct expression of the constancy of M_x. The function obtained by applying M_x to ψ_{nlm} can easily be shown to reduce to a linear combination $\sum_{m'=-l}^{+l} C_{m'}\psi_{nlm'}$ of the $2l+1$ functions ψ_{nlm} associated with the z-axis.

7. Characteristic Functions and Values of Operators; Operational Equations; Constants of the Motion

In general the equation $F\psi = \text{const.}\,\psi$ can only be satisfied by functions ψ of a special type which depend upon the nature of the operator F and are therefore called the *characteristic functions* of this operator ('Eigenfunktionen' of the German authors—often translated into English as 'proper functions'). The corresponding values of the constant factor are called the *characteristic values* of F. As an example we may take Schrödinger's equation $H\psi = W\psi$. In this equation the wave functions describing the stationary states of motion are the characteristic functions of the energy operator H, and the energy-levels W are its characteristic values. In the case of H, as well as in the case of any other operator, these values and the functions associated with them can form both a discrete and a continuous set. The characteristic functions are fully determined by an operator F for a one-dimensional problem, involving one coordinate only. In three-dimensional problems there remains in general a certain ambiguity in the choice of the functions ψ, as determined by a single equation of the type $F\psi = \text{const.}\,\psi$, an ambiguity which is known as 'degeneracy' if F is the energy operator H. Thus, for example, the operator $M_z = \dfrac{h}{2\pi i}\dfrac{\partial}{\partial \phi}$ specifies the corresponding characteristic functions only with regard to their dependence upon m, defining them as $\psi = f(r, \theta)e^{im\phi}$ where $f(r, \theta)$ is an arbitrary function of r and θ. The operator M^2 likewise determines the dependence of the characteristic functions on the angles θ, ϕ only, the equation $M^2\psi = \text{const.}\,\psi$ being satisfied by $\psi = f(r)Y_l(\theta, \phi)$ where $f(r)$ is an arbitrary function of r, and $Y_l(\theta, \phi)$ is an arbitrary spherical harmonic of order l, which can be expressed as a sum of $2l+1$ functions of the type $P_{lm}(\theta)e^{im\phi}$ with arbitrary coefficients.

Now we have also seen that Schrödinger's equation $H\psi = \text{const.}\,\psi$ in the case of a hydrogen-like atom has for each characteristic value of $H = W_n$ a solution of the form $\psi_n = f_n(r)\,Y(\theta, \phi)$, where $Y(\theta, \phi)$ is a sum of n^2 spherical harmonic functions of the type $P_{lm}(\theta)e^{im\phi}$ with arbitrary coefficients $(l = 0, 1, ..., n-1;\ m = -l, ..., +l)$. We cannot therefore completely specify the functions ψ_{nlm} describing the stationary states of a hydrogen atom by taking one of the three equations

$$H\psi = \text{const.}\,\psi, \qquad M^2\psi = \text{const.}\,\psi, \qquad M_z\psi = \text{const.}\,\psi, \qquad (41)$$

but only by taking all three equations together. The functions ψ_{nlm} then appear as the 'simultaneous characteristic functions' of the operators H, M^2, and M_z, each of these functions belonging to a 'triplet' of characteristic values W_n, $(M^2)_l = l(l+1)h^2/4\pi^2$, and $(M_z)_m = mh/2\pi$.

Another simple example of this relationship is provided by the operators p_x, p_y, p_z. The characteristic functions of these operators are obviously $f_1(y,z)e^{i2\pi g_x x/h}$, $f_2(z,x)e^{i2\pi g_y y/h}$, $f_3(x,y)e^{i2\pi g_z z/h}$; f_1, f_2, f_3 being arbitrary functions of the corresponding arguments. Taken together the three equations

$$p_x\psi = g_x\psi, \qquad p_y\psi = g_y\psi, \qquad p_z\psi = g_z\psi, \qquad (41\,\text{a})$$

where g_x, g_y, g_z are constants, specify unambiguously the function

$$\psi = \text{const.}\ e^{i2\pi(g_x x + g_y y + g_z z)/h}, \qquad (41\,\text{b})$$

which describes the uniform rectilinear motion of a particle with the momentum components g_x, g_y, g_z, and which is a *particular* solution of Schrödinger's equation $H\psi = W\psi$ with $H = (p_x^2 + p_y^2 + p_z^2)/2m$, i.e. with $U = 0$, corresponding to free motion.

It should be mentioned that the expression (41 b) for ψ is still incomplete (as well as the expression $\psi = f_n(r)Y_{lm}(\theta, \phi)$ for the hydrogen-like atom functions) inasmuch as it does not contain the *time*. The latter can be introduced by the additional relation

$$-p_t\psi = W\psi,$$

giving $\psi \sim e^{-i2\pi Wt/h}$. The constant W is, however, *not independent*, but is connected with g_x, g_y, g_z by the relation $W = (g_x^2 + g_y^2 + g_z^2)/2m$.

If F is an ordinary function of the coordinates (or of the time too) which does not contain the elementary differential operators p_x, p_y, p_z, then the equation $F\psi = \text{const.}\,\psi$ has no solutions of the ordinary continuous type. The only possible solutions—except the trivial one $\psi = 0$ —are those for which the function ψ is different from zero on the surface $F = \text{const.}$ and vanishes outside this surface (which can be displaced by varying arbitrarily the value of the constant).

Another interesting case is provided by operators which satisfy the equation $F\psi = C\psi$ *identically*, i.e. irrespective of the choice of the function ψ, and therefore do not determine this function at all. $F = p_x x - x p_x$ is the simplest example of such an operator. Applying it to some function ψ, we get

$$F\psi = \frac{h}{2\pi i}\left[\frac{\partial}{\partial x}(x\psi) - x\frac{\partial}{\partial x}\psi\right] = \frac{h}{2\pi i}\,\psi.$$

Thus we see that this operator has one *single* characteristic value $C = h/2\pi i$ with which *any* function can be associated as a 'characteristic function'. The preceding equation can be written symbolically in the form

$$p_x x - x p_x = \frac{h}{2\pi i}, \tag{42}$$

which is obtained by omitting the arbitrary function ψ to which the left- and right-hand sides of this equation must be applied. We have, of course, similar equations for the two other coordinates and the corresponding components of the momentum-operator: $p_y y - y p_y = h/2\pi i$ and $p_z z - z p_z = h/2\pi i$. In addition we have the 'operational' equations $p_x y - y p_x = 0$ or $p_x y = y p_x$, etc., which express the fact that the order in which the operators p_x and y are applied to any function $\psi(x, y, z)$ is immaterial (since x and y are independent variables). The equations $p_x p_y - p_y p_x = 0$ are quite similar to the equations $xy - yx = 0$ expressing the commutative law of ordinary multiplication. Two operators F and G which, when applied successively in the order F, G to any function ψ give the same result as when applied in the opposite order G, F, are said to be *commutable*. This property is expressed symbolically by the operational equation

$$FG = GF, \tag{42 a}$$

which means that the ordinary equation

$$FG\psi = GF\psi$$

is satisfied *identically*, i.e. for any function ψ.

In general, the fact that the equation $A\psi = B\psi$ is satisfied *identically* with respect to the function ψ, A and B being two outwardly different operators, is expressed symbolically by the equation $A = B$. We shall now give a few examples of such operational equations.

Let us consider first of all the operator $F = p_x f - f p_x$ where $f(x, y, z)$ is an arbitrary (continuous) function of the coordinates. Applying it to an arbitrary function ψ, we get

$$F\psi = \frac{h}{2\pi i}\left[\frac{\partial}{\partial x}(f\psi) - f\frac{\partial \psi}{\partial x}\right] = \frac{h}{2\pi i}\frac{\partial f}{\partial x}\psi,$$

so that
$$p_x f - f p_x = \frac{h}{2\pi i}\frac{\partial f}{\partial x}, \tag{43}$$

which means that the operator $p_x f - f p_x$ is equivalent to the multiplier $\frac{h}{2\pi i}\frac{\partial f}{\partial x}$.

The preceding equation is often written in the form
$$\frac{\partial f}{\partial x} = [p_x, f], \tag{43a}$$

where the bracket expression on the right side is defined by
$$[p_x, f] = \frac{2\pi i}{h}(p_x f - f p_x). \tag{43b}$$

If, in the above definition of F, we replace f by x and p_x by p_x^n [which means differentiation of the nth order with regard to x, combined with a multiplication by $(h/2\pi i)^n$], we get
$$F\psi = \left(\frac{h}{2\pi i}\right)^n \left[\frac{\partial^n}{\partial x^n}(x\psi) - x\frac{\partial^n}{\partial x^n}\psi\right] = \left(\frac{h}{2\pi i}\right)^n n\frac{\partial^{n-1}}{\partial x^{n-1}}\psi = \frac{h}{2\pi i}np_x^{n-1}\psi,$$

so that
$$p_x^n x - x p_x^n = \frac{h}{2\pi i}.np_x^{n-1}, \tag{44}$$

which can be rewritten symbolically in the form
$$xp_x^n - p_x^n x = -\frac{h}{2\pi i}\frac{\partial}{\partial p_x}p_x^n.$$

This formula can easily be generalized for any operator expressible as the sum of terms $a_n p_x^n$ with coefficients a_n which do not depend upon the coordinate x. Denoting this operator by $f(p_x, p_y, p_z; y, z)$, we get
$$xf - fx = -\frac{h}{2\pi i}\frac{\partial f}{\partial p_x}, \tag{44a}$$

an equation very similar to (43) with x playing the role of $-p_x$, and p_x the role of x. Putting
$$[x, f] = \frac{2\pi i}{h}(xf - fx) \tag{44b}$$

we can consider the equation
$$\frac{\partial f}{\partial p_x} = -[x, f] \tag{44c}$$

as the general definition of the operator $\partial/\partial p_x$. We shall write in general
$$[F, G] = \frac{2\pi i}{h}(FG - GF), \tag{45}$$

this 'bracket expression' introduced by Dirac as the quantum analogue of the Poisson brackets vanishing if the operators F and G commute with one another.

It should be noticed that an operational equation $A = B$ expresses the *identity* of the physical quantities represented by the operators A and B; the existence of such equations indicates that the same physical quantity can be represented in wave mechanics in a number of apparently different ways.

Another interesting and important illustration of operational equations is provided by the representation of the *angular momentum* of a particle.

From the definition (39) it follows that

$$M_x^2 = (yp_z - zp_y)^2 = (yp_z)^2 - (yp_z)(zp_y) - (zp_y)(yp_z) + (zp_y)^2$$
$$= y^2 p_z^2 + z^2 p_y^2 - y p_y p_z z - z p_z p_y y,$$

since p_y commutes with z and p_z, and p_z commutes with y and p_y. Taking into account the relations $p_z z = z p_z + h/2\pi i$ and $p_y y = y p_y + h/2\pi i$, we get

$$M_x^2 = y^2 p_z^2 + z^2 p_y^2 - 2yz p_y p_z - \frac{h}{2\pi i}(y p_y + z p_z),$$

whence the formula (39 b) can easily be obtained. We have in addition

$$M_x M_y = (yp_z - zp_y)(zp_x - xp_z) = y p_z z p_x - z p_y z p_x - y p_z x p_z + z p_y x p_z$$
$$= y p_x p_z z - z^2 p_y p_x - y x p_z^2 + z x p_y p_z,$$

whence

$$M_x M_y - M_y M_x = y p_x p_z z + z x p_y p_z - x p_y p_z z - z y p_x p_z,$$
$$= (y p_x - x p_y)(p_z z - z p_z) = \frac{h}{2\pi i}(y p_x - x p_y) = -\frac{h}{2\pi i} M_z.$$

Thus, according to (45),

$$[M_x, M_y] = -M_z. \tag{45 a}$$

In a similar way we can derive the relations $[M_y, M_z] = -M_x$ and $[M_z, M_x] = -M_y$, which can also be obtained from (45 a) by a cyclic permutation of the indices x, y, z. These three relations can be replaced by the symbolic vector equation

$$\mathbf{M} \times \mathbf{M} = -\frac{h}{2\pi i}\mathbf{M}, \tag{45 b}$$

where $\mathbf{A} \times \mathbf{B}$ is defined in the usual way as the vector product of $\mathbf{A}$ and $\mathbf{B}$.

Interesting results are obtained by calculating the bracket expressions for the components of the vector $\mathbf{M}$ on the one hand, and the components of the vector $\mathbf{r}(x, y, z)$ or $\mathbf{p}(p_x, p_y, p_z)$ on the other. We shall not go into these calculations (which can easily be carried out by the reader) but shall merely notice the following results:

$$[p^2, \mathbf{M}] = 0, \qquad [p^2, M^2] = 0, \tag{46}$$

where $p^2 = p_x^2 + p_y^2 + p_z^2$, the first of these equations being equivalent to the three equations $[p^2, M_x] = 0$, $[p^2, M_y] = 0$, $[p^2, M_z] = 0$. These equations express the fact that the angular momentum of a particle commutes with its kinetic energy $T = p^2/2m$ (more exactly we should speak of the *operators* representing the angular momentum and the kinetic energy). If the potential energy U is a function of the distance $r = \sqrt{\{x^2+y^2+z^2\}}$ alone (which corresponds to a central field of force), then we also have

$$[U, \mathbf{M}] = 0, \qquad [U, M^2] = 0, \tag{46 a}$$

and consequently

$$[H, \mathbf{M}] = 0, \qquad [H, M^2] = 0, \tag{46 b}$$

where $H = p^2/2m + U$ is the Hamiltonian operator representing the total energy of the particle.

The relations (46 b) can be obtained very simply by using *polar* coordinates to represent H and $\mathbf{M}$. Then

$$H = \frac{1}{2m}\left(\frac{h}{2\pi i}\right)^2\left[\frac{\partial^2}{\partial r^2} + \frac{2}{r}\frac{\partial}{\partial r} + \frac{1}{r^2}\Omega^2\right] + U(r),$$

$$M_z = \frac{h}{2\pi i}\frac{\partial}{\partial \phi}, \qquad M^2 = -\frac{h^2}{4\pi^2}\Omega^2,$$

and so

$$[H, M_z] = \frac{1}{2m}\left(\frac{h}{2\pi i}\right)^3\frac{1}{r^2}\left[\Omega^2, \frac{\partial}{\partial \phi}\right], \qquad [H, M^2] = \frac{1}{2m}\left(\frac{h}{2\pi i}\right)^4\frac{1}{r^2}[\Omega^2, \Omega^2],$$

both bracket expressions $[\Omega^2, \partial/\partial\phi]$ and $[\Omega^2, \Omega^2]$ obviously vanishing.†

The equations (46 b) must be naturally related to the fact that $\mathbf{M}$ and M^2 represent quantities which are constants of the motion (in the case of a radially symmetrical field of force). An equation of the type

$$[H, F] = 0, \tag{47}$$

i.e. the commutability of an operator F with the energy operator H, can actually be considered as the most *general expression of the fact that F represents a constant of the motion* determined by the operator H, i.e. by Schrödinger's equation $H\psi = W\psi$.

In fact, applying the operator F to both sides of this equation, we have $FH\psi = WF\psi$ or, if $HF = FH$, we obtain $H(F\psi) = W(F\psi)$. This shows that the function $F\psi$ satisfies the same equation as the function

---

† In order to obtain (46 a) without the use of polar coordinates we need only notice that $[U, M_z] = [U, yp_x - zp_y] = y[U, p_x] - z[U, p_y] = z\dfrac{\partial U}{\partial y} - y\dfrac{\partial U}{\partial z}$ according to (43 a).

ψ with the same characteristic value of the energy operator H. If there is no degeneracy, i.e. if there is but *one* function ψ associated with the characteristic value W, then $F\psi$ can differ from ψ by a constant factor only (which is immaterial so far as the equation $H\psi = W\psi$ is concerned). Thus in this case we get $F\psi = \text{const.}\,\psi$, which is the original condition for the constancy of the quantity represented by F in the motion described by ψ. In the general case, i.e. when there is degeneracy, the function $F\psi$ must obviously be equal to a linear combination of all the functions ψ_1, ψ_2,..., ψ_r associated with the same characteristic value of H, i.e. satisfying the equation $H\psi_k = W\psi_k$ $(k = 1, 2, ..., r)$, with the same value of the energy. Applying F to one of these functions we thus get, if $FH = HF$,

$$F\psi_k = \sum_{l=1}^{r} c_{kl}\psi_l, \qquad (47\,\mathrm{a})$$

where c_{kl} are constant numbers, the matrix

$$\begin{pmatrix} c_{11} & c_{12} & . & . & . & c_{1r} \\ c_{21} & c_{22} & . & . & . & c_{2r} \\ . & . & . & . & . & . \\ c_{r1} & c_{r2} & . & . & . & c_{rr} \end{pmatrix}$$

replacing the single constant C of the non-degenerate case.

The fact that the equations (47 a) actually express the constancy of F can be proved by reducing them to a system of the standard form

$$F\psi'_n = c'_n \psi'_n, \qquad (47\,\mathrm{b})$$

where ψ'_n $(n = 1, 2, ..., r)$ are a set of r new characteristic functions of H belonging to the same energy-level W as the original functions $\psi_1, ..., \psi_r$ and therefore equal to certain linear combinations of the latter. In order to determine them, we shall first consider the inverse transformation, i.e. we shall express the original functions as linear combinations of the new ones by means of the formulae

$$\psi_k = \sum_{n=1}^{r} a_{kn}\psi'_n. \qquad (48)$$

If these expressions are substituted in equations (47 a), then, in conjunction with (47 b), we get

$$\sum_n a_{kn} c'_n \psi'_n = \sum_l \sum_n c_{kl} a_{ln} \psi'_n.$$

Equating the coefficients of the same ψ'_n and dropping the index n, we get

$$\sum_{l=1}^{r} c_{kl} a_l = c' a_k \qquad (k = 1, 2, ..., r). \qquad (48\,\mathrm{a})$$

This is a system of r linear homogeneous equations for the determina tion both of the transformation coefficients a and of the characteristic values c'. The compatibility condition for equations (48 a)

$$
\begin{vmatrix}
c_{11}-c', & c_{12} & \cdots & c_{1r} \\
c_{21}, & c_{22}-c' & \cdots & c_{2r} \\
\cdots & \cdots & \cdots & \cdots \\
c_{r1}, & c_{r2} & \cdots & c_{rr}-c'
\end{vmatrix} = 0 \tag{48 b}
$$

gives r (in general different) values for the unknown c', and to each of these values c'_n there belongs a definite set of coefficients a_k, namely, $a_{1n}, a_{2n}, ..., a_{rn}$. By solving equations (48) with respect to the ψ'_n, we can obtain the explicit expressions for the new functions in terms of the original ones.

Summing up the preceding results, we can say that the condition $[H, F] = 0$ expresses the constancy of F with respect to all such types of motion as are described by functions ψ satisfying simult..neously the equations $H\psi = \text{const.}\,\psi$ and $F\psi = \text{const.}\,\psi$. The functions ψ are thus simultaneously the characteristic functions of both H and $\cdot$

So far we have regarded the energy as the queen of all the ope..t..rs, but the above considerations seem to banish the energy from this supreme position and to reduce the Schrödinger equation $H\psi = \text{const.}\,\psi$ to the same humble role as that of any other equation $F\psi = \text{const.}\,\psi$ for the characteristic functions and values of any other operator F. Provided the operator F has a dynamical meaning, its characteristic functions will describe the motion just as well as the Schrödinger wave functions although perhaps less completely and from a different point of view. The product $\psi\psi^*$ will represent the probability of finding the particle in the volume-element dV even if ψ is a characteristic function of some operator F different from the energy without being simultaneously a characteristic function of the latter. The above-mentioned difference in the point of view is obviously as follows: if ψ is the characteristic function of Schrödinger's wave equation, then $\psi\psi^*\,dV$ measures the probability of finding the particle in the volume-element dV with a *specified energy* W (the characteristic value of H associated with ψ); if ψ is the characteristic function of some other operator F, then $\psi\psi^*\,dV$ measures the probability of finding the particle in the volume-element dV *with a specified value of the quantity represented by* F.

The fact that the probability determined by some 'wave function' ψ has a *conditional* character only, dependent upon the assumption of a certain specified value for the quantity or quantities by which (or rather by whose operators) the function ψ is characterized, is of fundamental importance for a deeper understanding and further development of wave-mechanical theory. We shall not stress this further here, but shall limit ourselves to the following remarks.

(1) In the case of a one-dimensional motion the Schrödinger wave functions are completely determined by *one* operator only, namely, the energy operator H. This means that the energy is the only *independent* constant of the motion, i.e. that any other operator F commuting with H represents simply a function of H. A function of this kind can be defined by the fact that its characteristic values are a definite function of the characteristic values of H. If, for instance, $H\psi = W\psi$, then

$$H^2\psi = H(H\psi) = HW\psi = WH\psi = W^2\psi, \qquad H^n\psi = W^n\psi,$$

and in general $\qquad\qquad F(H)\psi = F(W)\psi, \qquad\qquad\qquad (49)$

a result which can be proved directly if F is represented by a power series in H with constant coefficients and which can be used as a definition of $F(H)$ in the general case. The wave functions describing the motion of a particle in three dimensions are completely determined not by the energy operator alone, but by *three* independent mutually commuting operators which represent three constants of the motion—if one of them is the energy, or if they indirectly involve the energy, all the three commuting with the latter—such that their common characteristic functions are at the same time solutions of the Schrödinger equation $H\psi = W\psi$.

(2) If the function ψ does not satisfy this equation, then it does not describe the motion, and the operator or operators by which it is defined (according to the equations $F\psi = $ const. ψ) can be said to have *specified* values, but *not constant values*, i.e. values which are *not permanent in time*. Thus time appears as the correlate of energy—a fact which is obvious in view of the possibility of representing the energy not only by the Hamiltonian operator H, but also by the time derivative operator $-p_t = \dfrac{h}{2\pi i}\dfrac{\partial}{\partial t}$, the general form of the Schrödinger equation $(H+p_t)\psi = 0$ merely expressing the equivalence of the two representations with respect to a certain set of functions.

8. Probable Values of Physical Quantities and their Change with the Time

In classical mechanics time enjoys a supreme role entirely different from all the other variables, being actually the only independent variable. The main problem of mechanics is to determine how all the other variables—in particular the coordinates—change with the time. In wave mechanics the time seems, at first sight, to be reduced to a humbler role, since the spatial coordinates no longer depend on the time but are treated—so far as the wave-mechanical 'equation of motion' is concerned—as independent variables, that is, they appear on the same footing as the time itself.

This equivalence between the spatial coordinates and the time is restricted, however, as we know, to the wave equation $(H+p_t)\psi = 0$ and does not extend to the boundary conditions under which it has to be solved nor to the interpretation of its solutions. Thus a function $\psi(x, y, z, t)$ which satisfies the preceding equation is interpreted as the measure of the probability of finding the particle under consideration in a volume-element $dV = dx dy dz$ at a *definite instant of time*, the probability in question being defined as equal or proportional to $\psi\psi^*\, dV$. If time played the same role as the coordinates, we should not be able to refer the probability to a definite *instant* of time but should instead refer it to an *interval* of time dt, and define it as proportional to $\psi\psi^*\, dV dt$. There is, however, actually no reason why we should not be able to refer the probability of location to a given instant of time—for the particle must be *somewhere* at any moment. The exceptional role of the time becomes particularly clear if we restrict ourselves to solutions of the Schrödinger equation which vanish at infinite distance (they cannot vanish for $t = \pm\infty$ except in separate places!) in such a way as to ensure the convergence of the integral $\int \psi\psi^*\, dV$ extended over all space. Taking the time derivative of this integral and replacing $\partial(\psi\psi^*)/\partial t$ by $-\mathrm{div}\, j$, where $j = \dfrac{h}{4\pi i m}\,(\psi^*\nabla\psi - \psi\nabla\psi^*)$ is the probability current density, then, if the integration is first extended over a finite volume limited by a closed surface, we get

$$\frac{\partial}{\partial t}\int \psi\psi^*\, dV = -\oint j_n\, dS, \qquad (50)$$

where J_n is the normal component of j. When the surface S is removed to infinity the latter integral tends to zero (so long as ψ is supposed to be quadratically integrable), so that in the limit we get

$$\int_\infty \psi\psi^*\, dV = \mathrm{const.},$$

which enables one to normalize ψ to 1 by the condition

$$\int_\infty \psi\psi^*\, dV = 1. \qquad (50\,\mathrm{a})$$

It should be remarked that this result holds for the motion of the particle not only in a constant field of force (this case has been considered in § 17, Part I), but also in a variable field of force.

Now if $\int \psi\psi^* \, dV$ is constant, it is futile to consider the integral $\iint \psi\psi^* \, dVdt$ with a view to normalizing the function ψ in such a way that the time would appear on the same footing as the coordinates. The Hamiltonian operator H, which, as we have seen, is intimately connected with the time, must therefore play an exceptional role in determining the permanence or non-permanence in time of different quantities connected with the motion.

As has been shown before, this permanence is determined by the condition $HF - FH = 0$, where F is the operator representing the quantity in question. We are now going to generalize this result for quantities which are not constants of the motion, i.e. quantities for which the condition $HF - FH = 0$ is not fulfilled.

In classical mechanics such quantities can be determined as functions of the time. In wave mechanics such a determination is only possible for their probable values, as defined by

$$\overline{F} = \int \psi^* F \psi \, dV,$$

under the condition (50 a) (which is fulfilled for a motion restricted to a finite region or represented by a wave packet).

Differentiating $\overline{F}$ with regard to the time, and taking into account the equations $\left(H + \dfrac{h}{2\pi i} \dfrac{\partial}{\partial t}\right)\psi = 0$, $\left(H - \dfrac{h}{2\pi i} \dfrac{\partial}{\partial t}\right)\psi^* = 0$, we get

$$\frac{d\overline{F}}{dt} = \frac{2\pi i}{h} \int [(H\psi^*)(F\psi) - \psi^* F(H\psi)] \, dV.$$

Now it can easily be proved that

$$\int (H\psi^*)(F\psi) \, dV = \int \psi^* H(F\psi) \, dV.$$

In fact, putting $F\psi = f_1$, $\psi^* = f_2$, and writing the operator H in the form

$$H = \frac{1}{2m}\left(\frac{h}{2\pi i}\right)^2\left(\frac{\partial^2}{\partial x^2} + \frac{\partial^2}{\partial y^2} + \frac{\partial^2}{\partial z^2}\right) + U,$$

we find

$$\begin{aligned}
\int (f_1 H f_2 - f_2 H f_1) \, dV &= \frac{1}{2m}\left(\frac{h}{2\pi i}\right)^2 \int \left[\frac{\partial}{\partial x}\left(f_1 \frac{\partial}{\partial x} f_2 - f_2 \frac{\partial}{\partial x} f_1\right) + \right.\\
&\quad \left. + \frac{\partial}{\partial y}\left(f_1 \frac{\partial}{\partial y} f_2 - f_2 \frac{\partial}{\partial x} f_1\right) + \frac{\partial}{\partial z}\left(f_1 \frac{\partial}{\partial z} f_2 - f_2 \frac{\partial}{\partial z} f_1\right)\right] dV \\
&= \frac{1}{2m}\left(\frac{h}{2\pi i}\right)^2 \int \operatorname{div} \mathbf{f}_{12} \, dV,
\end{aligned}$$

where $$\mathbf{f}_{12} = f_1 \nabla f_2 - f_2 \nabla f_1.$$

If the integral $$\int_\infty f_1 f_2 \, dV$$

is convergent, then the integral $\int \operatorname{div} \mathbf{f}_{12} \, dV = \int f_{12n} \, dS$ must vanish when the integration is extended over all space (the surface S receding to infinity), so that we get

$$\int f_1 H f_2 \, dV = \int f_2 H f_1 \, dV. \tag{51}$$

It should be mentioned that all operators having the property expressed by this equation are called 'self-adjoint'. Strictly speaking, the self-adjointness of an operator H is expressed by the fact that the difference $f_1 H f_2 - f_2 H f_1$ is equal to the *divergence* of some vector; this condition leads to (51) when combined with the condition

$$\int f_1 f_2 \, dV = \text{finite.} \tag{51 a}$$

The latter condition is certainly fulfilled for $f_1 = F\psi$ and $f_2 = \psi^*$ so long as (50 a) is fulfilled.

We thus can rewrite the above expression for $d\bar{F}/dt$ in the form

$$\frac{d\bar{F}}{dt} = \frac{2\pi i}{h} \int \left[\psi^* H(F\psi) - \psi^* F(H\psi)\right] dV,$$

or

$$\frac{d\bar{F}}{dt} = \frac{2\pi i}{h} \int \psi^* (HF - FH)\psi \, dV. \tag{52}$$

It follows from this formula that $d\bar{F}/dt = 0$, which means that F is a constant of the motion, if $HF = FH$. This agrees with the result found before. According to the general definition of the probable value of a quantity represented by some operator F, we can define the right-hand side of (52) as the average value of the operator

$$\frac{2\pi i}{h}(HF - FH) = [H, F].$$

Therefore

$$\frac{d\bar{F}}{dt} = \overline{[H, F]},$$

or

$$\frac{dF}{dt} = [H, F], \tag{52 a}$$

if dF/dt is regarded as an operator *defined* by equation (52 a) and satisfying the condition

$$\frac{\overline{dF}}{dt} = \frac{d}{dt} \bar{F}.$$

In the derivation of (52 a) we have tacitly assumed that F did not contain the time explicitly. If it does contain the time, then equation (52 a) must be replaced by

$$\frac{dF}{dt} = \frac{\partial F}{\partial t} + [H, F]. \tag{52 b}$$

For example, let us put $F = x$. The time derivative of x as a *quantity* is equal to zero, since x is independent of t. Regarding x, or rather dx/dt, as an operator, however, we have

$$\frac{dx}{dt} = [H, x] = -[x, H],$$

or according to (44 c)

$$\frac{dx}{dt} = \frac{\partial H}{\partial p_x}, \tag{53}$$

which, with

$$H = \frac{1}{2m}(p_x^2 + p_y^2 + p_z^2) + U(x, y, z),$$

gives

$$\frac{dx}{dt} = \frac{1}{m} p_x. \tag{53 a}$$

This equation coincides superficially with the classical relation between velocity and momentum, considered as *definite quantities*. In wave mechanics, however, they are indefinite quantities represented by the operators $d\mathbf{r}/dt$ and $\mathbf{p} = m d\mathbf{r}/dt$. Putting $F = p_x$, we have

$$\frac{dp_x}{dt} = [H, p_x] = [U, p_x] = -[p_x, U]$$

or, according to (43 a),

$$\frac{dp_x}{dt} = -\frac{\partial H}{\partial x} = -\frac{\partial U}{\partial x}. \tag{53 b}$$

Equations (53) and (53 b), together with the corresponding equations for the y and z components, are formally identical with the classical equations of motion in the 'canonical' form (see preceding chapter, § 5). If the classical quantity represented by the operator F is defined as a function of the time and of the (classical) variables x, p_x; y, p_y; z, p_z, we have

$$\frac{dF}{dt} = \frac{\partial F}{\partial t} + \sum_{x,y,z} \left(\frac{\partial F}{\partial x}\frac{dx}{dt} + \frac{\partial F}{\partial p_x}\frac{dp_x}{dt} \right) = \frac{\partial F}{\partial t} + \sum_{x,y,z}\left(\frac{\partial H}{\partial p_x}\frac{\partial F}{\partial x} - \frac{\partial H}{\partial x}\frac{\partial F}{\partial p_x} \right) \tag{53 c}$$

according to (53) and (53 b). Comparing this with (52 b) we see that the classical analogue of the quantum bracket expression $[H, F]$ is the sum $\sum_{x,y,z}\left(\frac{\partial H}{\partial p_x}\frac{\partial F}{\partial x} - \frac{\partial H}{\partial x}\frac{\partial F}{\partial p_x} \right)$ which is the classical Poisson bracket expression.

Equation (52 a) looks very similar to equation (43) and the equations corresponding to the other two coordinates, namely,

$$\frac{\partial f}{\partial x} = [p_x, f], \qquad \frac{\partial f}{\partial y} = [p_y, f], \qquad \frac{\partial f}{\partial z} = [p_z, f], \tag{54}$$

the time t being related to the energy operator H in the same way as the coordinates x, y, z are related to the operators p_x, p_y, p_z representing the components of momentum. This relationship seems very natural from the point of view of the relativity theory and seems to indicate that time and energy must be treated on the same footing as the spatial coordinates and the components of the momentum. The similarity between the relations $dF/dt = [H, F]$ and $\partial f/\partial x = [p_x, f]$ is, however, only apparent—for in the latter case f denotes a function or operator depending explicitly upon x, and $\partial/\partial x$ denotes partial differentiation with regard to x, while in the former case F is a function or operator which does *not* contain t explicitly. The time equivalent of equations (54) is easily seen to be

$$\frac{\partial f}{\partial t} = [p_t, f]. \tag{54 a}$$

This equation follows immediately from the definition of the operator $p_t = \frac{h}{2\pi i}\frac{\partial}{\partial t}$. Replacing $\partial F/\partial t$ in (52 b) by $[p_t, F]$, we get

$$\frac{dF}{dt} = [(H + p_t), F]. \tag{54 b}$$

It should be noticed that the operator $H + p_t$ *does not vanish* identically, as might appear from the equation $(H + p_t)\psi = 0$, but only with respect to the functions defined by this equation and describing the general type of motion determined by the Hamiltonian H. The fact that there are actually *two different* operators H and $-p_t$ representing the same quantity, i.e. the energy, and equivalent to one another with respect to the wave functions describing the motion of the particle, suggests the possibility of restoring the symmetry between time and space which is required by the relativity theory by introducing certain operators G_x, G_y, G_z which, though entirely different from p_x, p_y, p_z, would represent the same thing as the latter, i.e. the components of the momentum. The operators G would have to be defined so as to be equivalent to the corresponding p with respect to the *same wave functions* as the operators H and $-p_t$. If this were possible, we could replace the time in its exceptional role by any one of the three coordinates x, y, z, e.g. we could define the wave functions by an equation of the type

$(G_x - p_x)\psi = 0$, and interpret $\psi\psi^*\, dydzdt$ as the probability of finding the particle in the region specified by dy, dz, and dt for a definite value of its x-coordinate. We could further define the average or probable value of an operator by the formula $\bar{F} = \iiint \psi^* F \psi\, dydzdt$ as a definite function of x and obtain for its derivative with respect to x an expression similar to (52) or (52 b), i.e.

$$\frac{dF}{dx} = \frac{\partial F}{\partial x} + [G_x, F] = [G_x + p_x, F],$$

provided the operator G_x were self-adjoint, in the same sense as H.

This relativistic symmetry between space and time, as expressed by the equal eligibility of any one of the four quantities x, y, z, t, and the associated quantities G_x, G_y, G_z, H to the presidential role which has hitherto been enjoyed only by t and H, cannot, however, be attained if we retain the definition of the Hamiltonian operator

$$H = \frac{1}{2m}(p_x^2 + p_y^2 + p_z^2) + U$$

which has so far been used and which corresponds to pre-relativistic classical mechanics. This follows from the unsymmetrical way in which the operators p_x, p_y, p_z, and p_t are involved in the equation $(H + p_t)\psi = 0$.

It is possible, however, to modify the Schrödinger equation so as to secure the desired symmetry enabling one to formulate it in either of the four equivalent ways $(G_x - p_x)\psi = 0$, $(G_y - p_y)\psi = 0$, $(G_z - p_z)\psi = 0$, $(H + p_t)\psi = 0$ in agreement with the relativity theory. This modification (due to Dirac) will be considered later (Chap. VI).

9. The Variational Form of the Schrödinger Equation and its Application to the Perturbation Theory

If the potential energy U does not involve the time explicitly, then the equation $(H + p_t)\psi$ has, as we know, particular solutions of the type $\psi = \psi^0(x, y, z)e^{-i2\pi Wt/h}$, where the 'amplitude' function $\psi^0(x, y, z)$ satisfies the equation $H\psi^0 = W\psi^0$ (which has been written before in the equivalent form $H\psi = W\psi$). Multiplying it by ψ^{0*} and integrating over the whole space, then if, as we shall assume in future, $\int \psi^{0*}\psi^0\, dV = 1$, we get

$$\int \psi^{0*} H \psi^0\, dV = W. \tag{55}$$

This is just what we should expect, since, according to the general definition of probable (average) values, the integral

$$\int \psi^{0*} H \psi^0\, dV = \int \psi^* H \psi\, dV = \bar{H}$$

is the probable value W of the energy which is a constant of the motion. We shall now show that the function ψ^0, which may be called the characteristic function of the operator H (the time factor being irrelevant so far as the equation $H\psi = W\psi$ is concerned), can be determined from the variational principle

$$\delta\bar{H} \equiv \delta \int \psi^{0*}H\psi^0 \, dV = 0, \qquad (55\,\text{a})$$

in conjunction with the normalization condition

$$\int \psi\psi^* \, dV = 1. \qquad (55\,\text{b})$$

We have in fact

$$\delta\bar{H} = \int \delta\psi^{0*}H\psi^0 \, dV + \int \psi^{0*}H\delta\psi^0 \, dV,$$

or, according to (51), i.e. because of the self-adjointness of H and because of the convergence of the integral $\int \psi^{0*}\delta\psi^0 \, dV$,

$$\delta\bar{H} = \int \delta\psi^{0*}H\psi^0 \, dV + \int \delta\psi^0 H\psi^{0*} \, dV. \qquad (56)$$

Further, (55 b) gives

$$\int \delta\psi^{0*}\psi^0 \, dV + \int \delta\psi^0\psi^{0*} \, dV = 0. \qquad (56\,\text{a})$$

So long as the function ψ^0 is looked for as a complex quantity, it is equivalent to *two* real functions. We could therefore consider ψ^0 and ψ^{0*} as two *independent* unknown functions, and treat their variations as arbitrary independent infinitesimal quantities, were it not for the condition (56 a). According to the Lagrange 'method of multipliers', this dependence can be removed by multiplying (56 a) by some constant factor C and subtracting the result from (56). This gives

$$\int \delta\psi^{0*}(H\psi^0 - C\psi^0) \, dV + \int \delta\psi^0(H\psi^{0*} - C\psi^{0*}) \, dV = 0,$$

and since $\delta\psi^{0*}$ and $\delta\psi^0$ can now be regarded as completely arbitrary, we must have $H\psi^0 = C\psi^0$ and $H\psi^{0*} = C\psi^{0*}$.

Thus from (55 a) and (55 b) we have obtained the Schrödinger equation for the function ψ^0 and its conjugate complex function. The energy W appears in the variational method as the value of Lagrange's multiplier associated with the function ψ^0, and the Schrödinger equation appears as the variational equation of Euler and Lagrange corresponding to the 'conditional extremum' of the integral $\bar{H} = \int \psi^{0*}H\psi^0 \, dV$. This integral can be written in a somewhat different form—a form which contains only the first derivatives of the functions ψ^0 and ψ^{0*} (as it must do if the variational equation is of the second order). We have in fact

$$\psi^{0*}\frac{\partial^2}{\partial x^2}\psi^0 = \frac{\partial}{\partial x}\left(\psi^{0*}\frac{\partial\psi^0}{\partial x}\right) - \frac{\partial\psi^{0*}}{\partial x}\frac{\partial\psi^0}{\partial x},$$

and consequently

$$\int \psi^{0*}H\psi^0\,dV$$

$$= \frac{1}{2m}\left(\frac{h}{2\pi i}\right)^2\left[\int \operatorname{div}(\psi^{0*}\nabla\psi^0)\,dV - \int \nabla\psi^{0*}\nabla\psi^0\,dV\right] + \int U\psi^{0*}\psi^0\,dV,$$

or, since the first integral in the square brackets vanishes,

$$\bar{H} = \int \left(\frac{h^2}{8\pi^2 m}\nabla\psi^{0*}\nabla\psi^0 + U\psi^{0*}\psi^0\right)dV. \tag{57}$$

Putting $\mathbf{p} = \frac{h}{2\pi i}\nabla$, we can rewrite this expression in the form

$$\bar{H} = \int \left(\frac{1}{2m}|\mathbf{p}\psi^0|^2 + U|\psi^0|^2\right)dV, \tag{57a}$$

where $|\mathbf{p}\psi^0|^2$ is the scalar product of the vector $\mathbf{p}\psi^0$ and the conjugate complex vector $\mathbf{p}^*\psi^{0*} = -\frac{h}{2\pi i}\nabla\psi^{0*}$. If, in addition, we introduce the function $S = \frac{h}{2\pi i}\log\psi^0$, and so replace $\mathbf{p}\psi^0$ by $\psi^0\nabla S$, we get

$$\bar{H} = \int \left(\frac{1}{2m}|\nabla S|^2 + U\right)|\psi^0|^2\,dV. \tag{57b}$$

The integrand of this expression looks exactly like the classical expression for the total energy (S_0 being the Hamilton-Jacobi action function) multiplied by $|\psi^0|^2$. It is worthy of remark that Schrödinger first obtained his wave equation by applying the variation principle to the integral (57 b), without fully realizing at that time (beginning of 1926) its physical meaning.

The variational equation $\delta\bar{H} = 0$ does not mean that the values of $\bar{H} = W$ obtained from it (with the condition $\int \psi^0\psi^{0*}\,dV = 1$) are minimum or maximum values compared with those corresponding to slightly varied functions ψ^0. In order to find out whether we actually have an extremum or only a stationary value, we must calculate the variation of $\bar{H}$ to the second approximation, i.e. to the second order of the small quantities $\delta\psi^0$ and $\delta\psi^{0*}$.

We thus get

$$\Delta\bar{H} = \int (\psi^{0*}+\delta\psi^{0*})H(\psi^0+\delta\psi^0)\,dV - \int \psi^{0*}H\psi^0\,dV,$$

$$= \int \delta\psi^{0*}H\psi^0\,dV + \int \psi^{0*}H\delta\psi^0\,dV + \int \delta\psi^{0*}H\delta\psi^0\,dV.$$

On the other hand, we must have

$$\int (\psi^{0*}+\delta\psi^{0*})(\psi^0+\delta\psi^0)\, dV - \int \psi^{0*}\psi^0\, dV$$

$$= \int \delta\psi^{0*}\psi^0\, dV + \int \psi^{0*}\delta\psi^0\, dV + \int \delta\psi^{0*}\delta\psi^0\, dV = 0.$$

Multiplying this equation by the value of W corresponding to the function ψ^0 and subtracting it from the first, we get, since ψ^0 and ψ^{0*} satisfy the equations $H\psi^0 = W\psi^0$, $H\psi^{0*} = W\psi^{0*}$,

$$\Delta\bar{H} = \int \delta\psi^{0*}(H-W)\delta\psi^0\, dV, \tag{58}$$

which can also be written in the form

$$\Delta\bar{H} = \int \left[\frac{1}{2m}\,|\mathbf{p}\delta\psi^0|^2 + (U-W)|\delta\psi^0|^2\right] dV. \tag{58a}$$

This expression can be considered as the second variation of $\bar{H}$, since it is a small quantity of the second order. Its sign is, in general, uncertain: it may be positive for some variations $\delta\psi$ and negative for others. The values $\bar{H} = W$ given by the variational principle $\delta\bar{H} = 0$ must therefore be regarded as *stationary* and not as minimum or maximum values. The preceding results are simplified if we assume (as we·are usually entitled to do when we are dealing with stationary states with no magnetic field present) that the wave function ψ^0 is real; we need hardly however, restate them in this simplified form.

The variational principle provides us with a very simple and important method for obtaining approximate solutions of Schrödinger's equation and determining the corresponding energy values—or rather for *improving* such approximate solutions and energy values after they have been obtained by some other method.† Thus the variational method is useful in determining the motion due to a field of force which is slightly different from some simpler field of force for which the motion is supposed to be known. The solution of this question is one of the two main problems of the *perturbation theory*, the other problem being the determination of transition probabilities which has already been considered briefly in Part I. We shall give a detailed treatment of the perturbation theory in a later chapter. At present we shall briefly indicate those of its results which can be obtained, in a straightforward way, by the variational method.

---

† The method of reducing the solution of a differential equation of the type $H\psi^0 = W\psi^0$ to a variational problem has been worked out by Lord Rayleigh and much later by W. Ritz in connexion with the problems of the vibration of elastic bodies, which are formally very similar to the problem of the motion of a particle in wave mechanics.

Let us suppose that, somehow or other, we have obtained a function $\phi^0(x, y, z; a)$ which we know to be capable of approximately representing one of the characteristic functions of the operator H provided the undetermined parameter a, contained in it, is suitably chosen. Then this particular value of a can be determined from the equation

$$\frac{\partial \overline{H}(a)}{\partial a} = W \frac{\partial E(a)}{\partial a}, \tag{59}$$

where

$$\overline{H}(a) = \int \phi^{0*}(x, y, z; a) H \phi^0(x, y, z; a) \, dV, \tag{59 a}$$

and

$$E(a) = \int \phi^{0*} \phi^0 \, dV, \tag{59 b}$$

in conjunction with the relation $\overline{H}(a) = W$, which gives the corresponding value of the energy. If the function is normalized to 1 (according to $E = 1$) for every value of a, equation (59) can be replaced by $\partial H(a)/\partial a = 0$.

This method, which is often used in practice, can be generalized to include the case when the function ϕ^0 contains many unknown parameters $a_1, a_2, ..., a_r$, the closeness of the approximation in general increasing with the number r of these parameters. We come upon a particularly simple and interesting case of such an approximation in the perturbation theory of a *degenerate* motion, where we have, in the absence of the perturbation, a set of wave functions $\psi_1^0(x, y, z)$, $\psi_2^0(x, y, z), ..., \psi_r^0(x, y, z)$ representing different states of motion with the same energy W. Let us assume that the potential energy U has been replaced by U', the difference $U' - U$ corresponding to a small perturbing field of force (for example, an external electric field of force). The energy operator $H = p^2/2m + U$ must then be replaced by the operator $H' = p^2/2m + U' = H + U' - U$, and the functions $\psi_1^0, \psi_2^0, ..., \psi_r^0$ must be replaced by a set of r functions $\psi_1^{0\prime}, \psi_2^{0\prime}, ..., \psi_r^{0\prime}$ referring to r states of motion with nearly the same energy, i.e. belonging to r energy values $W_1', W_2', ..., W_r'$ which are slightly different from one another and from the approximate value W corresponding to the absence of perturbing forces (the latter are, of course, supposed to be independent of the time). Now the functions $\psi_l^{0\prime}$ can be represented approximately as linear combinations of the functions ψ_k^0 with unknown coefficients. Thus we may write

$$\psi_{k'}^{0\prime} = \sum_{k=1}^{r} a_{kk'} \psi_k^0, \tag{60}$$

the r coefficients $a_{1k'}, a_{2k'}, ..., a_{rk'}$ appearing in the expression of each function $\psi_l^{0\prime}$ playing the role of the r parameters mentioned above.

Dropping the index k' and substituting the expression $\psi^{0'} = \sum a_k \psi_k^0$ in the integrals

$$\overline{H}' = \int \psi^{0'*} H' \psi^{0'}\, dV \quad \text{and} \quad E' = \int \psi^{0'*} \psi^{0'}\, dV$$

we get

$$\overline{H}' = \sum_{k=1}^{r} \sum_{l=1}^{r} H_{kl}' a_k^* a_l, \tag{60 a}$$

$$E' = \sum_{k=1}^{r} \sum_{l=1}^{r} E_{kl} a_k^* a_l, \tag{60 b}$$

where

$$H_{kl}' = \int \psi_k^0{}^* H' \psi_l^0\, dV, \tag{60 c}$$

$$E_{kl}' = \int \psi_k^0{}^* \psi_l^0\, dV. \tag{60 d}$$

The expressions (60 c) are the matrix elements of the energy operator H' of the 'perturbed' motion with regard to the characteristic functions describing the unperturbed types of motion associated with the same energy W. Since these functions need not be orthogonal, the expressions E_{kl} may be different from zero for $k \neq l$.

The variational principle $\delta \overline{H}' = 0$, together with the condition $E' = 1$, gives the following equations:

$$\frac{\partial \overline{H}'}{\partial a_k^*} = W' \frac{\partial E'}{\partial a_k^*}, \qquad \frac{\partial \overline{H}'}{\partial a_l} = W' \frac{\partial E'}{\partial a_l},$$

i.e.

$$\sum_{l=1}^{r} (H_{kl}' - W' E_{kl}) a_l = 0 \qquad (k = 1, 2, ..., r), \tag{61}$$

$$\sum_{k=1}^{r} (H_{kl}' - W' E_{kl}) a_k^* = 0. \tag{61 a}$$

The second group can be obtained from the first by a change to conjugate complex quantities in conjunction with the 'Hermitian' relations (Part I, § 17) $H_{kl}'^* = H_{lk}'$ and $E_{kl} = E_{lk}^*$,

and therefore need not be considered separately. The compatibility condition for the r linear homogeneous equations (61) runs

$$\begin{vmatrix} H_{11}' - W' E_{11} & H_{12}' - W' E_{12} & \cdot & \cdot & \cdot & H_{1r}' - W' E_{1r} \\ H_{21}' - W' E_{21} & H_{22}' - W' E_{22} & \cdot & \cdot & \cdot & H_{2r}' - W' E_{2r} \\ \cdot & \cdot & \cdot & \cdot & \cdot & \cdot \\ H_{r1}' - W' E_{r1} & H_{r2}' - W' E_{r2} & \cdot & \cdot & \cdot & H_{rr}' - W' E_{rr} \end{vmatrix} = 0. \tag{61 b}$$

This is an equation of the rth degree for W'; its roots W_1', W_2',..., W_r are the required (approximate) values of the energy. The coefficients

$$a_{1k'}, a_{2k'}, ..., a_{rk'}$$

L

corresponding to $W' = W'_{k'}$ according to (61), specify, by means of equation (60), that type of perturbed motion which has the energy $W'_{k'}$. We thus see that the r types of unperturbed motion which have the same energy W and which are described by the functions $\psi_1^0,...,\psi_r^0$ actually give rise, under the influence of the perturbation, to the same number of different types of motion, but these, in general, now have different energies $W'_1,...,W'_r$. This phenomenon is denoted as the 'splitting up' of a multiple energy-level, by the influence of perturbing forces, into a number of 'sub-levels'. The Zeeman and Stark effects, i.e. the splitting of the spectrum lines under the influence of a magnetic or electric field, are examples of this.

It should be mentioned that if the functions ψ_k^0 are orthogonal and normalized to 1, i.e. if E_{kl} is equal to 0 for $k \neq l$ and to 1 for $k = l$, equations (61) assume the form

$$\sum_{l=1}^{r} H'_{kl} a_l = W' a_k \qquad (k = 1, 2,...,r), \qquad (62)$$

and the compatibility equation for determining the energy values reduces to

$$\begin{vmatrix} H'_{11} - W' & H'_{12} & . & . & . & H'_{1r} \\ H'_{21} & H'_{22} - W' & . & . & . & H'_{2r} \\ . & . & . & . & . & . & . & . \\ H'_{r1} & H'_{r2} & . & . & . & H'_{rr} - W' \end{vmatrix} = 0. \qquad (62\,a)$$

Equations (60), (62), and (62 a) closely resemble equations (48), (48 a), and (48 b) derived in § 7 for the determination of the characteristic values of an operator F which is a constant of a motion *involving degeneracy*. Actually they are identical, but this is slightly masked by a difference in notation. If we replace F by H', reverse the role of the 'old' and 'new' functions ψ and ψ', replacing the ψ by $\psi^{0'}$ and the ψ' by ψ^0, and in addition write H'_{kl} instead of c_{kl} and W' instead of c', then equations (48), (48 a), and (48 b) assume the form of (60), (62), and (62 a) respectively. This coincidence shows that the *operators H and H' must commute with one another*, i.e. that, to the degree of approximation obtained by the perturbation theory sketched above, the perturbation energy $H'-H$ is to be considered as *a constant of the unperturbed motion specified by H*.

This perturbation theory can easily be improved and generalized in such a way as to become what is called *a transformation theory*, the primary object of which is to derive exactly the characteristic functions and values of a certain operator H' from the characteristic functions and values of some other operator H. The solution of this problem is given by the preceding equations if, in the first place, we drop the assumption that the original (amplitude) functions $\psi_1^0, \psi_2^0, ..., \psi_r^0$ belong to the same energy-level, and if, in addition, we increase r to infinity, so as to use the *complete* set of functions and energy-levels belonging to the operator H. Equations (60) and (61) or (62), in conjunction with (61 b) or (62 a) will then determine the complete set of functions and energy values characteristic of the operator H'. Further generalizations of this transformation theory involving operators different from the energy and variables different from the coordinates will be examined later (Chap. IV).

It should be mentioned here that the reduction of an equation of the form $F\psi = C\psi$ to a variational principle of the form

$$\delta \overline{F} = \delta \int \psi^* F \psi \, dV = 0$$

(with the condition $\int \psi \psi^* \, dV = 1$) is possible not only when F is the energy operator H, but in the case of all operators which are 'self-adjoint', i.e. for which $f_1 \, F f_2 - f_2 \, F f_1 =$ the divergence of some vector. Actually it is not necessary for the integral $\int \psi \psi^* \, dV$ to converge. The only assumption which it is necessary to make in order to obtain the differential equation $F\psi = C\psi$ from the variational equation $\delta \overline{F} = 0$ is that $E = \int \psi \psi^* \, dV$ should be constant ($\delta E = 0$).

10. Orthogonality and Normalization of Characteristic Functions for Discrete and Continuous Spectra

The characteristic functions ψ^0 obtained by the variation principle, under the condition $\int \psi^0 \psi^{0*} \, dV = $ const., or by the direct solution of the equation $H\psi^0 = W\psi^0$, can form both a discrete and a continuous set corresponding to a discrete or a continuous set of energy values W. The energy values are therefore said to form a discrete or a continuous *spectrum* of the energy operator H. As we know from the general discussion of § 15, Part I, and from the examples of the oscillator and the hydrogen atom, a discrete spectrum is associated with characteristic functions which—because of 'total reflection'—vanish at infinity so rapidly that the integral $\int \psi^0 \psi^{0*} \, dV$ converges. This makes it possible to normalize them to 1 by means of the equation $\int \psi^0 \psi^{0*} \, dV = 1$. The characteristic functions corresponding to a continuous W-spectrum may also—although not necessarily—vanish at infinity, but not rapidly enough (because of the lack of total reflection) to ensure the convergence of the integral $\int \psi^0 \psi^{0*} \, dV$, so that their normalization to 1, or to any other finite value, is in this case impossible.

This relationship between the convergence or non-convergence of the integral $\int \psi^0 \psi^{0*} \, dV$ (which is a measure of the probability of finding the particle somewhere in the whole of space) and the discrete or continuous character of the energy spectrum is intimately connected with the relationship between the characteristic functions ψ_n^0 and ψ_m^0 which are associated with or 'belong to' *different* values of the energy W_n and W_m.

If the equation $H\psi_n^0 = W_n \psi_n^0$ which is satisfied by ψ_n^0 is multiplied by ψ_m^{0*} and subtracted from the equation $H\psi_m^{0*} = W_m \psi_m^{0*}$ multiplied by ψ_n^0, we get

$$\psi_n^0 H \psi_m^{0*} - \psi_m^{0*} H \psi_n^0 = (W_m - W_n)\psi_m^{0*}\psi_n^0.$$

Integrating over the whole space, and assuming the integrals $\int |\psi_n^0|^2 \, dV$ and $\int |\psi_m^0|^2 \, dV$ to be convergent, we get, because of the self-ajointness of the energy operator according to (51),

$$(W_m - W_n) \int \psi_m^{0*} \psi_n^0 \, dV = 0,$$

and since $W_m \neq W_n$,

$$\int \psi_m^{0*} \psi_n^0 \, dV = 0. \tag{63}$$

This is the 'orthogonality property' which has already been deduced for one-dimensional motion in § 17, Part I. As shown there, this property can still be retained even when the states are degenerate, i.e. when different functions ψ_m^0 and ψ_n^0 belong to the same energy-level, provided these functions are suitably chosen as linear combinations of the original ones (if the latter do not already satisfy the orthogonality condition). If the energy values corresponding to different functions are distinguished by different indices, irrespective of whether these values are actually different or identical, the orthogonality relation (63) and the normalization condition $\int \psi_n^0 \psi_n^{0*} \, dV = 1$ can be fused into a single equation

$$\int \psi_m^{0*} \psi_n^0 \, dV = \delta_{mn}, \tag{63 a}$$

where $\delta_{mn} = 1$ if $m = n$ and $\delta_{mn} = 0$ if $m \neq n$.

It should be mentioned that the existence of degeneracy must be regarded not as a general rule, but rather as an exceptional occurrence. It only arises in a few cases in which the particle is moving in an exceptionally simple field of force. Nevertheless, the simple types of the potential-energy function U corresponding to these simple fields of force are of great practical importance.

As shown in Part I when discussing examples of motion in three dimensions, the different characteristic functions are specified by the values of *three* quantum numbers n_1, n_2, n_3, which, from the geometrical point of view, give the number of nodal surfaces of the different kinds and which, from the dynamical point of view, specify the characteristic values of three operators F_1, F_2, F_3, representing three independent constants of the motion which is described by the corresponding characteristic function. The energy operator H can be defined as a certain function of the operators F_1, F_2, F_3, its characteristic values being equal to the same function of the characteristic values C'_{n_1}, C''_{n_2}, C'''_{n_3} of these three operators. The existence of such operators is connected with the existence of 'separable coordinates' q_1, q_2, q_3, these coordinates being such that each characteristic function of H can be represented as the product of three functions $\psi'_{n_1 n_2 n_3}(q_1)$, $\psi''_{n_1 n_2 n_3}(q_2)$, $\psi'''_{n_1 n_2 n_3}(q_3)$ satisfying the equations

$$F_k \psi^{(k)}_{n_1 n_2 n_3}(q_k) = C^{(k)}_{n_k} \psi^{(k)}_{n_1 n_2 n_3}(q_k) \qquad (k = 1, 2, 3). \tag{64}$$

Since
$$\psi^0_{n_1 n_2 n_3}(x, y, z) = \psi'_{n_1 n_2 n_3}(q_1)\psi''_{n_1 n_2 n_3}(q_2)\psi'''_{n_1 n_2 n_3}(q_3), \tag{64 a}$$

these become
$$F_k \psi^0_{n_1 n_2 n_3} = C^{(k)}_{n_k} \psi^0_{n_1 n_2 n_3},$$

with
$$H(F_1, F_2, F_3)\psi^0_{n_1 n_2 n_3} = W(C'_{n_1}, C''_{n_2}, C'''_{n_3})\psi_{n_1 n_2 n_3}, \tag{64 b}$$

where $W(C', C'', C''')$ is the same function of the numbers C', C'', C''' as H is of the operators F_1, F_2, F_3.

In the approximate quasi-classical determination of the function ψ in the form $e^{i 2\pi S/h}$, where S is the action function of the Hamilton-Jacobi theory, the product relation (64 a) corresponds to the additive relation

$$S_0(x, y, z) = S'(q_1) + S''(q_2) + S'''(q_3) \tag{64 c}$$

which serves to define the separable coordinates in the classical sense. The quantum numbers n_1, n_2, n_3 are introduced by the condition that the periodicity moduli of $S^{(k)}(q_k)$ must be integral multiples n_k of h. The energy $W(C', C'', C''')$ can be written as a function of the quantum numbers in the form $W_{n_1 n_2 n_3}$. We have degeneracy when the energy actually depends on only two or one of these numbers, or upon their sum—as in the case of a hydrogen-like atom, where we may assume that n_1 denotes the radial quantum number, $n_2 = l$ the angular quantum number, and $n_3 = m$ the axial quantum number, F_2 being the operator M^2 and F_3 the operator M_z, and hence

$$\psi''_{n_1 n_2 n_3}(q_2) = P_{lm}(\theta), \qquad \psi'''_{n_1 n_2 n_3}(q_3) = e^{im\phi}.$$

It is always possible to arrange the triplets of numbers n_1, n_2, n_3 in a single row and to specify the functions ψ^0 and the energy-levels W by a single index n indicating the position of the corresponding triplet in the row. The indices $n(\psi^0_n, W_n)$ so obtained will, of course, have no connexion with the quantum numbers. One can also use a kind of vector notation, writing n as an abbreviation for the three indices n_1, n_2, n_3. This is the notation used in § 17 of Part I, and we shall use it in future when dealing with states of motion belonging to a discrete spectrum.

A continuous spectrum of the energy operator H arises when at least one of the three operators F, corresponding to the separation coordinates, has a continuous spectrum of characteristic values, the spectra of the other two operators remaining discrete (although of course they may be continuous too). This case occurs with hydrogen-like atoms in the region of positive energy values, i.e. in the region corresponding to the non-periodic (hyperbolic) motions of the classical theory. The wave functions can still, in this case, be written in the form of a product (64 a), the radial quantum number (n_1) being replaced by a continuously variable parameter. We may take as this parameter the characteristic values C' of the operator F_1 itself, or the values of the energy which it determines in conjunction with the quantized parameters C'' and C'''. It will be convenient to use for the characteristic functions belonging to a continuous energy spectrum a notation similar to that corresponding to the discrete case, replacing the quantum numbers as indices by the characteristic values of the operators F and writing C as an abbreviation for the triplet C', C'', C''', so that the characteristic functions and energies are written $\psi_C^0(x, y, z)$ and W_C^0 respectively. If this abbreviation is not desired, it may be preferable to use a mixed notation involving continuously variable parameters as well as quantum numbers (e.g. the characteristic functions of the hydrogen-like atom can be written in the form ψ_{Wlm}^0, where the energy W stands for the continuously variable parameter C').

It should be mentioned that a continuous spectrum corresponds to non-quantizable or partially quantizable motions that can be described quasi-classically, i.e. with an approximately determined action function S_0, which is either single-valued, or has a many-valuedness of a kind restricted to one or two of the parts into which it is separated according to (64 c). The wave functions ψ_C^0 belonging to a continuous spectrum W_C do not possess the orthogonality property which is characteristic of the functions ψ_n^0 belonging to the discrete spectrum, since, as we saw when deriving the orthogonality relation (63), this relation depends not only upon the self-adjointness of the operator H, but also on the convergence of the integrals $\int |\psi^0|^2 \, dV$. These integrals converge for $\psi^0 = \psi_n^0$ but do not converge for $\psi^0 = \psi_C^0$.

The connexion between the lack of orthogonality and the continuous character of the energy spectrum can be illustrated by the following argument. Let us suppose that $\psi^0_{C_1}$ and $\psi^0_{C_2}$ are two functions belonging to two different energy-levels W_{C_1} and W_{C_2}. Since the latter form a continuous series, their difference can be made arbitrarily small. Now if the orthogonality relation (63) applies to the continuous case, then the integral $\int \psi^{0*}_{C_2} \psi^0_{C_1} dV$ would jump discontinuously from zero to infinity as we go from nearly equal values of C_1 and C_2 (corresponding to nearly equal values of the energy) to the limiting case $C_1 = C_2$.

It should also be mentioned that—with the exception of a motion with one degree of freedom, i.e. specified by one coordinate only—the continuous spectrum possesses a degeneracy of an infinitely high degree, in the sense that each energy value can be associated with an infinite number of different states of motion, represented by different functions ψ^0_C. In the case of a continuous energy spectrum it is possible, and indeed is often necessary, to consider not merely exactly defined states of motion corresponding to perfectly definite values of the continuously variable parameters C, but rather states of motion represented by a superposition of exactly defined states corresponding to a *very small* range ΔC of these parameters, i.e. by wave functions of the type

$$\int_{\Delta C} \psi_C \, dC = \phi_{\Delta C}, \qquad (65)$$

where the integration is extended over the range ΔC. The wave functions obtained in this way obviously represent a generalization of those functions which have been used in Part I to represent 'wave groups' or 'wave packets'. In defining these generalized 'wave-packet' functions, we must take into account the time factor in the expression $\psi_C = \psi^0_C e^{-i2\pi W_C t/h}$, since the energy W_C is also a function of C. So long, however, as the region ΔC is very small, the function (65) can be written in the form

$$\phi_{\Delta C} = \phi^0_{\Delta C} \, e^{-i2\pi W_{C_0} t/h}, \qquad (65\,a)$$

where C_0 denotes some arbitrarily chosen 'point' contained in ΔC, and $\phi^0_{\Delta C}$ is a certain function not only of the coordinates, but also of the *time*, representing the propagation of the wave packet.

For various reasons, it is usually more convenient to consider the functions $\phi^0_{\Delta C}$ at a particular instant $t = 0$, in which case they can be defined by the integral

$$\phi^0_{\Delta C} = \int_{\Delta C} \psi^0_C \, dC, \qquad (65\,b)$$

and to represent the inexactly defined states of motion for any time by the product of (65 b) by $e^{-i2\pi W_{C_0} t/h}$.

Let us imagine that the whole region formed by the variable parameters C (it may be a 'line', a 'surface', or a 'space'—depending upon the number of continuously variable parameters in the triplet denoted by C) is divided into very small elements ΔC_1, ΔC_2,..., ΔC_n which do not overlap, and let us consider instead of the exact states the inaccurately determined states which are represented by the amplitude functions $\int_{\Delta C_n} \psi_C^0 \, dC$ $(n = 1, 2, 3,...)$. These states can be associated with a discrete set of energy values W_n referring to certain (arbitrarily chosen) points of the corresponding elementary regions ΔC_n.

It can be shown that *in the limiting case when the size of each region is decreased to zero* (their number increasing to infinity) the functions

$$\bar{\psi}_n^0 = \frac{1}{\sqrt{(\Delta C_n)}} \int_{\Delta C_n} \psi_C^0 \, dC \tag{66}$$

behave in the same way as the ordinary amplitude functions ψ_n^0 belonging to a discrete spectrum, i.e. in such a way that the integrals $\int \bar{\psi}_n^{0*} \bar{\psi}_n^0 \, dV$ are convergent. This result follows from the oscillatory character of the functions ψ_C^0 at large distances (see below). Since the functions (66) satisfy in the limit the same equation as the corresponding exact functions (for $W = W_{C_n}$), it follows that they must be mutually orthogonal and further that they can be normalized to 1, so that we can put

$$\int \bar{\psi}_m^{0*} \bar{\psi}_n^0 \, dV = \delta_{nm}. \tag{66a}$$

Let us consider, for example, the functions

$$\psi_k = A(k)e^{i2\pi kx},$$

which describe a force-free one-dimensional motion with a momentum $g = hk$ and a kinetic energy $W = k^2 h^2 / 2m$.

If we regard A as a slowly varying function of k, we get

$$\phi^0 = \int_{k_1 - \frac{1}{2}\Delta k}^{k_1 + \frac{1}{2}\Delta k} \psi^0 \, dk = A(k_1) \int_{k_1 - \frac{1}{2}\Delta k}^{k_1 + \frac{1}{2}\Delta k} e^{i2\pi kx} \, dk = A(k_1)e^{i2\pi k_1 x}\frac{\sin \pi \Delta k \, x}{\pi x}.$$

We thus obtain, replacing the volume integration by an integration along the x-axis,

$$\int_{-\infty}^{+\infty} |\bar{\psi}^0|^2 \, dx = \frac{1}{\Delta k} \int_{-\infty}^{+\infty} |\phi^0|^2 \, dx = |A(k_1)|^2 \lim \Delta k \int_{-\infty}^{+\infty} dx \left(\frac{\sin \pi \Delta k \, x}{\pi \Delta k \, x}\right)^2$$

$$= |A(k_1)|^2 \frac{1}{\pi} \int_{-\infty}^{+\infty} \left(\frac{\sin \xi}{\xi}\right)^2 \, d\xi = |A(k_1)|^2,$$

i.e. by (66a), $|A(k_1)|^2 = 1.$

It should be noticed that the normalizing condition only determines the modulus of the coefficient $A(k)$. We can still multiply it by an arbitrary factor of the form $e^{if(k)}$.

Likewise we find for two intervals Δk_1 and Δk_2 about the different mean values k_1 and k_2:

$$\phi_1^{0*}\phi_2^0 = A_1^* A_2\, e^{i2\pi(k_2-k_1)x}\frac{\sin \pi \Delta k_1 x}{\pi x}\frac{\sin \pi \Delta k_2 x}{\pi x}.$$

If, for simplicity, we put $\Delta k_2 = \Delta k_1$ $(k_2 \neq k_1)$, then the integral $\dfrac{1}{\Delta k}\displaystyle\int \phi_1^{0*}\phi_2^0\, dx$ assumes the form

$$\int\limits_{-\infty}^{+\infty} e^{i\frac{2}{\Delta k}(k_2-k_1)\xi}\left(\frac{\sin \xi}{\xi}\right)^2 d\xi \qquad (\xi = \pi \Delta k\, x).$$

When $\Delta k \to 0$ the quantity $(k_2-k_1)/\Delta k$ becomes infinite and therefore this integral must in the limit be zero. These results can easily be generalized so as to apply to free motion in three dimensions, represented by a wave function of the form

$$\psi_{\mathbf{k}}^0 = A(\mathbf{k})e^{i2\pi \mathbf{k}\cdot \mathbf{r}} = A(k_x, k_y, k_z)e^{i2\pi(k_x x + k_y y + k_z z)},$$

since this function is equal to the product of three functions representing one-dimensional motions parallel to the three coordinate axes respectively, the integrals both with respect to k_x, k_y, k_z as well as with respect to x, y, z thus reducing to products of integrals for the separate components. (It should be remarked that ΔC must be defined in thi case as the product $\Delta k_x \Delta k_y \Delta k_z$.)

The general proof of the quadratic integrability of the functions (66) can be derived from a very simple physical consideration, namely, from the fact that, at very large distances, the motion represented by any function ψ_C must approximate to a force-free motion, at least in all problems of practical interest for which the field of force determining the motion of the particle is supposed to vanish at infinity.

Taking again the function $\psi_k^0 = e^{i2\pi k x}$ as a typical representative of wave functions belonging to a continuous spectrum (for the case of one-dimensional motion), let us consider the double integral

$$J = \iint \psi_{k_1}^{0*}\,\psi_{k_2}^0\, dx dk_2 = \iint e^{i2\pi(k_1-k_2)x}\, dx dk_2,$$

extended from $-\infty$ to $+\infty$ both with regard to k_2 and x. Since each of the simple integrals over k_2 and over x taken separately between these limits does not have a definite value, let us define the value of J as the limit of $J_k' = \displaystyle\int\limits_{-\infty}^{+\infty} dx \int\limits_{k_1-\frac{1}{2}k}^{k_1+\frac{1}{2}k} e^{i2\pi(k_2-k_1)x}\, dk_2$ for $k \to \infty$, or the limit of $J''_\xi = \int\limits_{-\infty}^{+\infty} dk_2 \int\limits_{-\xi}^{+\xi} e^{i2\pi(k_2-k_1)x}\, dx$ for $\xi \to \infty$. In the former case we have

$$\int\limits_{k_1-\frac{1}{2}k}^{k_1+\frac{1}{2}k} e^{i2\pi(k_2-k_1)x}\, dk_2 = \frac{\sin \pi k x}{\pi x},$$

and $\qquad J'_k = \int\limits_{-\infty}^{+\infty} \frac{\sin \pi k x}{\pi x}\, dx = \frac{1}{\pi} \int\limits_{-\infty}^{+\infty} \frac{\sin \rho}{\rho}\, d\rho = 1,$

independently of k, and therefore in particular for $k = \infty$, which gives $J = 1$. In the latter case we get similarly

$$\int\limits_{-\xi}^{+\xi} e^{i2\pi(k_2-k_1)x}\, dx = \frac{\sin 2\pi(k_2-k_1)\xi}{\pi(k_2-k_1)},$$

and $\qquad J''_\xi = \int\limits_{-\infty}^{+\infty} \frac{\sin 2\pi(k_2-k_1)\xi}{\pi(k_2-k_1)}\, dk_2 = \frac{i}{\pi} \int\limits_{-\infty}^{+\infty} \frac{\sin \rho}{\rho}\, d\rho = 1,$

independently of ξ, and in particular for $\xi = \infty$. The two definitions of J thus lead to the same result, namely, $J = 1$.

Let us now assume that $\psi_k = A(k)e^{i2\pi kx}$, where $A(k)$ is some relatively slowly varying (non-oscillatory) function of k, and let us define the double integral

$$\int\limits_{-\infty}^{+\infty} \int\limits_{-\infty}^{+\infty} \psi^*_{k_1} \psi_{k_2}\, dk_2\, dx$$

as the limit of $\qquad J_\xi = \int\limits_{-\infty}^{+\infty} dk_2 \int\limits_{-\xi}^{+\xi} \psi^*_{k_1} \psi_{k_2}\, dx$

for $\xi = \infty$. Then since

$$J_\xi = \int\limits_{-\infty}^{+\infty} A^*(k_1)A(k_2)\frac{\sin 2\pi(k_2-k_1)\xi}{\pi(k_2-k_1)}\, dk_2,$$

$$= \frac{1}{\pi}A^*(k_1) \int\limits_{-\infty}^{+\infty} A\left(k_1 + \frac{\rho}{2\pi\xi}\right)\frac{\sin \rho}{\rho}\, d\rho,$$

we get $\qquad J = A^*(k_1)A(k_1) = |A(k_1)|^2.$

Hence it follows that the 'normalization' $|A(k_1)|^2 = 1$ which has been derived above for the function $\psi^0_k = A(k)e^{i2\pi kx}$ with the help of (66) and (66 a) (with $n = m = k$) can be obtained just as well from the condition $\int\limits_{-\infty}^{+\infty} \int\limits_{-\infty}^{+\infty} \psi^{0*}_{k_1} \psi^0_{k_2}\, dk_2\, dx = 1$. This result can easily be generalized for *any* functions ψ^0_C belonging to a continuous energy spectrum, the normalization condition of the usual type for the quasi-discrete functions

$$\bar{\psi}_n^0 = \lim_{\Delta C \to 0} \frac{1}{\sqrt{(\Delta C_n)}} \int_{(\Delta C_n)} \psi_C^0 \, dC,$$

namely, $$\int \bar{\psi}_n^0 \bar{\psi}_n^{0*} \, dV = 1,$$

being equivalent to the condition

$$\iint \psi_{C_1}^{0*} \psi_{C_2}^0 \, dC_2 \, dV = 1. \tag{67}$$

The latter is similar to the equation

$$\sum_n \int \psi_m^{0*} \psi_n^0 \, dV = 1$$

for functions belonging to a discrete spectrum. This equation is an immediate consequence of the normalization and orthogonality relations

$$\int \psi_m^{0*} \psi_n \, dV = \delta_{mn}.$$

It is possible to treat equation (67) in a similar way, i.e. to consider it as a corollary following from an orthogonality and normalization relation for the functions ψ_C^0, which, according to Dirac, can be written in the form

$$\int \psi_{C_1}^{0*} \psi_{C_2}^0 \, dV = \delta(C_2 - C_1), \tag{67 a}$$

where $\delta(C)$ denotes a somewhat unusual type of function, rather defined by the left side of this equation (together with the condition (67)) than defining it. As a matter of fact, this function does not depend upon the particular type of the function ψ_C^0 so long as ψ_C^0 satisfies the condition (67) which reduces to

$$\int \delta(C_2 - C_1) \, dC_2 = 1,$$

or $$\int \delta(C) \, dC = 1, \tag{67 b}$$

the integration being extended over all values of the continuously variable parameter (or parameters) C.

It is obvious that for $C = 0$ (i.e. $C_2 = C_1$), the function $\delta(C)$ becomes infinite. It seems, however, impossible to assign to it a definite value for $C \neq 0$. Take, for example, the normalized function $\psi_k^0 = e^{i2\pi kx}$ (with $C = k$). According to the definition (67 a), we have

$$\delta(k_2 - k_1) = \int_{-\infty}^{+\infty} e^{i2\pi(k_2 - k_1)x} \, dx,$$

i.e. $$\delta(k) = \int_{-\infty}^{+\infty} e^{i2\pi kx} \, dx. \tag{68}$$

This expression has no definite value. We can, however, replace it, as we have actually done above in the evaluation of the integral J, by

$$\delta_\xi(k) = \int\limits_{-\xi}^{+\xi} e^{i2\pi kx}\, dx, \qquad (68\,\mathrm{a})$$

and pass to the limit $\xi \to \infty$ *after the completion of all the calculations in which the function* $\delta_\xi(k)$ *enters,* and in particular after integration over k (which always forms a part of these calculations). The result will have a perfectly definite value, and indeed *the same value as that which would be obtained by putting from the very beginning*

$$\left.\begin{array}{l} \delta(k) = 0 \quad \text{for} \quad k \neq 0 \\[2mm] \text{and} \qquad \displaystyle\int\limits_{-\infty}^{+\infty} \delta(k)\, dk = 1 \end{array}\right\} . \qquad (68\,\mathrm{b})$$

The above calculation of the integral $J = \displaystyle\int\limits_{-\infty}^{+\infty} \int\limits_{-\infty}^{+\infty} \psi_{k_1}^{0*}\psi_{k_2}^0\, dk_2\, dx$ for a function of the type $\psi_k^0 = A(k)e^{i2\pi kx}$, subject to the normalizing condition $J = 1$, serves to illustrate these relations.

We may thus say that the functions ψ_C^0 belonging to a continuous spectrum, though not orthogonal to one another in the strict sense of the term, can be treated *as if* they were orthogonal to one another and can be normalized according to the conditions (67 a) and (67 b) with $\delta(C) = 0$ for $C \neq 0$.

The usual normalization $\int \psi_n^0 \psi_n^{0*}\, dV = 1$ for a function belonging to a discrete spectrum is equivalent to putting the total probability of finding the particle under consideration somewhere in the whole of space equal to 1. The normalization (67) or (67 a) can be interpreted as expressing the fact that the relative probability of finding the particle within a finite region of space containing the field of force in which it is moving is infinitely small compared with the probability of finding it at infinity (where it moves practically as a free particle). Under these circumstances it is more convenient to normalize the total probability to infinity rather than to unity. This normalizing to infinity, corresponding to the relation (67) or (67 a), is equivalent to the usual type of normalization for the quasi-discrete functions $\dfrac{1}{\sqrt{(\Delta C)}} \displaystyle\int\limits_{\Delta C} \psi_C^0\, dC$, each of which represents a kind of 'frozen' wave packet.

III

MATRICES

11. Matrix Representation of Physical Quantities and Matrix Form of the Equations of Motion

If a particle is moving in a constant field of force, defined by a potential energy $U(x, y, z)$ which does not depend upon the time, its total energy W remains constant. A 'conservative motion' of this kind is described, in wave mechanics, by a particular solution of the equation $(H+p_t)\psi = 0$ of the type $\psi = \psi^0(x, y, z)e^{-i2\pi Wt/h}$, where the amplitude function ψ^0 and the associated energy constant satisfy the equation $H\psi^0 = W\psi^0$. If the particular solutions of the equation $(H+p_t)\psi = 0$, where the Hamiltonian H does not contain the time explicitly, form a discrete set corresponding to a discrete spectrum of W, then the general solution can be represented as a sum of these particular solutions with arbitrary constant coefficients. Thus we may write

$$\psi = \sum_n a_n \psi_n = \sum_n a_n \psi_n^0 e^{-i2\pi W_n t/h}, \tag{69}$$

the functions ψ_n^0 being supposed to be so normalized that they satisfy the condition $\int |\psi_n^0|^2 \, dV = 1$.

If the functions ψ form a continuous set, the summation must be replaced by an integration giving

$$\psi = \int a(C)\psi_C \, dC = \int a_C \psi_C^0 e^{-i2\pi W_C t/h} \, dC, \tag{69 a}$$

where C represents the continuously variable parameters. If some of the three parameters are quantized while the others are continuously variable, the summation must be replaced by a combined summation and integration. Thus, for example, we may have

$$\psi = \sum_{n_2} \sum_{n_3} \int a_{C_1 n_2 n_3} \psi_{C_1 n_2 n_3} \, dC_1, \tag{69 b}$$

the functions ψ_C^0 or $\psi_{C_1 n_2 n_3}^0$ being so normalized that they satisfy the condition (67), and $a(C) = a_C$ being arbitrary functions of the continuously variable parameters C.

If—as is generally the case—the energy spectrum consists of a discrete part W_n and a continuous part W_C, the general solution of the equation $(H+p_t)\psi = 0$ is represented by a sum of (69) and (69 a) or (69 b), so that

$$\psi = \sum_n a_n \psi_n + \int a_C \psi_C \, dC, \tag{69 c}$$

or $\qquad \psi = \sum_{n_1} \sum_{n_2} \sum_{n_3} a_{n_1 n_2 n_3} \psi_{n_1 n_2 n_3} + \sum_{n_2} \sum_{n_3} \int a_{C_1 n_2 n_3} \psi_{C_1 n_2 n_3} \, dC_1. \tag{69 d}$

We shall first examine the simplest case, i.e. the representation (69) corresponding to a discrete spectrum. As already explained in Part I, § 17, the summation, from the point of view of the probability theory, expresses the *alternative character* of the motions represented by the different functions ψ_n or ψ_n^0. The resulting function ψ can be normalized to unity in the same way as the separate functions ψ_n, i.e. it can be made to satisfy the condition

$$\int \psi\psi^* \, dV = 1. \tag{70}$$

According to (69), in conjunction with the orthogonality and normalizing relations $\int \psi_m^* \psi_n \, dV = \delta_{mn}$, it then follows that

$$\sum_n a_n a_n^* = 1. \tag{70a}$$

The quantities $a_n a_n^* = |a_n|^2$ can be interpreted, subject to this condition, as the probabilities of finding the particle in a state of motion specified by the function ψ_n, irrespective of its position in space.

The probable (or average) value of any quantity represented by an operator F is determined by the general formula

$$\bar{F} = \int \psi^* F \psi \, dV.$$

Putting $\psi = \sum_n a_n \psi_n$, we get

$$\bar{F} = \sum_m \sum_n a_m^* a_n F_{mn}, \tag{71}$$

where

$$F_{mn} = \int \psi_m^* F \psi_n \, dV. \tag{71a}$$

The F_{mn} are the 'matrix elements' of the quantity F with respect to the states of motion ψ_m and ψ_n. Putting

$$\psi_m = \psi_m^0(x,y,z)e^{-i2\pi W_n t/h} = \psi_m^0 e^{-i2\pi\nu_n t} \qquad (\nu_n = W_n/h),$$

we get

$$F_{mn} = F_{mn}^0 e^{i2\pi\nu_{mn}t}, \tag{71b}$$

with

$$F_{mn}^0 = \int \psi_m^{0*} F \psi_n^0 \, dV \tag{71c}$$

and

$$\nu_{mn} = \nu_m - \nu_n = \frac{W_m - W_n}{h}.$$

(cf. Part I, §§ 17 and 18).

So long as the operator F represents a *real* quantity, the matrix elements F_{mn}, as well as their amplitudes, are Hermitian, i.e. they satisfy the relations

$$F_{mn} = F_{nm}^*, \qquad F_{mn}^0 = F_{nm}^{0*}. \tag{72}$$

These relations are directly evident if F is a (real) function of the coordinates alone. To establish them for the general case, let us first put $F = p_x = \dfrac{h}{2\pi i}\dfrac{\partial}{\partial x}$. We then have

$$F_{nm} = \int \psi_n^* p_x \psi_m \, dV = \frac{h}{2\pi i} \int \psi_n^* \frac{\partial}{\partial x} \psi_m \, dV,$$

and consequently

$$F_{nm}^* = \int \psi_n p_x^* \psi_m^* \, dV = -\frac{h}{2\pi i} \int \psi_n \frac{\partial}{\partial x} \psi_m^* \, dV.$$

Now $\displaystyle \int \psi_n \frac{\partial}{\partial x} \psi_m^* \, dV = \int \frac{\partial}{\partial x}(\psi_n \psi_m^*)\, dV - \int \psi_m^* \frac{\partial}{\partial x}\psi_n \, dV,$

and since the first integral on the right vanishes, it follows that

$$F_{nm}^* = \frac{h}{2\pi i} \int \psi_m^* \frac{\partial}{\partial x}\psi_n \, dV = F_{mn},$$

and so we get (72). The proof can easily be extended to any function F of the operators p_x, p_y, p_z (and of the coordinates) not involving complex quantities (with the exception of the i in the expressions for p_x which is necessary to make these operators correspond to real quantities).

The relations (72) should not be confused with the self-adjointness relation (51) which, in the case of the integral (71 a), runs

$$\int \psi_m^* F \psi_n \, dV = \int \psi_n F \psi_m^* \, dV. \tag{72 a}$$

It is equivalent to (72) only when

$$F = F^*, \tag{72 b}$$

i.e. when F is a function of the coordinates alone, not involving the operators p_x, p_y, p_z or involving them in *even* powers only. In the latter case, which is met with, for example, when F is the energy operator

$$H = (p_x^2 + p_y^2 + p_z^2)/(2m) + U(x, y, z),$$

the Hermitian relations (72) actually reduce to the relation (72 a) expressing the self-adjoint character of F. Putting $F = H$, we have, since $H\psi_n = W_n \psi_n$,

$$H_{mn} = W_n \int \psi_m^* \psi_n \, dV.$$

Taking into account the orthogonality and normalizing relations for the functions ψ_n, this reduces to

$$H_{mn} = H_{mn}^0 = W_n \delta_{mn}. \tag{73}$$

We thus get by (71)

$$\overline{H} = \sum_n a_n a_n^* W_n = \sum_n |a_n|^2 W_n. \tag{73 a}$$

This equation shows that if $\bar{H}$ is to be interpreted as the probable value of the energy, then the number $|a_n|^2$ must actually be considered as the probability of finding the particle in the state of motion represented by the function ψ_n and associated with the exactly known value of the energy W_n.

Similar results hold for any operator F which represents a constant of the motion, i.e. which commutes with the energy operator. If there is no degeneracy, i.e. if the values of the energy W corresponding to different functions ψ_n are all different, then, as already shown in § 7, it follows from the relation $HF = FH$ that $F\psi_n = F_n\psi_n$, where F_n is a constant, namely, the value of the quantity represented by F for the state in question. We thus get, in the same way as before,

$$F_{mn} = \delta_{mn} F_n,$$

and
$$\bar{F} = \sum_n |a_n|^2 F_n.$$

These relations can still be retained when there is degeneracy provided the functions $\psi_1, \psi_2,..., \psi_r$ forming a degenerate set, i.e. belonging to the same value of the energy, are so defined that they satisfy the relations $F\psi_n = F_n\psi_n$ (this can always be done, as already shown in § 7). If they do not satisfy these relations, we have

$$F\psi_k = \sum_{l=1}^{r} C_{kl}\psi_l$$

[cf. eq. (47 b), § 7]. Multiplying this equation by ψ_m^*, where ψ_m is some function of the same degenerate set, and integrating, we get

$$\int \psi_m^* F\psi_k \, dV = \sum_{l=1}^{r} C_{kl} \int \psi_m^* \psi_l \, dV = C_{km},$$

since we can always suppose the functions ψ_m to be orthogonal to one another, irrespective of the degeneracy. We thus get $C_{km} = F_{mk}$ or

$$F\psi_k = \sum_{l=1}^{r} F_{lk}\psi_l. \tag{74}$$

If ψ_n is some function not belonging to the degenerate set $\psi_1, \psi_2,..., \psi_r$, it follows that

$$F_{nk} = \int \psi_n^* F\psi_k \, dV = \sum_{l=1}^{r} F_{lk} \int \psi_n^* \psi_l \, dV = 0.$$

The general expression (71) thus reduces to the sum of the expressions

$$\sum_{k=1}^{r} \sum_{l=1}^{r} a_k^* a_l F_{kl} = \sum_{k=1}^{r} \sum_{l=1}^{r} a_k^* a_l F_{kl}^0 \tag{74 a}$$

taken for *different* values of the energy W. The relation $F_{kl} = F_{kl}^0$ follows from $W_k = W_l$. Thus, irrespective of the degeneracy, the probable value of the operator F representing a constant of the motion is *independent* of the time. This independence of $\bar{F}$ of the time is therefore the general criterion of the fact that F is a constant of the motion and commutes with H. If there is no degeneracy, it means that all the matrix elements of F must vanish with the exception of the 'diagonal' elements (i.e. those with two identical indices). In the presence of degeneracy this restriction is too narrow, the constancy of F being consistent with non-vanishing values of the matrix elements of F for all those states for which the energy difference vanishes.

The relation (74) is a particular case of the general equation

$$F\psi_k = \sum_l F_{lk}\psi_l,\qquad(75)$$

where the summation is extended over *all* the characteristic functions of H, irrespective of whether they belong to the same energy or not. This relation (75) holds for any operator F, and reduces to (74) when F is a constant of the motion. Equation (75) is derived in the same way as (74) by *assuming* that the function $F\psi_k$ can be expanded in a series of the type $\sum_l C_{kl}\psi_l$ with coefficients C_{kl} which may be functions of the time but do not depend upon the coordinates.† This is equivalent to assuming that $F\psi_k^0$ can be expanded in a series of the type $\sum C_{kl}^0\psi_l^0$ with *constant* coefficients C_{kl}^0. In the latter case we obtain, by multiplication by ψ_m^{0*} and integration over the coordinates,

$$\int \psi_m^0 \, F\psi_k^0 \, dV = \sum_l C_{kl}^0 \int \psi_m^{0*}\psi_l^0 \, dV = C_{km}^0,$$

i.e.
$$C_{km}^0 = F_{mk}^0,$$

and
$$F\psi_k^0 = \sum_l F_{lk}^0 \psi^0. \qquad(75\,\text{a})$$

From this equation it is possible to derive (75) (provided F does not contain the operator p_l) with the help of the relations $\psi_k^0 = \psi_k \, e^{+i2\pi\nu_k t}$ and $F_{lk}^0 = F_{lk} \, e^{-i2\pi\nu_{lk}t}$, where $\nu_{lk} = \nu_l - \nu_k$.

If F is not a constant of the motion, the expression (71) for its probable value contains terms which represent harmonic oscillations with the 'transition' frequencies $\nu_{mn} = (W_m - W_n)/h$. (The meaning of this fact for the emission of light has been discussed in Part I, § 17.) Taking the derivative of $\bar{F}$ with respect to the time, we get, according to (71 b),

$$\frac{d\bar{F}}{dt} = \sum_m \sum_n a_m^* a_n \, 2\pi i \nu_{mn} F_{mn},$$

† This assumption can be justified for a very wide class of operators satisfying certain conditions which we shall not consider here and which are always fulfilled in practice.

or
$$\frac{d\overline{F}}{dt} = \frac{2\pi i}{h} \sum_m \sum_n a_m^* a_n (W_m - W_n) F_{mn}. \qquad (75\,\text{b})$$

It can easily be shown that the right side of this expression is equal to the probable value of $[H, F]$, i.e. to $2\pi i (\overline{HF} - \overline{FH})/h$. We have in fact

$$FH\psi_n = FW_n\psi_n = W_n F\psi_n,$$

and, according to (75),

$$HF\psi_n = \sum_k F_{kn} H\psi_k = \sum_k F_{kn} W_k \psi_k,$$

so that

$$(HF - FH)_{mn} = \int \psi_m^* (HF - FH)\psi_n \, dV$$

$$= \sum F_{kn} W_k \int \psi_m^* \psi_k \, dV - W_n \int \psi_m^* F\psi_n \, dV$$

$$= F_{mn}(W_m - W_n).$$

We may thus define the operator dF/dt by the matrix equation

$$\left(\frac{dF}{dt}\right)_{mn} = \frac{2\pi i}{h}(W_m - W_n)F_{mn} = \frac{d}{dt}(F_{mn}). \qquad (75\,\text{c})$$

If, in the preceding equations, we replace H by some other operator G, we get, by a twofold application of (75),

$$(FG)\psi_n = F \sum_k G_{kn}\psi_k = \sum_k G_{kn} F\psi_k = \sum_k G_{kn} \sum_k F_{mk}\psi_m,$$

$$= \sum_m (\sum_k F_{mk} G_{kn})\psi_m.$$

On the other hand, according to the same formula (75), we have

$$(FG)\psi_n = \sum_m (FG)_{mn}\psi_m,$$

where $(FG)_{mn}$ are the matrix elements of the compound operator FG. Therefore it follows that

$$(FG)_{mn} = \sum_k F_{mk} G_{kn}. \qquad (76)$$

If we put $\qquad F_{mk} = F_{mk}^0 e^{i2\pi\nu_{mk}t}, \qquad G_{kn} = G_{kn}^0 e^{i2\pi\nu_{kn}t},$

and take into account the relation

$$\nu_{mk} + \nu_{kn} = \frac{W_m - W_k}{h} + \frac{W_k - W_n}{h} = \frac{W_m - W_n}{h} = \nu_{mn}, \qquad (76\,\text{a})$$

we get $(FG)_{mn} = (FG)_{mn}^0 e^{i2\pi\nu_{mn}t}$, with

$$(FG)_{mn}^0 = \sum_k F_{mk}^0 G_{kn}^0. \qquad (76\,\text{b})$$

This relation can be obtained directly by applying the operator FG to ψ_n^0 instead of ψ_n and using (75 a) instead of (75).

It should be noticed that equations (76) or (76 b) coincide with equations of § 18, Part I, which were derived by combining the multiplication and addition laws for the 'probability amplitudes' for transitions from a certain state m to another state n through some intermediate state k. The matrix elements F_{mk} and G_{kn} were interpreted there as the 'probability amplitudes' for the simple transitions $m \to k$ and $k \to n$ under the influence of perturbing forces characterized by F and G respectively, and the matrix element $(FG)_{mn}$ as the probability amplitude of a transition which is a combination of the preceding two with the intermediate state k remaining unspecified.

We shall return to this interpretation in a later section.

Equations (76) or (76 b) express, from a purely formal point of view, the *multiplication law of matrices*. This matrix multiplication law (i.e. combination of the rows of the first matrix with the columns of the second) is quite similar to the multiplication law of *determinants*, which can be associated with the corresponding matrices. Hence the matrix of the operator FG is called the *product* of the matrices of F and G.

Matrix multiplication is, in general, *non-commutative*, just like multiplication (i.e. successive application) of the corresponding operators.

It must be mentioned further that the products of two Hermitian matrices FG and GF are in general *not* Hermitian, the conjugate complex of $(FG)_{mn}$ being equal to $(GF)_{nm}$. The two products are therefore Hermitian matrices only if they are identical, i.e. if F and G commute with each other.

If, instead of the product of two operators, we consider their *sum* $F+G$, which is obviously commutative in the sense that

$$(F+G)\psi = (G+F)\psi,$$

and form the matrix of this sum, we obtain the relation

$$(F+G)_{mn} = F_{mn} + G_{mn} = (G+F)_{mn}, \tag{76 c}$$

which expresses the *addition law of matrices*, this matrix addition satisfying the commutative law.

It can easily be shown that, for three or more factors, the associative law is satisfied both for operators and for the corresponding matrices, just as for ordinary numbers, so that, for example,

$$(EF)G = E(FG),$$

and therefore

$$[(EF)G]_{mn} = \sum_k (EF)_{mk} G_{kn} = \sum_k \sum_l E_{ml} F_{lk} G_{kn}$$
$$= \sum_l E_{ml}(FG)_{ln} = [E(FG)]_{mn}.$$

We thus see that *there exists a one-to-one correspondence between different operators and the associated matrices, both with respect to addition and multiplication.* This correspondence enables us to replace the operator representation of physical quantities, which we introduced in the preceding chapter, by a *matrix representation,* each physical quantity, whether numerically expressible, i.e. having a definite value, or not, being represented by an array of matrix elements

$$
\left\|
\begin{array}{cccccc}
F_{11}, & F_{12}, & F_{13}, & . & . & . \\
F_{21}, & F_{22}, & F_{23}, & . & . & . \\
F_{31}, & F_{32}, & F_{33}, & . & . & . \\
. & . & . & . & . & . \\
. & . & . & . & . & .
\end{array}
\right\|,
\tag{77}
$$

or

$$
\left\|
\begin{array}{cccccc}
F^0_{11}, & F^0_{12}, & F^0_{13}, & . & . & . \\
F^0_{21}, & F^0_{22}, & F^0_{23}, & . & . & . \\
F^0_{31}, & F^0_{32}, & F^0_{33}, & . & . & . \\
. & . & . & . & . & . \\
. & . & . & . & . & .
\end{array}
\right\|.
\tag{77 a}
$$

These will be denoted in future by single letters F and F^0 respectively, and will be used in exactly the same way as the operator representing the physical quantity in question, without *direct* reference to characteristic functions of any kind.

It should, however, be kept in mind that such functions are *indirectly* implied in the very definition of the matrices F or F^0, being the characteristic functions of the energy operator H. Referred to these particular functions, the energy is represented by a *diagonal* matrix

$$
H = \left\|
\begin{array}{cccccc}
W_1 & 0 & 0 & . & . & . \\
0 & W_2 & 0 & . & . & . \\
0 & 0 & W_3 & . & . & . \\
. & . & . & . & . & . \\
. & . & . & . & . & .
\end{array}
\right\|,
\tag{77 b}
$$

i.e.
$$
H_{mn} = \delta_{mn} W_n,
$$

where
$$
\delta = \left\|
\begin{array}{cccccc}
1 & 0 & 0 & . & . & . \\
0 & 1 & 0 & . & . & . \\
0 & 0 & 1 & . & . & . \\
. & . & . & . & . & . \\
. & . & . & . & . & .
\end{array}
\right\|
$$

is the so-called 'unit-matrix', which in future will sometimes be denoted by $\mathbf{1}$ ($\delta_{mn} = \mathbf{1}_{mn}$).

The matrix elements of (77 b), i.e. the energy-levels W_n, appear in the relations
$$F_{mn} = F^0_{mn} e^{i2\pi(W_m - W_n)t/h} \qquad (77\,c)$$
between the elements of (77) and (77 a)—the latter being simple *numbers*. The absolute values of the energy cannot, however, be derived from these relations, which contain their differences only.

To distinguish the quantities F_{mn} and F^0_{mn}, we shall call the F_{mn} the matrix *components* and the F^0_{mn} the matrix *elements* of the quantity F. For the energy as well as for any other constant of the motion, the matrix components coincide with the corresponding elements, so that we can then put
$$F = F^0.$$

The representation of physical quantities by means of operators (including functions of the coordinates alone) differs from the representation by means of matrices in that the representation by operators is *absolute*, while the representation by matrices is *relative*. By relative we mean that the matrix elements of a quantity are defined with respect to a particular set of stationary states which are specified by the characteristic functions of a particular operator—or a system of commutable operators (like H, M_z, and M^2). We shall see later that this distinction is not so fundamental as it seems. The operator representation given above is based upon the use of the coordinates (and the time) as the directly observable quantities. But this is not necessary. Certain other quantities—e.g. the momentum components—can assume the role of directly observable quantities. The coordinates then become represented as operators in terms of these new quantities. Leaving this aside, and retaining the variables x, y, z, t as the primary and directly observed quantities, we can maintain the above distinction as a fundamental one.

Now it can easily be shown that the determination of the matrix elements of any operator F with respect to the characteristic functions of some other operator H (or of a system of three commutable operators) does not necessarily require an actual knowledge of these functions. It is in fact sufficient to know that they are such as to make the matrix of H *diagonal*. If, moreover, both H and F are explicitly defined as functions of the coordinates x, y, z and of the elementary operators p_x, p_y, p_z, then, taking into account the commutation relations
$$p_x x - x p_x = \frac{h}{2\pi i}\mathbf{1}, \qquad p_y y - y p_y = \frac{h}{2\pi i}\mathbf{1}, \qquad p_z z - z p_z = \frac{h}{2\pi i}\mathbf{1}, \quad (78)$$

$$p_x y - y p_x = 0, \text{ etc.,} \qquad (78\,\text{a})$$

$$xy - yx = 0, \qquad p_x p_y - p_y p_x = 0, \text{ etc.,} \qquad (78\,\text{b})$$

(in the *matrix* representation) we can calculate, *with the help of the matrix addition and multiplication laws* together with the condition that x, y, z, p_x, p_y, p_z *shall all be Hermitian matrices*, the matrix elements both of H and of any other non-diagonal matrix F. After the matrix *elements* of H and F have been determined, we can then calculate the matrix *components* of F (those of H coinciding with the elements).

So far, therefore, as the determination of the matrix elements or components of any physical quantity with respect to the stationary states defined by some energy operator H is concerned, we can replace the solution of Schrödinger's equation $H\psi^0 = W\psi^0$ and the subsequent integration $F^0_{mn} = \int \psi^{0*}_m F \psi_n \, dV$ by the following problem:

(1) To determine the matrix elements of the quantities x, y, z, p_x, p_y, p_z, subject to the commutation conditions (78), (78 a), (78 b), in such a way that the matrix of the function $H(x, y, z; p_x, p_y, p_z)$ shall be diagonal, i.e. that $H_{nm} = 0$ unless $n = m$.

(2) Knowing the matrices x, y, z, p_x, p_y, p_z, to calculate the matrix elements (or components if the H-matrix is added to the list) of any given function $F(x, y, z; p_x, p_y, p_z)$.

In this way the functions ψ^0_n, specifying the stationary states to which the matrix elements refer, can be completely eliminated from the matrix theory, and the latter built up as a closed and consistent theory, in the air, as it were, by the logical attraction of its elements, and not requiring the use of any ideas extraneous to it for its support.

It should be noticed that the two parts of the above problem are, in a certain sense, reciprocal to one another—for in the first part we are concerned with the solution of a system of matrix equations for the unknown matrices x, y, z, p_x, p_y, p_z, and in the second with the calculation of an explicitly given function of these fundamental matrices.

In problems with one degree of freedom (corresponding to the motion of a particle in one dimension, such as the linear oscillator) the condition 'H is a diagonal matrix', together with the commutation conditions (78), etc., provides the basis for a complete and physically unambiguous determination of the fundamental matrices, e.g. x and p_x, and consequently of the matrices representing, 'from the point of view of H' as it were, any other quantity $F(x, p_x)$. It should be noticed, however, that there remains a certain ambiguity which is irrelevant for the physical interpretation of the matrix elements, but which, as we shall see later on, is very important for the correct understanding of the relation between matrix theory and classical mechanics. If, in fact, x^0_{mn} and $(p_x)^0_{mn}$ are matrix elements which satisfy the conditions of the problem (or rather of its first part), then any elements of the type

$$x^0_{mn}\, e^{i(\alpha_m - \alpha_n)}, \qquad (p_x)^0_{mn}\, e^{i(\alpha_m - \alpha_n)},$$

where $\alpha_m, ..., \alpha_n$ are arbitrary real numbers, will also satisfy these conditions, the elements of any other matrix F^0_{mn} being replaced accordingly by $F^0_{mn}\, e^{i(\alpha_m - \alpha_n)}$. This result can easily be proved directly, or deduced from the original definition of the matrix elements in terms of the characteristic functions ψ^0_n if we use the fact that each of them can be replaced by its product by $e^{-i\alpha_n}$ without any violation of the orthogonality and normalizing relations. This amounts to the introduction of an arbitrary 'phase' into ψ_n (putting $\psi_n = \psi^0_n\, e^{-i(2\pi\nu_n t + \alpha_n)}$) or 'phase difference' into F_{mn} (putting $F_{mn} = F^0_{mn}\, e^{i(2\pi\nu_{mn} t + \alpha_m - \alpha_n)}$).

The 'phase' constants α vanish in the diagonal elements F^0_{nn} which, as we know, determine the *average* or *probable value* of the quantity represented by F in a stationary state with the energy W_n. The phase constants also vanish in the products $F^0_{mn} F^{0*}_{mn}$, i.e. in the squares of the moduli of the matrix elements referring to different stationary states $(W_n \neq W_m)$. These products determine the *probability* of a *transition* between the two states under the influence of a perturbation proportional to F.

In the general case of motion in three dimensions, the condition that the energy matrix should be diagonal (together with the commutation relations (78), etc.) is not always sufficient for a physically unambiguous determination of the matrices x, y, z, p_x, p_y, p_z, and it has then to be supplemented by a similar condition for one or two other matrices representing quantities which are constants of the motion, for instance, the z-component and the square of the angular momentum for motion in a central field of force. Such additional conditions are necessary in the case of degeneracy, the existence of which is revealed in the matrix theory, by the identity of several (diagonal) elements of the energy matrix. The matrices representing constants of the motion must of course—irrespective of the presence or absence of degeneracy—commute with the energy matrix, i.e. satisfy the relation

$$(HF)_{mn} = (FH)_{mn},$$

which corresponds to the operator relation $HF = FH$. The multiplication law (76), together with the condition that H is a diagonal matrix $(H_{mn} = W_n \delta_{mn})$, give

$$(HF)_{mn} = \sum_k H_{mk} F_{kn} = W_m F_{mn},$$

$$(FH)_{mn} = \sum_k F_{mk} H_{kn} = W_n F_{mn}.$$

The condition that F is a constant of the motion therefore reduces to

$$(W_m - W_n) F_{mn} = 0,$$

which means that $\qquad F_{mn} = F_{mn}^0,$

i.e. that the matrix elements of F vanish for all states except those which correspond to the same value of the energy. Therefore, if there is no degeneracy, the constants of the motion must be represented by diagonal matrices. If there is degeneracy they *may* but need not necessarily have a diagonal form.

The preceding result has already been obtained in a somewhat different manner [cf. (77 d)]. It should be remarked that a function $f(F)$ of a *diagonal* matrix is itself a diagonal matrix, the elements of which are equal to the same function of the corresponding elements of the argument matrix

$$[f(F)]_{nn} = f(F_{nn}).$$

This follows from the fact that the characteristic values of an operator $f(F)$ must be equal to the same function of the characteristic values of F. This result has already been stated when discussing the energy operator (§ 7). It can be obtained directly from the matrix multiplication law which gives, when F is a diagonal matrix,

$$(F^2)_{mn} = \sum_k F_{mk} F_{kn} = F_{mm} F_{mn} = F_{nn}^2 \delta_{mn},$$

$$(F^3)_{mn} = \sum_k (F^2)_{mk} F_{kn} = F_{nn}^3 \delta_{mn}, \text{ etc.},$$

so that, if $f(F)$ can be expanded in the form $\sum a_k F^k$ where a_k are numerical coefficients, we have $\left(\sum_k a_k F^k\right)_{mn} = \left(\sum_k a_k F_{nn}^k\right)\delta_{mn}.$

As has been pointed out at the beginning of this section, matrices representing real physical quantities must satisfy the Hermitian condition. The products of two such matrices F and G (unless they commute with each other) FG and GF cannot therefore represent a real physical quantity. Representation of real physical quantities can be obtained, however, by taking the *sum* of the two products, or their *difference* multiplied by i. In the first case we get, on dividing by 2, the 'symmetrized' representation $\frac{1}{2}(FG+GF)$ of the classical product of the corresponding quantities. In the second case we get, with the additional factor $2\pi/h$, the bracket expression $[F, G]$ which has been already considered in § 8 and which corresponds to the Poisson-bracket expression of the classical theory.

12. The Correspondence between Matrix and Classical Mechanics

The matrix representation of physical quantities was introduced by W. Heisenberg towards the end of 1925. A few months later Schrödinger's wave-mechanical theory appeared, but nevertheless Heisenberg, Born, and Jordan continued, for some time during 1926, to develop their 'matrix theory', without seeing any connexion between it and the 'wave theory'. The connexion was finally discovered by Schrödinger (and independently by Pauli) who found that the Heisenberg-Born-Jordan matrix elements could be calculated from the wave functions by means of the formula $F^0_{mn} = \int \psi^{0*}_m F \psi^0_n \, dV$. This little bit of history serves to illustrate the fact that the matrix theory does not need a wave-mechanical support, but can be made completely 'self-supporting'. We shall see later that the connexion between the wave theory and the matrix theory can actually be reversed in the sense that the matrix theory, in a generalized form due to Dirac and Jordan, contains the wave-mechanical theory as a particular case (§ 14).

In his formulation of the matrix theory, Heisenberg was guided by Bohr's ideas concerning the correspondence between the quantum and the classical description of the phenomena of radiation. In 'the good old days' before the coming of the quantum theory, atomic phenomena, and in particular those connected with the emission or absorption of radiation, were described in terms of a steady motion of the electrons. To this idea of steady (or continuous) motion, Bohr added the idea of *transitions* from one state of motion to another. In this way, between the years 1913 and 1925, physicists gradually became accustomed to considering *two* types of mechanical quantities—classical and quantum-mechanical. On the one hand we had, for example, the classical frequencies or amplitudes referring to the steady motion (analysed by means of a Fourier series into a sum of harmonic vibrations), while on the other hand we had the quantum frequencies or amplitudes referring to the transitions.

By means of his 'correspondence principle', Bohr was able, in 1918, to establish an approximate relationship between the classical and the quantum-mechanical quantities. Advancing still further along the path

laid down by Bohr, Heisenberg rejected the classical quantities altogether, as devoid of physical meaning, and devised the matrix scheme
(improved a little later by Born and Jordan) for the direct calculation
of the quantum-mechanical quantities.

The correspondence principle can be explained in the simplest way
for a one-dimensional motion, restricted classically to a finite region,
e.g. lying between x' and x'', and therefore periodic. The coordinate x
of the particle can then be described classically as a periodic function
of the time and expanded in a Fourier series of the form

$$x(t) = \sum_{k=-\infty}^{k=+\infty} x^0(k)e^{i2\pi kvt}, \qquad (79)$$

where $v = 1/\tau$ is the fundamental frequency of oscillation (τ is the
period of oscillation, i.e. the duration of the 'round trip' from x' to x''
and back again to x'), and $x^0(k)$ is the amplitude of the kth harmonic
term having a frequency kv. The two complex terms with the frequencies $+kv$ and $-kv$ must, of course, combine to form a real term
of the type
$$a_{|k|}\cos 2\pi|k|vt + b_{|k|}\sin 2\pi|k|vt;$$
it follows that the amplitudes $x^0(+k)$ and $x^0(-k)$ must be conjugate
complex quantities
$$x^0(-k) = x^0(+k)^*, \qquad (79\,\mathrm{a})$$
giving $a_{|k|} = x^0(k)+x^0(k)^*, \qquad b_{|k|} = i[x^0(k)-x^0(k)^*].$

Bohr's theory, in so far as it was concerned with steady motions,
restricted these motions by quantum conditions which, in the present
case, reduce to the single equation

$$J \equiv \oint g\,dx = nh, \qquad (80)$$

specifying the quantized values of the energy $W = W_n$ and hence determining the fundamental frequencies $v = v_n$. Putting $g = \sqrt{\{2m(W-U)\}}$,
and differentiating the integral

$$J = \oint \sqrt{\{2m(W-U)\}}\,dx$$

with respect to W (considered as a parameter), we get

$$\frac{dJ}{dW} = \oint \frac{dx}{\sqrt{\{2(W-U)/m\}}} = \oint \frac{m\,dx}{g} = \oint \frac{dx}{v} = \oint dt,$$

i.e. $$\frac{dJ}{dW} = \tau,$$

or $$v = \frac{dW}{dJ}. \qquad (80\,\mathrm{a})$$

This relation is a special case of the general relations between the energy, the fundamental frequencies ν_1, ν_2, ν_3, and the fundamental moduli of periodicity J_1, J_2, J_3 of the action function S which were deduced, in an earlier chapter, for motion in three dimensions, with the help of the theory of canonical transformations (Chap. I, § 5).

Although the 'classical' frequency ν given by (80 a) refers to a steady motion, nevertheless it is expressed as the ratio of the differences of W and J for *two different*, though closely neighbouring, motions as if it were associated with a *transition* between them. In fact the relation (80 a) bears a striking resemblance to Bohr's frequency condition

$$\nu_{mn} = \frac{W_m - W_n}{h},$$

which gives the quantum frequency associated with a transition between two more or less widely different 'quantized' states m and n. Introducing the quantized values of the integral J, we can rewrite the preceding equation in the form

$$\nu_{mn} = (m-n)\frac{W_m - W_n}{J_m - J_n} = (m-n)\frac{\Delta W}{\Delta J}. \tag{80 b}$$

If W varies slowly with J, and if the quantum jump $m-n$ is not too large compared with m or n, then the difference ratio $\Delta W/\Delta J$ can be replaced approximately by the differential coefficient dW/dJ. From (80 a) we then get the following approximate relation between the classical and the quantum frequencies:

$$\nu_{mn} \cong (m-n)\nu. \tag{80 c}$$

We may regard this relation as indicating an approximate coincidence or a 'correspondence' between the quantum frequency associated with a k-fold jump and the classical frequency of the harmonic oscillation of the order k ($k = m-n$).

This correspondence between the classical and the quantum frequencies forms the nucleus of Bohr's correspondence principle. The principle is extended by asserting that, in addition to this correspondence between the frequencies, there is also a correspondence between the *amplitudes*.

Let us denote the functions $x(t)$ for the nth stationary state by $x_n(t)$ and the expansion coefficients $x^0(k)$ by $x_n^0(k)$. Formula (79) then becomes

$$x_n(t) = \sum_{k=-\infty}^{+\infty} x_n^0(k)e^{i2\pi k\nu t}. \tag{81}$$

Writing $m-n$ instead of k and putting

$$x_n^0(m-n) = x_{mn}^0, \tag{81 a}$$

formula (81) becomes

$$x_n(t) = \sum_{m=-\infty}^{+\infty} x_{mn}^0 \, e^{i2\pi(m-n)\nu t}. \tag{81 b}$$

Now if the classical frequency $(m-n)\nu$ corresponds to the quantum frequency ν_{mn} of the light emitted by the system under consideration (linear oscillator) as a result of the transition $m \to n$ (if $W_m > W_n$), then the classical amplitude x_{mn}^0 associated with this frequency must, according to Bohr, correspond to the quantum amplitude of the emitted light, the correspondence being such that the *intensity* of the emitted light must coincide approximately with the intensity calculated classically on the assumption that the motion of the particle (which is supposed to possess an electric charge without which there would be no radiation) is represented by the simple harmonic term

$$x_{mn} = x_{mn}^0 \, e^{i2\pi(m-n)\nu t}.$$

The approximation with regard to intensity must be the closer the closer the approximation with regard to frequency.

The ability of the correspondence principle to predict intensities has been verified in those cases where there is actually a close approximation between the classical and quantum frequencies. For example, it was able to predict successfully the relative intensities of the neighbouring lines appearing in the Stark effect. Nevertheless the nature of the correspondence established by Bohr remained mysterious, until Heisenberg, towards the end of 1925, unveiled it in a way worthy of admiration both for its simplicity and for its boldness. Basing his theory upon the principle that only those things have a real existence which can be observed, Heisenberg put forward the idea that classical quantities do not exist at all, since they do not produce any directly observed optical effects. In fact the position and intensity of the observed spectrum lines can only be expressed in terms of quantum or transition quantities.

From this point of view, the classical method of describing the motion of the particle by determining its coordinates for a given stationary state n as a certain function of the time $x_n(t)$, which could be expanded in a Fourier series (81 b), was to be considered as an approximation to the description of the motion by means of a double array or matrix components of the form

$$x_{mn} = x_{mn}^0 \, e^{i2\pi\nu_{mn}t}$$

'corresponding' to the totality of the classical harmonic terms for different values of m and n in the same sense in which an approximation corresponds to the truth.

At this point two different possibilities for reforming classical mechanics seemed to be open. The one consisted in assuming that the motion of the particle in a stationary state n can be described as a definite function or the time, namely, by the series

$$x_n(t) = \sum_{m=-\infty}^{+\infty} x_{mn}^0 e^{i 2 \pi \nu_{mn} t},$$

which should replace the simple Fourier series (81 b), and that the equations of motion should be so modified as to lead to solutions of this new type instead of solutions of the type (81 b).

The second possibility was to assume that the classical description of motion, establishing a definite dependence of the position of the particle upon the time, had to be abandoned and replaced by a quantum description in which the coordinate x was to be determined as a matrix, made up of components of the type $x_{mn}^0 e^{i 2 \pi \nu_{mn} t}$. In this case the external form of the classical equations of motion could be maintained and only their physical meaning altered, the variables x, p_x, H, etc., being regarded and determined not as ordinary quantities but as matrices.

With an unerring intuition Heisenberg chose the second way, thus giving up the very idea of motion in the classical sense (as being fundamentally unobservable and therefore devoid of physical meaning) and laying the foundation of the new quantum or matrix mechanics. The idea that the quantum description of motion amounts to the determination of quantities relating only to transitions between different states requires an important amendment, for besides such components a matrix contains diagonal components or elements relating to definite states taken separately. As we know, these diagonal elements are equal to the average or probable values of the quantity represented by the matrix for the corresponding states. This result, which has already been discussed in Chap. I, § 5, follows also from the preceding considerations connected with the correspondence principle. The time-average value of some quantity, e.g. x, as represented by a Fourier series (81), is obviously equal to that term of this series which does not depend upon the time, for which therefore $k = 0$. We thus have

$$\overline{x_n(t)} = x_n^0(0),$$

or, using the notation (81 a),

$$\overline{x_n(t)} = x_{nn}^0.$$

Having defined every physical quantity as a matrix, Heisenberg naturally enough replaced the usual multiplication law for ordinary numbers by the matrix multiplication law. In this he was guided by the necessity of securing the form

$$F_{mn} = F^0_{mn} e^{i 2 \pi \nu_{mn} t},$$

with the *same* transition frequencies ν_{mn} for the matrix representing any function $F(x)$ as those which appear in the matrix (82 a) for the coordinate x. Taking, for instance, $F(x) = x^2$ and using the matrix multiplication law, we get

$$(x^2)_{mn} = \sum_k x_{mk} x_{kn} = \left(\sum_k x^0_{mk} x^0_{kn} \right) e^{i 2 \pi \nu_{mn} t} = (x^2)^0_{mn} e^{i 2 \pi \nu_{mn} t}$$

as a consequence of the relations $\nu_{mk} = (W_m - W_k)/h$, $\nu_{kn} = (W_k - W_n)/h$, $\nu_{mn} = (W_m - W_n)/h = \nu_{mk} + \nu_{kn}$; cf. (76) and (76 b).

Having introduced matrices to represent physical quantities and the matrix multiplication law for the calculation of matrices representing functions of such quantities, Heisenberg kept unaltered the form of the equation of the motion

$$m \frac{d^2 x}{dt^2} = f(x),$$

understanding by x and $f(x)$ not the usual variables but the corresponding matrices, and put Bohr's quantum condition $\oint g \, dx = nh$ in the form

$$(gx - xg)_{nn} = \frac{h}{2 \pi i},$$

leaving the question of the non-diagonal elements of the matrix open. The commutation condition

$$gx - xg = \frac{h}{2 \pi i} \mathbf{1}$$

which also fixes the non-diagonal elements of this matrix (as equal to zero) was established by way of a generalization somewhat later by Born and Jordan, and still later was recognized (by Schrödinger and Eckart) as giving the key for the transition from matrix mechanics to wave mechanics, this transition consisting essentially in considering x as an ordinary variable and g as the operator $\dfrac{h}{2 \pi i} \dfrac{\partial}{\partial x}$ and further in replacing matrix equations by operator equations with the wave function to be operated upon.

The information obtained from the wave-mechanical treatment of a problem is more complete than that obtained from the matrix-mechanical treatment, for in addition to the matrix elements we obtain, in the former case, the wave functions which serve to determine the probable location of the particle, its probable velocity, and so on. In the matrix mechanics the notion of probability with reference to separate states appears only through the diagonal elements, representing probable values, while the non-diagonal elements can be interpreted under certain conditions as the probability amplitudes for transitions between different states. In Heisenberg's original theory, the matrix components of the coordinate were looked for as quantities which determine the intensity of radiation or, what amounts to the same thing, the probability of transitions with emission of light, it being assumed that the intensity of radiation associated with the matrix component $x_{mn} = x_{mn}^0 \, e^{i2\pi\nu_{mn}t}$ is the same as it would be on the classical theory if x_{mn} represented the actual motion of the particle as a harmonic function of the time. The result of this assumption is the same as that obtained in Part I in connexion with Schrödinger's theory of radiation, namely, that the probability of a spontaneous transition $m \to n$ with emission of energy in the form of monochromatic light of the frequency ν_{mn} is equal (per unit time) to

$$A_{mn} = \frac{64\pi^4}{3c^3} \frac{\nu_{mn}^3}{h} e^2 |x_{mn}^0|^2,$$

where e is the electrical charge of the particle [Part I, eq. (93)].

In the preceding sketch of the development of Heisenberg's matrix theory from Bohr's correspondence principle we did not attempt to give a direct proof of the latter so far as it refers to the connexion between the Fourier amplitudes and the matrix elements, having confined ourselves to the frequencies with respect to which the correspondence could be established by means of Bohr's own theory. This gap can be filled with the help of wave mechanics, or rather that approximate form of it which has been discussed in Chap. I, § 5, and which corresponds to the classical mechanics *together* with Bohr's quantum conditions.

We have already used this approximate form of the theory for comparing the classical time-averages (which are equal to the constant term in the Fourier expansion of the corresponding quantity F considered as a function of the time) with its probable values, defined by the integrals $\int \psi_n^* F \psi_n \, dx$, which are nothing else but the diagonal elements $F_{nn} = F_{nn}^0$ of the matrix representing F. We have found that to the approximation implied by the formula (23 a), § 4,

$$\psi_n = \frac{c_n}{\sqrt{|v_n|}} e^{i2\pi s_n(x,\,t)/h}, \tag{82}$$

where v_n is the velocity of the particle (defined by the equation

$v_n = \sqrt{\{2(W-U)/m\}}$ as a function of its position x) and

$$s_n(x, t) = s_n^0(x) - W_n t$$

the classical action function for the state in question (with the energy W_n), the classical time-average $\dfrac{1}{\tau} \displaystyle\int_0^\tau F(t)\,dt$ *coincides* with the probable value $\displaystyle\int_{x'}^{x''} F\psi_n^*\psi_n\,dx$ provided ψ_n is normalized to unity, that is, the coefficients c_n are set equal to $\sqrt{(2/\tau)}$.

$$\left(\int_{x'}^{x''} |\psi_n|^2\,dx = |c_n|^2 \int_{x'}^{x''} dx/v_n = |c_n|^2 \tfrac{1}{2}\tau = 1. \right)$$

In a similar way it is possible to ascertain the approximate equality between the Fourier coefficients in the expansion of $x(t)$, or any function of x supposed to be determined as a function of t according to the classical laws of motion, and the 'corresponding' matrix elements of this function $F(x)$.

In order to determine the Fourier coefficient $x^0(n)$ in the expansion (79) we multiply $x(t)$ by $e^{-i2\pi n\nu t}$ and notice that the constant term in the resulting expansion is just $x^0(n)$.

We thus get
$$x^0(n) = \frac{1}{\tau} \int_0^\tau x(t)\, e^{-i2\pi n\nu t}\,dt,$$

or, in the alternative notation corresponding to (81 b),

$$x_{mn}^0 = \frac{1}{\tau} \int_0^\tau x(t)\, e^{-i2\pi(m-n)\nu t}\,dt.$$

The coordinate x can be replaced here, as just mentioned, by any function of x (or of x and g) giving

$$F_{mn}^0 = \frac{1}{\tau} \int_0^\tau F(t)\, e^{-i2\pi(m-n)\nu t}\,dt. \qquad (82\,\mathrm{a})$$

On the other hand, we have by the definition of the matrix elements

$$F_{mn}^0 = \int_{x'}^{x''} \psi_m^{0*} F\psi_n^0\,dx,$$

or, according to (82), with $s(x, t) = s^0(x) - Wt$, $\psi_n^0 = \sqrt{\dfrac{2}{\tau}}\,\dfrac{1}{\sqrt{|v_n|}}\, e^{i2\pi s_n^0(x)/h}$,

$$F_{mn}^0 = \frac{2}{\tau} \int_{x'}^{x''} F(x)\, e^{i2\pi[s_n^0(x) - s_m^0(x)]/h}\, \frac{dx}{\sqrt{(v_n v_m)}}. \qquad (82\,\mathrm{b})$$

Now if the states n and m differ but little with respect to their energy, we can replace $\sqrt{(v_n v_m)}$ by a certain mean value of the velocity for an energy W lying between W_n and W_m, and put accordingly $dx/\sqrt{(v_n v_m)} = dt$ just as in the case $n = m$. We have further under the same condition

$$s_n^0(x) - s_m^0(x) = \frac{\partial s^0(x, J)}{\partial J}(J_n - J_m),$$

where J is the action variable (80) (introduced in Chap. II, § 5, for the general case of a three-dimensional motion), and $J_n = nh$, $J_m = mh$ its quantized values. In the case here considered of a one-dimensional motion the function $s^0(x)$ can be readily determined, from the equation $g = \partial s^0(x)/\partial x$ defining it, by the formula

$$s^0(x) = \int g\, dx = \int \sqrt{\{2m(W - U)\}}\, dx,$$

whence it follows [cf. the derivation of (80 a)] that

$$\frac{\partial s^0(x)}{\partial W} = \int \frac{dx}{\sqrt{\{2(W-U)/m\}}} = \int \frac{m\, dx}{g} = t + \text{const.},$$

and consequently (dropping the irrelevant constant)

$$\left(\frac{\partial s^0}{\partial J}\right)_{x=\text{const.}} = \frac{\partial s^0}{\partial W}\frac{dW}{dJ} = t\frac{dW}{dJ}.$$

We thus get with the above approximation

$$s_n^0(x) - s_m^0(x) = t\frac{dW}{dJ}(J_n - J_m),$$

or, since with the same approximation $(J_n - J_m)dW/dJ = W_n - W_m$,

$$s_n^0(x) - s_m^0(x) = (W_n - W_m)t. \qquad (82\,\text{c})$$

This gives, on substitution in (82 b),

$$F_{mn}^0 = \frac{2}{\tau}\int_0^{\frac{1}{2}\tau} F(t)\, e^{-i2\pi(W_m - W_n)t/h}\, dt,$$

which coincides with (82 a) when we remember that

$$(m - n)\nu \cong (W_m - W_n)/h.$$

The preceding results can easily be extended to the general case of the motion of a particle with three degrees of freedom in a limited region of space. According to classical mechanics such a motion can be described under certain very general assumptions as a 'conditionally periodic' motion, which means that the coordinates, or any function F of the latter, can be represented as a function of the time by a triple

Fourier series with three different (incommensurable) fundamental frequencies ν_1, ν_2, ν_3:

$$F_{n_1 n_2 n_3}(t) = \sum_{m_1} \sum_{m_2} \sum_{m_3} F^0_{m_1 m_2 m_3, n_1 n_2 n_3} e^{i2\pi[(m_1-n_1)\nu_1 + (m_2-n_2)\nu_2 + (m_3-n_3)\nu_3]t},$$

the coefficients F^0 being determined by the formula

$$F^0_{m_1 m_2 m_3, n_1 n_2 n_3} = \lim_{\tau \to \infty} \frac{1}{\tau} \int_0^\tau F_{n_1 n_2 n_3}(t) e^{-i2\pi[(m_1-n_1)\nu_1 + \dots]t} \, dt.$$

According to wave mechanics, a series of this kind, as a whole, will have no (or at least no exact) significance; the totality of the harmonic terms in all such series, corresponding to all possible states n_1, n_2, n_3, will, however, constitute an approximate expression of the matrix representing the quantity F. The exact expression of its matrix components can be obtained if we replace the classical frequencies $(m_1-n_1)\nu_1 + (m_2-n_2)\nu_2 + (m_3-n_3)\nu_3$ by the transition frequencies $(W_{m_1 m_2 m_3} - W_{n_1 n_2 n_3})/h$ and define the amplitudes $F^0_{m_1 m_2 m_3, n_1 n_2 n_3}$ by the integrals $\int \psi^{0*}_{m_1 m_2 m_3} F \psi^0_{n_1 n_2 n_3} \, dV$. The approximate equivalence of this definition to the classical one given above can be shown with the help of equations (32), (32 a), and (32 b) of § 5 in exactly the same way as before.

One might be tempted to think that it would be possible to give a correct wave-mechanical definition of the quantity F *as a function of the time* by replacing the classical amplitudes and frequencies in the preceding expression for $F_{n_1 n_2 n_3}(t)$ by the quantum ones, i.e. by putting

$$F_{n_1 n_2 n_3}(t) = \sum_{m_1} \sum_{m_2} \sum_{m_3} F^0_{m_1 m_2 m_3; n_1 n_2 n_3} e^{i2\pi(W_{m_1 m_2 m_3} - W_{n_1 n_2 n_3})t/h}.$$

The fact that no physical significance can be attached to this 'modified' Fourier series is, however, clearly illustrated by the possibility of multiplying the functions $\psi^0_{n_1 n_2 n_3}$ by arbitrary phase factors $e^{-i\alpha_{n_1 n_2 n_3}}$, resulting in the multiplication of the matrix elements by the phase factors $e^{i(\alpha_{m_1 m_2 m_3} - \alpha_{n_1 n_2 n_3})}$, which are completely irrelevant from the point of view of the wave-mechanical or the matrix theory, but profoundly influence the 'modified' definition of the function $F_{n_1 n_2 n_3}(t)$.

13. Application of the Matrix Method to Oscillatory and Rotational Motion

The matrix mechanics of Heisenberg, Born, and Jordan can be considered as a kind of 'skeleton' of Schrödinger's wave mechanics, complete in itself but nevertheless deprived of the flesh and blood of the probability conception, which forms the vital element of wave mechanics. In addition, the wave-mechanical theory has another advantage over the matrix theory, for, as a rule, it is easier to solve Schrödinger's equation for the characteristic functions of the energy operator and then to use these functions to calculate the matrix elements of any other operator by means of integration, than to determine these matrix elements from the condition that the matrix of the energy is diagonal, together with the commutation relations for the coordinates and momentum components, without knowing or using the characteristic functions at all.

The practical application of the matrix theory to concrete problems can, however, be made much easier and more convenient if instead of carrying out the matrix representation directly with respect to the fundamental operator relations $p_x x - x p_x = \dfrac{h}{2\pi i} \mathbf{1}$, etc., together with the condition that $H(x, y, z; p_x, p_y, p_z)$ is diagonal, it is carried out with respect to some other operator relations between certain more complicated functions F, G, etc., the choice of which depends upon the character of the problem [i.e. on the potential-energy function $U(x, y, z)$] if at least some of these functions commute with the energy, i.e. represent constants of the motion. If G is such a constant (it may, in particular, coincide with the energy H), and if some other function F (for instance, the coordinate x) has been found which satisfies a commutation relation of the form $GF - FG = \alpha F + \beta G$ where α and β are constant, the matrix interpretation leads very simply to the determination of the matrix elements both of G, which can be assumed to be diagonal, and of F. Applying the matrix multiplication rule to the left side of the preceding equation, we get

$$(GF - FG)_{mn} = (G_{mm} - G_{nn})F_{mn} = \alpha F_{mn} + \beta G_{nn} \delta_{mn},$$

whence it follows that all the matrix elements of F vanish with the exception of the diagonal elements which are equal to

$$F_{nn} = -\frac{\beta}{\alpha} G_{nn}$$

and those for which $G_{mm} - G_{nn} = \alpha.$

This equation leads very simply to the determination of the numbers G_{nn}—especially when n can be treated as a simple quantum number (and not as a set of several quantum numbers n_1, n_2, n_3 all of them different from the numbers m_1, m_2, m_3 represented by m). By a suitable labelling of the states associated with given values of G, we can make those states for which the values of G differ by α *successive*, i.e. having values of n and m differing by 1, so that the preceding equation will reduce to $G_{n+1,n+1} - G_{nn} = \alpha$. The solution of this equation is obviously of the form $G_{nn} = \alpha n + \gamma$, where γ is a certain constant. We shall not develop these general considerations but shall merely illustrate and amplify them by means of two special problems of outstanding simplicity and practical importance—namely, the problem of a linear harmonic oscillator and the problem of the rotational part of the motion of a particle in a central (radially symmetrical) field of force.

The energy of a linear harmonic oscillator is expressed by the operator or matrix (as we please)

$$H = \frac{1}{2m}p^2 + \tfrac{1}{2}(2\pi\nu_0)^2 mx^2, \tag{83}$$

where ν_0 is the natural vibration frequency of the classical theory. According to the matrix theory H has to be 'diagonalized' subject to the additional condition

$$px - xp = \frac{h}{2\pi i}\mathbf{1}, \tag{83a}$$

$\mathbf{1}$ being the unit matrix.

We shall put, for the sake of brevity,

$$2\pi\nu_0 mx = q, \qquad 2mH = K, \qquad h\nu_0 m = \omega,$$

so that (83) and (83a) can be written in the form

$$p^2 + q^2 = K, \qquad pq - qp = -i\omega, \tag{83b}$$

it being understood that ω denotes the product of the factor $h\nu_0 m$ and the unit matrix.

We shall now introduce the matrices

$$r = p + iq \quad \text{and} \quad s = p - iq \tag{84}$$

which are more convenient to deal with than p and q taken separately. Taking their product in the order rs, we get

$$rs = pp + iqp - ipq + qq = p^2 + q^2 - i(pq - qp),$$

i.e.
$$rs = K - \omega. \tag{84a}$$

Similarly we get
$$sr = K + \omega. \tag{84b}$$

Hence, using the associative law,

$$rsr = (rs)r = (K - \omega)r,$$
$$rsr = r(sr) = r(K + \omega),$$

i.e. putting $K - \omega = L$,
$$Lr - rL = 2r\omega. \tag{85}$$

Now since K and ω, and consequently L, are diagonal matrices, we have

$$(Lr - rL)_{mn} = (L_{mm} - L_{nn})r_{mn}$$

and $(r\omega)_{mn} = r_{mn}\omega$, where ω denotes now not the matrix but simply the number $h\nu_0 m$, so that the preceding equation can be written in the form

$$(L_{mm} - L_{nn} - 2\omega)r_{mn} = 0. \tag{85 a}$$

Thus either $r_{mn} = 0$, or $L_{mm} - L_{nn} = 2\omega$. In the same way we get

$$srs = (K+\omega)s = s(K-\omega)$$

and

$$(L_{mm} - L_{nn} + 2\omega)s_{mn} = 0, \tag{85 b}$$

so that either $s_{mn} = 0$ or $L_{mm} - L_{nn} = -2\omega$. Now

$$L_{mm} - L_{nn} = K_{mm} - K_{nn} = 2m(H_{mm} - H_{nn}) = 2m(W_m - W_n)$$

is the difference of the energy-levels for the states m and n multiplied by $2m$ (m being the *mass* and not the label number of the state!). We thus see that the energy-levels must form an arithmetical progression with the difference $2\omega/2m = h\nu_0$, so that we can put

$$W_n = nh\nu_0 + \text{const.} \tag{86}$$

With this labelling of the stationary states we must have

$$\left.\begin{array}{l} r_{mn} = 0, \quad \text{unless} \quad m = n+1 \\ s_{mn} = 0, \quad \text{unless} \quad m = n-1 \end{array}\right\}. \tag{86 a}$$

The value of the constant in the expression for W_n can be obtained from the condition that the lowest value of L_{nn} must be equal to zero. This condition follows from the equation

$$(rs)_{nn} = \sum_k r_{nk}s_{kn} = r_{n,n-1}s_{n-1,n} = L_{nn}$$

in conjunction with the fact that K_{nn} cannot assume negative values because the matrix K represents an essentially positive or rather non-negative quantity, namely, $2m(p^2+q^2)$ (with p and q both real). Hence we conclude that the series of stationary states must terminate with some state $n_{\min}$ which we can obviously label as $n = 0$. The matrix elements $r_{n,n-1}$ and $s_{n-1,n}$ must obviously vanish for $n \leqslant 0$, since the states $n \leqslant -1$ do not exist, whence it follows that $L_{00} = 0$, or $K_{00} = \omega$, and consequently $H_{00} = W_0 = \frac{1}{2}h\nu_0$, that is,

$$W_n = h\nu_0(n+\tfrac{1}{2}) \tag{86 b}$$

in agreement with the result obtained in Part I, § 13, by means of the wave-mechanical treatment of the problem of the linear oscillator.

Further, for $n > 0$ we get

$$r_{n,n-1}s_{n-1,n} = 2mh\nu_0 n. \tag{87}$$

Now from the definition of r and s according to (84) or

$$r_{n,n-1} = p_{n,n-1} + iq_{n,n-1},$$
$$s_{n-1,n} = p_{n-1,n} - iq_{n-1,n},$$

together with the Hermitian character of the matrices p and q (which expresses the reality of the quantities represented by them), it follows that

$$s_{n-1,n} = r_{n,n-1}^*. \tag{87 a}$$

We thus have $$|r_{n,n-1}| = |s_{n-1,n}| = \sqrt{(2mh\nu_0 n)}. \tag{87 b}$$

Coming back from r and s to p and q, we have $p = \frac{1}{2}(r+s)$, $q = -\frac{1}{2}i(r-s)$, and consequently

$$\left. \begin{array}{ll} p_{n,n-1} = \frac{1}{2}r_{n,n-1}, & p_{n-1,n} = \frac{1}{2}s_{n-1,n} \\ q_{n,n-1} = -\frac{1}{2}ir_{n,n-1}, & q_{n-1,n} = \frac{1}{2}is_{n-1,n} \end{array} \right\}, \tag{88}$$

all the other matrix elements p_{mn} and q_{mn} vanishing.

We thus get $$|p_{n,n-1}| = |q_{n,n-1}| = \sqrt{(\frac{1}{2}mnh\nu_0)} \tag{88 a}$$

and, returning to the original coordinate, $x = q/(2\pi\nu_0 m)$,

$$|x_{n,n-1}| = \sqrt{\left(\frac{h}{8\pi^2\nu_0 m}n\right)} = \frac{1}{2\pi\nu_0 m}|p_{n,n-1}|. \tag{88 b}$$

The latter relation between x and p can be obtained directly from the equation $p = mdx/dt$, which gives

$$p_{nk} = m2\pi i\nu_{nk}x_{nk},$$

i.e. since $\nu_{nk} = (W_n - W_k)/h = (n-k)\nu_0$,

$$p_{n,n-1} = 2\pi i\nu_0 x_{n,n-1}.$$

The derivation of the formulae (88) and (88 a) by the purely wave-mechanical method, i.e. through evaluation of the integrals

$$x_{mn} = \int_{-\infty}^{+\infty} x\psi_m^*\psi_n \, dx \quad \text{and} \quad p_{mn} = \frac{h}{2\pi i} \int_{-\infty}^{+\infty} \psi_m^* \frac{d}{dx}\psi_n \, dx,$$

where ψ_m and ψ_n are the normalized characteristic functions of the harmonic oscillator, would require a much larger amount of more complicated calculation.

In the case of the hydrogen-like atom, the wave-mechanical method, on the contrary, proves much more simple and convenient than the matrix method for the determination of the energy values and the matrix components. The matrix method can, however, be applied with advantage in this case, as well as in the general case of the motion of a particle in any central field of force, for the determination of quantities which wave-mechanically depend upon the *angular part* of the wave functions only [i.e. on the spherical harmonic functions $Y_{lm}(\theta, \phi)$].

Here·belong in the first place the components of the angular momentum M_x, M_y, M_z, or rather their matrix elements with regard to states differing from each other by the values of the axial quantum number m (or also of the angular quantum number l)—including, of course, their characteristic values.

The purely matrix determination of these quantities can be obtained most simply if one starts from the commutation relation

$$\mathbf{M} \times \mathbf{M} = -\frac{h}{2\pi i}\mathbf{M},$$

which has been deduced in the preceding chapter with the help of the operator definition of the vector $\mathbf{M}$.

We shall put, for the sake of brevity,

$$M_x = \frac{h}{2\pi}A, \qquad M_y = \frac{h}{2\pi}B, \qquad M_z = \frac{h}{2\pi}C,$$

so that the commutation relation above referred to assumes the form

$$AB - BA = iC, \qquad BC - CB = iA, \qquad CA - AC = iB, \qquad (89)$$

A, B, and C being regarded here as matrices.

We shall introduce the matrix

$$N = A^2 + B^2 + C^2 \qquad (89\,\mathrm{a})$$

which (multiplied by $h^2/4\pi^2$) represents the square of the total angular momentum (M^2), and shall show that it commutes with each of the matrices A, B, C (the proof is the same as if they were treated as operators).

We have, namely,

$$CA^2 - A^2C = (CA - AC)A + A(CA - AC) = +i(BA + AB),$$

and similarly

$$CB^2 - B^2C = (CB - BC)B + B(CB - BC) = -i(AB + BA).$$

Adding these equations to the equation $CC^2 - C^2C = 0$, we get

$$CN - NC = 0, \qquad (89\,\mathrm{b})$$

and in the same way $AN - NA = 0$ and $BN - NB = 0$.

Since, moreover, we know that N commutes with the energy matrix H, it must be a constant of the motion, and its characteristic values, together with the characteristic values of H, i.e. the diagonal elements of N and H in a matrix representation corresponding to characteristic functions of both H and N, can be used to specify the stationary states. We know, furthermore, that these characteristic functions can be chosen in such a way [by putting $Y_{lm}(\theta, \phi) = P_{lm}(\theta)e^{im\phi}$] that one of the three matrices A, B, C—C say—shall also be diagonal (corresponding to

$C\psi = \text{const.}\,\psi$). Using the results obtained before by the wave-mechanical method, we can thus define N and C as diagonal matrices with the elements

$$\left.\begin{aligned} N_{n,l,m;\,n,l,m} &= l(l+1) \\ C_{n,l,m;\,n,l,m} &= m \end{aligned}\right\}. \tag{89 c}$$

These results can be obtained independently by the purely matrix method, if we confine ourselves to matrix elements corresponding to the same energy values and assume both N and C to be diagonal matrices (which we obviously can do for the sake of simplicity, although this is by no means necessary).

We shall consider first such matrix elements of A and B as correspond to states with the same value of N and shall distinguish these states accordingly by one index m only, specifying the characteristic values (i.e. the diagonal elements) of C.

As in the case of the oscillator, we shall not consider A and B separately but in the conjugate complex combinations

$$A+iB = R, \qquad A-iB = S. \tag{90}$$

Replacing the K of the oscillator theory by C, we have, according to (89),

$$(A+iB)C-C(A+iB) = (AC-CA)+i(BC-CB) = -(iB+A),$$

i.e.
$$CR-RC = R, \tag{90 a}$$

and similarly
$$CS-SC = -S. \tag{90 b}$$

These equations are of exactly the same form as equation (85) for r and the corresponding equation for s, the constant ω being replaced by $\frac{1}{2}$. We thus get, in the same way as before,

$$C_{mm} = m+\text{const.}, \tag{91}$$

the non-vanishing elements of R and S being

$$R_{m,m-1} \quad \text{and} \quad S_{m-1,m}$$

and having the same numerical value since

$$R_{m,m-1} = S^{*}_{m-1,m}. \tag{91 a}$$

The latter, together with the value of the constant in (91), can be derived from the equation

$$RS = (A+iB)(A-iB) = A^2+B^2+C = A^2+B^2+C^2+\tfrac{1}{4}-(C^2-C+\tfrac{1}{4}),$$

i.e.
$$RS = N+\tfrac{1}{4}-(C-\tfrac{1}{2})^2. \tag{92}$$

Taking the diagonal elements of both sides, we get

$$(RS)_{mm} = R_{m,m-1}S_{m-1,m} = N+\tfrac{1}{4}-(C_{mm}-\tfrac{1}{2})^2, \tag{92 a}$$

where N now denotes not the matrix N but the diagonal element of this matrix corresponding to the state in question (with no subscript mm affixed to it because it does not depend upon m). In a similar way we find

$$(SR)_{mm} = S_{m,m+1} R_{m+1,m} = N + \tfrac{1}{4} - (C_{mm} + \tfrac{1}{2})^2. \qquad (92\,\mathrm{b})$$

It should be remarked that the same expression can be written in the form $(RS)_{m+1,m+1}$, so that we must have, according to (92 a),

$$(C_{mm} + \tfrac{1}{2})^2 = (C_{m+1,m+1} - \tfrac{1}{2})^2,$$

which is, of course, in agreement with (91).

Now since $A^2 + B^2 + C^2 = N$, the characteristic values of the operator C or, what is the same thing, the diagonal elements of the matrix C must lie within certain limits, the maximum value C' not exceeding $+N^{\frac{1}{2}}$ and the minimum value C'' being not smaller than $-N^{\frac{1}{2}}$. Denoting the corresponding limiting values of m by m' and m'' respectively, we must have

$$R_{m'+1,m'} = S_{m',m'+1} = 0 \quad \text{and} \quad R_{m'',m''-1} = S_{m''-1,m''} = 0.$$

This gives, according to (92 b),

$$C_{m'm'} = -\tfrac{1}{2} + \sqrt{(N+\tfrac{1}{4})},$$

and, according to (92 a),

$$C_{m''m''} = \tfrac{1}{2} - \sqrt{(N+\tfrac{1}{4})} = -C_{m'm'}, \qquad (93)$$

as would be expected from the fact that the relation $A^2 + B^2 + C^2 = N$ determines the square of C.

The difference $C_{m'm'} - C_{m''m''} = m' - m''$ is obviously an integral number, I say, equal to the number of states with different values of C_{mm} which are possible for a given value of N. We thus obtain the following condition for N:

$$2\sqrt{(N+\tfrac{1}{4})} = \text{integer} = I;$$

that is,

$$N = \tfrac{1}{4}(I^2 - 1) = \tfrac{1}{4}(I+1)(I-1). \qquad (93\,\mathrm{a})$$

This expression reduces to the usual form

$$N = l(l+1) \qquad (94)$$

if we put $I = 2l+1$, i.e. define I as an *odd* integer, giving for the limiting values of C_{mm}

$$C_{m'm'} = +l, \qquad C_{m''m''} = -l, \qquad (94\,\mathrm{a})$$

i.e. by (91) $m' = +l$, $m'' = -l$. We thus get

$$C_{mm} = m, \qquad (94\,\mathrm{b})$$

and consequently

$$M_z = \frac{h}{2\pi} C_{mm} = \frac{hm}{2\pi}, \qquad M^2 = \frac{h^2}{4\pi^2} N = \frac{h^2}{4\pi^2} l(l+1).$$

in accordance with our previous results. It is, however, important to notice that the matrix theory admits another possibility corresponding to I being an *even* integer, $2k$ say. We get, in this case,

$$N = (k+\tfrac{1}{2})(k-\tfrac{1}{2}) \qquad (95)$$

and $$C_{m'm'} = k-\tfrac{1}{2}, \qquad C_{m''m''} = -(k-\tfrac{1}{2}), \qquad (95\,a)$$

whence $$C_{mm} = m+\tfrac{1}{2} \qquad (95\,b)$$

with $m' = -k$ and $m'' = k-1$, or

$$C_{mm} = m-\tfrac{1}{2}$$

with $m' = -(k-1)$ and $m'' = k$. These results can be put in the same form as the preceding results if we define l as a *half-integral* angular quantum number

$$l = k-\tfrac{1}{2}$$

and m as a *half-integral* axial quantum number, varying between the limits $+l$ and $-l$.

We shall then get, as before, $C_{mm} = m$. We thus see, by this example, that the matrix theory is, in a certain respect, more general than the wave-mechanical theory—at least in that form in which it has been developed hitherto. We shall give in a later chapter a generalization of it which provides an equivalent for the half-integral values of l and m of the matrix theory of the angular momentum.

The non-diagonal matrices of the x and y components of the latter can easily be derived from (90), (91 a), and (92 a). We shall not, however, examine the matrices M_x and M_y separately, but shall examine their combinations

$$M_x+iM_y = \frac{h}{2\pi}\,R, \qquad M_x-iM_y = \frac{h}{2\pi}\,S$$

for the non-vanishing elements of which the following expressions are obtained

$$(M_x+iM_y)_{m+1,m} = \frac{h}{2\pi}\sqrt{\{(l+\tfrac{1}{2})^2-(m+\tfrac{1}{2})^2\}}e^{i\alpha_m} \qquad (96)$$

$$(M_x-iM_y)_{m,m+1} = \frac{h}{2\pi}\sqrt{\{(l+\tfrac{1}{2})^2-(m+\tfrac{1}{2})^2\}}e^{-i\alpha_m}, \qquad (96\,a)$$

where α_m is an arbitrary phase factor.

A derivation of these results by the usual wave-mechanical method, i.e. by means of the integral expressions for the matrix elements, would require a thorough knowledge of the spherical harmonic functions $Y_{lm} = P_{lm}(\theta)e^{im\phi}$ and would be much more laborious than the preceding calculations.

The preceding method can also be applied to the calculation of the matrix elements of the coordinates x, y, z and momentum components p_x, p_y, p_z—for such states at least as differ from each other in the quantum numbers m and l only (and which in the case of the hydrogen-like atom belong to the same energy-level). To do this we shall examine first the expressions $M_z x - x M_z$, $M_z y - y M_z$, and $M_z z - z M_z$. Since $\dfrac{2\pi i}{h}(M_z x - x M_z) = [M_z, x] = \dfrac{\partial M_z}{\partial p_x}$ and $M_z = x p_y - y p_x$, we get $[M_z, x] = -y$, and in the same way $[M_z, y] = +x$, $[M_z, z] = 0$. Putting

$$x + iy = \xi, \qquad x - iy = \eta \qquad (97)$$

we thus have
$$[M_z, \xi] = -y + ix = i(x + iy) = i\xi$$
$$[M_z, \eta] = -y - ix = -i(x - iy) = -i\eta$$

or, with $M_z = hC/2\pi$,

$$C\xi - \xi C = \xi, \qquad C\eta - \eta C = -\eta \qquad (97\,\text{a})$$

and
$$Cz - zC = 0. \qquad (97\,\text{b})$$

It follows immediately from these relations that, so far as the quantum number m is concerned (l being left undetermined), z is a diagonal matrix with non-vanishing elements z_{mm}, while ξ and η are matrices with non-vanishing elements of the form

$$\xi_{m,m-1} \quad \text{and} \quad \eta_{m-1,m},$$

as in the case of the harmonic oscillator.

Let us consider now the commutation relations between the quantities (operators, matrices) ξ, η on the one hand and R, S on the other. We have

$$[M_x + iM_y, \xi] = [M_x, \xi] + i[M_y, \xi]$$
$$= [M_x, x] + i[M_x, y] + i[M_y, x] - [M_y, y]$$
$$= i\left(\frac{\partial M_x}{\partial p_y} + \frac{\partial M_y}{\partial p_x}\right) = i(-z + z) = 0,$$

and similarly
$$[M_x - iM_y, \xi] = -2iz,$$

so that
$$R\xi - \xi R = 0, \qquad (98)$$
$$S\xi - \xi S = -2z. \qquad (98\,\text{a})$$

From the first of these equations we get

$$(R\xi)_{m+1,m-1} = R_{m+1,m}\,\xi_{m,m-1} = (\xi R)_{m+1,m-1} = \xi_{m+1,m}\,R_{m,m-1},$$

i.e.
$$\frac{\xi_{m+1,m}}{R_{m+1,m}} = \frac{\xi_{m,m-1}}{R_{m,m-1}} = \text{const.} = a,$$

and likewise from (98 a)

$$2z_{mm} = (\xi S)_{mm} - (S\xi)_{mm} = \xi_{m,m-1}\,S_{m-1,m} - S_{m,m+1}\,\xi_{m+1,m}$$
$$= a(R_{m,m-1}\,S_{m-1,m} - S_{m,m+1}\,R_{m+1,m}) = a[(RS)_{mm} - (RS)_{m+1\,m+1}].$$

We thus see that the non-vanishing matrix elements of the co-ordinates are determined, disregarding an irrelevant proportionality factor, by the matrix elements of the angular momentum. Substituting, in the preceding equations, the expressions for $R_{m,m-1}$ and $S_{m-1,m}$ derived before, we get $2z_{mm} = a\{[(l+\frac{1}{2})^2-(m-\frac{1}{2})^2]-[(l+\frac{1}{2})^2-(m+\frac{1}{2})^2]\}$, i.e.

$$z_{mm} = am$$
$$|\xi_{m+1,m}| = |\eta_{m,m+1}| = a\sqrt{\{(l+\tfrac{1}{2})^2-(m+\tfrac{1}{2})^2\}} \left.\right\} . \qquad (98\,\text{b})$$

In deriving these results it was tacitly assumed that the total momentum remained invariant, i.e. that the angular quantum number l preserved the same value in the different states to which the matrix elements (98 b) refer. Affixing the index l, we should have written the latter in the more complete form $z_{l,m;\,l,m}$, $\xi_{l,m+1;\,l,m}$, etc.

In order to find out the matrix elements which correspond to different values of l, we must take into account certain commutation relations containing the matrix of the total momentum, or its square N ($\times h^2/4\pi^2$). Taking, for instance, the relation

$$NR-RN = 0$$

(which follows from $NA-AN = 0$ and $NB-BN = 0$), we have, since N is a diagonal matrix with regard both to l and m (as a matter of fact not depending upon m),

$$(NR-RN)_{l',m';\,l'',m''} = \sum_{l'''m'''} (N_{l',m';\,l''',m'''} R_{l''',m''';\,l'',m''} - R_{l',m';\,l''',m'''} N_{l''',m''';\,l'',m''})$$
$$= (N_{l'l'}-N_{l'l''}) R_{l',m';\,l'',m''} = 0.$$

We thus see that $R_{l',m';\,l'',m''}$ vanishes unless $l' = l''$ as was assumed above. This assumption is therefore justified so far as the components of the angular momentum are concerned (it can be proved in the same way for S and C). It need not, however, hold for the coordinates, i.e. for the matrices ξ, η, z.

Taking, for instance, the $(l',m';l'',m'')$-element of (98), we have

$$\sum_{m'''} (R_{l',m';\,l',m'''} \xi_{l',m''';\,l'',m''} - \xi_{l',m';\,l'',m'''} R_{l'',m''';\,l'',m''}) = 0$$

or $R_{l',m';\,l',m'-1} \xi_{l',m'-1;\,l'',m''} - \xi_{l',m';\,l'',m''+1} R_{l'',m''+1;\,l'',m''} = 0.$

Now it can easily be seen that the results derived from (97 a) and (97 b) as to the non-vanishing elements of ξ, η, and z, so far as they are specified by the quantum number m, remain valid irrespective of the equality or inequality of the numbers l' and l'' (since these results depend solely upon the diagonal character of C with regard to m). The preceding equation need therefore be examined only for the case when

$m'' = m'-2$. Putting $m' = m+1$ and $m'' = m-1$, we get

$$R_{l',m+1;\,l',m}\,\xi_{l',m;\,l'',m-1} = \xi_{l',m+1,\,l'',m}\,R_{l'',m;\,l'',m-1}. \qquad (99)$$

The angular quantum number l represents the maximum absolute value of the axial quantum number m. This means that the matrix element $R_{l',m+1,\,l',m}$ will vanish unless *both* $|m| \leqslant l'$ and $|m+1| \leqslant l'$; likewise $\xi_{l',m,\,l'',m-1}$ will vanish unless $|m| \leqslant l'$ and $|m-1| \leqslant l''$, further $\xi_{l',m+1;\,l'',m}$ will vanish unless $|m| \leqslant l''$ and $|m+1| \leqslant l'$, and finally $R_{l'',m;\,l'',m-1}$ will vanish unless $|m| \leqslant l''$ and $|m-1| \leqslant l''$. Since equations (99) must hold for all values of m, both sides vanishing simultaneously, we can conclude that l' and l'' must be connected with each other in such a way that the violation of one of the conditions

$$|m| \leqslant l', \qquad |m+1| \leqslant l', \qquad |m-1| \leqslant l''$$

will entail the violation of one of the conditions

$$|m+1| \leqslant l', \qquad |m| \leqslant l'', \qquad |m-1| \leqslant l''.$$

This will obviously be the case if $l' = l''$, or $l' = l''+1$, or $l' = l''-1$.

We thus see that only those matrix elements of $\tilde{\xi}$ will be different from zero for which
$$l'-l'' = 0, +1, -1. \qquad (99\,\text{a})$$

For otherwise we could, by a suitable choice of m, make one side of (99) vanish while the other would be different from zero.

The same applies, of course, to the matrix elements of η and z, or, in other words, to the matrix elements of all the three coordinates.

Putting in (99) $l' = l$ and $l'' = l-1$, and replacing the matrix elements of R by their expressions (96), we get

$$\sqrt{\{(l+\tfrac{1}{2})^2-(m+\tfrac{1}{2})^2\}}\,\xi_{l,m;\,l-1,m-1} = \sqrt{\{(l-\tfrac{1}{2})^2-(m-\tfrac{1}{2})^2\}}\,\xi_{l,m+1;\,l-1,m},$$

or

$$\sqrt{\{(l+m+1)(l-m)\}}\,\xi_{l,m;\,l-1,m-1} = \sqrt{\{(l+m-1)(l-m)\}}\,\xi_{l,m+1;\,l-1,m}.$$

Replacing here the common factor $\sqrt{(l-m)}$ by $\sqrt{(l+m)}$, and taking into account that the expression $(l+m+1)(l+m)$ is obtained from $(l+m-1)(l+m)$ by replacing m by $m+1$, we can put

$$\xi_{l,m+1;\,l-1,m} = b\sqrt{\{(l+m)(l+m+1)\}}, \qquad (100)$$

where b is a proportionality coefficient which does not depend either on l or on m.

Substituting this expression in the equation

$$-2z_{l,m;\,l+1,m} = S_{l,m;\,l,m+1}\,\xi_{l,m+1;\,l-1,m} - \xi_{l,m;\,l-1,m-1}\,S_{l-1,m-1;\,l-1,m}$$

which follows from (98 a), and putting

$$S_{l,m-1;\,l,m} = R_{l,m;\,l,m-1} = \sqrt{\{(l+\tfrac{1}{2})^2 - (m-\tfrac{1}{2})^2\}},$$

we get

$$z_{l,m;\,l-1,m} = -b\sqrt{(l^2-m^2)}. \tag{100 a}$$

In a similar way for the case $l' = l-1$, $l'' = l$ we obtain

$$\xi_{l-1,m+1;\,l,m} = b'\sqrt{\{(l-m)(l-m-1)\}} \tag{100 b}$$

$$z_{l-1,m;\,l,m} = b'\sqrt{(l^2-m^2)}, \tag{100 c}$$

where b' is another coefficient of proportionality, which can be shown to have the same numerical value as b.

It is interesting to compare the preceding results† with the wave-mechanical method for the determination of matrix elements of the coordinates for a hydrogen-like atom.

We have, for instance,

$$z_{n,l,m;\,n',l',m'} = \int z\psi^*_{n,l,m}\psi_{n',l',m'}\,dV,$$

or, putting $\psi_{n,l,m} = f_n(r)P_{lm}(\theta)e^{im\phi}$, $dV = r^2\,dr d\omega$, $d\omega = \sin\theta\,d\theta d\phi$, and $z = r\cos\theta$,

$$z_{n,l,m;\,n',l',m'} = \int_0^\infty f_n(r)r^3\,dr \int_0^\pi P_{lm}(\theta)P_{l'm'}(\theta)\cos\theta\sin\theta\,d\theta \int_0^{2\pi} e^{i(m'-m)\phi}\,d\phi.$$

We see, first of all, that on account of the last factor this expression vanishes unless $m' = m$. In addition it can be shown that the second factor also vanishes unles $l' = l\pm 1$. The proof is based on the fact that the product $\cos\theta\,P_{lm}(\theta)$ can be represented as the sum of two functions $P_{l+1,m}(\theta)$ and $P_{l-1,m}(\theta)$ with suitably chosen coefficients, and on the orthogonality of the functions $Y_l(\theta,\phi)$ corresponding to different values of l [as characteristic functions of the operator Ω^2 with the characteristic values $-l(l+1)$].

Replacing z by $\xi = (x+iy) = r\sin\theta(\cos\phi + i\sin\phi) = r\sin\theta\,e^{i\phi}$, we get, in a similar way,

$$\xi_{n,l,m;\,n',l',m'} = \int_0^\infty f_n(r)r^3\,dr \int_0^\pi P_{lm}(\theta)P_{l'm'}(\theta)\sin^2\theta\,d\theta \int_0^{2\pi} e^{i(m'-m+1)\phi}\,d\phi.$$

The examination of the last factor shows at once that this expression vanishes unless $m' = m-1$; the second factor vanishes likewise if $l' \neq l\pm 1$.

The conditions relative to m coincide with those obtained by the matrix method for z and ξ; the condition $l' = l\pm 1$ is, however, more restrictive, since it excludes the case $l' = l$.

We see that here again, as for the values of l (integral or half-integral),

† Derived in the above way by Born and Jordan.

the matrix method leads to results of higher generality than the wave-mechanical method. It should not be inferred that the results obtained by the latter are incorrect. On the contrary, it is the results obtained by the matrix method which require some qualification. The reason for this is that the properties of the matrices which represent the components of the angular momentum of an electron are not completely specific, but, as we shall see later, are shared by matrices representing allied quantities of a more general character, which can be considered as the resultant of the angular momentum due to rotation about a fixed centre and the so-called 'intrinsic angular momentum' of the electron, whose origin is usually ascribed to its spin motion.

It is possible to generalize the wave-mechanical theory in such a way as to interpret this 'spin effect' and to incorporate the intrinsic momentum, allowing for the resultant angular quantum number or, as it is called, the 'inner quantum number' j both integral and half-integral values and allowing transitions, i.e. non-vanishing matrix elements of the coordinates, for which this number changes by ± 1 or remains constant. This does not, however, invalidate in the least the fact that the angular quantum number l, representing the 'orbital angular momentum' of the particle, can assume integral values only and obeys the restricted 'selection rule' $l' - l = \pm 1$.

The fact that we have obtained, by the matrix method, non-vanishing expressions (98 b) for the matrix elements of the coordinates in the case $l' - l = 0$ does not contradict the wave-mechanical theory, for these expressions contain a proportionality factor a, which has not been specified and which can easily be shown to be equal to zero in the case considered (if l denotes the orbital and not the total angular quantum number).

The matrix elements of the coordinates which we have calculated have a direct and indeed very important physical significance. They determine, according to the formula

$$A_{nn'} = \frac{64\pi^4}{3c^3} \frac{\nu_{nn'}^3 \, e^2}{h} |x_{nn'}|^2,$$

where e denotes the electric charge of the particle, the probability of a spontaneous transition with emission of light, i.e. they determine the intensity of the different lines in the emission spectrum of the corresponding system or the degree of their 'blackness' in the absorption spectrum [see Part I, § 13]. Such pairs of states n, n' for which the matrix elements $x_{n,n'}$ vanish do not combine with each other, in the sense that transitions between them connected with the emission or absorption of light, corresponding to oscillations in the x-direction, that is to say, 'polarized' in this direction, are impossible. The relations between the quantum numbers which characterize the 'allowed' transitions (corresponding to the non-vanishing matrix elements) are called 'selection rules'. The latter, as we have just seen, can be different for different coordinates. For instance, in the case of the z-coordinates (i.e. of light polarized in the z-direction) they amount to $l'-l = \pm 1$ and $m' = m$, while in the case of the x, y-coordinates they are $l'-l = \pm 1$ and $m' = m \pm 1$.

This distinction between the different coordinates is a purely formal one in the case of a radially symetrical field of force—because of the degeneracy connected with such a field. This degeneracy—with respect to the different values of m—can be eliminated, as will be shown later, by the presence of a magnetic field parallel to the z-axis (Zeeman effect). If the latter is weak enough, the preceding expressions for the matrix elements of z and of $x \pm iy$ will remain approximately valid and will determine the intensity of the spectrum lines linearly polarized in the direction of the magnetic field or circularly polarized about this direction.

14. Matrix Representation in the Case of a Continuous Spectrum

We have limited ourselves hitherto to the matrix representation of physical quantities where the states concerned form a discrete set, corresponding to a discrete spectrum of the energy operator H.

The case of a continuous spectrum corresponding to a continuous or 'mixed' set of states specified by functions of the type ψ_C^0 or $\psi_{C,n_2 n_3}^0$, etc. (§ 11), can be dealt with in a similar manner. The matrix elements of any operator F are defined in this case in exactly the same way as in the preceding case, i.e. by integrals of the form

$$F_{C'C''}^0 = \int \psi_{C'}^{0*} F \psi_{C''}^0 \, dV \qquad (101)$$

or $$F_{C_1' n_2' n_3';\, C_1'' n_2'' n_3''}^0 = \int \psi_{C_1' n_2' n_3'}^{0*} F \psi_{C_1'' n_2'' n_3''}^0, \qquad (101\,\text{a})$$

and so on.

These integrals as a rule do not converge, and are similar to the Dirac function $\delta(C'-C'')$ which was introduced and discussed in § 10, and to which the matrix elements of F actually reduce if F represents the energy H or any other constant of the motion commuting with H and satisfying the equation $F\psi_C = F_C\psi_C$. We then get, according to (101),

$$F^0_{C'C''} = F_{C''} \int \psi^{0*}_{C'}\psi^0_{C''}\, dV,$$

that is, $$F^0_{C'C''} = F_{C''}\,\delta(C'-C''). \tag{101 b}$$

This expression corresponds to a 'diagonal matrix' of the discrete case, just as $\delta(C'-C'')$ corresponds to the unit matrix.

The somewhat indefinite character of the matrix elements $F^0_{C'C''}$ can be removed in the same way as in the simplest case $F = 1$ when $F^0_{C'C''}$ reduces to the function $\delta(C'-C'')$—namely, by extending the integration in (101) over a *finite* volume, and passing to the limit $V \to \infty$ after completing the integration over C' or C'' which always occurs in problems of physical interest.† The simplest example of such a problem is the calculation of the probable value of some quantity F for a motion specified by a wave function of the type

$$\psi = \int a_C \psi_C\, dC, \tag{102}$$

which can be considered as the superposition of a large number of 'wave packets' corresponding to very small intervals of the parameter C. Although the integrals $\int |\psi_C|^2\, dV$ diverge, the integral $\int |\psi|^2\, dV$ remains in general finite and can be normalized to 1, just as in the discrete case when $\psi = \sum c_n\psi_n$.

We have in fact, reversing the order of integration with respect to V and C,

$$\int_V |\psi|^2\, dV = \int_{C'} a^*_{C'}\, dC' \int_{C''} a_{C''}\, dC'' \int_V \psi^*_{C'}\psi_{C''}\, dV$$

$$= \int_{C'} a^*_{C'}\, dC' \int_{C''} a_{C''}\, dC''\, \delta_V(C'-C'').$$

Instead of first performing the integration with regard to C' and C'' and then passing to the limit $V \to \infty$, we can in this case replace the (perfectly definite) function $\delta_V(C'-C'')$ at once by the Dirac function $\delta(C'-C'')$, which gives

$$\int |\psi|^2\, dV = \int a^*_{C'} a_{C'}\, dC'. \tag{102 a}$$

We thus see that the first integral converges along with the integral

---

† In some cases it is preferable to modify the definition of the wave functions ψ so as to make them vanish on a certain surface S beyond which the forces can be assumed to vanish. The problem is thus reduced to one characterized by a discrete spectrum. Such quantities as possess a *direct* physical interest are usually only slightly affected by the value of the volume V enclosed by S, so long as it is sufficiently large. Their exact values can be easily calculated by passing to the limit $V \to \infty$.

$\int |a_C|^2 \, dC$. The convergence of the latter can, however, always be secured by a reasonable choice of the function a_C. The normalization condition thus reduces to the equation

$$\int |a_C|^2 \, dC = 1, \tag{102 b}$$

which replaces the equation $\sum |a_n|^2 = 1$ of the discrete case, and shows that the product

$$|a_C|^2 \, dC \tag{102 c}$$

can be considered as the probability that the particle is in a state of motion specified by the interval $(C, C+dC)$.

The expression (102 c) is of the same form as the expression $|\psi|^2 \, dV$ for the probability of a position specified by the volume element dV; in both cases we have to deal with continuously variable parameters (C or the coordinates x, y, z), and therefore in both cases it has a meaning to talk of probability with reference not to a definite state or position, but to a definite *interval* of states or positions, the probability in question being proportional to the magnitude of the interval.

Subject to the condition (102 b), the probable value of a quantity F can be defined by the usual formula

$$\overline{F} = \int \psi^* F \psi \, dV, \tag{103}$$

which can be rewritten in the form

$$\overline{F} = \int_{C'} a_{C'}^* \, dC' \int_{C''} a_{C''} \, dC'' \int_V \psi_{C'}^* \, F \psi_{C''} \, dV,$$

i.e.

$$\overline{F} = \int\!\!\int a_{C'}^* \, a_{C''} \, F_{C'C''} \, dC' dC''. \tag{103 a}$$

In the simplest case, when F represents a constant of the motion, we get, according to (101 b),

$$\overline{F} = \int |a_C|^2 F_C \, dC, \tag{103 b}$$

in agreement with the above interpretation of the product $|a_C|^2 \, dC$.

If, however, F is not a constant of the motion, the integral (103 a) representing its probable value cannot be evaluated directly and we must have recourse to the method indicated above (*first* integration over finite volume, then over C'' or both C'' and C', and finally passage to the limit $V \to \infty$).

If the 'C-space' is subdivided into infinitely small intervals $\Delta C'$, $\Delta C''$, etc., and a wave packet is built up for each interval, according to the formula

$$\check{\psi}_{C'} = \lim_{\Delta C' \to 0} \frac{1}{\sqrt{\Delta C'}} \int_{\Delta C} \psi_C \, dC, \tag{104}$$

we can replace the matrix components of F with respect to the functions $\psi_{C'}$ by matrix components with respect to the 'quasi-discrete' functions $\tilde{\psi}_{C'}$ (normalized to unity):

$$\bar{F}_{C'C''} = \int \tilde{\psi}_{C'}^* F \tilde{\psi}_{C''} \, dV. \qquad (104\,a)$$

The connexion between these matrix components and those discussed above is given by the formula

$$\bar{F}_{C'C''} = \lim \frac{1}{\sqrt{(\Delta C' \Delta C'')}} \int_{\Delta C'} \int_{\Delta C''} F_{C'C''} \, dC' dC'', \qquad (104\,b)$$

whence it follows that the probable value of F can be written in the form

$$\bar{F} = \lim \sum_{\Delta C'} \sum_{\Delta C''} \sqrt{(\Delta C' \Delta C'')} \bar{F}_{C'C''} a_{C'}^* a_{C''}. \qquad (104\,c)$$

The matrix components—or elements—of a real quantity with respect to states of a continuous set must, of course, satisfy the Hermitian relations

$$F_{C'C''}^* = F_{C''C'}$$

just as in the case of a discrete spectrum.

'Continuous matrices' cannot be conveniently represented by a square array of elements or components, such as are used for discrete matrices. This, however, does not invalidate the analytical results which have been established in § 11; the only amendment which they require consists in the replacement of the unit matrix δ_{mn} by the Dirac function $\delta(C' - C'')$ and of summation with respect to discretely variable indices by an integration with respect to the continuously variable indices wherever the latter occur in the place of the former.

This has already been illustrated by the preceding examples. In a similar way we get instead of (75)

$$F\psi_{C'} = \int F_{C''C'} \psi_{C''} \, dC'', \qquad (105)$$

and instead of (76)

$$(FG)_{C'C''} = \int F_{C'C} G_{CC''} \, dC \qquad (105\,a)$$

(multiplication law for continuous matrices).

The seemingly unimportant formal difference between the continuous (or mixed) and discrete case is connected, however, with a fundamental difference in the physical meaning both of the wave functions and of the matrix elements. The essence of this difference consists in the fact that, while to states belonging to a discrete set there corresponds in classical mechanics periodic or quasi-periodic motion in a limited region of space, states belonging to a continuous set correspond to aperiodic motions of the classical theory, i.e. to types of motion for which the kinetic energy remains positive at infinity and which approximate therefore at infinite distance (so far as the forces vanish there) to free motion.

Motions of this type were not considered in the old quantum theory. The latter did not encroach upon the holy laws of classical mechanics, but merely added to them certain quantum restrictions when the motion was confined to a limited region of space and accordingly displayed certain periodicities corresponding to the many-valuedness of the action function S. As already shown above, Bohr's quantum conditions amounted to the condition of single-valuedness for the function $e^{i2\pi S/h}$.

In the case of aperiodic motions, starting at infinity and ending at infinity, the action function S remains single-valued, so that quantum restrictions of any kind are unnecessary.

The coordinates of a particle describing such an aperiodic motion, considered as functions of the time t, cannot, of course, be expanded in a Fourier series. The latter can be replaced, however, in this case by a *Fourier integral*. Limiting ourselves, for the sake of simplicity, to motion in one dimension, e.g. parallel to the x-axis, we can write instead of (79), § 12,

$$x(t) = \int_{-\infty}^{+\infty} x^0(\nu) e^{i2\pi\nu t}\, d\nu, \tag{106}$$

and instead of (81 b)

$$x_{\nu'}(t) = \int_{-\infty}^{+\infty} x^0_{\nu''\nu'} e^{i2\pi(\nu''-\nu')t}\, d\nu'', \tag{106 a}$$

where $x^0_{\nu''\nu'} = x^0_{\nu'}(\nu''-\nu')$, the product $x^0_{\nu''\nu'}\, d\nu''$ replacing the amplitude x_{mn}; $\nu' = W'/h$ is the frequency associated with the energy $W = W'$, which is supposed to be the energy of the motion represented by (106 a). As to the frequency $\nu'' = \nu'+\nu$, it is natural to assume that it coincides approximately with W''/h, where W'' denotes the energy of a state, a transition from which to the state W' corresponds, with regard to frequency and intensity of the emitted light, to the element $x^0_{\nu''\nu'} e^{i2\pi(\nu''-\nu')t}\, d\nu''$ of the integral (106 a). The question of the degree of approximation between ν'' and W''/h (if $\nu' = W'/h$) has no definite meaning in the present case with a continuously variable W, for equations (80), (80 a), (80 b), and (80 c) cannot be applied to it, the integrals $\oint$ referring to 'round trips' only. We are therefore entitled to assume that ν'' coincides *exactly* with W''/h, i.e. that there is not only a 'correspondence' but an actual *identity* between the classical frequencies occurring in (103) and the quantum frequencies $(W''-W')/h$. The responsibility for the disagreement between the classical and the quantum theory can thus be shifted entirely on to the amplitude coefficients $x^0_{\nu''\nu'}$, which can be supposed to 'correspond', i.e. to be approximately equal to the matrix elements of x with regard to the states W' and W''

$$\int\limits_{-\infty}^{+\infty} x\psi^{0*}_{\nu''}\,\psi^0_{\nu'}\,dx.$$

The correspondence with these elements can actually be established with the help of the approximate expressions of the wave functions ψ^0_ν in a way similar to that used in § 12 for the case of a discrete spectrum.

We shall put accordingly

$$\psi_{\nu'} = \frac{C_{\nu'}}{\sqrt{v_{\nu'}}}\,e^{i2\pi\{s^0_{\nu'}(x)-W_{\nu'}t\}/h}, \tag{107}$$

where the coefficients $C_{\nu'}$ must be determined by the condition

$$\int\limits_{-\infty}^{+\infty} \psi^{0*}_{\nu''}\,\psi^0_{\nu'}\,dx = \delta(\nu'-\nu''). \tag{107 a}$$

Taking into account the relation

$$s^0_{\nu'}(x)-s^0_{\nu''}(x) = (W_{\nu'}-W_{\nu''})t, \tag{107 b}$$

which can easily be shown to hold approximately (for two states not far removed from each other) irrespective of the periodic or aperiodic character of the motion,[†] we get in the case of neighbouring values of ν' and ν'':

$$F^0_{\nu''\nu'} = \int\limits_{-\infty}^{+\infty} F(x)\psi^{0*}_{\nu''}\,\psi^0_{\nu'}\,dx \cong \sqrt{C_{\nu'}\,C_{\nu'}}\int\limits_{-\infty}^{+\infty} F(t)e^{-i2\pi(W_{\nu''}-W_{\nu'})t/h}\,dt. \tag{108}$$

On the other hand, the Fourier coefficients in the integral representing a function $F_{\nu'}(t)$:

$$F_{\nu'}(t) = \int\limits_{-\infty}^{+\infty} F^0_{\nu''\nu'}\,e^{i2\pi(\nu''-\nu')t}\,d\nu''$$

are determined by the formula

$$F^0_{\nu''\nu'} = \int\limits_{-\infty}^{+\infty} F_{\nu'}(t)e^{-i2\pi(\nu''-\nu')t}\,dt, \tag{108 a}$$

which coincides with the' preceding expression for $F_{\nu''\nu'}$ if we put

[†] Cf. § 12. Since in the present case the integral $J = \oint g\,dx$ is non-existent, we can put directly
$$s^0_{\nu'}(x)-s^0_{\nu''}(x) \cong \frac{\partial s^0_\nu(x)}{\partial W}(W_{\nu'}-W_{\nu''}).$$
We have further, from the definition $\dfrac{\partial s^0}{\partial x} = g = \sqrt{[2m(W-U)]}$,
$$\frac{\partial s^0(x)}{\partial W} = \frac{\partial}{\partial W}\int \sqrt{[2m(W-U)]}\,dx = t,$$
in the same way as before.—The relation (107 b) can be proved in a somewhat more complicated manner for the general case of a (non-periodic) three-dimensional motion.

$\nu'' - \nu' = (W'' - W')/h$ and $C_\nu^2 = 1$. The latter condition can easily be shown to follow from (107 a). In fact the main contribution to the integral (107 a) must be due to distant points where the functions $s^0(x)$ reduce to gx with a constant value of g (corresponding to a constant potential energy). Replacing g by hk, where k is the wave number, we get, according to (23 a), Chap. I,

$$\int_{-\infty}^{+\infty} \psi_{\nu'}^{0*}\, \psi_{\nu'}^{0}\, dx \cong \frac{\sqrt{(C_{\nu'}\,C_{\nu''})}}{\sqrt{(v_{\nu'}\,v_{\nu''})}} \int_{-\infty}^{+\infty} e^{i2\pi(k'-k'')x}\, dx$$

$$= \frac{\sqrt{(C_{\nu'}\,C_{\nu''})}}{\sqrt{(v_{\nu'}\,v_{\nu''})}} \delta(k'-k'') = \delta(\nu'-\nu''),$$

whence

$$\int_{-\infty}^{+\infty} \sqrt{\left(\frac{C_{\nu'}\,C_{\nu''}}{v_{\nu'}\,v_{\nu''}}\right)} \delta(k'-k'')\, d\nu'' = \int \sqrt{\frac{C_{\nu'}\,C_{\nu''}}{(v_{\nu'}\,v_{\nu''})}}\left(\frac{d\nu}{dk}\right)'' \delta(k'-k'')\, dk'' = 1,$$

or, since $\int \delta(k'-k'')\, dk'' = 1$,

$$\frac{C_\nu^2}{v_\nu}\frac{d\nu}{dk} = 1.$$

Taking into account the relation $\nu = hk^2/(2m)$, we get

$$d\nu/dk = hk/m = v_\nu,$$

(group velocity = corpuscular velocity) and consequently

$$C_\nu^2 = 1.$$

The integral (108) expressing the Fourier components of a function $F_\nu(t)$ converges and has a definite value only when this function vanishes for $t = \pm\infty$. This condition is not satisfied for most of the quantities referring to aperiodic motion. In the simplest case of uniform motion we have, for instance, $x = vt$ and $x_{\nu''\nu'}^0 = v_{\nu'}\int_{-\infty}^{+\infty} t e^{-i2\pi(\nu''-\nu')t}\, dt$ the integral obviously diverging. If, further, F denotes a constant of the motion—e.g. the energy H—we get

$$H_{\nu''\nu'}^0 = W_{\nu'}\int_{-\infty}^{+\infty} e^{-i2\pi(\nu''-\nu')t}\, dt = W_{\nu'}\,\delta(\nu''-\nu'),$$

in exact agreement with the result (101 b) obtained from the matrix definition of $H_{\nu''\nu'}^0$.

These considerations give a new explanation of the fact, already mentioned, that the matrix elements of various quantities in the case of a continuous energy spectrum do not in general have definite values, being expressed by non-converging integrals over oscillatory functions of the $e^{i2\pi kx}$ type.

IV

TRANSFORMATION THEORY

15. Restricted Transformation Theory; Matrices defined from different 'Points of View'

Let us consider two operators H and K which we shall assume to represent the energy of the same particle moving in different fields of force with the potential-energy functions $U(x, y, z)$ and $V(x, y, z)$, both being independent of the time and limiting its movement classically to a finite region.

The characteristic values of H, which in this case will form a discrete set, will be denoted by H' or H'', etc. (the dashed letters referring not to a particular characteristic value, but to any one of them). The corresponding characteristic functions will be denoted by

$$\psi'_H = \psi^0_{H'}(x, y, z)e^{-i2\pi H't/h},$$

etc. A similar notation will be used for the characteristic values K' and functions $\phi_{K'} = \phi^0_{K'}(x, y, z)e^{-i2\pi K't/h}$ of the operator K.

If there is no degeneracy, the functions $\psi_{H'}$ will be completely specified by the attached value of the operator to which they belong. In case of degeneracy we must add to the energy operator one or two other operators, representing independent constants of the motion, for example the z-component of the angular momentum M_z and its square M^2 if the potential energy U depends upon the distance r alone (central field of force). To avoid unnecessary complication, we shall in such cases understand by H the set of all these three mutually commutable operators H_1, H_2, H_3, and by H' a set of their characteristic values H'_1, H'_2, H'_3 corresponding to the same function $\psi_{H'} = \psi_{H'_1 H'_2 H'_3}$ (in the sense of the simultaneous validity of all the three equations $H_1\psi_{H'} = H'_1\psi_{H'}, H_2\psi_{H'} = H'_2\psi_{H'}, H_3\psi_{H'} = H'_3\psi_{H'}$ which we shall write as a single equation $H\psi_{H'} = H'\psi_{H'}$). The same remark applies to the operator K, its characteristic values K', and its characteristic functions $\phi_{K'}$.

In addition, let us consider some quantity represented by an operator F and let us introduce its matrix representation with the help of the functions $\psi_{H'}$ on the one hand and of the functions $\phi_{K'}$ on the other. We shall thus get two different matrices which we shall denote by F_H and F_K respectively and refer to as the matrix of F 'from the point of view' of H and the matrix of F from the point of view of K.

The components (or elements) of these matrices will be denoted by $F_{H'H''}$ ($F_{H'H''}^0$) and $F_{K'K''}$ ($F_{K'K''}^0$). We shall thus have

$$\left. \begin{array}{ll} F_{H'H''} = \int \psi_{H'}^* F \psi_{H''} \, dV, & F_{H'H''}^0 = \int \psi_{H'}^{0*} F \psi_{H''}^0 \, dV \\[2mm] F_{K'K''} = \int \phi_{K'}^* F \phi_{K''} \, dV, & F_{K'K''}^0 = \int \phi_{K'}^{0*} F \phi_{K''}^0 \, dV \end{array} \right\} \quad (109)$$

with

$$F_{H'H''} = F_{H'H''}^0 \, e^{i2\pi(H'-H'')t/h}, \qquad F_{K'K''} = F_{K'K''}^0 \, e^{i2\pi(K'-K'')t/h}. \quad (109\,a)$$

In particular we shall have

$$\bar{H}_{H'H''} = H' \delta_{H'H''}, \qquad K_{K'K''} = K' \delta_{K'K''}, \quad (109\,b)$$

since H and K are diagonal matrices from their own point of view, the elements of these matrices being identical with the respective characteristic values.

The transformation theory in its simplest form consists in the establishment of a certain connexion between the two 'points of view', i.e. of certain relations between the functions $\psi_{H'}$ and the functions $\phi_{K'}$, as well as between the matrices F_H and F_K. With the help of equations (109), the second part of this problem can be reduced to the first. However, we shall see later that it can be solved independently without the use of the functions ψ and ϕ, on the basis of the conditions (109 b).

The fundamental assumption of the transformation theory is that the *amplitude* functions $\phi_{K'}^0(x,y,z)$ can be expressed *as linear combinations* of the amplitude functions $\psi_{H'}^0(x,y,z)$ according to the equation

$$\phi_{K'}^0 = \sum_{H'} a_{H'K'} \psi_{H'}^0 \quad (110)$$

with constant coefficients $a_{H'K'}$. We shall not try to justify this assumption on formal grounds for the general case of any operators H and K but shall be content with the following remarks.

(*a*) The assumption (110) leads to an unambiguous determination of the expansion coefficients $a_{H'K'}$. Indeed, multiplying (110) by $\psi_{H''}^{0*}$ and supposing the different functions $\psi_{H'}$ to be orthogonal to each other (which we can always do), we get upon integration

$$a_{H'K'} = \int \psi_{H'}^{0*} \phi_{K'}^0 \, dV. \quad (110\,a)$$

It is clear from this that equation (110) can hold only when the summation is extended over *all* the values of H', i.e. over all the stationary states, defined by the operator H (and those representing other independent constants of the motion, if there is degeneracy).

(*b*) For our assumption to be justified it is necessary and sufficient that the series (110) with the coefficients determined according to (110 a) should be *convergent*.

We shall argue in future as if this convergence condition were satisfied. It can be shown to be actually satisfied in most cases of practical importance corresponding to a small difference between K and H due to some weak 'perturbing' forces. In this particular case the transformation theory we are developing reduces to the so-called *perturbation theory*.

If the transformation (110) holds, then the reciprocal transformation

$$\psi^0_{H'} = \sum_{K'} a^{-1}_{K'H'} \phi^0_{K'} \tag{111}$$

must also hold with the coefficients

$$a^{-1}_{K'H'} = \int \phi^{0*}_{K'} \psi^0_{H'} \, dV. \tag{111a}$$

Comparing this with (110 a), we get the relation

$$a^*_{H'K'} = a^{-1}_{K'H'}. \tag{112}$$

On substituting the expressions (111) in (110) or (110) in (111), we get—in the first case—

$$\phi^0_{K'} = \sum_{H'} a_{H'K'} \sum_{K''} a^{-1}_{K''H'} \phi^0_{K''} = \sum_{K''} \left(\sum_{H'} a^{-1}_{K''H'} a_{H'K'} \right) \phi^0_{K''},$$

i.e.

$$\sum_{H'} a^{-1}_{K''H'} a_{H'K'} = \delta_{K''K'}, \tag{112a}$$

and in the second case

$$\sum_{K'} a_{H''K'} a^{-1}_{K'H'} = \delta_{H''H'}. \tag{112b}$$

Replacing $a^{-1}_{K'H'}$ by $a^*_{H'K'}$ according to (112), we obtain the relations

$$\sum_{H'} a_{H'K'} a^*_{H'K''} = \delta_{K'K''} \tag{113}$$

$$\sum_{K'} a_{H''K'} a^*_{H'K'} = \delta_{H''H'}, \tag{113a}$$

which express the *orthogonality and normalization* of the coefficients $a_{H'K'}$ (or $a^{-1}_{K'H'}$).

Another—equivalent—form of these relations is obtained by multiplying $\phi^0_{K'}$ in (110) by its conjugate complex and summing over K'. This gives $\sum_{K'} \phi^{0*}_{K'} \phi^0_{K'} = \sum_{H'} \sum_{H''} \sum_{K'} (a^*_{H''K'} a_{H'K'}) \psi^0_{H'} \psi^0_{H''}$, i.e. according to (112 c),

$$\sum_{K'} \phi^{0*}_{K'} \phi^0_{K'} = \sum_{H'} \psi^{0*}_{H'} \psi^0_{H'}. \tag{113b}$$

Before proceeding further in the formal development of the theory, we shall examine the physical meaning of the assumption implied by the transformation equations (110) and (111).

It should be noticed first of all that the latter have an external

S

resemblance to the representation of the general solution of the wave equation $\left(H + \dfrac{h}{2\pi i}\dfrac{\partial}{\partial t}\right)\psi = 0$ in the form of a sum of its particular solutions, i.e. to the equation

$$\psi(x,y,z,t) = \sum_{H'} C_{H'}\psi_{H'} = \sum_{H'} C_{H'}\psi_{H'}^0\, e^{-i2\pi H't/h}. \tag{113c}$$

The fundamental difference between the two cases is that the time t enters as an essential factor in equation (113 c), while the transformation equations (110) or (111) do not contain it at all. If, however, we put in (113 c) $t = 0$ or $t = t_0$, i.e. consider the function ψ at a definite instant of time, we see that by a suitable choice of the amplitude coefficients $C_{H'}$ it can be made to coincide with any one of the amplitude functions $\phi_{K'}^0$, so far as the latter are actually expressible by a series of the type (110). The physical meaning of the assumption implied in formula (110) is that any stationary state defined by the operator K, according to the equation $K\phi_{K'} = K'\phi_{K'}$ can be represented as a superposition of the alternative states defined by the operator H (according to $H\psi_{H'} = H'\psi_{H'}$) at a certain instant of time. Such a coincidence, even if achieved at a definite instant $t = t_0$, will, however, not persist unless the coefficients $C_{H'}$ are allowed to vary with the time in an adequate manner. In this case the function ψ defined by (113) will no longer represent a general solution of the equation $\left(H + \dfrac{h}{2\pi i}\dfrac{\partial}{\partial t}\right)\psi = 0$; it seems, however, natural to suppose that, with a suitable definition of the functions $C_{H'}(t)$, it will represent the general or a particular solution of the equation $\left(K + \dfrac{h}{2\pi i}\dfrac{\partial}{\partial t}\right)\phi = 0$.

The latter assumption reduces to the equation

$$\phi_{K'} = \sum_{H'} C_{H'K'}(t)\psi_{H'}, \tag{113d}$$

or

$$\phi_{K'}^0\, e^{-i2\pi K't/h} = \sum_{H'} C_{H'K'}(t)\psi_{H'}^0\, e^{-i2\pi H't/h},$$

which becomes identical with (110) if we put

$$C_{H'K'}(t) = a_{H'K'}\, e^{i2\pi(H'-K')t/h}. \tag{113e}$$

In the same way we can replace the equations of the reciprocal transformation (111) by

$$\psi_{H'} = \sum C_{K'H'}^{-1}(t)\phi_{K'} \tag{114}$$

with

$$C_{K'H'}^{-1} = a_{K'H'}^{-1}\, e^{i2\pi(K'-H')t/h}. \tag{114a}$$

We thus see that our fundamental assumption as to the existence of a linear relation (110) or (111) between the amplitude functions $\phi_{K'}^0$ and

$\psi^0_{H'}$ is equivalent to the assumption that the same motion, whether it be determined by an energy operator H or K, can be described from the point of view of the other operator, in the sense that a stationary state of the set determined by K (or H) can be represented as a super-position of stationary states determined by H (or K) with variable amplitude coefficients $C_{H'K'}$ (or $C^{-1}_{K'H'}$).

If the latter were constant, then (113 c) would represent some general solution of the equation $\left(H + \dfrac{h}{2\pi i}\dfrac{\partial}{\partial t}\right)\psi = 0$ corresponding to the pos-sibility of finding the particle in one of the *alternative* (mutually excluding) states of motion defined by the different functions $\psi_{H'}$. The coefficients $C_{H'K'}$, provided they satisfy the normalizing relation $\sum_{H'} |C_{H'K'}|^2 = 1$, would in this case represent the 'probability ampli-tudes' of the different alternative states $\psi_{H'}$, the probability of these states being equal to the square of the moduli of $C_{H'K'}$.

It is natural to preserve this interpretation in the present case when the $C_{H'K'}$ are functions of the time defined by (113 b). This dependence upon the time does not affect their moduli, which remain constant and equal to the moduli of the transformation coefficients $a_{H'K'}$—the nor-malization condition $\sum |C_{H'K'}|^2 = 1$ being satisfied in virtue of the relations (113) (with $K'' = K'$).

In defining the quantities $|C_{H'K'}|^2$ or $|a_{H'K'}|^2$ as the probabilities of the different states of the H-set, we must not forget that all these states are associated with a definite K-state, as indicated by the second sub-script in $a_{H'K'}$. The quantity $|a_{H'K'}|^2$ is not to be regarded as the probability of the state H' *per se* irrespective of any accessory con-ditions—for such *unconditioned* probability has no definite value—but as the probability of the state H' subject to the accessory condition that the particle is *actually* in a state of motion specified by value K' of K or by the function $\phi_{K'}$.

Instead of talking of the states as described by the wave functions $\phi_{K'}$ or $\psi_{H'}$, it is often more convenient to speak of the *values* of certain quantities F, H, K associated with these states. The fact that a definite state is actually realized can be expressed by saying that the probability of this state is equal to unity. We can thus say that $|a_{H'K'}|^2$ is the probability that the quantity H has the value H' if it is *known* (with a probability amounting to certainty, i.e. equal to unity) that the quantity K has the value K'.

It is perfectly natural that the determination of the probability of a certain value of some quantity, e.g. H, must imply an assumption about the probability of a given value of some other quantity K—for the probability theory does not *create* probabilities, but only correlates them.

From the relations (112), it follows that $|a_{H'K'}|^2 = |a_{K'H'}^{-1}|^2$. This equation can be interpreted from the probability point of view as the expression of the 'reciprocity law', which means that the probability of H having the value H' when K is *known* to have the value K' is equal to the probability of K having the value K' when H is known to have the value H'.

This feature of the coefficients $a_{H'K'}$ reveals a close similarity between them and the amplitude functions $\psi_{H'}^0$ (or $\phi_{K'}^0$). As a matter of fact, the latter also depend upon *two* arguments, or sets of arguments—one of them, x, y, z, specifying the *position* and the other, H' (or H_1', H_2', H_3'), the energy and some quantities commuting with it (i.e. representing constants of the motion defined by the energy operator H). Further, the function $|\psi_{H'}^0(x, y, z)|^2$, or more exactly its product with the volume-element dV, does not determine the probability of a position specified by dV irrespective of any other circumstances, but subject to the explicitly stated condition that H is known to have the value H'. To give an adequate formal expression to this analogy between the coefficients $a_{H'K'}$, $a_{K'H'}^{-1}$ on the one hand, and the functions $\psi_{H'}^0(x, y, z)$, $\phi_{K'}^0(x, y, z)$ on the other, we shall introduce for the latter the following notation:

$$\psi_{H'}^0(x', y', z') = \psi_{x'H'}^0, \qquad \phi_{K'}^0(x', y', z') = \phi_{x'K'}^0, \qquad (115)$$

using x' to represent a set of values of the three coordinates x, y, z in the same way as H' or K' is used to represent a set of values of the three quantities H_1, H_2, H_3 or K_1, K_2, K_3.

The analogy between the functions $\psi_{x'H'}^0$ and the coefficients $a_{H'K'}$ or $a_{K'H'}^{-1}$ seems to indicate that a set of values of the coordinates x (x, y, z) can specify a 'state' of the particle just as well as a set of characteristic values of any other three mutually commuting operators H_1, H_2, H_3 or K_1, K_2, K_3. We are thus led, in a very natural manner, to revise the conception of a 'state' or 'stationary state' which we have been using hitherto, in the sense that it is not determined by a function $\psi_{x'H'}^0$ or $\phi_{x'K'}^0$, which refers to *two* states of *two different sets* like the transformation coefficients—or probability amplitudes—$a_{K'H'}^{-1}$ and $a_{H'K'}$, but simply by the values of *three* quantities (corresponding to the three degrees of freedom) which are represented by *three independent mutually commuting operators* such as the three spatial coordinates of the particle, or its energy, z-component of the angular momentum, and square of the

latter (in the case of a motion in a central field of force), and so on.
A 'state' defined in this more general way must no longer be necessarily
associated with the idea of *motion*. As a matter of fact the idea of
motion—in the sense of a change of the position with the time—has no
meaning in wave mechanics, being replaced by the idea of the probability of finding the particle in a given position when its energy and
two other quantities commuting with the energy have given values.
The functions $\psi^0_{x'H'}$ do not have to be associated with motion any more
than the coefficients $a^{-1}_{K'H'}$. They are to be interpreted simply as the
probability amplitudes for a state defined by the position x' (or volume-
element dV') subject to the condition that $H = H'$, just as the coefficients $a^{-1}_{K'H'}$ determine the probability of the value K' of K if H is
known to have the value H'.

It should be remarked that in all these considerations the time does
not play any role whatever so long as it does not appear explicitly in
H or in the other operators concerned.

We are thus driven by the inner logic of the ideas embodied in the
wave-mechanical theory to consider it as a special case of a general
physical theory—let us call it quantum mechanics—whose problem
consists in determining the probability of a certain value of some
quantity or of a set of quantities when a set of some other quantities is assumed to have given values. This general problem reduces to
the usual wave-mechanical problem when the first three quantities
are the coordinates of the particle, and the second three are its energy
and some other two quantities which are represented by operators
commuting with the energy operator.

The condition that the three quantities of each set—those whose
values are supposed to be known or those for which the probability of
certain values is being determined—should be represented by mutually
commuting operators seems to be essential for the problem to have a
physical meaning. It is customary to express the possibility of fixing
simultaneously the value of two or more quantities by saying that they
can be simultaneously *observed* or *measured*; this can be regarded as
the experimental equivalent for the mathematical idea of 'mutual commutability', connected with the operator or the matrix representation
of the quantity in question. I should like, however, to warn the reader
against the conclusion, often implied in the above expression, that in
discussing elementary phenomena, we must keep in mind the observer
or experimenter as an essential part of these phenomena, supposed to
be responsible through his interference with them for the indeterminate-

ness by which they are characterized—and which, as a matter of fact, is only *revealed* and not *produced* by his observations.

This indeterminateness constitutes the characteristic feature of the new quantum or wave mechanics, which distinguishes it from classical mechanics. In the case of a particle moving in a given field of force with three degrees of freedom, the classical mechanics assumed the possibility of fixing simultaneously the values of *six* quantities—for instance, the three coordinates x, y, z and the three components of the momentum g_x, g_y, g_z (or the energy H, the z-component of the angular momentum M_z, and the square of the latter M^2), whereby the motion was *completely* determined—while the wave or quantum mechanics is less ambitious and restricts the number of quantities whose values can be fixed (arbitrarily, or by observation) to *three*, making up for the resulting incompleteness or indeterminateness in the description of the motion by probability considerations as to some other set of three quantities.

Another distinction between classical and quantum mechanics which must be borne in mind refers to the role played by the time. In the former case this role seems to be much more fundamental and important than in the second. As a matter of fact, the time seems to have been completely eliminated from the scope of the quantum mechanics as it has been specified above. This is, however, not quite true. First of all the time enters *implicitly* in the definition of such quantities as the components of velocity (or momentum) and various functions of them (such as energy, etc.), although these quantities are represented by operators which do not contain the time explicitly. And secondly we have supposed from the very beginning of this section that the potential energy of the field of force in which the particle is supposed to move does not contain the time explicitly, i.e. *it depends upon the coordinates alone*. It is only subject to this condition that the time can be practically eliminated from the theory; it becomes, however, a vital element of the latter when the potential energy is a function not only of the coordinates but also of the time. In this case Schrödinger's equation $\left(H + \dfrac{h}{2\pi i}\dfrac{\partial}{\partial t}\right)\psi = 0$ does not have particular solutions of the form $\psi = \psi_{H'}^0\, e^{-i2\pi H't/h}$ with $\psi_{H'}^0(x, y, z)$ satisfying the equation $H\psi_{H'} = H'\psi_H$. Characteristic values of the energy do not exist, or putting it in another way, values of the energy, if it is not a constant of the motion, cannot be measured, and the question of determining the probability of an arbitrarily chosen position $x'(x', y', z')$ for a given (supposedly known) value of the energy becomes meaningless.

We shall now come back to our original assumption, that neither H nor K contain the time explicitly and that they possess a discrete set of characteristic values $H'(H_1', H_2', H_3')$ and $K'(K_1', K_2', K_3')$ which determine two discrete sets of 'states'. We have been led to the conclusion that the coordinates of the particle can be used for the definition of a third set of states, specified merely by the position of the particle in space. Since any values of the coordinates $x'(x', y', z')$ are possible, these values can be regarded as constituting a 'continuous spectrum'. This distinction between H and K on the one hand, and x on the other hand is reflected in the fact that in determining the probabilities we must speak of definite values of H and K and of a definite *range* of the values of x, i.e. of a volume-element dV in which the particle is supposed to be situated. We thus have the expressions: $|a_{H'K'}|^2$ for the probability of $H = H'$ if it is known that $K = K'$, or of $K = K'$ if it is known that $H = H'$; $|\psi_{x'H'}^0|^2 \, dV'$ for the probability that x is enclosed in the range $(x', x'+dx')$ if it is known that $H = H'$ $(dV' = dx'dy'dz')$; $|\phi_{x'K'}^0|^2 \, dV'$ for the probability that x is enclosed in the range $(x', x'+dx')$ if it is known that $K = K'$.

Generalizing the reciprocity law which has been established in the case of $|a_{H'K'}|^2$, we can define $|\psi_{x'H'}^0|^2 \, dV'$ and $|\phi_{x'K'}^0|^2 \, dV'$ as the probabilities of $H = H'$ or $K = K'$ when it is known that the particle is located in the volume-element dV'.

The similarity between the functions $\psi_{x'H'}^0$ or $\phi_{x'K'}^0$ and the coefficients $a_{K'H'}^{-1}$ or $a_{H'K'}$ is revealed also by the fact that they satisfy similar orthogonality and normalizing relations, which in the former case are expressed either by means of integrals (over x') instead of sums (over H' or K') or by functions $\delta(x'-x'')$ instead of $\delta_{H'H''}$ or $\delta_{K'K''}$——corresponding to the fact that H' and K' form a discrete and x' a·continuous set of values. We have, namely, the relation (113a), which can be written in the form

$$\sum_{K'} a_{K'H'}^{-1} a_{K'H''}^{-1*} = \delta_{H'H''},$$

and to which there correspond the usual orthogonality and normalizing relations for the 'wave function' ψ

$$\int \psi_{x'H'}^0 \psi_{x'H''}^{0*} \, dx' = \delta_{H'H''} \qquad (dx' = dV'). \tag{116}$$

Besides the preceding relation, the coefficients $a_{K'H'}^{-1}$ also satisfy the 'reciprocal' relation (113) or

$$\sum_{H'} a_{K'H'}^{-1} a_{K''H'}^{-1*} = \delta_{K'K''},$$

to which an analogue is found in the relation

$$\sum_{H'} \psi_{x'H'}^0 \psi_{x''H'}^{0*} = \delta(x'-x''), \tag{116a}$$

where $\delta(x'-x'')$ is an abbreviation for the product of the three Dirac functions $\delta(x'-x'')$, $\delta(y'-y'')$, $\delta(z'-z'')$ (just as $\delta_{K'K''}$ is actually an abbreviation for the product of the three expressions of this type for the three quantities implied in K).

The proof of the relations (116 a) [i.e. of their equivalence to (116)] is obtained by multiplying them by $\psi^0_{x''H''}$, where H'' is any fixed value of H, and integrating over x''. This gives, in view of (116),

$$\int \sum_{H'} \psi^0_{x'H'} \psi^0_{x''H''} \psi^{0*}_{x''H'} \, dx'' = \sum_{H'} \psi^0_{x'H'} \int \psi^0_{x''H''} \psi^0_{x''H'} \, dx'' = \psi^0_{x'H''},$$

which, according to the definition of the function $\delta(x''-x')$, agrees with $\int \psi^0_{x''H''} \delta(x''-x') \, dx''$. The remaining difference between the probability amplitudes $a_{H'K'}$, $\psi^0_{x'H'}$, $\phi^0_{x'K'}$ vanishes if we abandon our initial assumption as to the discreteness of the spectrum of H and K and suppose that one of these quantities, e.g. H, has a continuous spectrum, being in this respect equivalent to x (the spectrum of K will be assumed for a while to remain discrete).

The transformation equations (110) which, with our new notation, could be written in the form

$$\phi^0_{x'K'} = \sum_{H'} \psi^0_{x'H'} a_{H'K'},$$

must now be replaced by†

$$\phi^0_{x'K'} = \int \psi^0_{x'H'} a_{H'K'} dH'. \tag{117}$$

Multiplying this equation by $\psi^{0*}_{x'H''}$ and integrating over $x'(x', y', z')$ $(dx' = dV')$, we get

$$\int \psi^{0*}_{x'H''} \phi^0_{x'K'} \, dx' = \int a_{H'K'} \, dH' \int \psi^{0*}_{x'H''} \psi^0_{x'H'} \, dx' = \int a_{H'K'} \delta(H'-H'') \, dH',$$

that is $\qquad\qquad a_{H''K'} = \int \psi^{0*}_{x'H''} \phi^0_{x'K'} \, dx'$

as before.‡ Since the form of the reciprocal transformation

$$\psi^0_{x'H'} = \sum_{K'} a^{-1}_{K'H'} \phi^0_{x'K'} \tag{117 a}$$

remains unchanged (so long as K is supposed to have a discrete spectrum), we get the previous relation between the coefficients a and a^{-1}, namely, $a^{-1}_{K'H'} = a^*_{H'K'}$, leading to the reciprocity law $|a^{-1}_{K'H'}|^2 = |a_{H'K'}|^2$.

---

† This transition is quite similar to a transition from a Fourier series to a Fourier integral, which as a matter of fact forms a special case of the transformation or 'expansion' (117) and (117 a).

‡ It should be noticed that the former coefficient $a_{H'K'}$ actually corresponds to the product of the present coefficient with dH', this difference being compensated for by the difference between the previous and the present form of the orthogonality and normalizing relation for $\psi_{H'}$.

Substituting the preceding expression in (117 a), we get

$$\phi^0_{x'K'} = \sum_{K''} \phi^0_{x'K''} \int a^{-1}_{K''H'} a_{H'K'} \, dH',$$

whence it follows that

$$\int a^{-1}_{K''H'} a_{H'K'} \, dH' = \delta_{K''K'},$$

or $$\int a^*_{H'K''} a_{H'K'} \, dH' = \delta_{K''K'}. \qquad (118)$$

This orthogonality-normalizing relation, which replaces (113), is identical with the corresponding relation for the function $\phi^0_{x'K'}$, x' being replaced by K' [cf. (116)]. In a similar way (through substitution of (117 a) in the reciprocal expansion) we find the relation

$$\sum_{K'} a_{H'K'} a^*_{H''K'} = \delta(H'-H''), \qquad (118\,\text{a})$$

which is the complete analogue of (116 a) with x' replaced by H' and H' by K'.

If both H and K have a continuous spectrum, the relations (118) and (118 a), as well as (116) and (116 a), are replaced by relations of the form

$$\int a^*_{H'K''} a_{H'K'} \, dH' = \delta(K''-K'),$$

$$\int a^*_{H''K'} a_{H'K'} \, dK' = \delta(H''-H'),$$

$$\int \psi^0_{x'H'} \psi^{0*}_{x'H''} \, dx' = \delta(H''-H'),$$

$$\int \psi^0_{x'H'} \psi^{0*}_{x''H'} \, dH' = \delta(x''-x'),$$

etc., all the sums being replaced by integrals and all the $\delta_{K'K''}$-numbers by $\delta(K'-K'')$-functions. All the transformation or expansion formulae acquire in this case the same form (117 a).

From the complete analogy between $a_{H'K'}$ and $\psi^0_{x'H'}$ or $\phi^0_{x'K'}$, it follows in particular that we must have, in addition to the equations

$$\phi^0_{x'K'} = \int \psi^0_{x'H'} a_{H'K'} \, dH', \qquad \psi^0_{x'H'} = \int \phi^0_{x'K'} a^{-1}_{K'H'} \, dK', \qquad (119)$$

the equation $$a_{H'K'} = \int \psi^{0(-1)}_{H'x'} \phi^0_{x'K'} \, dx', \qquad (119\,\text{a})$$

where $\psi^{0(-1)}_{H'x'} = \psi^{0*}_{x'H'}$. In fact, this equation is nothing else but the expression (110 a) for the coefficients $a_{H'K'}$. We can thus consider this equation as a 'transformation' between the functions $a_{H'K'}$ and $\phi^0_{x'K'}$, $\psi^{0(-1)}_{H'x'}$ playing the role of the transformation coefficients, or as a transformation between the functions $a_{H'K'}$ and $\psi^{0(-1)}_{H'x'}$, the role of the transformation coefficients being played in this case by $\phi^0_{x'K'}$.

It should be mentioned that (119 a) still holds when H and K have discrete spectra, equation (119) being replaced by (117) and its reciprocal

$$\psi^0_{x'H'} = \sum_{K'} \phi^0_{x'K'} a^{-1}_{K'H'}. \tag{119b}$$

After we have thus settled the physical meaning of the 'transformation coefficients' or 'wave functions' as the probability amplitudes for the values of one of the quantities concerned when the value of the other is supposed to be fixed, we obtain an extremely simple and illuminating interpretation of the various 'transformation equations' connecting these probability amplitudes. All these equations can be considered, namely, as *the expression or rather the direct consequence of the addition and multiplication law of the new probability theory* (which deals with the probability amplitudes in the same way as the old theory dealt with the probabilities themselves).

Taking the last equation, for example, we see that the product $\phi^0_{x'K'} a^{-1}_{K'H'}$ can be interpreted as the probability amplitude that x will be equal to x' if $K = K'$ and that at the same time K will have the value K' if H is known to be equal to H'. Keeping the latter value as well as that of x fixed, and summing the products $\phi^0_{x'K'} a^{-1}_{K'H'}$ for all possible values of K, we must obviously obtain the probability amplitude of $x = x'$ subject to the assumption that $H = H'$, in agreement with (119b).

16. Transformation of Matrices

We shall now return to the beginning of the preceding section, i.e. we shall again assume the values of H and K to be discrete, and we shall examine the transformation equations for the *matrices* representing different quantities F from the point of view of H and K. Before doing this we must point out the fact that the transformation coefficients $a_{H'K'}$ and $a^{-1}_{K'H'}$ can also be considered as the matrix elements of a certain matrix a and its reciprocal a^{-1} respectively, in the same way as $F_{H'H'}$ or $F_{K'K'}$ are the matrix elements of F_H or F_K. The main difference between them is that, in the latter case, the two indices (H', H'' or K', K'') refer to states of the *same set*, defined *either* by H *or* by K, whereas in the former case the first index refers to a state of the one set and the second to a state of the other set.

Another difference (closely related to the preceding one) is that while the matrix elements $F_{K'K'}$ or $F_{H'H'}$ are Hermitian, i.e. satisfy the conditions $F_{K'K'} = F^*_{K'K'}$, $F_{H'H'} = F^*_{H'H'}$, the coefficients (or matrix elements) $a_{H'K'}$ are *not* Hermitian, as shown by the relations (112).

The matrix which is obtained from F (or a) by interchanging the rows and the columns is called the transposed matrix of F and is denoted (usually) by $\widetilde{F}$. A matrix $\widetilde{F}^*$ which is obtained from the transposed $\widetilde{F}$ by taking the conjugate complex of its elements is called, according to Jordan, the 'adjoint' matrix of F ('conjugate imaginary' according to Dirac) and denoted by $F^\dagger$. Using this notation, we can write the Hermitian condition in the form

$$F^\dagger = F, \qquad (120)$$

while the condition (112) can be written in the form

$$a^\dagger = a^{-1}. \qquad (120\,a)$$

Matrices a satisfying this condition are called 'unitary', because the product of such a matrix with its adjoint matrix, which is the analogue of the square of the modulus of an ordinary complex number, is equal to unity (i.e. to the unit matrix).

It is self-evident that the multiplication of the matrices of the type a which do not correspond to a definite 'point of view' (H or K) but serve to connect two different points of view must be performed according to the usual rule of matrix multiplication, i.e. by combining the rows of the first factor with the columns of the second. This means that the elements of the product of two matrices a and b must have the form

$$(ab)_{mn} = \sum_k a_{mk} b_{kn},$$

i.e. that the second index of the elements of the first factor should coincide with the first index of the elements of the second factor, this common index being the index of summation.

From the point of view of this definition, the product of a 'mixed' matrix such as a by itself or its conjugate complex a^* would have no meaning, since the two indices refer to states of different sets, and therefore cannot be identified. We can, however, form the product of a with its transposed ($\widetilde{a}$) or adjoint matrix ($a^\dagger$), since the first index of the latter two refers to a state of the same set as the second index of the former and vice versa. The expression $\sum_{K'} a_{H'K'} \widetilde{a}_{K'H''}$ can thus be considered as the (H', H'') element of the product matrix $a\widetilde{a}$ which is of the same 'pure' type as the matrix F_H. The same refers to the matrix $aa^\dagger$ or aa^{-1}, if the elements of the reciprocal matrix a^{-1} are labelled with the indices H' and K' in the order opposite to that which refers to the matrix a (as has actually been done in the preceding section). It can easily be shown that the matrix $aa^\dagger$ is Hermitian (while $a\widetilde{a}$ is *not*). In fact, taking its adjoint matrix, which is obviously equal to the product of the adjoint matrices of the two factors taken in the *reverse* order, we get

$$(aa^\dagger)^\dagger = a^{\dagger\dagger}a^\dagger = aa^\dagger,$$

in agreement with (120).

It should be noticed that the two matrices $aa^\dagger$ and $a^\dagger a$ are, in general, entirely different, the former belonging to the same type as F_H and the latter belonging to the same type as F_K.

In the particular case of a *unitary* matrix, satisfying the conditions (120 a), we get

$$(a^\dagger a)_{K'K''} = \sum_{H'} a^\dagger_{K'H'} a_{H'K''} = \sum_{H'} a^{-1}_{K'H'} a_{H'K''} = \delta_{K'K},$$

$$(aa^\dagger)_{H'H''} = \sum_{K'} a_{H'K'} a^\dagger_{K'H''} = \sum_{K'} a_{H'K'} a^{-1}_{K'H''} = \delta_{H'H''},$$

according to (112 a)–(113 a), or in matrix notation

$$aa^\dagger = \delta_H, \qquad a^\dagger a = \delta_K, \tag{120 b}$$

where δ_H and δ_K denote the 'unit matrix' as defined from the 'point of view' of H or K. Neglecting the physical meaning implied in this difference one often identifies the two unit matrices and writes

$$aa^\dagger = a^\dagger a = \mathbf{1},$$

which occasionally can lead to misunderstandings.

The possibility of treating the transformation coefficients as the elements of a (mixed) matrix and of applying to the latter the usual rule of matrix multiplication is substantiated by the results obtained in two or more successive transformations. Let L be an operator (or set of three operators L_1, L_2, L_3) of the same kind as H or K, with the (discrete) characteristic values L' and characteristic functions $\chi^0_{L'}$. These functions can be 'transformed' to those of K by means of the equations $\chi^0_{L'} = \sum_{K'} b_{K'L'} \phi^0_{K'}$, and further to those of H by means of the equations $\phi^0_{K'} = \sum_{K'} a_{H'K'} \psi^0_{H'}$. Combining them together, we obtain a direct transformation from L to H,

$$\chi^0_{L'} = \sum_{H'} c_{H'L'} \psi^0_{H'},$$

with the coefficients $c_{H'L'} = \sum_{K'} a_{H'K'} b_{K'L'}$. The matrix of these coefficients is thus equal to the product of the matrices a and b taken in the order stated, and calculated according to the ordinary rule. Using the matrix representation for the transformation coefficients, we can thus define the matrix of two successive transformations as the product of the matrices of each of the separate transformations. This holds, in particular, for the case which has been considered above, where the second transformation is the reciprocal of the first one.

We can now turn to the main object of this section—the transformation of the matrix representing the same quantity F in the transition from one 'point of view' specified by H to another, specified by K. Substituting (110) in the expression (109) for the elements of F_K, we get

$$F^0_{K'K''} = \sum_{H'} \sum_{H''} a^*_{H'K'} a_{H''K''} F_{H'H''}, \tag{121}$$

which can be written in the form

$$F^0_{K'K''} = \sum_{H'} \sum_{H''} a^\dagger_{K'H'} F^0_{H'H''} a_{H''K''}.$$

This expression can be interpreted, according to the matrix multiplication law, as the (K', K'')-element of the product of the matrices $a^\dagger$, F_H, and a taken in the order stated. We can thus put

$$F_K = a^\dagger F_H a. \tag{121 a}$$

Substituting (111) in (109), we get in the same way

$$F_H = a F_K a^\dagger. \tag{121 b}$$

This equation can be obtained from the preceding equation if the latter is multiplied by a on the left and by $a^\dagger$ on the right side and if the relations $a^\dagger a = a a^\dagger = 1$ are taken into account.

If we restrict ourselves to multiplying (121 a) by a on the left *or* by $a^\dagger$ on the right, we get

$$\left. \begin{aligned} F_H a &= a F_K \\ F_K a^\dagger &= a^\dagger F_H \end{aligned} \right\}. \tag{121 c}$$

and

The product matrices in these equations have all a mixed character, with elements of the type (H', K') in the case of the first and (K', H') in that of the second.

Written in matrix elements, these equations run

$$(F_H a)_{H'K'} = \sum_{H''} F_{H'H''} a_{H''K'} = \sum_{K''} a_{H'K''} F_{K''K'} = (a F_K)_{H'K'},$$

$$(F_K a^\dagger)_{K'H'} = \sum_{K''} F_{K'K''} a^\dagger_{K''H'} = \sum_{H''} a^\dagger_{K'H''} F_{H''H'} = (a^\dagger F_H)_{K'H'}.$$

If in (121 c) we put, in particular, $F = K$ or $F = H$, we get

$$K_H a = a K_K, \qquad a H_K = H_H a, \tag{122}$$

and two similar equations with $a^\dagger$ instead of a.

Taking the element (H', K') of the first equation (122), we get, since $K_{K'K''} = \delta_{K'K''} K'$,

$$\sum_{H''} K_{H'H''} a_{H''K'} = K' a_{H'K'}. \tag{122 a}$$

In the same way we obtain from the second equation (122)

$$\sum_{K''} a_{H'K''} H_{K''K'} = a_{H'K'} H'. \qquad (122\,\text{b})$$

The equations (122 a) have exactly the same form for all values of K'. Dropping K' as second index in the coefficients a, we can rewrite them as a single system of linear homogeneous equations (corresponding to different values of H') for a set of variables $a_{H'}$

$$\sum_{H''} K_{H'H''} \cdot a_{H''} = K' a_{H'} \qquad (123)$$

with a parameter K'.

This system of equations can serve for the direct determination both of the transformation coefficients $a_{H'K'}$ and of the values K' if the matrix elements of K_H are known. We have, indeed, as the condition of the compatibility of equations (123) the vanishing of the determinant,

$$\begin{vmatrix} K_{H'H'} - K' & K_{H'H''} & K_{H'H'''} & . & . & . \\ K_{H''H'} & K_{H''H''} - K' & K_{H''H'''} & . & . & . \\ K_{H'''H'} & K_{H'''H''} & K_{H'''H'''} - K' & . & . & . \\ . & . & . & . & . & . & . & . & . \\ . & . & . & . & . & . & . & . & . \end{vmatrix} = 0, \qquad (123\,\text{a})$$

which is an equation for the determination of the possible values of K' (K'', K''', etc.). To each of these values there corresponds a set of values of the variables $a_{H'}$ which we can identify, under certain conditions, with the transformation coefficients $a_{H'K'}$ ($a_{H'K''}$, $a_{H'''K'}$, etc.). These conditions amount to the relations $a^\dagger a = a a^\dagger = 1$, which can be shown to be verified if the solutions of (123) are normalized according to the equation

$$\sum_{H'} a_{H'} a_{H'}^* = 1 \qquad (123\,\text{b})$$

for every value of K'.

Let us first of all make sure of the fact that the values K' obtained from (123 a) are real. To show this we take the equations

$$\sum_{H''} K_{H'H''} a_{H''K'} = K' a_{H'K'},$$

$$\sum_{H''} K_{H'H''}^* a_{H''K'}^* = K'^* a_{H'K'}^*$$

(the first of which can be considered as an identity, resulting from (123) for a particular value of K', and the second as its conjugate complex), multiply them respectively by $a_{H'K'}^*$ and $a_{H'K'}$, sum over H', and finally subtract one from the other. This gives

$$(K' - K'^*) \sum_{H'} a_{H'K'} a_{H'K'}^*$$
$$= \sum_{H'} \sum_{H''} K_{H'H''} a_{H''K'} a_{H'K'}^* - \sum_{H'} \sum_{H''} K_{H'H''}^* a_{H''K'}^* a_{H'K'}.$$

Taking into account the Hermitian condition $K^*_{H''H'} = K_{H''H'}$, we can rewrite the second double sum on the right side in the form $\sum_{H'}\sum_{H''} K_{H''H'} a_{H'K'} a^*_{H''K'}$ which becomes identical with the first double sum if we interchange the summation indices H' and H''. We thus get

$$(K' - K'^*) \sum_{H'} a_{H'K'} a^*_{H'K'} = 0,$$

or, since the sum $\sum_{H'} a_{H'K'} a^*_{H'K'} = \sum_{H'} |a_{H'K'}|^2$ is essentially positive,

$$K' - K'^* = 0.$$

This equation expresses the fact that K' is real.

If, in the preceding argument, we replace the second equation by an equation (identity)

$$\sum_{H'} K^*_{H'H''} a^*_{H''K''} = K'' a^*_{H'K''}$$

corresponding to some value of K'' different from K', multiply it by $a_{H'K'}$, sum over H', and subtract from the first equation multiplied by $a^*_{H'K''}$ and also summed over H', we get

$$(K' - K'') \sum_{H'} a_{H'K'} a^*_{H'K''}$$
$$= \sum_{H'}\sum_{H''} K_{H'H''} a_{H''K'} a^*_{H'K''} - \sum_{H'}\sum_{H''} K^*_{H'H''} a^*_{H''K''} a_{H'K'}.$$

In view of $K^*_{H'H''} = K_{H''H'}$ and the interchangeability of the summation indices H', H'', the right side vanishes just as in the case $K' = K''$, and we get

$$(K' - K'') \sum_{H'} a_{H'K'} a^*_{H'K''} = 0,$$

which, since $K' - K''$ is assumed to be different from zero, reduces to

$$\sum a_{H'K'} a^*_{H'K''} = 0$$

or

$$\sum a^\dagger_{K''H'} a_{H'K'} = 0 \qquad (K'' \neq K').$$

This relation expresses the mutual 'orthogonality' of the different sets of solutions of the system of equations (123). Together with the normalizing condition (123 b), it can be written in the form

$$a^\dagger a = \delta_K,$$

whereby the identity of the coefficients $a_{H'K'}$ obtained from equations (123), (123 a), and (123 b), with those defined at the outset with the help of the wave functions $\psi^0_{H'}$ and $\phi^0_{K'}$ by means of equations (110 a) and (111 a), is demonstrated.

At the same time we have demonstrated the possibility of effecting the transformation of the matrix F_H representing an arbitrary physical quantity F 'from the point of view of H' (i.e. with regard to states defined by H) to the matrix F_K representing the same quantity 'from the point of view of K' without the use of the wave functions characteristic of H and K, but by a purely matrix method, based upon the matrix representation of all quantities—including the key one K— 'from the point of view of H'. The transition from this point of view to that of K can be effected by means of the equations (123), (123 a), (123 b), which determine the transformation matrix a, and further by means of equation (121 a), giving the new matrix elements of any quantity F in terms of the old matrix elements.

In view of the relation $a^\dagger = a^{-1}$, this formula can also be written in the form

$$F_K = a^{-1}F_H\, a. \qquad (124)$$

The transformation matrix a can actually be defined by the condition

$$a^{-1}K_H\, a = K_K \text{ (a diagonal matrix)} \qquad (124\,\text{a})$$

which leads, after a left-handed multiplication by a, to the equation $K_H\, a = aK_K$, i.e. to the system of equations (123); the unitary character of the matrix a, expressed by the relation $a^\dagger a = 1$, can be considered as a consequence of these equations.

A transformation of the type (124) is generally called a *canonical matrix transformation*. It has an interesting feature which does not depend upon a being a unitary matrix (i.e. satisfying the relation $a^\dagger = a^{-1}$), namely, of leaving invariant all the functional relations between the original matrices, the same functional relations holding between the transformed matrices. This can be proved directly by putting in (124) $F = E+G$ or $F = EG$. In the first case we get, since $F_H = E_H + G_H$,

$$F_K = a^{-1}(E_H + G_H)a = a^{-1}E_H\, a + a^{-1}G_H\, a = E_K + G_K;$$

in the second case we have, using $(EG)_H = E_H\, G_H$,

$$F_K = a^{-1}E_H\, G_H\, a.$$

Now we can insert between E_H and G_H the product aa^{-1}, since it is equal to the unit matrix δ whose product with any other matrix is identical with the latter (just as in the case of the multiplication of ordinary numbers by an ordinary unity). We thus get, by the associative law, $$F_K = (a^{-1}E_H\, a)(a^{-1}G_H\, a) = E_K\, G_K.$$

This proof can easily be extended by induction to any function F of E and G, so that, putting (in the operator representation) $F = f(E, G)$, we have

$$f(E_K, G_K) = a^{-1}f(E_H, G_H)a \qquad (124\,\text{b})$$

or $$a^{-1}f(E_H, G_H)a = f(a^{-1}E_H\, a, a^{-1}G_H\, a).$$

It follows from these equations that, in particular, the transformation

(124) does not affect the validity of the commutation relations between the coordinates and the components of the momentum; the original relations $(p_x x - x p_x)_H = \dfrac{h}{2\pi i}\, \delta_H$ are transformed into $(p_x x - x p_x)_K = \dfrac{h}{2\pi i}\, \delta_K$.

Canonical transformations of the above type should be distinguished from canonical transformations of the variables x, y, z, p_x, p_y, p_z in the sense corresponding to the general definition of a canonical transformation in classical mechanics (see § 5). In the former case the canonically conjugate variables are supposed to remain unaltered, the transformation referring to the *matrices* only by which they are represented from the point of view of *different energy operators* (H or K). In the latter case, on the contrary, the variables x,..., p_z are themselves transformed into a new set of canonically conjugate variables ξ, η, ζ, π_ξ, π_η, π_ζ, the *energy operator $H_{(x)} = H(x,...,p_z)$ remaining essentially the same* and only changing its *external form* because the old variables defining it are replaced by their expressions in terms of the new variables. We thus get for it a new function, $H_{(\xi)}$ say, of the variables ξ,..., π_ζ, which is, however, numerically equal to $H_{(x)}$ for the corresponding values of the original variables. This numerical equality of the classical theory is replaced in quantum mechanics by the equality of the characteristic values of the operators $H_{(x)}$ and $H_{(\xi)}$. The condition expressing the canonical character of the transformation from the original variables to the new ones consists in the fact that the matrices representing the latter (from any point of view) should satisfy the same commutation relations $\pi_\xi \xi - \xi \pi_\xi = h\delta/2\pi i$, etc., as those representing the old variables. This means that the new matrices (of ξ,..., π_ζ) can be derived from the old ones (of x,..., p_z) by a canonical transformation in the first sense, i.e. in the sense of the equation (124). The *physical meaning* of such a transformation will, however, be entirely different from the case to which (124) refers, the two kinds of transformation bearing but a formal resemblance to each other.—We shall come back to the transformations of the second kind in the next section.

In the case of a degeneracy of the original energy matrix H_H, i.e. when some of its diagonal elements coincide, it is necessary to consider it simultaneously with one or two other matrices, which represent independent constants of the motion specified by H. We must therefore replace the operator H by the three operators H_1, H_2, H_3 and define the matrix representation of any quantity F from the 'point of view' of this 'trio', writing $F_{H_1 H_2 H_3}$ instead of F_H. The transformation matrix corresponding to a transition to the 'point of view' of some other trio, e.g.

K_1, K_2, K_3, will then be unambiguously determined by the simultaneous equations

$$
\left.\begin{array}{l}
a^{-1}K_{1(H_1,H_2,H_3)}a = K_{1(K_1,K_2,K_3)} \\
a^{-1}K_{2(H_1,H_2,H_3)}a = K_{2(K_1,K_2,K_3)} \\
a^{-1}K_{3(H_1,H_2,H_3)}a = K_{3(K_1,K_2,K_3)}
\end{array}\right\} \qquad (124\,\mathrm{c})
$$

with the condition that all the three matrices on the right side should be diagonal (which can always be satisfied if the corresponding operators K_1, K_2, K_3 commute with each other). Each of the equations (124 c), taken separately, will leave a certain amount of ambiguity in the shape of the matrix a, which can be removed by means of one or both of the others; if we do not desire a diagonal representation of the corresponding quantities we can remove this ambiguity in a perfectly arbitrary manner consistent with the condition $a^{-1} = a^\dagger$.

The preceding considerations can easily be generalized for the case when either or both of the operators (or the operator trios) H and K have a continuous spectrum. Let us assume, for instance, that the values of H form a continuous set, while those of K remain discrete. We then have, instead of (110) and (111), the transformation equations (117) and (117 a) with a semi-continuous transformation matrix $a_{H'K'}$ satisfying the orthogonality and normalizing relations (118) and (118 a). The latter can be put in the same form,

$$
aa^\dagger = \delta_H, \qquad a^\dagger a = \delta_K,
$$

as in the discrete case, if δ_H is considered as a continuous unit matrix, i.e. as a Dirac function

$$
\delta_{H'H''} = \delta(H'-H''),
$$

while $\delta_{K'K''}$ is the usual discrete unit matrix, and if, further, the matrix multiplication law is defined in the usual way corresponding to discrete matrices in the case of $aa^\dagger$:

$$
(aa^\dagger)_{H'H''} = \sum_{K'} a_{H'K'} a^\dagger_{K'H''},
$$

and in the way corresponding to continuous matrices in the case of $a^\dagger a$:

$$
(a^\dagger a)_{K'K''} = \int a^\dagger_{K'H'} a_{H'K''}\, dH'
$$

[cf. eq. (105 a), § 14].

We get further, instead of (121),

$$
F^0_{K'K''} = \iint a^*_{H'K'} a_{H''K''} F^0_{H'H''}\, dH'dH'',
$$

or

$$
F^0_{K'K''} = \iint a^\dagger_{K'H'} F^0_{H'H''} a_{H''K''}\, dH'dH'',
$$

which, as in the discrete case, can be written in the matrix form

$$F_K = a^\dagger F_H a,$$

it being understood that the matrix multiplication must be carried out according to the rule for continuous matrices whenever the 'summation' indices are continuously variable. From this equation we can derive the equations (122), the second of which, when reduced to matrix elements, runs exactly as before [eq. (122 b)], while the first assumes the form

$$\int K^0_{H'H''} \cdot a_{H''K'} \, dH'' = K' a_{H'K'},$$

instead of (122 a). Dropping the index K' of the coefficients $a_{H'K'}$, we get

$$\int K^0_{H'H''} \cdot a_{H''} \, dH'' = K' a_{H'}, \qquad (125)$$

which can be considered as an *integral equation* for the determination of the functions $a_{H'}$ and the characteristic values K', replacing the system of algebraic equations (123). The result of the elimination of the functions $a_{H'}$ from (125) cannot be written in the form of a determinant (123 a) unless we adopt a generalized definition of 'continuous determinants' corresponding to continuous matrices. Writing the right side of (125) in the form $\int K' a_{H''} \cdot \delta(H''-H') \, dH''$, we could then replace the compatibility equation (123 a), which serves for the determination of the characteristic values of K ($K' = K_{K'K'}$), by a symbolic equation of the type

$$|K_{H'H''} - K'\delta(H'-H'')| = 0, \qquad (125\,a)$$

indicating the general element of the determinant. In the corresponding notation for the discrete case, equation (123 a) would run as follows:

$$|K_{H'H''} - K'\delta_{H'H''}| = 0.$$

Of course (125 a) cannot be used for the actual calculation of the values K'; but this is also true of equation (123 a), since it refers to a determinant which consists of an *infinite* number of discrete elements.

We shall indicate later the method which can be used for the approximate calculation of the admissible values of K' when K differs but little from H (as is the case in problems of the perturbation theory). It should be remarked here that *both for a discrete and a continuous spectrum of H the characteristic values of K may form a discrete as well as a continuous spectrum* (contrary to the assumption which was made at the beginning about the discreteness of the K-spectrum).

It can easily be proved that if the functions $a_{H'}$ ['characteristic functions' of the integral equation (125)] corresponding to a particular value K' are labelled with this value as second index, they will form an orthogonal set—discrete or continuous, together with the set of values of K'—and normalizable to unity, i.e. satisfying the relations

$$\int a_{H'K'} a^*_{H'K''} \, dH' = \delta_{K'K''} \quad \text{or} \quad \delta(K'-K'')$$

and

$$\sum_{K'} a_{H'K'} a^*_{H''K'} \quad \text{or} \quad \int a_{H'K'} a^*_{H''K'} \, dK' = \delta(H'-H'')$$

as the case may be.

The proof is obtained in exactly the same way as in the case of a discrete H'-spectrum dealt with above and therefore will not be reproduced here. It should be remarked incidentally that the results referring to the latter case must be amended to allow for the possibility of K having a continuous spectrum with $K_{K'K''} = \delta(K'-K'')$.

Summing up, we can say that both with a discrete and a continuous spectrum of the 'basic quantity' (or basic trio) H, it is possible to calculate the matrix elements of any quantity F from the point of view of some other 'basic quantity' (or basic trio) K, without the knowledge of the characteristic functions of either H or K; the only thing which it is necessary to know in order to carry out the transformation from F_H to F_K is the matrix K_H. The transformation coefficients $a_{H'K'}$ can be found from the condition that K_K is a diagonal matrix of the discrete or of the continuous type (which need not and cannot be specified beforehand).

17. Transformation Theory of Matrices as a Generalization of Wave Mechanics; Transformation of Basic Quantities

It thus appears that the matrix theory, so far as the transformation from one point of view to another is concerned, can be considered as a logically closed self-supporting structure, which does not need the wave-mechanical basis upon which we have built it up. We have already met with a similar situation in the preceding chapter, when we were discussing the question of the actual determination of the matrices corresponding to a given energy operator and found it possible to achieve this result by determining the fundamental Hermitian matrices of the coordinates and the momentum-components in such a way as to make the energy matrix diagonal subject to the commutation conditions $p_x x - x p_x = h/2\pi i$, etc.

In the light of the transformation theory developed in this chapter, it appears, first of all, that if the latter problem has been solved for some simple type of motion specified by the energy operator H, it can be solved for any other type of motion, specified by some more complicated energy operator K, by the method of the transformation theory, without getting back to fundamental matrices (x, p_x) and commutation conditions (which, as has been shown above, are invariant with respect to canonical transformations). It is just this method of solution which is used by the perturbation theory, when the difference between the operators K and H is sufficiently small.

Besides furnishing a simple and practically the only workable method for the solution of such perturbation problems, the transformation theory reveals a new *connexion between the matrix and the wave-mechanical method, reducing the latter to a particular case of the former*—as was pointed out in the preceding section. We have seen, namely, that the characteristic functions or probability amplitudes of the wave-mechanical theory $\psi^0_{x'H'}$ can be considered as the transformation coefficients from the point of view of the 'energy-trio' H to that of the 'coordinate-trio' x (provided that such a thing as the energy exists, i.e. that the energy operator H does not contain the time)—in the same sense as the probability amplitudes $a_{H'K'}$ are the transformation coefficients from the point of view of the energy-trio H to that of the energy-trio K. This means that the wave-mechanical method can be completely replaced by the matrix method involving the transformation of the matrices F_x to the matrices F_H or vice versa.

The wave-mechanical theory, considered as a special case of the matrix transformation theory, has to solve the following problem: Suppose the matrices of all quantities, and in particular of the energy H, to be known from the point of view of the coordinates, we have to find the matrices representing them from the point of view of H. The solution of this problem reduces to the solution of the linear integral equation,

$$\int H^0_{x'x''} \psi^0_{x''} \, dx'' = H' \psi^0_{x'}, \tag{126}$$

which is obtained from (125) if K is replaced by H, H by x, and $a_{H'}$ by $\psi^0_{x'}$, and which obviously must be equivalent to the Schrödinger equation†

$$H\psi^0_{x'} = H'\psi^0_{x'} \qquad (\psi^0_{x'} = \psi^0_{x'H'}). \tag{126 a}$$

The equivalence of these equations can be proved directly with the help of the general definition of the elements of a matrix F_C by means of the integral

$$F^0_{C'C''} = \int \psi^{0*}_{x'C'} F\psi^0_{x'C''} \, dx'. \tag{127}$$

† We mean here and in the sequel Schrödinger's equation *not involving the time* (and serving to define the stationary states only). This circumstance is indicated by affixing to all the quantities connected—directly or indirectly—with the energy operator K the additional (upper) index 0.

This definition has been used until now only in connexion with such 'key' or 'basic' quantities C, one of which at least could be regarded as the energy. This restriction does not seem, however, to be necessary, and the formula (127) can be applied to quantities C of any type (provided the operators by which they are represented commute with each other). We can, in particular, put $C = x$ (i.e. $C_1 = x$, $C_2 = y$, $C_3 = z$), subject to the condition that the variables x' and C' in $\psi^0_{x'C'}$ *should be considered as independent*. This means that the two indices (or arguments) in the function $\psi^0_{x'C'}$ *need not* necessarily refer to the same point.

We can thus in (127) put $C' = x''$ and $C'' = x'''$, or, denoting the integration variable by x''' instead of x', write

$$F^0_{x'x'} = \int \psi^{0*}_{x'''x'} F \psi^0_{x'''x'} \, dx''', \qquad (127\,\mathrm{a})$$

where the operator F is understood to refer to the point x''', i.e. to be a function of x''' and of the elementary operators $p_{x'''} = \dfrac{h}{2\pi i} \dfrac{\partial}{\partial x'''}$.

The functions $\psi^0_{x'''x'}$ must obviously represent the *identical* transformation (from the point of view of x''' to that of x'), or, in other words, the probability amplitudes that x should be equal to x''' when it is known that it has the value x'. Since one and the same particle cannot be *simultaneously* in two different places, this means that $\psi^0_{x'''x'}$ must vanish when $x''' \neq x'$ and become infinite when $x''' = x'$ (in view of the fact that x is a continuous variable). We can thus identify $\psi^0_{x'''x'}$ with the 'unit matrix' of the continuous case, i.e. put

$$\psi^0_{x'''x'} = \delta(x''' - x'). \qquad (128)$$

This expression can be derived from the general formula

$$\phi^0_{x'''C'} = \int \psi^0_{x'''H'} a_{H'C'} \, dH'$$

[cf. (119), § 15] if we put $C' = x'$ and accordingly $a_{H'K'} = a^{(-1)*}_{K'H'} = \psi^{0*}_{x'H'}$ in conjunction with the orthogonality and normalizing relation $\int \psi^0_{x'''H'} \psi^{0*}_{x'H'} \, dH' = \delta(x''' - x')$, the $\phi^0_{x'''K'}$ being in this case obviously identical with $\psi^0_{x'''x'}$.

It is easy to see that, defined in this way, the function $\phi^0_{x'''C'} = \psi^0_{x'''x'}$ also satisfies the usual orthogonality and normalizing relations:

$$\int \phi^{0*}_{x'''C'} \phi^0_{x'''C''} \, dx''' = \delta(C' - C''), \qquad \int \phi^{0*}_{x'C'} \phi^0_{x''C'} \, dC' = \delta(x' - x'').$$

In fact, putting $C' = x'$ and $C'' = x''''$, we get, according to (128),

$$\int \phi^{0*}_{x'''C'} \phi^0_{x'''C''} \, dx' = \int \delta(x' - x''') \delta(x''' - x'''') \, dx''' = \delta(x' - x'''')$$

and, putting $C' = x'''$,

$$\int \phi^{0*}_{x'C'} \phi^0_{x''C'} \, dC' = \int \delta(x'''-x')\delta(x''-x''') \, dx''' = \delta(x'-x'').$$

We thus see that the elements of a matrix F_x can be defined according to (127 a) and (128) by the integral

$$F^0_{x'x''} = \int \delta(x'-x''')F\delta(x'''-x'') \, dx'''; \qquad (128\,\mathrm{a})$$

so that, in particular, we have

$$H^0_{x'x''} = \int \delta(x'-x''')H\delta(x'''-x'') \, dx''', \qquad (128\,\mathrm{b})$$

where H denotes the usual Hamiltonian function of the coordinates x and of the 'components of the momentum' $p_x = \dfrac{h}{2\pi i}\dfrac{\partial}{\partial x}$, both *referred to the point* $x = x'''$ (dx''' indicates the volume-element enclosing this point).

It can now easily be shown that the integral equation (126), together with the expression (128 b) for its 'nucleus', actually reduces to the differential equation (126 a).

Let us first take that part of H which depends upon the coordinates, that is, the potential energy $U(x,y,z)$. We then get, according to (128 a),

$$U^0_{x'x''} = \int U(x''')\delta(x'-x''')\delta(x'''-x'') \, dx''' = U(x'')\delta(x''-x'),$$

which, on substitution in (126), gives

$$\int U^0_{x'x''} \psi^0_{x''} \, dx'' = U(x')\psi^0_{x'}.$$

Putting, further, $F = \partial/\partial x$, we have

$$F^0_{x'x''} = \int \delta(x'-x''') \frac{\partial}{\partial x'''} \delta(x'''-x'') \, dx''' = -\int \delta(x'-x''') \frac{\partial}{\partial x''} \delta(x'''-x'') \, dx''',$$

since, obviously,

$$\frac{\partial}{\partial x'''} \delta(x'''-x'') = -\frac{\partial}{\partial x''} \delta(x'''-x''),$$

and consequently,

$$\int F^0_{x'x''} \psi^0_{x''} \, dx'' = -\int \psi^0_{x''} \, dx'' \int \delta(x'-x''') \frac{\partial}{\partial x''} \delta(x'''-x'') \, dx'''$$

$$= -\int \delta(x'-x''') \, dx''' \int \psi^0_{x''} \frac{\partial}{\partial x''} \delta(x'''-x'') \, dx''.$$

Now integrating by parts, we have

$$\int \psi^0_{x''} \frac{\partial}{\partial x''} \delta(x'''-x'') \, dx'' = -\int \delta(x'''-x'') \frac{\partial}{\partial x''} \psi^0_{x''} \, dx'',$$

because the product $\psi_{x''}^0 \delta(x'''-x'')$ vanishes at the limits of integration (or at infinity). We thus get

$$\int F_{x'x''}^0 \psi_{x''}^0 \, dx'' = \int dx'' \frac{\partial \psi_{x''}^0}{\partial x''} \int dx''' \, \delta(x'-x''')\delta(x'''-x'')$$

$$= \int dx'' \frac{\partial \psi_{x''}^0}{\partial x''} \delta(x'-x'') = \frac{\partial}{\partial x'} \psi_{x'}^0.$$

In the same way it can be shown that

$$\int F_{x'x''}^0 \psi_{x''}^0 \, dx'' = \left(\frac{\partial}{\partial x'}\right)^2 \psi_{x'}^0$$

if $F = (\partial/\partial x)^2$, and so on. Putting finally $F = \dfrac{1}{2m} \sum \left(\dfrac{h}{2\pi i} \dfrac{\partial}{\partial x}\right)^2 + U = H$

we get $\int H_{x'x''}^0 \psi_{x''}^0 \, dx'' = H\psi_{x'}^0$. It should be mentioned that this formula holds *identically*, i.e. irrespective of the shape of the function $\psi_{x'}^0$. The latter is determined in fact as $\psi_{x'H'}^0$, by the condition that $H\psi_{x'}^0$ should be equal to the product $H'\psi_{x'}^0$.

The generalization of the matrix theory which has been considered hitherto consisted, in the main, in admitting quantities other than the energy and those commuting with the energy to the role of the 'basic quantities' determining the matrix representation of all other quantities and being themselves represented by diagonal matrices. In the case just considered, this role of basic quantities was switched over to the coordinates. The matrices representing the latter x_x (or x_{xyz}, y_{xyz}, z_{xyz}) are obviously defined by the equations [cf. (101 b), § 14]

$$x_{x'x''} = x'\delta(x'-x''), \tag{129}$$

or, written out in detail:

$$\left. \begin{array}{l} x_{x'y'z';\,x''y''z''} = x'\delta(x'-x'')\delta(y'-y'')\delta(z'-z'') \\ y_{x'y'z';\,x''y''z''} = y'\delta(x'-x'')\delta(y'-y'')\delta(z'-z'') \\ z_{x'y'z';\,x''y''z''} = z'\delta(x'-x'')\delta(y'-y'')\delta(z'-z'') \end{array} \right\} \tag{129 a}$$

The coordinates have, however, preserved at the same time another fundamental role in which they have been employed from the very beginning—namely, that of the arguments of the functions $\psi_{x'C'}^0$ (with $C = H$, x, or any other 'basic trio') which can serve for the direct determination of the elements of a matrix F_C by means of equation (127). This second role of the coordinates is intimately connected with the initially adopted representation of physical quantities by means of operators, defined as functions of the (rectangular) coordinates x, y, z and of the elementary differential operators $p_x = \dfrac{h}{2\pi i}\dfrac{\partial}{\partial x}$, $p_y = \dfrac{h}{2\pi i}\dfrac{\partial}{\partial y}$, $p_z = \dfrac{h}{2\pi i}\dfrac{\partial}{\partial z}$, which replace the components of the momentum.

These functions were supposed to be known, being in fact identified with the functions representing the same quantities in the classical theory (on the ground that $F(x, p_x)\psi$ reduces to the product $F(x, g_x)\cdot\psi$ if ψ is replaced by its approximate expression $\psi = e^{i2\pi S/h}$, where S is the action function of classical mechanics).

We must now consider a further generalization of the transformation theory, consisting in the replacement of the coordinates in this second role, connected with the usual operator representation, by some other quantities, e.g. Q, associated with operators which contain derivatives with regard to Q.

The possibility—and, more than that, the necessity—of such a generalization clearly follows from the fact that the functions $\psi^0_{x'C'}$, considered as transformation coefficients 'from the point of view of C to that of x,', or as probability amplitudes for one of these two quantities having a given value when the value of the other is known, are practically symmetrical with regard to both quantities. Instead of—or rather together with—the functions $\psi^0_{x'C'}$, we must consider the functions $\psi^{0(-1)}_{C'x'}$ which are simply equal to the conjugate complex of the former and which correspond to the reciprocal transformation. In these functions, however, it is the quantities C which play the role of the coordinates, while the latter appear in the role of the 'basic quantities' instead of C.

Replacing the Schrödinger wave functions $\psi^0_{x'H'}$ by transformation coefficients or probability amplitudes of the most general type $a_{Q'C'}$, we can define the matrix elements of a certain quantity F with respect to C by the formulae

$$F^0_{C'C''} = \int a^*_{Q'C'} F a_{Q'C''}\, dQ',$$

or

$$F^0_{C'C''} = \sum_{Q'} a^*_{Q'C'} F a_{Q'C''},$$

according as C has a continuous or a discrete spectrum.

This definition will, however, remain meaningless so long as F is not specified as an operator 'from the point of view' of Q, i.e. as a certain function of $Q\,(Q_1, Q_2, Q_3)$ and the derivatives $\partial/\partial Q$. The operators which have been considered hitherto have always been specified from the point of view of the coordinates x, and obtained from the classical functions $F(x, g_x)$ by a simple substitution of $p_x = \dfrac{h}{2\pi i}\dfrac{\partial}{\partial x}$ for g_x. Adopting what can be denoted as the 'principle of relativity' with regard to the 'basic quantities' which specify the operator representation, we shall denote the operator representing a certain quantity F 'from the point of view of Q' by $F_{(Q)}$, where the brackets are introduced to distinguish this operator from the corresponding matrix F_Q. The operators defined in the usual way, i.e. from the point of view of the coordinates, should be denoted accordingly by $F_{(x)}$ and the general definition of the elements of the matrix F_C by means of the operator $F_{(Q)}$ should run as follows:

$$F^0_{C'C''} = \int a^*_{Q'C'} F_{(Q)} a_{Q'C''} \, dQ' = \int a^{-1}_{C'Q'} F_{(Q)} a_{Q'C''} \, dQ' \qquad (130)$$

if the spectrum of Q is continuous, or

$$F^0_{C'C''} = \sum_{Q'} a^*_{Q'C'} F_{(Q)} a_{Q'C''} = \sum_{Q'} a^{-1}_{C'Q'} F_{(Q)} a_{Q'C''} \qquad (130\,a)$$

if it is discontinuous.

Another obvious condition for the operators $F_{(Q)}$ is that the matrix elements of F_C defined by the preceding equations should not depend upon the choice of the quantities Q.

Equations (130) and (130a) bear a striking resemblance to the transformation equations

$$F^0_{C'C''} = \iint a^{-1}_{C'Q'} F^0_{Q'Q''} a_{Q''C''} \, dQ'dQ'',$$

and

$$F^0_{C'C''} = \sum_{Q'} \sum_{Q''} a^{-1}_{C'Q'} F^0_{Q'Q''} a_{Q''C''},$$

or, in the abbreviated notation based on the matrix multiplication law,

$$F_C = a^{-1} F_Q a = a^\dagger F_Q a,$$

with a denoting the transformation matrix $a_{Q'C'}$.

The equations of both types actually become identical if the operators $F_{(Q)}$ satisfy the condition

$$F_{(Q)} a_{Q'C''} = \int F^0_{Q'Q''} a_{Q''C''} \, dQ'', \qquad (131)$$

or

$$F_{(Q)} a_{Q'C''} = \sum_{Q''} F^0_{Q'Q''} a_{Q''C''}. \qquad (131\,a)$$

These conditions are a generalization of the equation

$$\int H^0_{x'x''} \psi^0_{x''} \, dx'' = H\psi^0_{x'},$$

which has already been obtained in connexion with the proof of the equivalence of the Schrödinger equation (126a) with the integral equation (126). It should be observed that, according to the present notation, we must write $H_{(x)}$ for the energy operator, and $a_{x'H'}$ for the wave functions $\psi^0_{x'}$. Further, we easily get as a generalization of equation

(128 b) the following relation between the operator $F_{(Q)}$ and the matrix F_Q:

$$F^0_{Q'Q''} = \int \delta(Q'-Q''')F_{(Q)}\delta(Q'''-Q'')\,dQ''', \qquad (131\,b)$$

where the functions $\delta(Q'-Q'')$ can be considered as the transformation coefficients $a_{Q'Q''}$ on the assumption that the spectrum of Q is continuous. The formula (131 b) can be considered as the direct consequence of (130).

Putting $F = C$ in (131) and taking into account that

$$\int C^0_{Q'Q''}a_{Q''C''}\,dQ'' = C''a_{Q'C''}$$

according to the definition of the transformation coefficients $a_{Q'C''}$ [cf. equations (125) and (126)], we get

$$C_{(Q)}a_{Q'C''} = C''a_{Q'C''}. \qquad (132)$$

This equation is the broadest generalization of Schrödinger's equation, with C standing for H, Q for x, and the probability amplitudes $a_{Q'C''}$ (which could also be denoted by $\psi^0_{Q'C''}$) for the usual 'wave functions' $\psi^0_{x'H''}$. If the form of the operator $C_{(Q)}$ as a function of Q and of $\dfrac{h}{2\pi i}\dfrac{\partial}{\partial Q}$ is known, equation (132) can serve to determine the functions $a_{Q'}(= a_{Q'C''})$ and the characteristic values C'' of the operator $C_{(Q)}$. It should be remarked that these characteristic values *do not depend upon the choice of the basic quantities* Q (i.e. are invariant with regard to the transformation of the latter), being as a matter of fact nothing else but the characteristic values of the operator $C_{(C)}$, or, in other words, the (diagonal) elements of the matrix C_C. This corresponds to the physical meaning of the characteristic values of a quantity, as the values which this quantity can possibly assume, irrespective of the values which can be, or actually are, assumed by any other quantities.

In deriving equation (132), we have assumed that the characteristic values of Q constitute a continuous set. If they constitute a discrete set, the differential operator representation of different quantities F with regard to Q becomes *impossible*, for the application of the derivative operators $\partial/\partial Q$ to functions of Q becomes meaningless. Equation (131 a) can hold accordingly only when the operator $F_{(Q)}$ reduces to a function of Q. The same refers to the equation, $F^0_{Q'Q''} = \sum\limits_{Q'''} \delta_{Q'Q'''}F_{(Q)}\delta_{Q'''Q''}$, which should replace equation (131 b) and which is meaningless, unless the operator $F_{(Q)}$ reduces to a function of Q (not containing the derivatives

$\partial/\partial Q$), in which case it reduces to

$$F^0_{Q'Q''} = F(Q'')\delta_{Q'Q''},$$

meaning that F_Q is a diagonal matrix.

This example shows that the matrix theory, which we initially developed on the basis of the operator theory, starting with the energy operator $H_{(x)}$ and the wave functions defined by it according to Schrödinger's equation $H_{(x)}\psi^0_{x'} = H'\psi^0_{x'}$, is actually more general than the operator theory even in its generalized form corresponding to the replacement of the coordinates x by some other trio of quantities with *continuously* variable values.†

Another and perhaps logically more satisfactory procedure would be to start (following Heisenberg, Jordan, and Dirac) from the other end, i.e. with the matrix representation of physical quantities, deriving the operator representation as an alternative form of it for the case when the basic quantities admit continuously variable values, and using the transformation theory for the definition of the probability amplitudes $a_{Q'C'}$ and, in particular, of the wave functions $\psi^0_{xH'}$ of the de Broglie-Schrödinger wave-mechanical theory.

This purely deductive method has, however, from a didactic point of view, the disadvantage of being too abstract and of starting with ideas completely alien to customary or 'classical' conceptions. The inductive method, which is adopted in this book, and which makes an appeal not only to the logic but also to the intuition of the reader, gradually leading him from the concrete customary conceptions to the abstract new ideas, may prove more helpful for those who have to get used to these new ideas and perform the logically simple but psychologically difficult task of getting rid of the old conceptions.

To this it should be added that the matrix theory remains an empty scheme so long as no concrete assumptions are made about the commutation properties and the functional relationship of the matrices concerned, the problem consisting in the actual determination of the elements of these matrices from a certain 'point of view' (after which a transition to some other point of view and the determination of the corresponding probability amplitudes can be made with the help of the transformation theory). These assumptions, however, involve considerations which lie outside the logical realm of the matrix theory and can hardly be understood without the fundamental idea of the wave-

---

† It would be possible to extend the operator theory to the discrete case if differential coefficients were replaced by finite differences.

mechanical theory, namely, that the motion of a particle in a given field of force is determined in terms of probabilities by the propagation of the associated waves.

This refers in particular to the commutation relations between the fundamental matrices x and p,

$$px - xp = \frac{h}{2\pi i} \, \delta \qquad (133)$$

in conjunction with the fact that the latter have to be defined as the components of the momentum in the classical expression of the energy H (replaced by the matrix H_x).

After these relations, which correspond to the quantum conditions of Bohr's theory, have been established, the whole problem of the wave-mechanical theory can be stated as the transformation of all the matrices involved (and in the first place of x, p, and H) from the point of view of x to that of H, the transformation coefficients $\psi^0_{x'H'}$ being the probability amplitudes of finding the particle in a given position when its energy is known or with a given energy if its position is known. The actual solution of this problem is usually reduced to the solution of Schrödinger's equation involving the operator $H_{(x)}$.

As an illustration of the 'principle of relativity' with respect to the basic quantities in the operator representation, we shall consider the results which are obtained if the coordinates are replaced in this role by the momenta p. The latter must be considered in this case as ordinary quantities ($= Q$), while the coordinates, in order that the 'quantum conditions' (133) should be satisfied, must be defined as differential operators according to the formulae

$$x = -\frac{h}{2\pi i} \frac{\partial}{\partial p_x}, \qquad y = -\frac{h}{2\pi i} \frac{\partial}{\partial p_y}, \qquad z = -\frac{h}{2\pi i} \frac{\partial}{\partial p_z}. \qquad (133\,a)$$

The energy operator $H_{(p)}$ can be determined accordingly as the operator resulting from the substitution in the classical Hamiltonian function $(p_x^2 + p_y^2 + p_z^2)/(2m) + U(x, y, z)$ of the elementary operators (133 a) for the coordinates. The new wave functions $\psi^0_{p'H'}$ corresponding to this definition of the energy operator are determined by the differential equation [cf. (132)]:

$$H_{(p)}\psi^0_{p'} = H'\psi^0_{p'}, \qquad (133\,b)$$

which in general is entirely different from that of Schrödinger—since the kinetic energy $(p_x^2 + p_y^2 + p_z^2)/(2m)$ which in the x-representation reduced to the Laplacian differential operator of the wave theory

∇^2 [multiplied by $-h^2/(8\pi^2 m)$], in the p-representation remains an ordinary quantity, or more exactly an ordinary factor which has to be multiplied by the function ψ_p^0, while the potential energy becomes a differential operator acting on this function, the result of the operation $H_{(p)}$ being equivalent to the multiplication of ψ_p^0 by a constant factor H'—one of the characteristic values of H. As stated above, these characteristic values must be the same whether we start with the basic quantities x or p.

The probability amplitudes $\psi_{p'H'}^0$ are, however, in general, functions of p' entirely different from the ordinary wave functions $\psi_{x'H'}^0$ (with the exception of the case of the harmonic oscillator, where the potential energy is the same quadratic function of the coordinates as the kinetic energy is of the momentum components). According to the fundamental equation of the transformation theory [see, for instance, (119 b)] they must be connected with each other by the relations

$$\left.\begin{aligned} \psi_{x'H'}^0 &= \int a_{x'p'}\,\psi_{p'H'}^0\,dp' \\ \psi_{p'H'}^0 &= \int a_{p'}^{-1}\cdot\psi_{x'H'}^0\,dp' = \int a_{x'p'}^*\,\psi_{x'H'}\,dx' \end{aligned}\right\}, \qquad (134)$$

where the transformation coefficients $a_{x'p'}$ can be defined by the operator equation,

$$p_{(x)}a_{x'} = p'a_{x'}, \qquad (134\,\text{a})$$

that is,

$$\frac{h}{2\pi i}\frac{\partial}{\partial x}a_{x'y'z'} = p_x'\,a_{x'y'z'},$$

$$\frac{h}{2\pi i}\frac{\partial}{\partial y}a_{x'y'z'} = p_y'\,a_{x'y'z'},$$

$$\frac{h}{2\pi i}\frac{\partial}{\partial z}a_{x'y'z'} = p_z'\,a_{x'y'z'}.$$

This gives

$$a_{x'p'} = \frac{1}{\sqrt{h}}e^{i2\pi p'x'/h}, \qquad (134\,\text{b})$$

$p'x'$ denoting the scalar product of the vectors $\mathbf{p}$ and $\mathbf{r}$, i.e. the sum $p_x'x'+p_y'y'+p_z'z'$. The coefficient $1/\sqrt{h}$ follows from the orthogonality and normalizing relation

$$\int a_{x'p'}a_{x'p''}^*\,dx' = \delta(p'-p''), \quad \text{or} \quad \int a_{x'p'}a_{x''p'}^*\,dp' = \delta(x'-x'').$$

The same result is obtained if the functions $a_{x'p'}$, or rather $a_{p'x'}^{-1}$, are defined by the operator equation

$$x_{(p)}a_p^{-1} = x'a_p^{-1},$$

which, because $x_p = -\dfrac{h}{2\pi}\dfrac{\partial}{\partial p}$, gives

$$a_{p'x'}^{-1} = \frac{1}{\sqrt{h}}\,e^{-i2\pi x'p'/h}, \tag{134 c}$$

in agreement with the relation $a_{p'x'}^{-1} = a_{x'p'}^{*}$.

Substituting these expressions in (134), we get

$$\psi_{x'H'}^{0} = \frac{1}{\sqrt{h}}\int \psi_{p'H'}^{0}\,e^{i2\pi p'x'/h}\,dp'$$

$$= \frac{1}{\sqrt{h}}\int \psi_{p'H'}^{0}\,e^{i2\pi(p_x'\,x' + p_y'\,y' + p_z'\,z')/h}\,dp_x'\,dp_y'\,dp_z' \tag{135}$$

$$\psi_{p'H'}^{0} = \frac{1}{\sqrt{h}}\int \psi_{x'H'}^{0}\,e^{-i2\pi p'x'/h}\,dx' = \frac{1}{\sqrt{h}}\int \psi_{x'H'}^{0}\,e^{-i2\pi(p_x'\,x' + p_y'\,y' + p_z'\,z')/h}\,dx'dy'dz'. \tag{135 a}$$

The first of these formulae can obviously be regarded as the expansion of the function $\psi_{x'H'}^{0}$ in a Fourier integral with the amplitude coefficients $\dfrac{1}{\sqrt{h}}\psi_{p'H'}^{0}$, while the second gives the explicit expression of these coefficients. Remembering the wave-mechanical interpretation of the vector $\mathbf{p}'/h$ as equal to the reciprocal of the wave-length and pointing in the direction of the propagation of the waves associated with the motion of the particle, we can regard the transformation coefficients $a_{x'p'}$ as *plane sine waves* (without the time factor, however!), and we can interpret the transformation equation (135) as the representation of the wave function $\psi_{x'H'}$ by means of a superposition of plane sine waves with appropriate amplitudes and travelling in appropriate directions. This physical interpretation is in complete harmony with the physical meaning of the Fourier amplitudes $\psi_{p'H'}^{0}$ as the probability amplitudes for the particle to have a definite momentum p' (irrespective of its position) for a given value H' of its total energy to which the function $\psi_{x'H'}^{0}$ refers.

We shall not consider in further detail the generalized transformation theory and its application to operators other than x, p, and H. There is, however, one particular class of transformations which have been alluded to at the end of § 16 as 'canonical transformations of the second kind' and which deserve special notice. They consist in a transition from the original trio of (rectangular) coordinates (x) and the associated momentum operators $\left(p_x = \dfrac{h}{2\pi i}\dfrac{\partial}{\partial x}\right)$ to some new basic trio of mutually commuting coordinates (Q) and mutually commuting momenta (P)

satisfying the commutation relation

$$PQ - QP = \frac{h}{2\pi i}\delta \tag{136}$$

for a *given motion* specified by a definite energy operator

$$H_{(x)} = H_{(x)}(x, y, z; p_x, p_y, p_z)$$

which is thereby transformed into $H_{(Q)} = H_{(Q)}(Q_1, Q_2, Q_3; P_1, P_2, P_3)$.

The quantities P and Q satisfying the above relations are said to be 'canonically conjugate' with each other. From the point of view of the new coordinates (Q) the new momenta (P) are represented by the operators $P_{(Q)} = \dfrac{h}{2\pi i}\dfrac{\partial}{\partial Q}$ (just as the Q's are represented from the point of view of the P's by the operators $Q_{(P)} = -\dfrac{h}{2\pi i}\dfrac{\partial}{\partial P}$). An operator representation of the P's from the point of view of the original co-ordinates (x) is, however, possible in the particular case only when the Q's are defined as certain functions of the x's not involving the p_x's or the P's. In this case, which corresponds to the 'point transformation' of the classical theory, the new momenta (P) can be expressed as certain functions of the original ones p_x (involving as parameters the co-ordinates x or Q). In the general case of a canonical transformation corresponding to a 'contact transformation' of the classical theory such a relationship between the new and the old variables does not exist and some kind of matrix representation must be used for the definition of the latter. The relationship between the new and the old variables can be expressed with the help of a certain *transformation matrix* Φ according to the equations $\quad Q = \Phi^{-1}x\Phi, \qquad P = \Phi^{-1}p_x\Phi,$ that is,

$$\left.\begin{array}{lll} Q_1 = \Phi^{-1}x\Phi, & Q_2 = \Phi^{-1}y\Phi, & Q_3 = \Phi^{-1}z\Phi \\ P_1 = \Phi^{-1}p_x\Phi, & P_2 = \Phi^{-1}p_y\Phi, & P_z = \Phi^{-1}p_z\Phi \end{array}\right\} \tag{136a}$$

These equations automatically secure the fulfilment of the commutation relations which must exist between the new variables

$$Q_iQ_k - Q_kQ_i = 0, \quad P_iP_k - P_kP_i = 0, \quad P_iQ_k - Q_kP_i = \frac{h}{2\pi i}\delta_{ik} \tag{136b}$$

as a consequence of those existing between the original ones.

In order that the new variables should be represented by Hermitian matrices just as the original ones, the transformation matrix Φ must be *unitary*, i.e. satisfy the relation $\Phi^{-1} = \Phi^\dagger$.

The equations (136 a) are thus formally quite similar to the equations

(124) of § 16. They have, however, an entirely different physical meaning. While the transformation matrix a in (124) has a mixed character referring to two different sets of states, the elements of the matrix Φ refer to the same set of states specified by the characteristic values of some basic quantity which serves for the definition of the matrices x, p_x, Q, P, and H (this basic quantity can in particular coincide with the invariable energy H).

The equations (136 a) must be considered as corresponding to the classical equations $p_x = \dfrac{\partial \Phi}{\partial x}, \ldots, Q = \dfrac{\partial \Phi}{\partial P}$ [cf. (31 a), § 4] defining a contact transformation with the help of an arbitrary function Φ. In the quantum theory the latter is replaced by the likewise arbitrary transformation matrix Φ.

In the classical theory a canonical transformation is characterized by the fact that it does not alter the canonical form of the equations of motion. The same criterion is easily seen to apply to the canonical transformation (136 a) of the quantum theory.

We have, in fact, differentiating Q and P with respect to the time t,

$$\frac{dQ}{dt} = [H, Q], \qquad \frac{dP}{dt} = [H, P],$$

which in virtue of (136) can be written in the form

$$\frac{dQ}{dt} = \frac{\partial H}{\partial P}, \qquad \frac{dP}{dt} = -\frac{\partial H}{\partial Q}$$

[cf. § 7, eqs. (43 a) and (44 c)].

An equivalent form of the condition that the variables P and Q should be canonically conjugate (in the classical sense), i.e. that they should satisfy the canonical equations of motion, is that the Poisson bracket expression

$$[A, B] = \sum_{x, y, z} \left(\frac{\partial A}{\partial p_x} \frac{\partial B}{\partial x} - \frac{\partial A}{\partial x} \frac{\partial B}{\partial p_x} \right)$$

should be equal to 1 for $A = P_i$, $B = Q_i$ ($i = 1, 2, 3$) and to 0 for all the other combinations of the variables P, Q. This condition corresponds to the commutation conditions (136 b) which can be written in the form $[Q_i, Q_k] = 0$, $[P_i, P_k] = 0$, $[P_i, Q_k] = \delta_{ik}$, the classical Poisson bracket being the analogue of the quantum bracket expression $[A, B] = \dfrac{2\pi i}{h}(AB - BA)$ (cf. § 8).

18. Geometrical Representation of the Transformation Theory

The understanding of the generalized matrix theory, connected with the 'principle of relativity' in the choice of the basic quantities and with the transformation from one 'basis' to another, can be greatly facilitated by the use of a geometrical picture, or rather of a geometrical language, suggested by the formal similarity between the equations of the transformation theory developed in the preceding sections and the theory of linear orthogonal transformations of ordinary analytical geometry. The nucleus of this analogy is that in both cases the transformation equations are linear (and homogeneous) and that the transformation coefficients satisfy similar orthogonality and normalizing relations. (The mere idea of 'orthogonality' is suggestive of mutually perpendicular axes.)

The choice of the basic quantities in the present theory corresponds to the choice of the coordinate system in the geometrical theory, and the relativity in the choice of these basic quantities corresponds to the relativity in the choice of the coordinate system—or, in other words, to the equivalence of all the directions in space.

It will be remembered that in analytical geometry a linear orthogonal transformation means a set of linear homogeneous equations between the coordinates $x = x_1$, $y = x_2$, $z = x_3$ of an arbitrarily chosen point with respect to one system of axes, S, say, and the coordinates of the same point $\xi = \xi_1$, $\eta = \xi_2$, $\zeta = \xi_3$ with respect to another system Σ, both systems being orthogonal and having the same origin. These equations can be written in the form

or
$$\left. \begin{array}{l} \xi_\nu = \sum_n a_{n\nu} x_n \\[2mm] x_n = \sum_\nu a_{\nu n}^{-1} \xi_\nu \end{array} \right\} , \qquad (137)$$

with
$$a_{n\nu} = a_{\nu n}^{-1} = \cos(x_n, \xi_\nu). \qquad (137\,\text{a})$$

The relations $a_{n\nu} = a_{\nu n}^{-1}$, which are geometrically evident, can be obtained analytically from the orthogonality condition

$$\sum_n x_n^2 = \sum_\nu \xi_\nu^2, \qquad (137\,\text{b})$$

which gives, in conjunction with (137),

$$\sum_{\nu} a_{n'\nu} a_{n''\nu} = \delta_{n'n''}, \qquad \sum_n a_{\nu'n}^{-1} a_{\nu''n}^{-1} = \delta_{\nu'\nu''}. \qquad (137\,\text{c})$$

On the other hand, substituting the expressions of the ξ's in those of the x's and vice versa, we have

$$\sum_\nu a_{n'\nu} a_{\nu n''}^{-1} = \delta_{n'n''}, \qquad \sum_n a_{\nu'n}^{-1} a_{n\nu''} = \delta_{\nu'\nu''}. \qquad (137\,\text{d})$$

The comparison of these equations with the preceding equations leads to the relations (137 a), without, of course, the geometrical interpretation with which we started.

The transformation theory which has been developed in the preceding sections can be obtained from this elementary theory of linear orthogonal transformations by a twofold generalization.

Firstly, by making the number of coordinates specifying a point *infinite*, i.e. by considering, instead of the ordinary three-dimensional space, a fictitious space with infinitely many dimensions.

Secondly, by considering the coordinates of a point as *complex* quantities and by defining the square of its distance from the origin, not as the sum of the squares of the coordinates, but as the sum of the squares of their *moduli*, thus replacing the orthogonality condition (137 b) by the following condition:

$$\sum_n x_n x_n^* = \sum_\nu \xi_\nu \xi_\nu^*, \qquad (138)$$

the summation being extended over all the coordinates. We get in this case, instead of (137 c),

$$\sum_\nu a_{n'\nu} a_{n''\nu}^* = \delta_{n'n''}, \qquad \sum_n a_{\nu'n}^{-1} a_{\nu''n}^{-1*} = \delta_{\nu'\nu''},$$

and, since equations (137 d) are not altered,

$$a_{\nu n}^{-1} = a_{n\nu}^* \quad \text{or} \quad a_{n\nu} = a_{\nu n}^{-1*}, \qquad (138\,\text{a})$$

that is, $a^{-1} = a^\dagger.$

In the special case of real coordinates x, ξ, this 'unitary' transformation reduces to the usual orthogonal transformation (though with an unlimited number of variables), and we get $a^\dagger = \tilde{a}^* = \tilde{a}$ (transposed matrix), that is, $a^{-1} = \tilde{a}$, which is another expression of the relations (137 a). Although a geometrical interpretation cannot be associated with an infinite number of complex variables x, ξ, connected with each other by a unitary transformation, yet, since the number of variables does not make any difference from the purely analytical point of view (so long as it is larger than 1), we can preserve, if not a geometrical picture, at least a geometrical language with respect to the variables x, ξ and the transformation coefficients $a_{n\nu}$. We can accordingly regard (or rather denote) the former as the coordinates of a point in a space of infinitely many dimensions with respect to two orthogonal systems of coordinates S and Σ, while the latter can still be regarded (or denoted) as the cosines of the angles between the old and the new coordinate axes. The variables x_n and ξ_ν can be defined also as the projections (or components) of a certain vector $\mathbf{r}$ on these axes.

In the simplest matrix transformation problem which was considered at the beginning of § 15, the role of the coordinates x_n and ξ_ν is played by the characteristic functions (or rather amplitudes) $\psi^0_{H'}$, $\phi^0_{K'}$. This is clearly seen from the fact that they are transformed according to equations (110) and (111) which are the analogues of equations (137), and that they satisfy the orthogonality relation (113) which is exactly of the same type as (138). We can thus describe the matrix transformation theory in a very suggestive geometrical language, according to the following principles.

Each stationary state specified by a wave function $\psi^0_{H'}$ can be represented geometrically by a certain *direction* or *axis* H' in a space of infinitely many dimensions, which we shall call the *state-space*. The states specified by the different functions $\psi^0_{H'}$ are represented by axes H' which are perpendicular to each other, the complete set of states defined by the operator H forming a *complete* orthogonal system of coordinate axes in the state-space, which we shall also denote by the letter H. The 'completeness' of the system means that *any* 'vector' in the state-space can be represented as the geometrical sum of its components along the axes of H.

This applies in particular to vectors drawn in the directions of another complete orthogonal system of axes K', which represent geometrically the stationary states defined by the operator K. The transformation coefficients $a_{H'K'}$ can be regarded as the projections of a unit vector in the direction of a definite axis K' on the different axes H' or, loosely speaking, as the cosines of the angles between the axes K' and H'. The latter expression requires, however, a correction, inasmuch as the coefficients $a^{-1}_{K'H'} = a^*_{H'K'}$ can also pretend to the same role, for they represent the projection of a unit vector in the direction of a certain axis H' on the different axes K'. This interpretation of $a_{H'K'}$ and $a^{-1}_{K'H'}$ immediately follows from the comparison of the transformation equations $\phi^0_{K'} = \sum_{H'} a_{H'K'} \psi^0_{H'}$ and $\psi^0_{H'} = \sum_{K'} a^{-1}_{K'H'} \phi^0_{K'}$ with (137).

It should be remembered that the quantities $\psi^0_{H'}$ and $\phi^0_{K'}$ appearing in these equations in the role of rectangular coordinates of a point in the state-space are functions of the ordinary spatial coordinates x, y, z, and that, moreover, they refer to the *same* (arbitrarily chosen) *point*.

So long as this point remains unspecified, $\psi^0_{H'}$ and $\phi^0_{K'}$ can be treated as *vectors*, but as soon as we specify it, putting $x = x'$, we get *numbers* $\psi^0_{x'H'}$ and $\phi^0_{x'K'}$ which, as we know, both with regard to their physical meaning (as probability amplitudes) and analytical properties (as transformation coefficients), are wholly similar to the numbers $a_{H'K'}$. We can regard them accordingly as the components of the vectors $\psi_{H'}^0$ and $\phi_{K'}^0$ along the axes of a third coordinate system X in the state-space, each axis x' of this system specifying a definite position $x = x'$, $y = y'$, $z = z'$ of the particle in the ordinary space. The axes of this new system X must be regarded as orthogonal (i.e. mutually perpendicular) in spite of the fact that they correspond not to a discrete set of states, like the axes of the system H or K, but to a continuum of states.

Since the functions $\psi_{x'H'}^0$ and $\phi_{x'K'}^0$ are normalized to unity, both with respect to x and to H or K, the vectors $\psi_{H'}^0$, $\phi_{K'}^0$, as well as $\psi_{x'}^0$, $\phi_{x'}^0$ (the latter specifying a certain position in space irrespective of the values of the energy H or K) can be regarded as *unit* vectors (i.e. having the length unity) and the numbers $\psi_{x'H'}^0$ and $\phi_{x'K'}^0$ interpreted geometrically in the same way as the numbers $a_{H'K'}$, namely, as the cosines of the angles between the axes x' (not in the ordinary space of course, but in the state-space!) on the one hand, and between the axes H' or K' on the other.

From this point of view the transformation equations

$$\left.\begin{aligned} \phi_{x'K'}^0 &= \sum_{H'} \psi_{x'H'}^0 \, a_{H'K'} \\ \psi_{x'H'}^0 &= \sum_{K'} \phi_{x'K'}^0 \, a_{K'H'}^{-1} \end{aligned}\right\} \tag{139}$$

acquire an extremely simple geometrical meaning: they become, namely, the generalization of the well-known formula of analytical geometry for the cosine of the angle between two directions, x' and K', say, expressed in terms of the cosines of the angles between these directions and a complete set of mutually perpendicular directions constituting a co-ordinate system H.

In fact, if we write $\cos(x', K')$, $\cos(x', H')$, and $\cos(H', K')$ instead of $\phi_{x'K'}^0$, $\psi_{x'H'}^0$, and $a_{H'K'}$ respectively, the first of equations (139) assumes the familiar form

$$\cos(x', K') = \sum_{H'} \cos(x', H') \cos(H', K').$$

It becomes, however, necessary to distinguish two different cosines between the same two directions (corresponding to the projection of the first on the second or the second on the first), since $a_{K'H'}^{-1} = \cos(K', H')$ is not equal to $a_{H'K'} = \cos(H', K')$ but to its conjugate complex: $\cos(K', H') = \cos^*(H', K')$. (The same refers, of course, to the functions $\psi_{x'H'}^0$ and $\psi_{H'x'}^{0(-1)}$ or $\phi_{x'H'}^0$ and $\phi_{K'x'}^{0(-1)}$.)

Following Dirac, we shall often use in future the simplified notation

$(K'|H')$ and $(H'|K')$ for these two 'cosines' or transformation coefficients; we shall write likewise

$$\phi^0_{x'K'} = (x'|K') \qquad \phi^{0*}_{x'K'} = (K'|x')$$
$$\psi^0_{x'H'} = (x'|H') \qquad \psi^{0*}_{x'H'} = (H'|x'),$$

thus avoiding the unnecessary complications arising from the use of different letters, a, ψ^0, ϕ^0, etc. The unit vector (in the state-space) defining a certain state x', H', or K' *per se*, i.e. irrespective of the other states with which it can be associated, will be denoted accordingly by the symbols $(x'|)$, $(H'|)$, $(K'|)$ or $(|x')$, $(|H')$, $(|K')$. This notation has the advantage of representing the same thing by the same symbol (or two 'conjugate' symbols), while in our previous notation the same state corresponding to a given position x' was described by two different symbols $\psi^0_{x'}$ or $\phi^0_{x'}$, depending upon the 'coordinate system' H or K which we had in mind.

With the new notation the transformation equations (139) can be written in the form

$$\left.\begin{aligned}
(x'|K') &= \sum_{H'} (x'|H')(H'|K') \\
(x'|H') &= \sum_{K'} (x'|K')(K'|H')
\end{aligned}\right\} \tag{139a}$$

Since the three coordinate systems H, K, and x are equivalent to each other, we could write by analogy a third relation of the same form, namely,

$$(H'|K') = \sum_{x'} (H'|x')(x'|K'),$$

if x' were discretely variable, like H' and K'. Since, however, x' is continuously variable, we must replace the sum by an integral over x', which gives

$$(H'|K') = \int (H'|x')(x'|K')\,dx', \tag{139b}$$

or, in the previous notation,

$$a_{H'K'} = \int \psi^{0*}_{H'}(x)\phi^0_{K'}(x)\,dV,$$

which is nothing else but the formula (110a) obtained at the beginning of §15, and again in the way just shown—but without the associated geometrical interpretation—somewhat later.

The preceding equations (139a) and (139b) hold, of course, for any three sets of states which may be specified by three basic 'trios'. It should be remembered that, from the physical point of view, they express *the addition and multiplication law for the probability amplitudes*. The geometrical interpretation of the probability amplitudes

$(Q'|C')$ as the cosines between the directions $Q = Q'$ and $C = C'$ in the state-space is in perfect harmony with the initial interpretation of the orthogonality between two functions representing two different states as the expression of the *alternative* character of these states. All those states which are represented by mutually perpendicular directions in the state-space are alternative or mutually exclusive—in the sense that the probability of finding the particle in one of them when it is known to be in another is equal to zero. All such states may always be referred to the same set.

Having elucidated the geometrical meaning of the probability amplitudes—or transformation matrices—we shall now turn to the geometrical interpretation of the ordinary matrices, which represent physical quantities from one or the other point of view. This interpretation is again determined by the transformation equations (121) which show that Hermitian matrices can be considered as a generalization of the so-called *tensors*, or more exactly *symmetrical tensors*, of the elementary three-dimensional analytical geometry.

A tensor can be defined as a composite quantity with a number of components, each of which refers to two axes of the same system of coordinates, and behaves with respect to a transformation of the coordinate system in the same way as the product of the components of two vectors along the corresponding axes.

Let us consider again the two coordinate systems S and Σ and denote the components of the same vector, $\mathbf{f}$, say, along the axes of S and Σ by f_n and f_ν respectively. If $\mathbf{g}$ is some other vector, and if we form the products of all the components of f with all the components of g, *referred to the same system*, we shall obtain a set of 9 quantities

$$T_{mn} = f_m g_n \quad \text{or} \quad T_{\mu\nu} = f_\mu g_\nu, \tag{140}$$

which can be considered as the components of the *same* tensor T referred to, or represented from the point of view of, the coordinate system S or Σ. Taking into account the transformation equations,

$$f_\mu = \sum_m a_{m\mu} f_m, \qquad g_\nu = \sum_n a_{n\nu} g_n,$$

with the coefficients $a_{n\nu} = a_{\nu n}^{-1} = \cos(x_n, \xi_n)$ as before, we get

$$T_{\mu\nu} = \sum_m \sum_n a_{m\mu} a_{n\nu} T_{mn} = \sum_m \sum_n a_{\mu m}^{-1} T_{mn} a_{n\nu}, \tag{140a}$$

and

$$T_{mn} = \sum_\mu \sum_\nu a_{\mu m}^{-1} a_{\nu n}^{-1} T_{\mu\nu} = \sum_\mu \sum_\nu a_{m\mu} T_{\mu\nu} a_{\nu n}^{-1}. \tag{140b}$$

These transformation equations can serve to define a tensor T in the general case, when its components cannot be put in the simple form

(140). These equations can obviously be written in the following matrix form:

$$T_\Sigma = a^{-1}T_S a, \qquad T_S = aT_\Sigma a^{-1},$$

which makes it evident that a matrix F_C representing some quantity F from the point of view of some other basic quantity C, can be interpreted geometrically as a certain tensor F in the state-space referred to a system of coordinates whose axes represent the states specified by the characteristic values of C.

The matrices F_C representing real quantities are Hermitian, i.e. satisfy the relation

$$F_{C''C'} = F^*_{C'C''},$$

which can be considered as the generalization of the condition

$$T_{mn} = T_{nm}, \qquad T_{\mu\nu} = T_{\nu\mu}$$

for the symmetrical tensors of ordinary analytical geometry.

Now such tensors admit of a very simple and suggestive geometrical illustration, namely, that of a *central quadric* (ellipsoid, hyperboloid), defined by the equation

$$\sum_m \sum_n T_{mn} x_m x_n = 1, \qquad (140\,c)$$

in the coordinate system S, or

$$\sum_\mu \sum_\nu T_{\mu\nu} \xi_\mu \xi_\nu = 1, \qquad (140\,d)$$

in the coordinate system Σ.

The fact that these two equations represent *the same surface*, i.e. that the coefficients T_{mn} and $T_{\mu\nu}$ are transformed into each other according to equations (140a) and (140b), can be proved by substituting in (140 d) the expressions $\xi_\mu = \sum_m a_{m\mu} x_m$, $\xi_\nu = \sum_n a_{n\nu} x_n$, which gives

$$\sum_\mu \sum_\nu \sum_m \sum_n T_{\mu\nu} a_{m\mu} a_{n\nu} x_m x_n = 1,$$

or, changing the order of summation with regard to the Greek and Latin indices,

$$\sum_m \sum_n x_m x_n \Big(\sum_\mu \sum_\nu T_{\mu\nu} a_{m\mu} a_{n\nu} \Big) = 1,$$

which, in view of (140a), coincides with (140 c).

The components of a symmetrical tensor referred to a system of coordinates can thus be interpreted as the coefficients in the equation of a certain central quadric referred to the same coordinate system; this makes it possible to *visualize a symmetrical tensor, without any reference to a system of coordinates, as the quadric surface which it defines*.

It should be mentioned that a quadric surface can be defined, according to (140 c), by a non-symmetrical tensor just as well as by a symmetrical one. But it will actually contain the *sum* of the components $T_{mn}+T_{nm}$ referring to the coordinates x_m and x_n as the coefficient of their product $x_m x_n$. The asymmetry of T, if any, will therefore not be manifested in the shape of the surface, or, in other words, the latter will define only the symmetrical part of T. Thus a tensor can be completely specified by a quadric surface only when it is symmetrical.

Every central surface of the second order has three mutually perpendicular axes of symmetry, which can be defined by the condition that, referred to a system of coordinates Σ whose axes coincide with its symmetry axes, the equation of the quadric reduces to the 'canonical' form

$$\sum_\mu T_{\mu\mu}\xi_\mu^2 = 1,$$

not containing products of different coordinates.

This can be expressed by saying that the matrix T_Σ considered from this point of view is diagonal. The possibility of reducing the equation of a central quadric to the canonical form, i.e. the existence of symmetry axes, is proved by a well-known method which at the same time leads to the actual determination of the cosines between these axes and the original axes x_n, i.e. of the coefficients of the orthogonal transformation $S \to \Sigma$, and of the diagonal elements of the transformed matrix, or, in other words, of the characteristic values of the tensor T, $T_{\mu\mu} = T'$.

This method consists in defining the vertices of the quadric—i.e. the end-points of the symmetry axes—by either one of the following conditions:

(1) The normals to the surface at the vertices coincide in direction with the radii vectores from the centre. This condition leads to the equations

$$\frac{\partial F}{\partial x_m}\text{ proportional to } x_m,$$

where F denotes the left side of equation (140 c), or, if the proportionality factor is denoted by T':

$$\sum_n T_{mn} x_n = T' x_m. \tag{141}$$

So long as we are dealing with ordinary three-dimensional space, this is a set of three linear equations which are compatible with each other if their determinant vanishes. The latter condition gives a cubic equation for T', and to the three roots of it there correspond three sets of x_n values, $x_{nT'}$, say, which define three mutually perpendicular vectors, and reduce to the cosines of the angles between the old axes and the symmetry axes if normalized to unity. The three values of T' turn out to be the three non-vanishing diagonal elements of the transformed matrix or tensor T_Σ.

(2) The distances of the vertices from the centre or their squares $r^2 = \sum x_m^2$ have the largest or smallest possible values, consistent with the equation

$$F \equiv \sum_{mn} T_{mn} x_m x_n = 1.$$

This gives, with the help of Lagrange's method of undetermined multipliers, a system of equations derived from

$$\delta r^2 + \lambda \delta F = 0 \tag{141 a}$$

by equating to zero the coefficients of the variations of the separate coordinates with a properly chosen value of the coefficient λ. Putting $\lambda = -T'$, we again get equations (141).

It should be mentioned that the variational equation (141 a) can be interpreted as the condition that F should have a maximum, minimum, or stationary value while r^2 is kept constant, for instance equal to unity.

(3) Finally we could find the symmetry axes of T by defining the transformation coefficients $a_{n\nu}$ in equations (140 a) in such a way that the three transformed non-diagonal components of T vanish, or, in other words, that the transformed matrix T_Σ be diagonal. This again, as can easily be shown, leads to equations (141) or, more exactly, to

$$\sum_n T_{mn} x_{nT'} = T' x_{mT'}.$$

These equations, as well as equations (141), are obviously of the same type as equations (122 b) or (123) of § 16 defining the transformation of the matrix K_H to the diagonal matrix K_K. They only differ in the number of dimensions, this being equal to three in the case of ordinary space and to infinity in the case of the state-space to which the latter equations refer. Another difference between them and the corresponding elementary equations is that the vectors and tensors with which we have to do in the case of the state-space are complex, the symmetry condition for the ordinary tensors being replaced by the Hermitian condition for the tensors in the state-space.

With this amendment, which from the purely analytical point of view is merely a trivial generalization of the ideas and relations of ordinary analytical geometry, we can apply the tensor idea and the idea of a quadric central surface in the state-space for the representation of physical quantities which have hitherto been represented by Hermitian matrices. The idea of a tensor, together with the 'principle of relativity' in the choice of the coordinate system, is actually equivalent to the idea of a matrix in conjunction with the principle of relativity of the basic quantities which determine the coordinate system.

The additional feature of the geometrical representation derived by generalizing the ordinary geometrical theory is the possibility of thinking of a quantity F as pictured, as it were, by a central quadric surface in the state-space, the axes of symmetry of this surface representing the different states specified by the characteristic values of F, and these characteristic values being inversely proportional to the squares of the length of these axes drawn from the centre to the vertices (without being prolonged to infinity). The latter relation follows from the fact that in the canonical form of the equation of the quadric $\sum_{\mu} T_{\mu\mu} \xi_{\mu}^2 = 1$ the coefficients $T_{\mu\mu}$ which are obviously the reciprocals of the squares of the lengths of the axes (with positive or negative sign) represent at the same time the characteristic values T' (or T', T'', T''') of the tensor T.

The equation of a quadric surface representing in the state-space a certain quantity F referred to the symmetry axes of the quadric surface which represents some other quantity, C, say, can be written in the form

$$\sum_{C'} \sum_{C''} F^0_{C'C''} a^*_{C'} a_{C''} = \text{const.}, \tag{142}$$

if the values of C form a discrete set, or in the form

$$\iint F^0_{C'C''} a^*_{C'} a_{C''} \, dC' dC'' = \text{const.}, \tag{142a}$$

if they vary in a continuous manner, while the expression

$$E = \sum_{C'} a^*_{C'} a_{C'} \tag{142b}$$

or

$$E = \int a^*_{C'} a_{C'} \, dC' \tag{142c}$$

can be interpreted as the square of the distance from the common centre of the two surfaces to some point with the coordinates $a_{C'}$.

The characteristic values of F and the states specified by them can be found by transforming the quadric (142) to the canonical form, i.e. to the symmetry axes of F. This problem, as we know already, is solved by the transformation equations

$$\left. \begin{array}{l} \sum_{C''} F^0_{C'C''} a_{C''} = F' a_{C'} \\ \int F^0_{C'C''} a_{C''} \, dC'' = F' a_{C'} \end{array} \right\}, \tag{143}$$

the resulting normalized $a_{C'} = a_{C'F'} = (C'|F')$ being the cosines of the angles between the symmetry axes of C and those of F, or, from the physical point of view, the probabilities of getting a certain value for C when that of F is supposed to be known.

An important relationship between the two quantities is expressed by the *coincidence of the symmetry axes* of the associated surfaces. This means the coincidence of the states specified by the corresponding characteristic values of F and C and is equivalent to the condition that F and C, defined as matrices or operators from any common point of view (Q say), *commute with each other*. To prove this we shall first put $Q = C$. The matrices F_C and C_C, being both diagonal, must commute with each other, since their product is also a diagonal matrix, independent of the order of the factors:

$$(FC)_{C'C''} = F_{C'C'} C_{C''C''} \delta_{C'C''} = (CF)_{C'C''}.$$

Now when $Q \neq C$ one can always define a (unitary) transformation matrix b which will transform C into Q according to the equation $Q = bCb^{-1}$. According to the invariance property with regard to canonical transformations of this form expressed by equation (124 a), we must have

$$F_Q C_Q - C_Q F_Q = b(F_C C_C - C_C F_C)b^{-1} = 0.$$

The transformation equations from C to F in the general case when these quantities do not commute can be derived from a variational principle of the same type as that which serves to determine the vertices of a quadric in ordinary analytical geometry. We can put, namely, $\delta E = 0$, subject to the condition (142) or (142 a) giving

$$\delta \overline{F} - F' \delta E = 0, \tag{143 a}$$

where $\overline{F}$ denotes the left-hand side of (142) or (142 a) and E the expression (142 b) or (142 c) respectively, while F' is an undetermined multiplier. This equation can also be interpreted as expressing the fact that $\delta \overline{F} = 0$ subject to the condition that $E = \text{const.}$ ($= 1$, say). The variations of $a_{C'}$ and a_C^* must be considered as independent of each other and their coefficients in (143 a) set equal to zero, which leads to the transformation equations (143) and their conjugate complex (i.e. the equations of the reciprocal transformation).

The 'conditioned' variational equations $\delta E = 0$ with $\overline{F} = \text{const.}$, or $\delta \overline{F} = 0$ with $E = \text{const.}$, can be replaced by the 'unconditioned' variational equation

$$\delta(\overline{F}/E) = 0 \tag{143 b}$$

which automatically provides for the normalization of the functions $a_{C'}$ so far as the value of $\overline{F}$ is concerned. If, indeed, the $a_{C'}$ are not normalized, then the functions $a_{C'}/\sqrt{E}$ can be considered as their normalized values and $\bar{F}/E$ as the value of $\bar{F}$ subject to the appropriate normalization conditions $\left(\sum\limits_{C'} a_{C'}^* a_{C'} = 1 \text{ or } \int a_{C'}^* a_{C'} \, dC'' = 1 \right)$.

It is obvious from the comparison of (143 b) with (143) that the stationary values of $\bar{F}/E$ are just equal to the characteristic values F'— a fact which can be ascertained directly with the help of the transformation equations. Taking, for instance, $\bar{F} = \sum\limits_{C'} \sum\limits_{C''} F_{C'C''} a_{C'}^* a_{C''}/E$, then, since $\sum\limits_{C''} F_{C'C''} a_{C''} = F' a_{C'}$, we get $\bar{F} = F' \sum\limits_{C'} a_{C'}^* a_{C'}/E = F'$.

The variational principle which we have just considered is a generalization of the variational principle for the energy, which was considered in the preceding chapter under the form $\delta \bar{H} = 0$, with $\bar{H} = \int \psi^{0*} H \psi^0 \, dV$ and $E = \int \psi^{0*} \psi^0 \, dV = 1$. It reduces to the preceding form if ψ^0 is replaced by the sum $\sum\limits_{C'} a_{C'} \psi_{x'C'}^0$, $\psi_{x'C'}^0$ being the characteristic functions of the operator $C_{(x)}$ which may be supposed to represent a Hamiltonian slightly different from that represented by the operator H or, more exactly, $H_{(x)}$.

This leads to a problem of the perturbation theory, which, from the geometrical point of view, outlined in this section, can be regarded as the problem of finding the symmetry axes of the quadric surface H, whose equation is referred to the symmetry axes of a slightly different quadric C.

More generally we can say that from this geometrical point of view *the quantum mechanics can be regarded as the analytical geometry of central quadric surfaces in the state-space*; the symmetry axes of each such surface specify, by their length, the characteristic values of the physical quantity represented by this surface, and, by their direction, the associated states; while the cosines between the symmetry axes of two different surfaces represent the probability amplitudes for a certain value of one quantity (or set of three quantities) when the other quantity (or set of three quantities) is known to have a given value.

In conclusion a few remarks should be added on the question of notations. Dirac and following him many other authors denote the elements of a matrix F_C by the symbol $(C'|F|C'')$ which is equivalent to the symbol $F_{C'C''}^0$ used in this chapter, and which has the advantage of being closely connected with the symbol $(F'|C')$ for the probability amplitudes $\psi_{F'C'}^0$. Using Dirac's notation, we can write the transformation equations connecting the matrices F_H and F_K in the following form:

$$(K'|F|K'') = \sum_{H'} \sum_{H''} (K'|H')(H'|F|H'')(H''|K''),$$

if the spectrum of H is discrete, or

$$(K'|F|K'') = \iint (K'|H')\, dH'\, (H'|F|H'')\, dH''\, (H''|K''),$$

if it is continuous.

The index ^{0} in our notation serves to indicate that the time, which is supposed not to appear in the equations of this chapter, is ignored. We shall take it into account in a later section.

Another remark refers to a type of vector notation applied by Dirac to vectors and tensors in the state-space and quite similar to that used in the ordinary three-dimensional vector and tensor analysis.

A state—in the quantum-mechanical sense—is specified by a vector, ψ, say, of unit length and of a definite direction in the state-space. The components of this vector with respect to a system of coordinates C may be denoted by $\psi_{C'}$. The same state can, however, be specified by the conjugate complex of ψ, which is a vector ψ^* with the components $\psi^*_{C'}$.

The sum $\sum\limits_{C'} \psi^*_{C'}\psi_{C'}$ or the integral $\int \psi^*_{C'}\psi_{C'}\, dC'$ which is the measure of the square of the common length of the vectors ψ^* and ψ will be denoted as their 'scalar product' $\psi^*\psi$. In a similar way the scalar product of two different vectors ψ_1 and ψ_2 referring to two different states will be denoted by $\psi^*_2 \psi_1$ or $\psi^*_1 \psi_2$, which means, in the coordinate representation, $\sum\limits_{C'} \psi^*_{2C'}\psi_{1C'}$ or $\sum\limits_{C'} \psi^*_{1C'}\psi_{2C'}$ (the sums being again replaced by integrals in the case of a continuous C-spectrum).

These expressions (which are conjugate complex with regard to each other) can be regarded, from the physical point of view, as the probability amplitudes for the simultaneous occurrence of the two states (a measure of the 'mutual compatibility' of the latter). If these states are alternative (mutually exclusive), the vectors ψ_1 and ψ_2 are mutually orthogonal, which means that $\psi^*_2 \psi_1 = \psi^*_1 \psi_2 = 0$.

Further, let F denote a tensor representing not a state, such as ψ, but a certain physical quantity (an 'observable' or 'dynamical variable' according to Dirac), with the components $F_{C'C''}$ along the axes (= states) of C (we are dropping for convenience the superscript zero). The sum $\sum\limits_{C'} F_{C'C''}\psi_{C''}$ (or integral $\int F_{C'C''}\psi_{C''}\, dC''$) can be considered as the C'-component of another vector, ϕ, say, specifying some state, in general different from ψ. This vector will be called *the product of the tensor F and the vector ψ* and denoted by $F\psi$ [so that $(F\psi)_{C'} = \sum\limits_{C''} F_{C'C''}\psi_{C''}$].

The conjugate complex of ϕ can be defined in a similar way as the product of F and ψ^* *taken in the inverse order*, i.e. by the formula

$\phi^* = \psi^* F$, which means, in the coordinate representation,

$$\phi_{C'}^* = (\psi^* F)_{C'} = \sum_{C''} \psi_{C''}^* F_{C''C'} \quad \left(\text{or } \int \psi_{C''}^* F_{C''C'}\, dC''\right).$$

This gives

$$\phi^*\psi = \sum_{C'} \phi_{C'}^* \psi_{C'} = \sum_{C'} (\psi^* F)_{C'} \psi_{C'} = \sum_{C'} \sum_{C''} \psi_{C''}^* F_{C''C'} \psi_{C'}$$

$$\left(\text{or } \iint \psi_{C''}^* F_{C''C'} \psi_{C'}\, dC' dC''\right),$$

which will be denoted simply as $\psi^* F \psi$.

We get further (taking for the sake of simplicity the case of a discrete C-spectrum)

$$\phi^*\phi = \sum_{C'} \phi_{C'}^* \phi_{C'} = \sum_{C'} \sum_{C''} \sum_{C'''} \psi_{C''}^* F_{C''C'} F_{C'C'''} \psi_{C'''}$$

or, since

$$\sum_{C'} F_{C''C'} F_{C'C'''} = (F^2)_{C''C'''},$$

we get

$$\phi^*\phi = \psi^* F^2 \psi.$$

The preceding formula is the simplest example of a 'tensor product'. The product of two tensors F and G taken in the order stated is defined as a tensor with the components

$$(FG)_{C''C'''} = \sum_{C'} F_{C''C'} G_{C'C'''} \quad \text{or} \quad \int F_{C''C'} G_{C'C'''}\, dC'.$$

This definition of tensor multiplication is identical with the definition of matrix multiplication if F and G are considered not as tensors but as matrices.

The matrix representation can also be applied to vectors such as ψ if we generalize the conception of a matrix by admitting matrices which consist not of a square array of numbers (elements, components) but of a rectangular array (with a different number of rows and columns) and, in particular, of a *linear array* with one row or one column only. If we wish to preserve the general multiplication law, i.e. that the product of two matrices shall be a matrix obtained by combining the *rows* of the first factor with the *columns* of the second, we must represent the vector ψ and its conjugate complex ψ^* by linear matrices of different kinds, the one, considered as the first factor, consisting of one row only and the second of one column only.

Taking the components of ψ and ψ^* along the C-axes as the elements of the matrices ψ_C and ψ_C^*, we shall put accordingly

$$\psi_C^* = \{\psi_{C'}^*, \psi_{C''}^*, \psi_{C'''}^*, \ldots\}$$

and

$$\psi_C = \left\{ \begin{matrix} \psi_{C'} \\ \psi_{C''} \\ \psi_{C'''} \\ \vdots \end{matrix} \right\},$$

which means that in multiplying two vectors or a vector and a tensor we must always start with the conjugate complex (ψ^*, ϕ^*) and finish with the original ones. From the matrix point of view we should write $\psi^\dagger$ (adjoint matrix) instead of ψ^*, for the matrix ψ^* defined above is obtained from the matrix ψ not only by taking the conjugate complex of its elements, but also by an interchange of the rows and columns (cf. § 16). With this convention the scalar product of two vector-matrices ψ and ϕ can be written in the form $\psi^\dagger\phi$ or $\phi^\dagger\psi$, while the symbols $\psi\phi^\dagger$ or $\phi\psi^\dagger$ have no meaning. Taking the components of $\psi^\dagger\phi$ in the usual way, we get

$$(\psi^\dagger\phi)_{mn} = \sum_{C'} \psi^\dagger_{mC'}\phi_{C'n},$$

which is equal to zero unless $m = 1$ (first row of $\psi^\dagger$) and $n = 1$ (first column of ϕ).

The product of a vector ψ and a tensor F must be represented accordingly in either of the two forms $F\psi$ or $\psi^\dagger F$, the former being a matrix of the same form as ψ and the latter a matrix of the same form as $\psi^\dagger$. The two matrices are, of course, adjoint with regard to each other, so that we can write

$$(\psi^\dagger F)^\dagger = F\psi,$$

which is quite natural since $F^\dagger = F$ (so long as F is a Hermitian matrix).

It should be mentioned finally that the linear matrices with the elements $\psi_{1C'} = \psi_{C'}$ can be replaced by 'square' matrices with the elements $\psi_{Q'C'}$ representing a set of vectors, which correspond to different values of Q', or, in other words, the cosines between the directions Q' and C'. Such matrices are not hermitian but unitary, i.e. satisfy the relation $\psi^\dagger = \psi^{-1}$ ($\psi^{-1}_{C'Q'} = \psi^*_{Q'C'}$). The preceding formulae, relating to the products of the type $\phi^\dagger\psi$ or $F\psi$, etc., remain valid with this interpretation of the ψ, i.e. not as vectors specifying states, but as cosines between two sets of axes specifying two sets of states and measuring the probability amplitudes of their coexistence. The transformation equations $\phi^0_{K'} = \sum a_{H'K'}\psi^0_{H'}$, can be written accordingly in the form $\phi^0_{x'K'} = \sum_{H'} \psi^0_{x'H'}a_{H'K'}$, or $\phi = \psi a$ (the order of the factors on the right side being opposite to that which corresponds to the product of ψ considered as a vector with a matrix representing a tensor).

V

PERTURBATION THEORY

19. Perturbation Theory not involving the Time (Method of Stationary States)

The exact determination of the wave functions $\psi^0_{x'H'} = (x'|H')$ which specify the motion of a particle in a complicated field of force is usually impossible on account of analytical difficulties. But even if these difficulties could be overcome, it would hardly be possible to use the results, and especially to visualize them, on account of their complicated character. Thus both for mathematical and physical reasons it is desirable, in the case of a complicated field of force, to use an approximative method of determining the functions ψ^0, starting with an exact determination of the latter for the motion in a simplified field of force, and introducing corrections to represent the effect of the 'perturbing forces', i.e. those forces which have been left out of account at the beginning.

The energy operator corresponding to the 'unperturbed', i.e. simplified, motion will be denoted by H ($= H_{(x)}$) and its characteristic functions by $\psi^0_{H'}$ ($= \psi^0_{x'H'}$). The energy operator corresponding to the actual or 'perturbed' motion will be denoted by K ($= K_{(x)}$) and its characteristic functions by $\phi^0_{K'}$ ($= \phi^0_{x'K'}$).

The difference $K - H = S$ will thus represent the additional or 'perturbation' energy; it is usually defined as the potential energy of the perturbing forces.

This perturbation energy must, of course, be regarded as 'small'. The exact meaning of this condition will become apparent as we develop the problem by the method of the perturbation theory.

As already mentioned, the perturbation theory (so far as H and K do not involve the time) amounts to a transformation of all physical quantities, considered as matrices, from the point of view of H to the point of view of K, which is supposed to be but slightly different from H, so that the actual calculations can be carried out by means of the method of successive approximations.

The principle of this method consists in regarding all quantities involving S, for instance the matrix elements $S_{H'H''}$, as small quantities of the first order and splitting up the exact equations into a chain of approximate equations containing small quantities of the same order.

We shall first assume that H has a discrete spectrum and that the *unperturbed motion is not degenerate*, the characteristic values of H being thus sufficient for the complete specification of the corresponding states.

The fundamental part of our problem will consist in the transformation of the matrix K_H to the diagonal form K_K and in the determination of the transformation matrix a, according to the general equation

$$K_K = a^\dagger K_H a \qquad (a^\dagger = a^{-1}), \tag{144}$$

or
$$K_H a = a K_K, \tag{144a}$$

that is [cf. (123), § 16],

$$\sum_{H''} K^0_{H'H''} a_{H''K'''} = K''' a_{H'K'''}. \tag{144b}$$

We must, first of all, fix the 'zero approximation' which corresponds to $S = 0$, i.e. to the actual coincidence of K and H. Assuming the identical states to be labelled by the letters K or H *with the same number of dashes* ($K' = H'$, $K'' = H''$, $K''' = H'''$, etc.), we can put, in this case,
$$a = \delta,$$

that is,
$$a_{H'K'''} = \delta_{H'K'''}, \tag{145}$$

where δ is the mixed unit matrix with the diagonal elements $\delta_{H'K'} = \delta_{H''K''} = 1$ (all the others being equal to zero).

Equations (144 b) reduce, in this case, to

$$K^0_{H'H'''} = K''' a_{H'K'''},$$

that is, to
$$K^0_{H'H'} = K', \tag{145a}$$

which is the same thing as $K' = H'$, since $K_{H'H'} = H_{H'H'} = H'$.

We shall now consider the actual case in which $S \neq 0$, assuming that there still exists in this case a one-to-one correspondence between the unperturbed states H', H'', H''',... and the perturbed states K', K'', K''',... —in the sense that the states labelled by the letter K or H with the same number of dashes coincide with each other when the perturbation energy S tends to zero.

We shall put accordingly

$$K_{K'K'} = K' = H' + \Delta H', \tag{146}$$

where $\Delta H'$ denotes the change of the energy-levels due to the perturbation, and
$$a = \delta + \Delta a, \quad \text{i.e.} \quad a_{H'K''} = \delta_{H'K''} + \Delta a_{H'K'}, \tag{146a}$$

the corrections $\Delta a_{H'K'}$ being assumed to be small (compared with 1). We have further

$$K_H = H_H + S_H, \quad \text{i.e.} \quad K^0_{H'H''} = H^0_{H'H''} + S^0_{H'H''}. \tag{146b}$$

Substituting these expressions in equations (144 b) and taking into account that $H^0_{H'H''} = H'\delta_{H'H''}$, we get

$$H'(\delta_{H'K'''}+\Delta a_{H'K'''}) + \sum_{H''} S^0_{H'H''}\delta_{H''K'''} + \sum_{H''} S^0_{H'H''}\Delta a_{H''K'''}$$

$$= (H'''+\Delta H''')(\delta_{H'K'''}+\Delta a_{H'K'''}).$$

Since $\delta_{H''K'''} = 0$ unless $H'' = K'''$ when it is equal to 1, and $(H'''-H')\delta_{H'K'''} = 0$ both when $K''' = K'$ (because then $H''' = H'$) and when $K''' \neq K'$, we get

$$S^0_{H'H'''} + \sum_{H''} S^0_{H'H''}\Delta a_{H''K'''}$$
$$= \Delta H'''(\delta_{H'K'''}+\Delta a_{H'K'''}) + (H'''-H')\Delta a_{H'K'''}. \quad (147)$$

These equations can be solved by successive approximations, if we assume that the quantities $S_{H'H''}$ (i.e. the matrix elements of the perturbation energy 'from the point of view' of the unperturbed energy) are small quantities of the same (first) order of magnitude and expand $\Delta H'$ and Δa in series of the form

$$\left.\begin{array}{c} \Delta H' = \Delta_1 H' + \Delta_2 H' + \ldots \\ \Delta a = \Delta_1 a + \Delta_2 a + \ldots \end{array}\right\}, \quad (147\,\text{a})$$

where $\Delta_n H'$ and $\Delta_n a$ are corrections of the nth order (that is, of the same order of magnitude as the nth power of the elements of S_H).

Substituting (147 a) in (147) and dropping terms of the second and higher orders of magnitude, we obtain as a *first approximation* the equations

$$S^0_{H'H'''} = \Delta_1 H'''\delta_{H'K'''} + (H'''-H')\Delta_1 a_{H'K'''}. \quad (148)$$

Putting $K''' = K'$ (and consequently $H''' = H'$), we get

$$\Delta_1 H' = S^0_{H'H'}. \quad (148\,\text{a})$$

This formula determines, to the first approximation, the change of the energy-levels produced by the perturbation.

If K''' is different from K' (and consequently H''' is different from H'), equation (148) reduces to

$$S^0_{H'H'''} = (H'''-H')\Delta_1 a_{H'K'''},$$

that is,

$$\Delta_1 a_{H'K'''} = -\frac{S^0_{H'H'''}}{H'-H'''}, \quad (148\,\text{b})$$

giving the first-order expressions for the transformation coefficients $a_{H'K'''}$.

If we preserve in (147) terms of the second order, dropping terms of the third and higher orders, and take account of the first-order equations

(148), we get the second-order equations:

$$\sum_{H''} S^0_{H'H''} \Delta_1 a_{H''K'''}$$
$$= \Delta_2 H''' \delta_{H'K'''} + \Delta_1 H''' \Delta_1 a_{H'K'''} + (H''' - H') \Delta_2 a_{H'K'''}. \quad (149)$$

It should be remarked that these equations, as well as the equations of the succeeding orders, can be obtained from (147) by substituting the expressions (147 a) and dropping all terms with the exception of those of the order in question.

Putting $K''' = K'$ (and $H''' = H'$) in (149), we get

$$\sum_{H''} S^0_{H'H''} \Delta_1 a_{H''K'} = \Delta_2 H' + \Delta_1 H' \Delta_1 a_{H'K'},$$

or, on account of the relation (148 a),

$$\Delta_2 H' = \sum_{H'' \neq H'} S^0_{H'H''} \Delta_1 a_{H''K'}.$$

Substituting the expressions (148 b) with K''' replaced by K' and H' by H'', we get

$$\Delta_2 H' = - \sum_{H'' \neq H'} \frac{S^0_{H'H''} S^0_{H''H'}}{H'' - H'} = \sum_{H'' \neq H'} \frac{|S^0_{H'H''}|^2}{H' - H''}. \quad (149\,a)$$

With K''' different from K', equation (149) reduces to

$$\sum_{H''} S_{H'H''} \Delta_1 a_{H''K'''} = \Delta_1 H''' \Delta_1 a_{H'K'''} + (H''' - H') \Delta_2 a_{H'K'''},$$

giving, with the help of (148 a) and (148 b), the following expression for the second-order correction in the coefficients a:

$$\Delta_2 a_{H'K'''} = \sum_{H'' \neq H'''} \frac{S^0_{H'H''} S^0_{H''H'''}}{(H' - H''')(H'' - H''')} - \frac{S^0_{H'H'''} S^0_{H'''H'''}}{(H' - H''')^2},$$

or $$\Delta_2 a_{H'K'''} = \sum_{H'' \neq H', H'''} \frac{S^0_{H'H''} S^0_{H''H'''}}{(H' - H''')(H'' - H''')}. \quad (149\,b)$$

In carrying out the summation over H'' we must drop the term $H'' = H'''$ (as well as $H'' = H'$) because the formula

$$\Delta_1 a_{H''K'''} = - \frac{S^0_{H''H'''}}{H'' - H'''}$$

holds for the case $H'' \neq H'''$ only, while for $H'' = H'''$ we have

$$\Delta_1 a_{H'''K'''} = 0. \quad (150)$$

This equation can be obtained from the normalization condition which must be satisfied by the matrix a, namely,

$$\sum_{H'} a_{H'K'} a^*_{H'K''} = 1.$$

Putting $a_{H'K''} = \delta_{H'K''} + \Delta a_{H'K'}$, then since $\delta_{H'K''} = 1$ when $H' = H''$ and 0 when $H' \neq H''$, we get

$$\Delta a_{H''K''} + \Delta a^*_{H''K''} + \sum_{H'} \Delta a_{H'K''} \Delta a^*_{H'K''} = 0, \quad (150\,a)$$

whence it follows that

$$\Delta_1 a_{H'K''} + \Delta_1 a^*_{H'K''} = 0.$$

Since the diagonal elements of the matrix a must be real $(a^*_{H'K''} = a_{H'K''})$, we have

$$\Delta_1 a_{H'K''} = 0.$$

The formula (149) likewise leaves undetermined the diagonal elements of $\Delta_2 a_{H'K'''}$. They can be determined, however, with the help of the equation (150 a) or rather the equation

$$2\Delta_2 a_{H'K''} + \sum_{H''} \Delta_1 a_{H'K''} \Delta_1 a^*_{H'K''} = 0,$$

which is obtained from it as a second approximation (dropping all terms save those of the second order) and which, in conjunction with (148 b), gives

$$\Delta_2 a_{H'K''} = -\frac{1}{2} \sum_{H'' \neq H'} \frac{|S^0_{H'H''}|}{(H'-H'')^2}. \tag{150 b}$$

The formula (150) follows in a quite obvious manner from the geometrical interpretation of the coefficients $a_{H'K'}$ as the cosines of the angles between the symmetry axes of the quadric surfaces representing (in the state-space) the energy H and the energy K. Since, by definition, H and K must differ very little from each other, the corresponding axes H' and K' (or H'' and K'', etc.) must have approximately the same direction, while the non-corresponding axes (H' and K'') must be nearly perpendicular to each other. Denoting the angle between H' and K' by $\alpha_{H'K'}$ and considering it as a small quantity of the first order, we get

$$a_{H'K'} = \cos \alpha_{H'K'} = 1 - \frac{(\alpha_{H'K'})^2}{2} + \dots,$$

which means that the first-order correction $\Delta_1 a_{H'K'}$ vanishes, while $\Delta_2 a_{H'K'} = -\frac{1}{2}(\alpha_{H'K'})^2$. Comparing this with (150 b), we can put

$$(\alpha_{H'K'})^2 = \sum_{H'' \neq H'} \frac{|S^0_{H'H''}|^2}{(H'-H'')^2}. \tag{151}$$

This formula shows that the angles between the corresponding symmetry axes of H and K are of the same order of magnitude as the ratios of the matrix elements of the perturbation energy S with respect to different H-states to the difference between the characteristic values of H for these states.

The same result, in a still simpler form, is obtained from a consideration of the first approximation values of the coefficients $a_{H'K''} = \Delta a_{H'K''}$ ($K'' \neq K'$). Putting $a_{H'K''} = \cos \alpha_{H'K''}$ and $\alpha_{H'K''} = \frac{1}{2}\pi + \Delta\alpha_{H'K''}$, where $\Delta\alpha_{H'K''}$ denotes a small angle, we get

$$a_{H'K''} = -\sin \Delta\alpha_{H'K''} \cong -\Delta_1 \alpha_{H'K''},$$

whence, according to (148 b),

$$\Delta_1 \alpha_{H'K'} = \frac{S^0_{H'H''}}{H'-H''}. \tag{151 a}$$

This angle should not be confused with the angle through which the axis H'' has to be rotated in order to coincide with K'' and which is equal to $\alpha_{H'K'} = \Delta \alpha_{H''K'}$. The comparison of equations (151) and (151 a) shows that the latter angle can be regarded as the (geometrical) sum of mutually perpendicular angular displacements of the type $\Delta \alpha_{H'K'}$ for different values of H' ($\neq H''$). In other words, the angular displacement $\Delta \alpha_{H'K'}$ can be considered as the component along the H'-axis of the elementary rotation $\alpha_{H''K'}$. We thus obtain the law of the vector composition of elementary rotations about different (mutually perpendicular) axes, which is a generalization of the corresponding law for ordinary three-dimensional space.

In the latter case, an infinitesimal rotation of the coordinate system can be specified by a certain vector $\boldsymbol{\omega}$, which determines the (apparent) change of a fixed vector $\mathbf{r}$ by means of the formula $\Delta \mathbf{r} = -\boldsymbol{\omega} \times \mathbf{r}$. So far as the first approximation is concerned, *the components of $\boldsymbol{\omega}$ and $\Delta \mathbf{r}$ along the old and new axes can be identified with each other*. Written in components along the old axes, the preceding formula gives the following equations:

$$\Delta x_1 = \xi_1 - x_1 = -\omega_2 x_3 + \omega_3 x_2$$
$$\Delta x_2 = \xi_2 - x_2 = -\omega_3 x_1 + \omega_1 x_3$$
$$\Delta x_3 = \xi_3 - x_3 = -\omega_1 x_2 + \omega_2 x_1$$

which can be considered as a particular or rather as a limiting case of an orthogonal transformation for the case when the two systems (S and Σ) differ very little from each other. Putting

$$\omega_1 = \alpha_{23} = -\alpha_{32}, \qquad \omega_2 = \alpha_{31} = -\alpha_{13}, \qquad \omega_3 = \alpha_{12} = -\alpha_{21},$$

we can rewrite the preceding equations in the form

$$\Delta x_{n'} = -\sum \alpha_{n''n'} x_{n''}. \tag{152}$$

Comparing equations (152) with the exact transformation equations

$$\xi_{\nu'} = \sum_{n''} a_{n''\nu'} x_{n''},$$

we see that they can be obtained from the latter if we put

$$a_{n'\nu'} = \delta_{n'n''} - \alpha_{n'n''}, \qquad \xi_{\nu'} = \xi_{n'},$$

where ν' and n' denote corresponding axes of the new and old system, i.e. such axes as were initially coincident. The angles $\alpha_{n'\nu'} = \alpha_{n'n'}$ must approximately vanish for the normalizing and orthogonality relations to be satisfied.

We thus see that an infinitesimal orthogonal transformation in ordinary space can be treated as an infinitesimal rotation of the original coordinate systems, specified both with regard to the direction of the rotation axis and the angle of rotation about it by the (infinitely small) vector $\boldsymbol{\omega}$ with the components ω_1, ω_2, ω_3, or by the 'antisymmetrical tensor' α with the components $\alpha_{n'n''} = -\alpha_{n''n'}$, referred to the original axes.

These results can easily be extended to the infinitesimal orthogonal transformations in the 'state-space', corresponding to a transition from the symmetry axes of the quadric surface representing the unperturbed energy H, to the symmetry axes of the quadric representing the perturbed energy $K = H + S$.

Leaving the perturbation energy S unspecified, we can represent the (apparent) change of the components of any vector ψ due to the small rotation of the coordinate axes by an equation wholly similar to (152), namely,

$$(\Delta\psi)_{H'} = - \sum_{H''} \alpha_{H''H'}\psi_{H''}, \qquad (152\,\text{a})$$

where α denotes an 'anti-Hermitian' tensor (which is a generalization of the antisymmetric one) satisfying the condition

$$\alpha_{H'H''} = -\alpha_{H''H'}^*, \qquad (152\,\text{b})$$

or $\qquad\qquad \alpha^\dagger = -\alpha.$

These results can be obtained in the same way as in the three-dimensional case from the exact transformation equation,

$$\psi_{K'} = \sum_{H''} a_{H''K'}\psi_{H''},$$

by putting $\psi_{K'} = \psi_{H'} + \Delta\psi_{H'}$ and $a_{H''K'} = \delta_{H''H'} - \alpha_{H''H'}$, where the α denote small quantities of the first order. Substituting the latter expressions in the orthogonality and normalizing conditions,

$$\sum_{K'} a_{H''K'} a_{H'''K'}^* = \delta_{H''H'''},$$

and neglecting second-order terms, we get, if the summation index K' is replaced by H',

$$\sum_{H'} \delta_{H''H'}\alpha_{H'''H'}^* + \sum_{H'} \alpha_{H''H'}\delta_{H'''H'} = 0,$$

that is, $\qquad\qquad \alpha_{H'''H''}^* + \alpha_{H''H'''} = 0,$

which is equivalent to (152 b).

As a matter of fact, from (148 b) and because $\alpha_{H''H'} = -\Delta_1 a_{H''K'}$, we have

$$\alpha_{H''H'} = \frac{S_{H''H'}^0}{H'' - H'}, \qquad (152\,\text{c})$$

so that the condition (152 b) is actually satisfied.

It should be mentioned that in the case of a generalized space with more than three dimensions an antisymmetrical tensor is no longer equivalent to a vector.† It is therefore impossible to represent the rotation of the quadric surface H into such a position that its axes coincide (in direction but not in length!) with those of the quadric K by means of a *vector* corresponding to ω, or to specify the rotation by its components along the different *axes* of H. Instead of using the coordinate axes, we can, however, use for the same purpose the *coordinate planes* (in the case of ordinary space the number of these planes is equal to the number of axes, which explains the possibility of representing the former by the latter). The quantities $\alpha_{H''H'}$ can be interpreted as the projections of the rotation $H \to K$ on the planes (H'', H'). The angle through which H'' must be rotated to coincide with K'' is given by the equation

$$\alpha^2_{H''K''} = \sum_{H'} |\alpha_{H''H'}|^2,$$

which is similar to the ordinary equation for the composition of elementary rotations considered as vectors (for instance, $\omega^2 = \omega_1^2 + \omega_2^2 + \omega_3^2$) because in the preceding equation one of the axes (H'') remains fixed and the summation over the different planes passing through it is equivalent to a summation over all the axes different from H''.

The expressions (152 c) for the elementary rotations, as well as the corresponding (first-order) corrections for the energy values $\Delta H' = K' - H'$, can be obtained in a somewhat simpler way than before by starting from the expressions (152 a) and using the equations $H\psi_{H'} = H'\psi_{H'}$ and $K\phi_{K'} = K'\phi_{K'}$.

Putting in the latter equation $\phi_{K'} = \psi_{H'} + \Delta\psi_{H'}$, $K' = H' + \Delta H'$, and $K = H + S$, we have

$$H\psi_{H'} + S\psi_{H'} + H\Delta\psi_{H'} + S\Delta\psi_{H'} = H'\psi_{H'} + \Delta H'\psi_{H'} + H'\Delta\psi_{H'} + \Delta H'\Delta\psi_{H'},$$

or dropping terms of the second order of smallness (i.e. the products $S\Delta\psi_{H'}$ and $\Delta H'\Delta\psi'$):

$$S\psi_{H'} + H\Delta\psi_{H'} = \Delta H'\psi_{H'} + H'\Delta\psi_{H'}. \tag{153}$$

Now by the definition of matrix elements we have

$$S\psi_{H'} = \sum_{H''} S^0_{H''H'}\psi_{H''}.$$

On the other hand we get, according to (152 a),

$$H\Delta\psi_{H'} = -\sum_{H''} \alpha_{H''H'} H\psi_{H''} = -\sum_{H''} \alpha_{H''H'} H''\psi_{H''}.$$

---

† If n is the number of dimensions, then the number of different non-vanishing components of an antisymmetric tensor is equal to $\frac{1}{2}n(n-1)$, which is equal to the number (n) of components of a vector only when $n = 3$.

Thus (153) can be written in the form

$$\sum_{H''} (S^0_{H''H'} - H''\alpha_{H''H'})\psi_{H''} = \Delta H'\psi_{H'} - H'\sum_{H''}\alpha_{H''H'}\psi_{H''},$$

or

$$\sum_{H''} [S^0_{H''H'} - (H''-H')\alpha_{H''H'}]\psi_{H''} = \Delta H'\psi_{H'} = \sum_{H''}\delta_{H''H'}\Delta H''\psi_{H''}. \quad (153\,\text{a})$$

Equating the coefficients of $\psi_{H''}$ on both sides, we get

$$\left.\begin{array}{c} S^0_{H'H'} = \Delta H' \\ S^0_{H''H'} = (H''-H')\alpha_{H''H'} \end{array}\right\}, \quad (153\,\text{b})$$

in agreement with the results previously found.

The fact that equation (153 a) splits up into equations (153 b) for the coefficients of the separate $\psi_{H''}$ is due, as already pointed out, (Part I, § 18), to the *mutual orthogonality* of the functions $\psi_{H''}$ (as functions of the coordinates x, y, z). If we have an equation of the type $\sum_{H'} a_{H'}\psi_{H'} = \sum_{H'} b_{H'}\psi_{H'}$ which holds identically (i.e. for all values of x, y, z), then multiplying it by $\psi^*_{H''}$ and integrating over x, y, z, we get $a_{H''} = b_{H''}$, all the other terms vanishing.

We have assumed, hitherto, that the unperturbed problem was 'non-degenerate', i.e. that all the characteristic values of H were different. The essential character of this assumption is clearly seen from the fact that the equations $a_{H''H'} = \dfrac{S^0_{H''H'}}{H''-H'}$, become meaningless (unless $S^0_{H''H'}$ vanishes) when $H'' = H'$, while the two states $\psi_{H''}$ and $\psi_{H'}$ remain different. It is, moreover, impossible to specify the different states, as has been done so far, by the value of the energy alone. We shall therefore add to it some other quantity C, which commutes with it (i.e. represents a constant of the motion) and which can be supposed to have different values for different states which have the same energy.

The alterations in the treatment of a perturbation problem which are necessitated by the presence of degeneracy in the unperturbed problem can best be understood with the help of the geometrical interpretation. If the energy H is represented as a quadric surface in the state-space, with symmetry axes whose lengths are inversely proportional to the corresponding characteristic values of H, then degeneracy means that a few of these axes have the same length, the corresponding section of the surface, comprising all the equal axes, being 'circle-like' A degeneracy of this sort is met with in ordinary analytical geometry in the case of an ellipsoid with two or three equal axes, the ellipsoid degenerating into a spheroid or into a sphere.

So long as the surface is not degenerate, the directions of its symmetry axes are perfectly definite. Degeneracy involves an arbitrariness in the choice of the symmetry axes within the 'circle-like' section, any orthogonal system of axes being appropriate. It may be mentioned that this corresponds to the „physical indeterminateness of the corresponding states and to the necessity of specifying them with the help of some other quantity, C say, which can also be imagined to be represented by a certain quadric surface. The commutability of H and C means, as we know, that the symmetry axes of the corresponding surfaces have the same directions; if one of them has a 'circular' section its axes within this section can be identified with those of the other.

Let us assume that the surface representing the energy K of the perturbed motion is non-degenerate. We shall then find two types of relations between its symmetry axes and those of H. So long as the latter are intrinsically determined—i.e. apart from the circular sections —the axes K' must differ but very little from the corresponding axes H', as has been supposed hitherto. So far, however, as a set of equal H-axes is concerned, a set contained within a circular section and fixed more or less arbitrarily, the angles between them and the set of K-axes corresponding to this section *need not be small*. The process of successive approximations, which was based on the assumption that all the angles $\alpha_{H'K'''}$ were small, must therefore, in general, lead to wrong results. That it does lead to wrong results is clear from the formula (152 c) which gives an infinitely large value for $\alpha_{H''H'}$ if the difference $H''-H'$ (for two different states) vanishes, *unless* $S^0_{H''H'}$ *also vanishes*.

It is thus clear that before starting on the process of successive approximations based upon the assumption of the smallness of the angles, one must make them actually small by transforming the sets of axes which refer to 'circular' sections in such a way that they approximately coincide with the corresponding set of K-axes. ˡ This 'preliminary' or zero-order transformation can be carried out for each circular section independently, i.e. by dropping from the general equation of the K-quadric, or rather from the equations of the $K_H \to K_K$ transformation, all the terms which connect different circular sections with each other (or with individual axes, if any). In fact the transformation coefficients $a_{H'K'''}$ and $a_{H''K'''}$, where H' and H'' refer to one circular section and K''' to another 'nearly' circular section, must be very small of the first order (the two sections being 'nearly' perpendicular to each other) and can therefore be neglected compared with the coefficients $a_{H'K''}$ or $a_{H''K''}$, where K'' refers to the nearly circular section of K which approximately coincides with the circular section of H containing the axes H' and H''.

It will be convenient to alter our previous notation and to denote the r' axes of a circular section corresponding to the value $H = H'$ by $C_1', C_2',...,C_{r'}'$. The r' axes of the corresponding nearly circular section of K will be denoted accordingly by $K_1', K_2',..., K_{r'}'$. There is, in general, no one-to-one correspondence between these r' K'-axes and the r' C'-axes. They form two different orthogonal systems and the preliminary transformation which we are looking for is precisely the transformation $C' \rightarrow K'$ carried out for each circular section separately.

The exact equations of the transformation $H \rightarrow K$ are thus split up into a set of 'zero-order' equations of the following form:

$$\sum_{n=1}^{r'} K_{C_m' C_n'} a_{C_n' K'} = K' a_{C_n' K'}, \qquad (154)$$

where $m = 1, 2, 3,..., r'$.

For each of the 'multiple' values of H corresponding to r' different states, we thus get a system of r' linear homogeneous equations involving states *of this set only*. These equations are quite similar to the general transformation equations for the case of no degeneracy,

$$\sum_{H''} K_{H'H''}^0 a_{H''K'''} = K''' a_{H'K'''},$$

differing from them solely by the fact that they refer to a *finite* number of states—a fact which makes it possible to solve them exactly without the use of the method of successive approximation (whose application has to be postponed).

Putting $K = H + S$ and $K' = H' + \Delta H'$ in (154), then since $H_{C_m' C_n'} = H' \delta_{mn}$, we get

$$\sum_{n=1}^{r'} S_{C_m' C_n'}^0 a_{C_n' K'} = \Delta H' a_{C_n' K'}. \qquad (154\,\text{a})$$

For the sake of simplicity, we shall rewrite this equation, or rather the set of r' equations, in the form

$$\sum_{n=1}^{r'} S_{mn}^0 a_n = \Delta H' a_m, \qquad (154\,\text{b})$$

where m is an abbreviation for C_m' and the index K' is dropped. Their compatibility condition

$$\begin{vmatrix} S_{11}^0 - \Delta H' & S_{12}^0 & . & . & . & S_{1r'}^0 \\ S_{21}^0 & S_{22}^0 - \Delta H' & . & . & . & S_{2r'}^0 \\ . & . & . & . & . & . \\ S_{r'1}^0 & S_{r'2}^0 & . & . & . & S_{r'r'}^0 - \Delta H' \end{vmatrix} = 0 \qquad (154\,\text{c})$$

gives r' values for the 'additional' energy $\Delta H'$, which are, in general, different from each other. This is expressed by saying that the perturbation splits up each multiple energy-level H' into a number (r') of different sub-levels $K' = H' + \Delta H'_1,\ H' + \Delta H'_2, ..., H' + \Delta H'_r$.

To each value of $\Delta H'$, $\Delta H'_s$ say, there corresponds a set of values of the r' coefficients a_n:

$$a_{ns} = a_{1s},\ a_{2s},\ ...,\ a_{r's}.$$

As in the general case, each of these sets must be normalized to 1, the different sets being orthogonal to each other. We thus get for each r'-fold value of the unperturbed energy H' a *unitary transformation matrix* a of order r', which serves to transform the original r' functions $\psi_{C'_1}, \psi_{C'_2}, ..., \psi_{C'_r}$, associated with the energy-level H' into new functions $\psi'_{K'_1}, \psi'_{K'_2}, ..., \psi'_{K'_r}$, associated with the different sub-levels into which these levels are split up. Using the one-row matrix notation for the two sets of functions, we can write the relation between them in the form

$$\psi' = a\psi \quad \text{or} \quad \psi'^\dagger = \psi^\dagger a^\dagger.$$

The preceding results are identical with those obtained in Chap. II, § 9, by means of the variational method.

It should be understood that the functions ψ' do not represent a set of K-states, but another degenerate set of H-states which only approximate to the corresponding K-states. Starting with these functions, it is possible, in the usual way, to obtain higher approximations. It is important to note that the first approximation values for the energy are determined, according to (154 c), in conjunction with the 'zero approximation' for the characteristic functions.

It can easily be shown that the H-states specified by the new functions ψ' are such that the matrix of the perturbation energy S with respect to them is diagonal. This follows from the fact that equations (154 a) are of the same form as the equations for the transformation of the matrix K_H to the diagonal form K_K, K being replaced by S, K' by $\Delta H'$, and the whole quadric K by its 'nearly circular' section. Denoting the transformed matrix of the perturbation energy (for the r' states ψ') by S', we have

$$S' = a^{-1}Sa = a^\dagger Sa.$$

The diagonal elements of S' are equal to the values of $\Delta H'$ for the corresponding states, so that we can put

$$S'_{K'_s K'_s} = \Delta H'_s,$$

which is exactly of the same form as equation (148 a), referring to the case in which there is no degeneracy.

These equations have a very simple physical meaning, which can be expressed by saying that *the additional energy due to perturbing forces is equal, in the first approximation, to the average value of the perturbation energy S for the unperturbed motion.*† When there is no degeneracy, the latter is specified unambiguously by a function $\psi_{H'}$ referring to one definite state. In the presence of degeneracy these unperturbed states have to be defined by means of the preliminary transformation, and are, in general, different from the original states.

We are now in a position to formulate the conditions under which a perturbation can be treated as weak. This weakness must obviously correspond to the smallness of the angles between the symmetry axes of the surfaces K and H and also to a smallness of the difference between the lengths of these axes. The 'circular' sections of H corresponding to degeneracy need not be taken into account, since the directions of the axes lying within them remains arbitrary and can always be adjusted to be close to those of the corresponding section of K.

Now we have seen that, to a first approximation, the angles $\alpha_{H'K'}$ are equal to $S^{0}_{H'H''}/(H'-H'')$ and the differences $K_{K'K'}-H_{H'H'}=K'-H'$ are equal to $S^{0}_{H'H'}$. It follows from this that the perturbation can be considered as weak if the matrix elements of the perturbation energy S with respect to different values of H are small compared with the difference between these values, and the diagonal elements are small compared with the corresponding values of H.

The smallness of S in this sense does not exclude the possibility that S, considered as a function of the coordinates of the particle (i.e. in the classical sense), should become very large and even infinite at certain points or regions. This makes the range of applicability of the wave-mechanical perturbation theory infinitely broader than that of the classical mechanics, which is restricted by the condition that S should be small compared with H' at all points of the unperturbed path.

20. Extension of the Preceding Theory to the Case of 'Relative Degeneracy' and Continuous Spectra; Effect of Perturbation on Various Physical Quantities.

In many non-degenerate problems we meet with the case of a perturbation which cannot be described as weak—in the above sense—with

---

† It should be mentioned that the same result holds in the perturbation theory of classical mechanics, the average value of S being defined here as the average value with respect to the time.

regard to pairs of (unperturbed) states belonging to certain sets, while it remains weak with regard to pairs of states belonging to different sets. This means that the matrix elements of S with respect to the different states of the same set are large—or at least not small—compared with the energy differences between these states, while the matrix elements of S with respect to states belonging to any two different sets are small compared with the corresponding energy differences. In the limiting case when the energy differences between the states of the same set vanish, we get back to the 'degenerate' problem considered before. It is plain, however, that the same method can be applied approximately when these energy-differences do not exactly vanish but are small compared with the corresponding matrix elements of S, so that without sensible error the (unperturbed) energies of the states in question can be identified with each other.

This serves to show that the notion of 'degeneracy' can be visualized as a *relative* one, from the point of view of the perturbation energy S which we are interested in, the 'absolute' degeneracy which has been considered hitherto forming but the limiting case of this relative degeneracy. If, for instance, S contains a continuously variable parameter (an electric or magnetic field, say), we can pass, by steadily increasing it, from a practically non-degenerate problem to a practically degenerate one, the degeneracy extending over certain sets of states whose energy-differences become small, as S increases, with respect to the corresponding matrix elements of S, while the matrix elements of the same function remain small compared with the energy-differences between states of different sets.†

We shall assume that such a subdivision of the various unperturbed states into relatively narrow sets, which lie wide apart from each other on the energy scale, is possible, and shall denote these states as *multiplets*. When the perturbation energy (defined by the value of its matrix elements with respect to the corresponding states) is small compared with the distance between the different multiplets and not small (without necessarily being large) compared with the 'widths' of the separate multiplets, the perturbation theory given in the preceding section is no longer applicable, and must be replaced by a more general method.

This generalized perturbation method (which has been pointed out by Lennard-Jones and by Jones) is extremely simple and consists in

† A typical example of this condition is found in the transition from a weak to a strong magnetic field in the theory of the Zeeman effect (or Paschen-Back effect).

splitting up the exact system of the transformation equations

$$\sum_{H''} K^0_{H'H''} a_{H''K'''} = K''' a_{H'K'''}$$

into a number of approximate systems, referring to the separate multiplets and obtained from the above equations by *confining the summation over H'' for each value of H' to such states only as belong to the same multiplet as H'*.

This is exactly what we have done before in writing down the equations (154) which refer to the limiting case of absolute degeneracy. They are applicable, however, just as well to the more general case of a relative degeneracy if the letters $C'_1, C'_2,..., C'_{r'}$ are used to denote the states of the same 'multiplet', with energy-values $H'_1, H'_2,..., H'_{r'}$ lying close to a certain value H' and far away from the energy values, specifying all the other unperturbed states. To prove this we need but note the fact that the matrix elements of the total energy K with respect to states of different sets are relatively small and can therefore be neglected compared with those which refer to the same set (multiplet).

In the geometrical representation of the unperturbed and the perturbed states as the axes of the quadric surfaces H and K in the statespace, a multiplet corresponds to a 'nearly' circular section of the former. So long as each such section is nearly parallel to a certain also nearly circular section of the K-surface, we have to deal with a perturbation which can be considered as weak with regard to the different multiplets. It can be, however, at the same time strong with regard to the states of the same multiplet, if the symmetry axes of the corresponding nearly circular sections of H and K have entirely different directions. A one-to-one correspondence between the unperturbed states of each multiplet and the perturbed ones cannot be traced in this case, just as in the case of an absolute degeneracy. The difference between the two cases lies only in the fact that in the former case the unperturbed states are fixed unambiguously, while in the latter they are represented by a perfectly arbitrary set of mutually perpendicular axes in the corresponding exactly circular section of the quadric H.

As has just been mentioned, the equations (154) still hold for the case of the 'relative degeneracy' if the letters $C'_1,..., C'_{r'}$ serve to distinguish the states of a multiplet belonging to neighbouring values of the energy $H'_1,..., H'_{r'}$. The equations (154 a) or (154 b) are, however, not applicable to the general case, for we must take into account the differences between the various 'sub-levels' H'_n ($n = 1,...,r'$). To do this we need only replace $\Delta H'$ in (154 a) by $\Delta H'_m = K' - H'_m$, which gives, in the notation of (154 b),

$$\sum_{n=1}^{r'} S^0_{mn} a_n = \Delta H'_m a_m \qquad (155)$$

or

$$\sum_{n=1}^{r'} S^0_{mn} a_n = (\Delta \bar{H}' - \Delta \bar{H}'_m) a_m, \qquad (155\,a)$$

where $\Delta \bar{H}' = K' - \bar{H}'$ and $\Delta \bar{H}'_m = \bar{H}' - H'_m$,

$\bar{H}'$ denoting some average of the r' values H'_1, H'_2,..., $H'_{r'}$. The compatibility condition of the equations (155 a)

$$\begin{vmatrix} S^0_{11} + \Delta \bar{H}'_1 - \Delta \bar{H}' & S^0_{12} & . & . & S^0_{1r'} \\ S^0_{21} & S^0_{22} + \Delta \bar{H}'_2 - \Delta \bar{H}' & . & . & S^0_{2r'} \\ . & . & . & . & . \\ S^0_{r'1} & S^0_{r'2} & . & . & S^0_{r'r'} + \Delta \bar{H}'_{r'} - \Delta \bar{H}' \end{vmatrix} = 0 \qquad (155\,b)$$

differs from (154 c) by the additional terms $\Delta \bar{H}'_m$ in the diagonal elements of the determinant, and leads as before to r' (in general different) values of the perturbed energy $K' = \bar{H}' + \Delta \bar{H}'$. If the non-diagonal terms of the determinant are sufficiently small it reduces to the product of the diagonal terms leading to the expressions $\Delta \bar{H}' = S^0_{nn} + \Delta \bar{H}'_n$ or $\Delta H'_n = S^0_{nn}$ which have been obtained in the preceding section for the case of no degeneracy. If, on the contrary, the terms $\Delta \bar{H}'_m$ or rather $H'_m - H'_n$ are small compared with S^0_{mn}, equation (155 b) practically reduces to the equation (154 c) for the case of complete (absolute) degeneracy.

We have hitherto assumed that the wave functions $\psi_{H'}$ specifying the unperturbed states are orthogonal with respect to each other. The above theory can easily be extended to the case when the orthogonality condition is not fulfilled. We need not, however, consider this case in detail here, for it has been dealt with already in § 9 of Chap. II by the variational method. The results embodied in the equations (61) are a generalization of the equations (154), which differ from the (specialized) equations (62) in the notation only.

It should be mentioned that to the states defined by non-orthogonal wave functions there correspond in the state-space a system of non-orthogonal axes to which the energy quadrics H and K are referred. The non-orthogonality of these axes means physically that the corresponding states are not mutually excluded, the integral $\int \psi^*_{H'} \psi_{H''} \, dV$ measuring in fact the probability of one of them when the other is supposed to be realized.

So far we have dealt only with the case in which the unperturbed motion has a *discrete energy spectrum* (which corresponds, classically, to its being confined to a limited region of space). The case of a continuous H-spectrum could be treated on similar lines. It is, however, meaningless to determine the change ΔH of the energy-levels produced by the perturbation, when these levels form a continuous series. Thus one of the main problems of the perturbation theory relating to the case of discrete H-spectra, together with the complications arising in connexion with degeneracy, drops out. The other problem—that of the determination of the change $\Delta\psi$ of the wave functions specifying the stationary states—can be solved in the same way as before, i.e. by determining the transformation coefficients $a_{H'K''}$. In the present case the zero approximation is given by the formula

$$a_{H'K''} = \delta(H'-H''),$$

instead of $a_{H'K''} = \delta_{H'H''}$. Instead of equation (144 b), we have

$$\int K^0_{H'H''} a_{H''K'''} \, dH'' = K''' a_{H'K'''}.$$

Putting $a_{H''K'''} = \delta(H''-H''')+\Delta a_{H''K'''}$ and $K = H+S$, then since

$$H^0_{H'H''} = H'\delta(H'-H''),$$

we get

$$H'[\delta(H'-H''')+\Delta a_{H'K'''}]+S^0_{H'H'''}+\int S^0_{H'H''}\Delta a_{H''K'''}\, dH''$$
$$= K'''[\delta(H'-H''')+\Delta a_{H'K'''}],$$

which, with $K''' = H'''+\Delta H'''$, can be written in the form

$$S^0_{H'H'''}+\int S^0_{H'H''}\Delta a_{H''K'''}\, dH''$$
$$= \Delta H'''[\delta(H'-H''')+\Delta a_{H'K'''}]+(H'''-H')\Delta a_{H'K'''}.$$

This method can be conveniently applied only when the quantities $\Delta a_{H'K'''}$ are known to be small—a condition which is, in general, not satisfied.

An alternative method consists in the direct determination of the change of the functions $\psi_{H'}$, $\Delta\psi_{H'}$, which is produced by the perturbation, without the use of the integral representation

$$\Delta\psi_{H'} = \int \Delta a_{H'H''}\psi_{H''}\, dH''$$

(where $\Delta a_{H'H''} = \Delta a_{H'K'}$). This can be done with the help of the equation

$$(H+S-K')(\psi_{H'}+\Delta\psi_{H'}) = 0,$$

which can be written in the form

$$(H-K')\Delta\psi = -S(\psi_{H'}+\Delta\psi_{H'}) \qquad (156)$$

and which differs from the approximate equation (153) by leaving 'unsplit' the energy K' of the perturbed motion and by preserving the small term $S\Delta\psi'$. Dropping it, we get the equation of the first approximation:

$$(H-K')\Delta_1\psi = -S\psi_H. \tag{156 a}$$

Substituting on the right side the nth-order correction $\Delta_n\psi_{H'}$ for $\psi_{H'}$, we get the equation for the correction of the $(n+1)$th order,

$$(H-K')\Delta_{n+1}\psi_{H'} = -S\Delta_n\psi_{H'}, \tag{156 b}$$

the exact function $\psi_{H'}+\Delta\psi_{H'}$ being thus defined as the limit of the series

$$\psi_{H'}+\Delta_1\psi_{H'}+\Delta_2\psi_{H'}+\ldots.$$

This method has been worked out by Born in connexion with collision problems (see Part III). It can be applied also to the case of discrete spectra (thus enabling one to avoid the determination of the transformation coefficients a); but in this case it must be modified by putting $K' = H'+\Delta H' = H'+\Delta_1 H'+\Delta_2 H'+\ldots$, which leads to the equations

$$\left.\begin{aligned}
&(H-H')\Delta_1\psi_{H'} = -(S-\Delta_1 H')\psi_{H'} \\
&(H-H')\Delta_2\psi_{H'} = -(S-\Delta_1 H')\Delta_1\psi_{H'}+(\Delta_2 H')\psi_{H'} \\
&\quad\cdot\quad\cdot\quad\cdot\quad\cdot\quad\cdot\quad\cdot\quad\cdot\quad\cdot\quad\cdot\quad\cdot\quad\cdot\quad\cdot\quad\cdot \\
&(H-H')\Delta_{n+1}\psi_{H'} \\
&\quad = -(S-\Delta_1 H')\Delta_n\psi_{H'}+(\Delta_2 H')\Delta_{n-1}\psi_{H'}+\ldots+(\Delta_{n+1} H')\psi_{H'}
\end{aligned}\right\} \tag{157}$$

The problem becomes more complicated, for we must determine not only the functions $\Delta_1\psi_{H'}$, $\Delta_2\psi_{H'}$, etc., but at the same time the numbers $\Delta_1 H'$, $\Delta_2 H'$,…. This can be done with the help of the so-called orthogonality property of the non-homogeneous linear equations of the form

$$(H-H')\chi = f. \tag{157 a}$$

This 'orthogonality' consists in the following: Multiplying the preceding equation by the solution of the corresponding homogeneous equation $(H-H')\psi_{H'} = 0$, or its conjugate complex $\psi_{H'}^*$, and integrating, we get, in view of the self-adjointness of the operator H,

$$\int \psi_{H'}^*(H-H')\chi\, dV = \int \chi(H-H')\psi_{H'}^*\, dV = 0,$$

and consequently

$$\int f\psi_{H'}^*\, dV = 0. \tag{157 b}$$

Applying this 'orthogonality property' to the first of equations (157), we get

$$\Delta_1 H' \int \psi_{H'}\psi_{H'}^*\, dV = \int \psi_{H'}^* S\psi_{H'}\, dV,$$

that is, $\Delta_1 H' = S_{H'H'}^0$. Applying it to the second, we get in a similar way

$$\Delta_2 H' = \int \psi_{H'}^*(S-\Delta_1 H')\Delta_1\psi_{H'}\, dV,$$

which can easily be evaluated after $\Delta_1 \psi_{H'}$ has been determined from the first of equations (157). This process can be prolonged as far as one may desire, the determination of $\Delta_n H'$ always preceding by one step that of $\Delta_n \psi_{H'}$.

If (157 a) is multiplied by $\psi_{H''}^*$ instead of $\psi_{H'}$, we obtain, on integration,

$$(H'' - H') \int \psi_{H''}^* \chi \, dV = \int \psi_{H''}^* f \, dV. \tag{157 c}$$

This gives, if applied to the first of equations (157),

$$\int \psi_{H''}^* \Delta_1 \psi_{H'} \, dV = -\frac{S_{H''H'}^0}{H'' - H'},$$

i.e. the expression for the coefficient $\Delta_1 a_{H''K'}$. This is quite natural, for if we put $\Delta_1 \psi_{H'} = \sum_{H''} \Delta_1 a_{H''K'} \psi_{H''}$, then, in view of the orthogonality of the functions $\psi_{H'}$ and $\psi_{H''}$, we get $\int \psi_{H''}^* \Delta_1 \psi_{H'} \, dV = \Delta_1 a_{H''K'}$.

The preceding results obviously hold for the case only when the unperturbed problem is not degenerate, and must be modified if there is degeneracy—either absolute or relative.

We shall, however, leave that case aside and shall briefly examine the approximate effect produced by the perturbation on any physical quantity F described as a matrix, from the point of view of H in the case of the unperturbed motion and that of K in that of the perturbed one. This can be readily done after we have succeeded in determining the supposedly small quantities $\Delta a_{H'K''}$ or $\Delta \psi_{H'}$. Putting

$$F_{K'K''}^0 - F_{H'H''}^0 = \Delta F_{H'H''}^0,$$

we have

$$\Delta F_{H'H''}^0 = (a^\dagger F a - F)_{H'H''}^0,$$

or, since $a = \delta + \Delta a$ and $\delta^\dagger F = F \delta = F$,

$$\Delta F_{H'H''}^0 = (F \Delta a + \Delta a^\dagger F)_{H'H''}^0 + (\Delta a^\dagger F \Delta a)_{H'H''}^0.$$

This gives, to the first order of approximation,

$$\Delta_1 F_{H'H''}^0 = (F \Delta_1 a + \Delta_1 a^\dagger F)_{H'H''}^0,$$

or in the case of a discrete H-spectrum (with no degeneracy or a degeneracy accounted for by a preliminary transformation), according to (148 b):

$$\Delta_1 F_{H'H''}^0 = \sum_{H'''} \frac{F_{H'H'''}^0 S_{H'''H''}^0}{H'' - H'''} + \sum \frac{S_{H'H'''}^0 F_{H'''H''}^0}{H' - H'''}, \tag{158}$$

since $\Delta_1 a_{H'H'''}^\dagger = \Delta_1 a_{H'''H'}^* = -\Delta_1 a_{H'H'''} = \dfrac{S_{H'H'''}^0}{H' - H'''}$. Putting $H'' = H'$ and writing H'' for H''' we obtain, in particular,

$$\Delta_1 F_{H'H'}^0 = \sum_{H''} \frac{F_{H'H''}^0 S_{H''H'}^0 + S_{H'H''}^0 F_{H''H'}^0}{H' - H''}. \tag{158 a}$$

This formula determines the change of the average or probable values of F for the different unperturbed states as compared with the corresponding perturbed states. Putting $F = S$, we get

$$\Delta_1 S^0_{H'H'} = 2 \sum_{H''} \frac{|S^0_{H'H''}|^2}{H' - H''}.$$

Comparing this with (149 a), we obtain the following relation between the second-order correction for the energy and the first-order correction for $S^0_{H'H'}$:

$$\Delta_2 H' = \tfrac{1}{2} \Delta_1 S^0_{H'H'}. \tag{158 b}$$

This formula is quite similar to

$$\Delta_1 H' = S^0_{H'H'},$$

and can be further generalized with the result

$$\Delta_n H' = \frac{1}{n} \Delta_{n-1} S^0_{H'H'}$$

if higher-order corrections for the matrix elements are taken into consideration, according to (157 a). We shall not, however, consider in detail this question which can easily be solved by substituting in (157 a) the expressions $\Delta a = \Delta_1 a + \Delta_2 a + \dots$.

For the sake of illustration we shall apply the preceding equations to the case of a hydrogen-like atom, perturbed by a homogeneous electric field E parallel to the x-axis. We have in this case $S = -eEx$, where x is the coordinate of the electron with respect to the nucleus. Putting in (158 a) $F = ex$, we obtain the expression for the additional electric moment induced by the field when the atom is supposed to remain in the (non-degenerate) unperturbed state H':

$$ex_{H'H'} = 2e^2 E \sum_{H''} \frac{|x_{H'H''}|^2}{H'' - H'} = \alpha E, \tag{158 c}$$

where α is the polarization (or susceptibility) coefficient. The corresponding energy must obviously be equal to $\tfrac{1}{2} \alpha E^2 = \tfrac{1}{2} \Delta_1 S^0_{H'H'}$ which is in agreement with the relation (158 b) since the energy in question corresponds to the second-order correction $(\Delta_2 H')$.

The same results are obtained, of course, if instead of the transformation coefficients the transformed functions ψ, or rather the corrections $\Delta\psi$, are used. Limiting ourselves to the first approximation, we get

$$F^0_{K'K''} = \int (\psi^*_{H'} + \Delta\psi^*_{H'}) F (\psi_{H''} + \Delta\psi_{H''}) \, dV$$

$$\cong \int \psi^*_{H'} F \psi_{H''} \, dV + \int \Delta_1 \psi^*_{H'} F \psi_{H''} \, dV + \int \psi^*_{H'} F \Delta_1 \psi_{H'} \, dV,$$

that is, $\Delta_1 F^0_{H'H''} = \int \Delta_1 \psi^*_{H'} F \psi_{H''} \, dV + \int \psi^*_{H'} F \Delta_1 \psi_{H''} \, dV.$ $\tag{159}$

These expressions can be used in the case of continuous H-spectra when the functions $\Delta_1 \psi_{H'}$ are determined directly by Born's method. If they are determined with the help of the transformation coefficients, we get, as before, $\Delta_1 F^0_{H'H''} = (F\Delta_1 a + \Delta_1 a^* F)^0_{H'H''}$, which means in the present case

$$\Delta_1 F^0_{H'H''} = \int \left(\frac{F^0_{H'H'''} S^0_{H'''H''}}{H'' - H'''} + \frac{S^0_{H'H'''} F^0_{H'''H''}}{H' - H'''} \right) dH''' \qquad (159\,\text{a})$$

instead of (158).

In conclusion the following remark should be made. It can happen that, while the unperturbed motion is confined to a finite region and has accordingly, within a certain interval of energy values, a discrete spectrum, the perturbed motion has, within the same interval, a continuous energy spectrum, which means that the perturbing forces, *even when small*, can extract the particle and drive it to infinity. An example of this condition is furnished by the action of a homogeneous electric field on a hydrogen atom. In the region of low energy values the continuous energy spectrum, corresponding to the presence of the electric field, practically reduces to a discrete one, with each H-level split up (as a consequence of degeneracy) into several sub-levels. This phenomenon is known as the *Stark effect*. The sub-levels in question have, however, a certain effective *width* which increases with the strength of the electric field and which corresponds to the phenomenon of *predissociation*, discussed in Part I, § 16. This means that there exists a certain probability for the atom to be ionized by the electric field even if the unperturbed state of the atom corresponds to the lowest energy. The width of the energy-levels becomes, however, marked for unperturbed states, which correspond to comparatively high energy-levels, where the energy spectrum of the perturbed atom becomes practically continuous. In the case of the unperturbed atom, the continuous spectrum starts at the point where the energy is equal to zero, while for a perturbed atom it starts below this point—and indeed the more below, the larger the perturbing electric field.

21. Perturbation Theory involving the Time; General Processes; Theory of Transitions

In all the foregoing developments the time has been completely ignored. This has been possible because we have limited ourselves to the consideration of such physical quantities as do not depend upon the time. It may seem, at first sight, that the introduction of the time as an independent variable into the expression of an operator, $F_{(x)}$ say, representing some variable physical quantity, would only have the effect of making its characteristic values, and consequently the states specified by them, functions of the time. That this is not so is clear, however, from the example of the energy. If the energy operator K contains the time explicitly, then an equation of the type $(K-K')\phi_{K'} = 0$ has no physical meaning and must be replaced by the general equation of motion

$$(K+p_t)\phi = 0, \qquad (160)$$

where $p_t = \dfrac{h}{2\pi i}\dfrac{\partial}{\partial t}$. The equation $(K-K')\phi_{K'} = 0$ would correspond to the treatment of the time as a simple *parameter*; from the purely mathematical point of view, the appearance of the time would have no particular meaning, save that of making the characteristic values K' and the characteristic functions $\phi_{K'}(t)$ definite functions of the time. These functions, as well as the corresponding characteristic values $K'(t)$, would, however, have nothing to do with those functions $\phi(x,t)$ which describe wave-mechanically the motion determined by the energy operator K and which are the solutions of equation (160).

So long as K depends upon the time, this equation does not admit particular solutions of the type $\phi = \phi_{K'}^0(x)e^{-i2\pi K't/h}$, which means, from the physical point of view, that K has no characteristic values, or, in other words, *that the values of a variable energy cannot be specified*.

This result constitutes one of the fundamental differences between wave mechanics and classical mechanics, where the value of a variable energy can always be ascertained as a definite function of the time. The same refers to other operators involving the time as an independent variable.

It is true that the energy is more intimately connected with the time than any other operator. It seems, however, doubtful whether an equation of the form $F_{(x)}\psi = F'\psi$ defining the characteristic values of an operator $F_{(x)}$ has any meaning if $F_{(x)}$ depends upon the time—so long at least as the latter is treated on an entirely different basis from that of the coordinates x, y, z. The exceptional role of the time is revealed by the fact that, in contradistinction to the coordinates, it cannot be used for the specification of the states, the latter being referred, in general, to a particular instant of time. The time, therefore, cannot be treated on the same lines as the coordinates and other physical quantities, and, in particular, it cannot be represented as an operator or a matrix with regard to some other basic quantity. Even when completely 'inactive', the time remains above the realm of ordinary quantities, ruling out the very possibility of their determination (so far

as *exact* and not probable values are concerned) by its active interference.

Nevertheless, the transformation theory which has been developed
in the preceding chapter can be applied in a somewhat modified and
generalized form to variable quantities and, in particular, to the energy
K of a particle moving in a variable field of force.

If the variable part of K refers to a comparatively small force, we
can regard the latter as a perturbing factor *causing transitions* between
the states specified by the part of K which does not contain the time.
This theory of transitions has been outlined already in Part I, § 14.
We shall now briefly recapitulate it, using the new notation, and we
shall point out its connexion with the transformation theory.

The variable part of K, which will be regarded as the perturbation
energy, will be denoted, as before, by S, and the constant part by H.
The function $\phi(x,t)$, which is the general solution of equation (160),
can be represented as a superposition of the (normalized) functions $\psi_{H'}$
which correspond to the different states specified by the operator H,
with suitably determined *variable coefficients*.

Taking first the case of a discrete H-spectrum, we shall put accordingly

$$\phi(x,t) = \sum_{H'} c_{H'}(t)\psi_{H'}, \qquad (160\,\text{a})$$

with
$$\psi_{H'} = \psi^0_{H'}(x)e^{-i2\pi H't/h},$$

or
$$\phi(x,t) = \sum_{H'} C_{H'}(t)\psi^0_{H'}, \qquad (160\,\text{b})$$

where
$$C_{H'}(t) = c_{H'}(t)e^{-i2\pi H't/h}. \qquad (160\,\text{c})$$

Substituting (160 a) in (160) and taking into account that the functions
$\psi_{H'}$ satisfy the equation $(H+p_t)\psi_{H'} = 0$, we have

$$(H+S+p_t)\sum_{H'} c_{H'}(t)\psi_{H'} = \sum_{H'}[(p_t c_{H'})\psi_{H'} + c_{H'}S\psi_{H'}] = 0.$$

Since
$$S\psi_{H'} = \sum_{H''} S_{H''H'}\psi_{H''},$$

we get
$$\sum_{H'}\sum_{H''} \psi_{H''}[\delta_{H'H''}p_t c_{H'} + c_{H'}S_{H''H'}] = 0,$$

whence
$$\sum_{H'}(\delta_{H'H''}p_t c_{H'} + c_{H'}S_{H''H'}) = 0,$$

or, interchanging H' and H''

$$-\frac{h}{2\pi i}\frac{dc_{H'}}{dt} = \sum_{H''} S_{H'H''}c_{H''}. \qquad (161)$$

It should be remembered that the quantities $S_{H'H''}$ represent not the
matrix *elements* but the matrix *components* of the perturbation energy,
so that $S_{H'H''} = S^0_{H'H''}e^{i2\pi(H'-H'')t/h}$. Further, so long as S contains the

time explicitly, the matrix elements $S^0_{H'H''} = \int \psi^{0*}_{H'} S\psi_{H''} \, dV$ must also be certain functions of the time, so that (161) can be written in the form

$$-\frac{h}{2\pi i}\frac{dc_{H'}}{dt} = \sum_{H''} S^0_{H'H''}(t) e^{i2\pi(H'-H'')t/h} c_{H''}. \qquad (161\,\mathrm{a})$$

If we substitute in (160) the expression (160 b) instead of (160 a), we get in the same way, without, however, separating K into the parts H and S,

$$(K+p_t)\sum_{H'} C_{H'}\psi^0_{H'} = \sum_{H'}(\psi^0_{H'}p_t C_{H'} + C_{H'}K\psi^0_{H'}) = 0,$$

or, since $K\psi^0_{H'} = \sum_{H''} K^0_{H''H'}\psi^0_{H''}$,

$$\sum_{H''}\psi^0_{H''}\sum_{H'}(\delta_{H'H''}p_t C_{H'} + K^0_{H''H'}C_{H'}) = 0,$$

or finally

$$-\frac{h}{2\pi i}\frac{dC_H}{dt} = \sum_{H''} K^0_{H'H''}C_{H''}. \qquad (161\,\mathrm{b})$$

This equation can be derived from (161 a)—or the latter from it—with the help of the relation (160 c) between the coefficients C and c and the relations

$$K^0_{H'H''} = H'\delta_{H'H''} + S^0_{H'H''}.$$

As already explained in Part I, § 17, the squares of the moduli of the coefficients $c_{H'}$ or $C_{H'}$, i.e. the quantities

$$N_{H'}(t) = C_{H'}C^*_{H'} = c_{H'}c^*_{H'}, \qquad (162)$$

can be interpreted as the probabilities of finding the particle at the instant t in the unperturbed state H', or, using the 'multiplex representation', as the *relative numbers of the copies* of the particle in the state H' at the instant $t = 0$. These numbers can be determined as functions of the time with the help of equations (161 b) or (161) if the initial values of the coefficients $C_{H'}$ (or $c_{H'}$) at some instant $t = 0$ are supposed to be known. We shall denote them in future by $C^0_{H'}$ and write accordingly $N_{H'}(0) = N^0_{H'}$.

The change of the numbers $N_{H'}$ with the time can be interpreted as the result of *transitions* induced by the perturbing forces. So long, however, as two or more of the numbers $N^0_{H'}$ are different from zero, it is impossible to ascertain the original state from which the transition to a given state takes place.

In order to be able to speak of *definite* transitions to a given final state from a given initial state, we must therefore assume that initially all the copies of the particle were in the same state, H' say. This means that all the coefficients $C^0_{H'}$ must be set equal to zero, with the exception of one of them, $C^0_{H'}$, which can be put equal to 1. This can be expressed by means of the formula

$$C^0_{H''} = \delta_{H''H'}, \tag{162a}$$

which serves to show that the coefficients $C_{H''}(t)$, not only for $t = 0$ but also for $t > 0$, can be considered as the elements of a matrix, which we shall call the *transition matrix* and shall denote by the same letter C. The value of the coefficient $C_{H''}$ at the time t, on the assumption of a definite initial state H', will thus be denoted by

$$C_{H'}(t) = C_{H''H'}(t), \tag{162b}$$

the initial value of the matrix C being δ (that is, 1).

The formula $\phi = \sum C_{H''}(t)\psi^0_{H''}$ represents the *general* solution of Schrödinger's equation (160). That particular solution of it which reduces to $\psi_{H'}$ at the initial instant $t = 0$ can conveniently be denoted by $\phi_{H'}(x, t)$. We thus get for particular solutions of this type, *which approximate* to the particular solutions of the equation of the unperturbed motion $(H + p_t)\psi = 0$, the following formula:

$$\phi_{H'} = \sum_{H''} C_{H''H'}\psi^0_{H''}, \tag{163}$$

which shows that the transition matrix $C(t)$ can be regarded as the transformation matrix from the wave functions $\psi^0_{H'}$ to the wave functions $\phi_{H'}$. The latter can no longer be denoted by $\phi_{K'}$, as was done before, since K has no characteristic values; these characteristic values can, however, be replaced by a kind of 'reminiscence' of the particular solutions of the equation $(K + p_t)\phi = 0$ about the H-state they represented at the instant $t = 0$.

It can easily be shown that the functions $\phi_{H'}$, $\phi_{H''}$, etc., are *mutually orthogonal*, just as are the functions $\phi_{K'}$, $\phi_{K''}$ considered before.

We have in fact

$$\left(K + \frac{h}{2\pi i}\frac{\partial}{\partial t}\right)\phi_{H'} = 0, \qquad \left(K - \frac{h}{2\pi i}\frac{\partial}{\partial t}\right)\phi^*_{H''} = 0.$$

Multiplying the first of these equations by $\phi^*_{H''}$ and the second by $\phi_{H'}$, subtracting one from the other, and integrating over the coordinates, we get

$$\int (\phi^*_{H''} K\phi_{H'} - \phi_{H'} K\phi^*_{H''})\, dV = -\int \frac{\partial}{\partial t}(\phi^*_{H''}\phi_{H'})\, dV,$$

or, since the left-hand side vanishes (so long as K, in spite of its dependence upon the time, preserves the property of self-adjointness), we get

$$\frac{d}{dt}\int \phi^*_{H''}\phi_{H'}\, dV = 0.$$

We thus see that the value of the integral $\int \phi_{H''}^* \phi_{H'} \, dV$ does not depend upon the time. Since at the initial moment $t = 0$ we have $\phi_{H'} = \psi_{H'}$ and $\phi_{H''} = \psi_{H''}$, it follows from this that the functions $\phi_{H'}$ satisfy, irrespective of the time, the same orthogonality and normalizing conditions

$$\int \phi_{H''}^* \phi_{H'} \, dV = \delta_{H''H'} \tag{163 a}$$

as the functions $\psi_{H'}$.

Substituting in these equations the expressions (163), we have further

$$\int \phi_{H''}^* \phi_{H'} \, dV = \sum_{H'''} \sum_{H''''} C_{H'''H'} \, C_{H''''H''}^* \int \psi_{H''''}^{0*} \psi_{H'''}^0 \, dV,$$

that is, $$\int \phi_{H''}^* \phi_{H'} \, dV = \sum_{H'''} C_{H'''H'} \, C_{H'''H''}^*,$$

and consequently $$\sum_{H'''} C_{H'''H''}^* \, C_{H'''H'} = \delta_{H''H'}. \tag{163 b}$$

This equation shows that the transition matrix is *unitary* ($C^\dagger = C^{-1}$), just as are the ordinary transformation matrices, which have been considered in the preceding sections and which do not depend upon the time. The transformation equations (163) can be written accordingly in the ordinary matrix form

$$\phi = \widetilde{C} \psi^0, \quad \text{or} \quad \phi^\dagger = \psi^{0\dagger} \widetilde{C}^\dagger. \tag{163 c}$$

It follows from these results that the functions $\phi_{H'}$ specify *perfectly definite states* in the same sense as those which would be represented by the functions $\phi_{K'}$ if K were independent of the time and had definite characteristic values; the only difference between them being that the former vary with the time while the latter should remain constant.

The set of states specified by the functions $\phi_{H'}$ can be represented geometrically as an orthogonal system of coordinates in the state-space, the transformation coefficients $C_{H''H'}$ denoting the cosines of the angles between the fixed axes which represent the states $\psi_{H''}^0$ and the movable axes which represent the states $\phi_{H'}$. This movable system of axes, rotating like a solid body in the state-space, can be regarded as the geometrical representation of the variable energy K.

One might be inclined to go a step further and to represent K by a quadric surface defined by the equation

$$\sum_{H'} \sum_{H''} K_{H'H''}^0 \, a_{H'}^* \, a_{H''} = \text{const.},$$

thus fixing not only the directions but also the lengths of the axes associated with K—i.e. the characteristic values of the latter. This argument is, however, fallacious because the preceding equation has nothing to do with the representation of the variable surface K, which we have been considering, but represents in reality the fictitious 'quasi-constant' energy operator K with the time treated as a simple parameter.

The fallacy of the above argument becomes especially apparent when K is *actually constant* (which can be considered as a special case of a variable K). The equation $\sum \sum K^0_{H'H''} a^*_{H'} a_{H''} = \text{const.}$ will then represent K as a quadric surface *fixed* in the state-space. Nothing, however, will prevent us from solving the equation $(K + p_t)\phi = 0$ in this case in the same way as in the preceding case, namely, by taking particular solutions not of the usual K-type, $\phi_{K'} = \phi^0_{K'} e^{-i2\pi K't/h}$, but of the H-type, i.e. such that, at the initial moment $t = 0$, ϕ coincides with one of the functions $\psi_{H'}$. The functions $\phi_{H'}$ so obtained will represent for $t \neq 0$ states entirely different both from those specified by the functions $\psi_{H'}$ and from those specified by the functions $\phi_{K'}$. In order to avoid confusion, we shall denote the characteristic functions of K (when they exist of course, i.e. when K is independent of the time) by $\chi_{K'}$ instead of $\phi_{K'}$. The connexion between these functions and the functions $\psi_{H'}$

$$\chi^0_{K'} = \sum_{H'} a_{H''K'} \psi^0_{H''}, \tag{164}$$

which has been investigated before, is represented by a constant transformation matrix a, which has nothing to do with the variable matrices C and c.

It should be remarked that the elements of these matrices are connected with each other, according to (160 c), by the relation

$$c_{H'H''} = C_{H'H''} e^{i2\pi H''t/h},$$

which is not symmetrical with regard to the two indices and is in agreement with the unitary character of the two matrices.

The transformation matrix a can be derived from the general equations (161 b) if the condition that the function ϕ should reduce to $\psi_{H'}$ for $t = 0$ is replaced by the condition that it should be a harmonic function of the time of the type

$$\phi = \chi_{K'''} = \chi^0_{K'''} e^{-i2\pi K'''t/h}. \tag{164 a}$$

This means, on account of the equation

$$\phi = \sum_{H'} C_{H'} \psi^0_{H'},$$

that all the coefficients $C_{H'}$ should also be of the type

$$C_{H'} = C^0_{H'} e^{-i2\pi K'''t/h}. \tag{165}$$

The differential equations (161 b) reduce, subject to this condition, to a system of ordinary algebraic equations for the amplitudes $C_{H'}^0$

$$K''' C_{H'}^0 = \sum_{H''} K_{H'H''}^0 C_{H''}^0, \qquad (165\,a)$$

which are obviously identical with the equations determining the transformation coefficients a.

We thus get $\qquad\qquad C_{H'}^0 = a_{H'},$

or more exactly $\qquad\qquad C_{H'K'''}^0 = a_{H'K'''}.$ $\qquad (165\,b)$

The relations between the functions $\chi_{K'} = \chi_{K'}^0 \, e^{-i2\pi K'l/h}$ and $\psi_{H''} = \psi_{H''}^0 \, e^{-i2\pi H''l/h}$ can be obtained from (164) if the coefficients $a_{H''K'}$ are replaced by

$$\zeta_{H''K'} = a_{H''K'} \, e^{i2\pi(H''-K')l/h}. \qquad (166)$$

These coefficients also constitute a unitary matrix ζ. Combining the matrix equations

$$\chi = \psi\zeta \quad \text{and} \quad \phi = \psi c,$$

we can easily obtain a direct relation between the functions ϕ and χ. We have, namely,

$$\psi = \chi\zeta^{-1} = \chi\zeta^{\dagger},$$

and consequently $\qquad\qquad \phi = \chi d,$

with the transformation matrix

$$d = \zeta^{\dagger}c.$$

Written in matrix elements, these equations run

$$\phi_{H'} = \sum_{K''} d_{K''H'} \chi_{K''}, \qquad (166\,a)$$

with $\qquad d_{K''H'} = \sum_{H'''} \zeta_{K''H'''}^{\dagger} c_{H'''H'} = \sum \zeta_{H'''K''}^* c_{H'''H'},$

or $\qquad d_{K''H'} = \sum_{H'''} a_{H'''K''}^* c_{H'''H'} \, e^{i2\pi(K''-H''')l/h}. \qquad (166\,b)$

Putting $\qquad\qquad d_{K''H'} = \eta_{K''H'} \, e^{i2\pi K''l/h},$

we can rewrite (166 a) in the more convenient form

$$\phi_{H'} = \sum_{K''} \eta_{K''H'} \chi_{K''}^0, \qquad (166\,c)$$

with $\qquad \eta_{K''H'} = \sum_{H'''} a_{H'''K''}^* C_{H'''H'}, \qquad (166\,d)$

showing that the dependence of $\phi_{H'}$ on the time is fully determined by the transformation coefficients $C_{H'''H'}$.

Equations of exactly the same type as (165 a) are obtained in classical mechanics for the amplitudes of the free oscillations of a system of particles held together by 'quasi-elastic' forces, i.e. forces which are proportional to their displacements both from the respective equilibrium positions and relative to each other. Such a system can be realized in the simplest form by a set of coupled pendulums which can oscillate in a definite plane under the influence of gravity and of forces due to their being coupled together (by means of lateral strings or otherwise).†

Let ξ_1, ξ_2,... be the displacements of the given particles—or pendulums—from their position of rest. Their dependence upon the time is determined by a system of equations of the form

$$-\frac{d^2\xi_n}{dt^2} = \sum_m \Phi_{nm}\xi_m. \tag{167}$$

The coefficients Φ_{nn} thus specify the binding of the separate particles to their positions of rest, and so determine the free vibrations which they would carry out in the absence of any coupling with the other particles. The coefficients $\Phi_{nm} = \Phi_{mn}$ $(m \neq n)$ describe, on the other hand, the perturbing coupling forces.

If we put

$$\Phi_{nn} = \Phi_{nn}^0 + \Phi_{nn}', \qquad \Phi_{nm} = \Phi_{nm}' \quad (n \neq m),$$

we can then regard the above equations as the equations of the *perturbed motion* of the given quasi-elastic system. By the unperturbed motion we are to understand the vibrations determined by the equations

$$-\frac{d^2\xi_n}{dt^2} = \Phi_{nn}^0 \xi_n.$$

In this case each particle (pendulum or current) vibrates quite independently of the others and with a frequency $\omega_n^0 = \frac{1}{2\pi}\sqrt{\Phi_{nn}^0}$.

In the presence of perturbing coupling forces such independent harmonic vibrations of the separate particles (or pendulums) are not possible. They become replaced by harmonic vibrations of a different kind—so-called 'normal vibrations' of the system—in which with regard to any kind of vibration characterized by the common frequency ω_k *all* particles participate with definite relative amplitudes and definite phase differences. The real amplitude and the initial phase (at time $t = 0$) of each particle can be defined respectively as the modulus and the argument of a complex amplitude $\gamma_n = |\gamma_n|e^{i\delta_n}$. These complex amplitudes and the corresponding frequencies of vibration can be determined from the equations of motion if we make the substitution

$$\xi_n = \gamma_n e^{-2\pi i\omega t}, \tag{167 a}$$

for the variables ξ_n. Equations (167) then reduce to the form

$$\sum_m \Phi_{nm}\gamma_m = \omega^2\gamma_n, \tag{167 b}$$

† Instead of a mechanical model we could use, for the illustration of the equations (165 a), an electric model, formed by a system of electrically coupled electric circuits.

and thus with $\omega^2 = K'''$ and $\Phi_{nm} = K^0_{H'H''}$ become identical with the 'wave mechanics' equations (165 a).

The general solution of the classical vibration problem (167)—just as of the corresponding 'wave mechanics' problem $(K+p_l)\chi = 0$—is obtained by superposition of all harmonic particular solutions (with arbitrary constant coefficients).

The similarity of the two problems enables us to relate the perturbation theory of quantum mechanics, in a very clear manner, to the classical theory of weakly coupled particles or pendulums. The 'pendulum model' (which can serve just as well for the illustration both of the wave-mechanical and the electromagnetic vibrations) proves to be especially convenient. Such a model consists of an infinite series of pendulums which are suspended along a horizontal line in the order of increasing frequencies of the unperturbed vibrations, i.e. in the order of decreasing lengths, and which can be bound to one another in pairs (see Fig. 2). Thus each pendulum corresponds to a definite quantized state of the unperturbed system (atom, molecule), i.e. to a definite characteristic function $\psi^0_{H'}$. In the case of 'degeneracy', i.e. when several different pendulums have the same unperturbed vibration frequency $\nu^0_{H'} = H'/h$, we can ascribe the same length to the corresponding pendulums (in general, however, a different mass) and place them beside one another transversely to the original direction of suspension.

If, under the given conditions of the motion, there exists, besides a discrete set of states, also a continuous set of stationary states, then the discrete pendulum series of our model must be supplemented by a continuous series, which can be conceived as a compact heavy fabric. For this fabric not to tear, the amplitudes and phases of the vibration of its vertical elements must be continuous functions of the (unperturbed) vibration frequency $\nu^0 = H'/h$.†

From the point of view of the wave conception, the correspondence between the vibrations of our pendulum model and the vibration process in the corresponding mechanical system is very straightforward and suggestive. Thus the different types of standing waves represented by the functions $\psi^0_{H'}$ play the role of the single pen-

---

† We could replace the pendulum model by a *string model* (limiting ourselves to the fundamental vibrations of each string). The continuous spectrum in this model would be represented by a *membrane*. Such a membrane must, however, possess quite unusual properties which are incompatible with the ordinary equations of the theory of elasticity (for these equations correspond to a coupling between the neighbouring elements of the elastic continuum only).

dulums; while the coefficients $C_{H''}$ (or $c_{H''}$) are the (complex) amplitudes of vibration.

This correspondence acquires a purely symbolic character, however, when we go over from the wave picture to the corpuscular picture. The amplitude coefficients then acquire a quite different physical meaning; for their norms $C_{H''} C_{H''}^* = |C_{H''}|^2$ then determine the relative number of the copies of the given particle which are in the corresponding state. To the continuous alteration of these coefficients with the time under the action of the perturbing forces there corresponds a series of forced transitions of these copies from one state to another. The derivative $d|C_{H''}|^2/dt$ then gives the probability, referred to unit time, that any

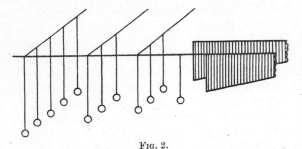

FIG. 2.

copy of the particle will go over *into* the state $\psi_{H''}^0$ if $d|C_{H''}|^2/dt > 0$ or *out of* this state if $d|C_{H''}|^2/dt < 0$.

One important difference between the pendulum model and the wave-mechanical vibrations it represents, consists in the normalization of the amplitudes of vibration to a definite value (1). A system of pendulums, as considered in classical mechanics, can be at rest; or if the system is vibrating, one has to distinguish not only the relative but also the *absolute* values of the amplitudes. So far as this model is used for the illustration of wave-mechanical vibrations a state of rest is excluded—for the particle must always be found in some one of the states represented by the pendulums. Moreover, only the *relative* values of the amplitudes have a physical significance as defining the probability amplitudes of the corresponding states—which can be taken into account by normalizing the sum of their norms once and for all to 1.

In the case of certain relations between the amplitudes γ_n of the various pendulums, these amplitudes can preserve constant values, as we have seen above. Such 'normal vibrations' of the system of pendulums correspond to stationary distributions of the copies of the particles among the different unperturbed states, and represent the stationary states in the presence of the perturbing forces (i.e. states defined by the energy K). If we introduce for the illustration of the perturbed motion, i.e. of the vibrations defined by the operator K, a pendulum model of the same kind as for the unperturbed motion (i.e. the H-vibrations), then any such stationary distribution, i.e. any normal vibration of the original model, will be represented by the vibrations of a single pendulum of the new model. These new pendulums, representing the transformed characteristic functions $\chi_{K'}$, must clearly be considered as uncoupled. This means that transitions between the new stationary states (which are the real stationary states) are impossible.

A transition between two different unperturbed states H' and H'' is possible in the first place if the corresponding matrix element of the perturbation energy $S^0_{H'H''}$ is different from zero. The coupling coefficients Φ'_{mn}, which represent these elements in our pendulum model, can be regarded as a measure of the probability amplitude for transitions between the corresponding states. It can easily be seen, however, that transitions are also possible between unperturbed states H' and H'' which are *only indirectly* coupled with each other, the matrix element $S^0_{H'H''}$ vanishing, but certain other elements of the type $S^0_{H'H'''}$ and $S^0_{H'''H''}$ being different from zero. Such 'indirect transitions' play, as we shall see later on, an important role in many physical phenomena.

In the case of the stationary K_K-states represented by a stationary distribution of the copies over the various H-states—or by normal vibrations of the pendulum-system—the transitions between different H-states can be imagined to be mutually compensated.

The *variable* K_H-states which are described by the functions $\phi_{H'}$ can be represented in our pendulum model by vibrations which at the initial time $t = 0$ involve one particular pendulum (H') only. As time goes on, the vibrations of this pendulum must be gradually transferred to other pendulums, this transference representing the gradual transition of the copies of the particle from the state H' in which they were initially supposed to be concentrated (whose probability, in other words, was initially equal to 1) to other states.

If the energy K, or what amounts to the same thing the perturbation energy S, depends upon the time, only K_H-states of this type can be defined and represented by means of the pendulum model, while normal vibrations corresponding to definite values of K are impossible.

It is natural to consider vibrations due to an external influence, specified as a given function of the time, as 'forced vibrations'. It must be borne in mind, however, that the forced vibrations we are referring to are not of the usual type described by the non-homogeneous equations

$$\frac{d^2\xi_n}{dt^2} = -\sum_m \Phi_{nm}\xi_m + F_n(t),$$

where $F_n(t)$ denotes the external force acting on the nth pendulum. Such external forces do not have any place in our model. They are replaced by a so-called 'parametric perturbation', i.e. by a change of the parameters Φ_{nm} which determine the *free* vibrations of the pendulums. In fact, the case of a perturbation energy depending upon the time can be represented, in the pendulum model, by a type of forced vibrations determined by the equations

$$\frac{d^2\xi_n}{dt^2} = -\sum_m \Phi_{mn}(t)\xi_m = -\Phi_{nn}^0\xi_n - \sum_m \Phi'_{mn}(t)\xi_m.$$

The model will, however, adequately reproduce the actual conditions only when the dependence of S upon the time is *harmonic* and if, besides, we restrict ourselves to the case of small perturbing forces; otherwise the agreement between the wave-mechanical equations (161 a) or (161 b) and the classical equations will be destroyed on account of the fact that in the former we have first derivatives with respect to the time (multiplied by $h/2\pi i$), while in the latter we have second derivatives ($d^2\xi_n/dt^2$). This difference is immaterial only in the case of harmonic vibrations represented by exponential functions of the type $e^{i2\pi\nu t}$, the differentiation with regard to the time being in both cases equivalent to multiplication by a real constant.

The preceding theory can easily be extended to the case of a continuous or mixed energy spectrum of the unperturbed motion.

Writing, for example,

$$\phi(x,t) = \sum_{H'} c_{H'}(t)\psi_{H'} + \int c_{H''}(t)\psi_{H''}\, dH'' \tag{168}$$

instead of (160 a), we get

$$(H+S+p_t)\phi$$
$$= \sum_{H'} [(p_t c_{H'})\psi_{H'} + c_{H'}S\psi_{H'}] + \int [(p_t c_{H''})\psi_{H''} + c_{H''}S\psi_{H''}]\, dH'' = 0.$$

We have further

$$S\psi_{H'} = \sum_{H'''} S_{H'''H'}\psi_{H'''} + \int S_{H''''H'}\psi_{H''''}\, dH'''',$$

$$S\psi_{H''} = \sum_{H'''} S_{H'''H''}\psi_{H'''} + \int S_{H''''H''}\psi_{H''''}\, dH'''',$$

where H' and H''' refer to the discrete and H'' and H'''' to the continuous region of the H-spectrum, and consequently

$$\left.\begin{aligned}
-\frac{h}{2\pi i}\frac{dc_{H'}}{dt} &= \sum_{H'''} S_{H'H''''}c_{H'''} + \int S_{H'H''''}c_{H''''}\,dH'''' \\
-\frac{h}{2\pi i}\frac{dc_{H''}}{dt} &= \sum_{H'''} S_{H''H''''}c_{H'''} + \int S_{H''H''''}c_{H''''}\,dH''''
\end{aligned}\right\}. \qquad (168\,a)$$

The only difference between the discrete and the continuous case is that in specifying the states we must, in general, replace the discrete values of H' by elementary regions or ranges of H'', the number of the copies belonging to the range $\Delta H''$ being equal to $\int_{\Delta H''} |c_{H''}|^2\,dH''$—provided the functions $\psi_{H''}$ are duly normalized according to the equation

$$\int \psi_{H''}^*\,\psi_{H''''}\,dV = \delta(H''-H'''') \quad \text{or} \quad \int \psi_{H''}^*\,\psi_{H''''}\,dH'''' = 1.$$

It should be remembered that this condition is equivalent to the usual normalizing condition $\int |\bar{\psi}_{H''}|^2\,dV = 1$ for the quasi-discrete functions

$$\bar{\psi}_{H''} = \lim \frac{1}{\sqrt{(\Delta H'')}} \int_{(\Delta H'')} \psi_{H''}\,dH''.$$

With the help of the latter the case of a continuous spectrum can be dealt with in exactly the same way as the discrete case, provided we start with finite ranges $\Delta H''$ and pass to the limit $\Delta H'' \to 0$ after having calculated the coefficients c.

The actual determination of the perturbed motion by the method of transitions explained above, both in the case of a variable energy K and in the special case of a constant K, can be carried out by means of a process of successive approximations, based upon the following consideration. If there were no perturbation, then the coefficients c (but not C!) would remain constant, preserving those values c^0 which they were supposed to have at the initial moment $t = 0$. The action of the perturbation will be to modify these values, so that we can put $c(t) = c^0 + \Delta c(t)$ and consider $\Delta c(t)$ as a small quantity—for sufficiently weak perturbing forces and, *in general, for sufficiently small values of t.* The latter condition constitutes an important restriction of the validity of the approximation method in question—a restriction that does not have any equivalent in the alternative method dealing with stationary states and not involving the time (if K does not depend upon the time).

It is, however, perfectly natural from the physical point of view, since, in the determination of transition probabilities, we have to limit ourselves to short intervals of time. Regarding the matrix components

$S_{H'H''}$ as small quantities of the first order, we can put

$$c_{H'}(t) = c_{H'}^0 + \Delta_1 c_{H'}(t) + \Delta_2 c_{H'}(t) + \cdots$$

and obtain the corrections $\Delta_1 c$, $\Delta_2 c$, etc., by the usual scheme of successive approximations.

Confining ourselves again, for the sake of simplicity, to the case of a *discrete* spectrum, we obtain a chain of equations starting with

$$-\frac{h}{2\pi i}\frac{d}{dt}\Delta_1 c_{H'} = \sum_{H''} S_{H'H''} c_{H''}^0 \tag{169}$$

(first approximation),

$$-\frac{h}{2\pi i}\frac{d}{dt}\Delta_2 c_{H'} = \sum_{H''} S_{H'H''} \Delta_1 c_{H''}, \tag{169a}$$

(second approximation), and so on. Since the matrix components $S_{H'H''}$ are known functions of the time, equations (169) can be integrated directly with the result

$$\Delta_1 c_{H'}(t) = -\frac{2\pi i}{h}\sum_{H''} c_{H''}^0 \int_0^t S_{H'H''}\, dt, \tag{170}$$

which, on substitution in (162 a), gives

$$\Delta_2 c_{H'}(t) = -\frac{4\pi^2}{h^2}\sum_{H''}\sum_{H'''} c_{H'''}^0 \int_0^t dt'\, S_{H'H''}(t') \int_0^{t'} dt''\, S_{H''H'''}(t''). \tag{170a}$$

In a similar way one can obtain an expression for $\Delta_n a_{H'}(t)$ which is of the nth order with respect to the small quantities $S_{H'H''}$, etc.

The function S can usually be represented in the form of a product of a function of the coordinates and a function of the time:

$$S = T(x,y,z)f(t), \tag{171}$$

or more generally as a sum of terms of this type. We get accordingly

$$S_{H'H''} = T_{H'H''}^0 f(t)e^{i2\pi(H'-H'')t/h}, \tag{171a}$$

and

$$\int_0^t S_{H'H''}(t')\, dt' = T_{H'H''}^0 f_{\nu_{H'H''}}(t), \tag{171b}$$

where $\nu_{H'H''} = (H'-H'')/h$ and

$$f_\nu(t) = \int_0^t f(t')e^{i2\pi\nu t'}\, dt', \tag{171c}$$

This function can be defined as the amplitude coefficient in the Fourier integral representation of the function $f(t')$ within the interval $0 \leqslant t' \leqslant t$, or more exactly of a function which is equal to $f(t')$ within this interval *and vanishes outside it.* The latter function

$$f_0^t(t') = \int\limits_{-\infty}^{+\infty} f_\nu(t)e^{-i2\pi\nu t'}\, d\nu$$

can replace the actual function $f(t)$ so far as we are interested in the results produced by the perturbation S during the limited time t.

Turning to the quantities $N_{H'} = |c_{H'}|^2$, we get

$$N_{H''} = |c_{H''}^0|^2 + (c_{H''}^{0*}\Delta_1 c_{H''} + c_{H''}^0 \Delta_1 c_{H''}^*) + |\Delta_1 c_{H''}|^2 +$$
$$+ (c_{H''}^{0*}\Delta_2 c_{H''} + c_{H''}^0 \Delta_2 c_{H''}^*) + \dots. \qquad (172)$$

Terms of higher order will not be needed in future and have accordingly been dropped. In the particular case when $c_{H''}^0 = 0$, this expression reduces to

$$N_{H''} = |\Delta_1 c_{H''}|^2. \qquad (172\,a)$$

If initially the particle were supposed to be in a definite state, H' say (so that $c_{H''}^0 = c_{H''H'}^0 = \delta_{H''H'}$), equations (170) and (170a) reduce to

$$\Delta_1 c_{H''H'} = -\frac{2\pi i}{h}\int\limits_0^t S_{H''H'}\, dt, \qquad (173)$$

(with H'' and H' interchanged) and

$$\Delta_2 c_{H''H'} = -\frac{4\pi^2}{h^2}\sum_{H'''}\int\limits_0^t dt'\, S_{H''H'''}(t')\int\limits_0^{t'} dt''\, S_{H'''H'}(t''). \qquad (173\,a)$$

These equations give the first and second approximation for the elements of the 'transition matrix' $c_{H''H'}$. We need not consider here their geometrical representation (as determining the angles between the fixed H-axes and the rotating K_H-axes in the state-space), since it is identical with that of the transformation coefficients a, discussed in § 19.

It is also hardly necessary to point out the way in which the preceding equations can be generalized to allow for the presence of a continuous or mixed spectrum; all we need to do in this case is to replace the sums wholly or partially by integrals extended over the continuously variable parameters.

The equations (173) and (173a), as well as the higher approximations for $c_{H''H'}$, can be obtained in a more straightforward, though somewhat symbolic, way by considering the coefficients $c_{H''H'}(t)$ as a matrix and writing the equations (161), which serve to define them, in the matrix form

$$-\frac{h}{2\pi i}\frac{dc}{dt} = Sc. \qquad (174)$$

We thus get, treating S as an ordinary function of the time,

$$c(t) = e^{-\frac{2\pi i}{h}\int_0^t S\,dt}\,c(0),\qquad\qquad (174\,\text{a})$$

or putting, for the sake of brevity, $\dfrac{2\pi}{h}\displaystyle\int_0^t S\,dt = R$ and expanding the exponential in a power series

$$c(t) = (1 - iR - \tfrac{1}{2}R^2 + ...)c(0).\qquad\qquad (174\,\text{b})$$

This formula contains the two equations (173) and (173 a) as corresponding to the terms of the first and second order in the expansion. It is self-evident that all the multiplications must be carried out in the order stated, according to the general rule of matrix multiplication, and that, moreover, the matrix $c(0)$ must be defined as the unit matrix

$$c_{H''H'}(0) = \delta_{H''H'}.$$

It may seem at first sight that there is a discrepancy between the expression (173 a) and the second-order term of (174 b)

$$\Delta_2 c_{H''H'} = -\tfrac{1}{2}(R^2\delta)_{H''H'} = -\tfrac{1}{2}\sum_{H'''} R_{H''H'''}R_{H'''H'},$$

i.e.

$$\Delta_2 c_{H''H'} = -\frac{2\pi^2}{h^2}\sum_{H'''}\int_0^t S_{H''H'''}\,dt''\int_0^{t'} S_{H'''H'}\,dt''.\qquad\qquad (174\,\text{c})$$

As a matter of fact, they are easily seen to be identical (by a generalization of the well-known relation for multiple integrals with the same variable).

Since the first factor in (174 a) is a pure imaginary, we get at once the relation

$$c^\dagger(t)c(t) = c^\dagger(0)c(0) = \delta,$$

which means that $\sum_{H''}|c_{H''H'}(t)|^2 = 1$ in agreement with the elementary theory of Part I (§ 18) or with the formula (163 b) of this section.

It should be mentioned, in conclusion, that the case of a variable perturbation can be dealt with by a method similar to that of Born for the case of a constant perturbation in the theory of stationary states (§ 20). We can, in fact, determine the functions $\phi_{H'}$, which are the particular solutions of the equation $(H+S+p_t)\phi = 0$ reducing to $\psi_{H'} = \psi_{H'}^0$ at the initial instant $t = 0$, by putting

$$\phi_{H'} = \psi_{H'} + \Delta_1\psi_{H'} + \Delta_2\psi_{H'} + ...,$$

and integrating successively the chain of equations

$$(H+p_t)\Delta_1\psi_{H'} = -S\psi_{H'},$$
$$(H+p_t)\Delta_2\psi_{H'} = -S\Delta_1\psi_{H'},$$

etc., subject to the condition that $\Delta_1\psi_{H'} = \Delta_2\psi_{H'} = \ldots = 0$ for $t = 0$. This method can be advantageously applied in the case of continuous spectra. It is, of course, completely equivalent to the method explained above, differing from it only by avoiding the use of the coefficients c.

22. First Approximation; Theory of Simple Transitions

The study of transitions produced by a perturbing force can conveniently be divided into two parts, corresponding to the first and to the second approximation of the general theory. The first-order terms determine the probability of simple (or direct) transitions between two states, which have been dealt with already to some extent in Part I, § 18; while the second-order terms mainly determine the probability of combined transitions, involving intermediate states.

So far as the action of variable forces is concerned, we shall restrict ourselves to the case of a harmonically oscillating force represented by the expression (171) with $f(t) = \cos(2\pi\nu t+\beta)$. In the general case of a force represented by a sum (or integral) of terms of this form with different frequencies ν, $\Delta_1 c_{H''H'}$ reduces to the sum (or integral) of parts corresponding to the separate harmonic terms of S.

Putting $f(t) = \frac{1}{2}\big[e^{i(2\pi\nu t+\beta)}+e^{-i(2\pi\nu t+\beta)}\big]$, we get, according to (170), (169 b), and (169 c),

$$\Delta_1 c_{H''H'} = -\tfrac{1}{2}T^0_{H''H'}\left[e^{i\beta}\frac{e^{i2\pi(H''-H'+h\nu)t/h}-1}{H''-H'+h\nu}+e^{-i\beta}\frac{e^{i2\pi(H''-H'-h\nu)t/h}-1}{H''-H'-h\nu}\right],$$

(175)

which can also be written in the form

$$\Delta_1 c_{H''H'} = -\frac{1}{2h}T^0_{H''H'}\left[e^{i\beta}\frac{e^{i2\pi(\nu_{H''H'}+\nu)t}-1}{\nu_{H''H'}+\nu}+e^{-i\beta}\frac{e^{i2\pi(\nu_{H''H'}-\nu)t}-1}{\nu_{H''H'}-\nu}\right],$$ (175 a)

involving the transition frequencies $\nu_{H''H'} = (H''-H')/h$ instead of the energy values.

As pointed out in Part I, § 18, these expressions, regarded as functions of the time, have two entirely different characters depending upon whether the absolute value of the transition frequency $\nu_{H''H'}$ coincides with ν ('resonance') or not.

In the latter case $\Delta_1 c_{H''H'}$ oscillates about the value zero, while $N_{H''}$, as determined by (172 a) (for a state H'' different from H'), oscillates about a small (positive) average value

$$\overline{N}_{H''} = |T^0_{H''H'}|^2 \left[\frac{1}{(H''-H'+h\nu)^2} + \frac{1}{(H''-H'-h\nu)^2} \right], \qquad (176)$$

representing the average number of copies of the particle in the initially vacant state H''.

In the case of resonance ($\nu = \pm\nu_{H''H'}$) one of the two terms in the square brackets becomes infinite, which means that a stationary distribution is impossible, i.e. that the number of copies in the state H'' is steadily increasing. With the help of the formula

$$\lim_{\xi\to 0} \frac{e^{i2\pi\xi t}-1}{\xi} = 2\pi i t,$$

we get in this case, according to (175),

$$\Delta_1 c_{H''H'} = -\frac{1}{2h} T^0_{H''H'}[e^{\pm i\beta}2\pi it + \text{periodic term}]$$

(the positive sign referring to $H'' > H'$ and the negative sign to $H'' < H'$), that is, dropping the periodic term which remains small while t increases:

$$N_{H''} = \frac{\pi^2}{h^2} |T^0_{H''H'}|^2 t^2. \qquad (176\,a)$$

A perturbing force is usually said to induce transitions from the state H' to H'' only when these transitions are manifested as a systematic increase of $N_{H''}$ with the time, i.e. in the case of resonance. In the old quantum theory the resonance or frequency condition was regarded as the expression of the law of the conservation of energy on the assumption that light of frequency ν can be absorbed or emitted in energy quanta of the magnitude $h\nu$. We see that this relation is by no means confined to light, being valid in the case of harmonic oscillations of any kind.—To the type of resonance implied there corresponds in our pendulum model not ordinary resonance between the external force and the free vibrations of a definite pendulum, but what in classical mechanics is denoted by 'parametric resonance', which means the coincidence of the frequency of the variation of the coupling $S^0_{H'H''}$ between two pendulums H' and H'' with the difference of the frequencies of their free vibrations (corresponding to the absence of the coupling). It can, in fact, easily be shown that under this condition even a very weak harmonic variation of the coupling coefficient ($\Phi_{H'H''}$) must produce a steady transfer of energy from the H'-pendulum (supposed to be initially the only one set in motion) to the H''-pendulum while all the other pendulums H''' for which the condition of parametric resonance is not fulfilled will perform oscillations of small amplitude without any tendency towards a steady increase.

The quadratic increase of $N_{H''}$ with the time according to (176 a) corresponds to a transition probability (referred to unit time)

$$\Gamma_{H''H'} = \frac{dN_{H''}}{dt} = \frac{2\pi^2}{h^2}|T^0_{H''H'}|^2t,$$

which is itself a linear function of the time.

This result is due to the exact coincidence between $\nu_{H''H'}$ and ν (*sharp resonance*), which is practically never realized in nature. It has been shown in Part I, § 18, that in the case of 'nearly-monochromatic' light, formed by a spectral line of finite width, $N_{H''}$ becomes a linear function of the time and the transition probability $\Gamma_{H''H'}$ becomes a constant. The same is true, of course, of any nearly-harmonic perturbation.

We shall return to this question in the second part of this section where it will be dealt with by a different method.

The preceding formula cannot be directly applied to the special case $\nu = 0$ corresponding to a perturbing force which does not depend upon the time. We must, namely, take into account the fact that in the case $\nu > 0$ only one term of (175) is effective in producing transitions from the state H' to the state with higher energy $H'' = H' + h\nu$, while the other would be effective in producing transitions from H' to the lower level $H'' = H' - h\nu$ (if such a level exists). Now when $\nu = 0$ both terms of (175) become equally effective for the transition $H' \to H''$ (more simply, the splitting of S into two terms becomes meaningless). We thus get

$$\Delta_1 c_{H''H'} = -S^0_{H''H'}\frac{e^{i2\pi(H''-H')t/h}-1}{H''-H'} = -\frac{S^0_{H''H'}}{h}\frac{e^{i2\pi\nu_{H''H'}t}-1}{\nu_{H''H'}}, \quad (177)$$

whence

$$\overline{N}_{H''} = \frac{2|S^0_{H''H'}|^2}{(H''-H')^2} \quad (177\,a)$$

if $H'' \neq H'$, and

$$N_{H''} = \frac{4\pi^2}{h^2}|S^0_{H''H'}|^2t^2 \quad (177\,b)$$

if $H'' = H'$, which is the resonance condition in the present case. This type of 'inner' resonance is faithfully reproduced in our pendulum model by the resonance between the pendulums representing the unperturbed states H' and H''. It will be noticed that the expression (177 b) differs from the corresponding expression (176 a) for the case $\nu > 0$ by a factor 4 in the numerator.

The quantities $S^0_{H'H'}$, $S^0_{H''H''}$, etc., have the effect of slightly disturbing the resonance between the corresponding pendulums, while the quantities $S^0_{H''H'}$ describe the perturbing *coupling* forces. As long as the latter are weak and there is no resonance, there corresponds to the unperturbed vibration of each pendulum (H') a perturbed normal vibration of the whole system (K') in which this particular pendulum plays the principal role, while all the others only faintly accompany it. This state of affairs is described by the formula $a_{H''K'} = \delta_{H''K'} + \Delta a_{H''K'}$ of § 19, where $a_{H''K'}$ are the transformation coefficients between the functions $\chi^0_{K'}$ and $\psi^0_{H''}$; the small quantities $\Delta a_{H''K'}$ represent the participation of the pendulums $H'' \neq H'$ in the normal vibration K', corresponding to the unperturbed oscillation of the pendulum H' alone. We might expect the quantities $N_{H''}$—or their average values—to be equal to the square of the moduli of these small quantities. As a matter of fact, we have, according to (148 b),

$$\Delta_1 a_{H''K'} = -\frac{S^0_{H''H'}}{H'' - H'}$$

and consequently $$|\Delta_1 a_{H''K'}|^2 = \frac{|S^0_{H''H'}|^2}{(H'' - H')^2},$$

which is equal to one-half of the value of $N_{H''}$ as determined by (177).

This discrepancy is explained by the fact that the quantities $|\Delta_1 a_{H''K'}|^2$ refer to the *stationary* states ($\chi_{K'}$) of the perturbed system, while the quantities (177 a) refer to the non-stationary states $\phi_{H'}$, or more exactly to the initial stages in the development of these states— as follows from the method of approximation used in deriving equation (177). The limitation to the initial stages is practically irrelevant so long as the quantities $c_{H''H'}$ remain small, i.e. so long as there is no resonance ($H'' \neq H'$). It becomes, however, of primary importance in the case of resonance, the formula (177 b) being valid for small values of t only.

The actual conditions met with in this case can be best understood with the help of the pendulum model. If initially only one pendulum, H' say, were set in motion, then, however small the perturbing forces which couple it with other pendulums, those which are in resonance with it will gradually acquire large vibration amplitudes (while the rest will but faintly accompany them as before). Resonance thus excludes the 'dominance' of one particular pendulum in the perturbed vibrations: all the pendulums which are in resonance with each other become equally important in the vibrations started by any one of them.

In the simplest case of two coupled pendulums in resonance we obtain the following well-known results: If originally (when $t = 0$) only *one* of the two pendulums was vibrating, then its vibration energy must gradually go over to the second pendulum. If both pendulums are identical, this process goes on until the first pendulum comes to a standstill and the second takes over its role. Similar *beats*, i.e. relatively slow periodic increases and decreases of the vibrations of one pendulum at the cost of the other, must take place with any relations between their initial amplitudes and phases—except in two cases: 'symmetrical' vibrations with equal (real) amplitudes and phases, and 'antisymmetrical' with equal amplitudes and opposite phases. In these exceptional cases the vibrations maintain a stationary character, i.e. their amplitudes remain constant. The symmetrical and antisymmetrical vibrations have somewhat different frequencies, both of which are, in general, different from the common unperturbed vibration frequency of the pendulums.

The non-stationary vibrations can be represented by a superposition of the two kinds of stationary vibrations. The frequency of the resulting 'beats' must obviously be equal to the difference of the two fundamental frequencies.

These results can easily be generalized to any finite number, r' say, of coupled pendulums in resonance. In the first approximation their coupling with other pendulums can be neglected. The resulting vibrations of the resonance group can be represented as a superposition of r' independent normal vibrations with different frequencies. By suitably adjusting the amplitudes (and phases) of these normal vibrations, a resulting vibration can be obtained such that, at the instant $t = 0$, one pendulum only—H' say—is in motion. The amplitudes of the others will then at the beginning increase linearly with the time and their energies increase proportionally to t^2, this dependence being restricted to such values of t as are small compared with the 'beat periods', that is, the reciprocals of the frequency-differences between the different normal modes of vibration.

These results can easily be obtained from the general theory embodied in equations (161 a) and (161 b) of § 21. It should be remarked that, although equations (161 a) must be used for the approximate calculation of the numbers $N_{H'}$ (for the coefficients $c_{H'}$ can be supposed to be approximately constant while the coefficients $C_{H'}$ cannot), equations (161 b), with the coefficients $K^0_{H'H'}$ which are independent of the time are more appropriate for the discussion of the case of resonance, because of their similarity to the equations which determine the vibrations of a system of coupled pendulums—the only modification consisting in replacing $\dfrac{d^2}{dt^2}$ by $\dfrac{h}{2\pi i}\dfrac{d}{dt}$.

If the coupling between the pendulums (i.e. H-states) not belonging to the resonance (degenerate) set in question and those which belong to this set is neglected, then the quantities $C_{H'}$ for the latter pendulums can be determined by the system of r' equations

$$-\frac{h}{2\pi i}\frac{d}{dt}C_{H'} = \sum_{H''=H'} K^0_{H'H''}\,C_{H''},$$

or in the notation corresponding to equation (154 b),

$$-\frac{h}{2\pi i}\frac{d}{dt}C_m = \sum_{n=1}^{r'} K^0_{mn}\,C_n \qquad (m = 1, 2, ..., r'). \tag{178}$$

With the help of the relations

$$C_m = c_m\,e^{-i2\pi H't/h} \quad \text{and} \quad K^0_{mn} = \delta_{mn}H' + S^0_{mn}$$

these equations can be reduced to the form

$$-\frac{h}{2\pi i}\frac{d}{dt}c_m = \sum_{n=1}^{r'} S^0_{mn}\,c_n. \tag{178a}$$

The latter equations can be derived directly from the general equations (161 a) in the same way as equations (178) have been derived from (161 b), in conjunction with the condition $H_m = H_n = H'$ (i.e. $S_{mn} = S^0_{mn}$), namely, by dropping terms connecting the states which belong to the same energy H' with those which belong to different energy-levels. We have preferred, however, the indirect derivation in order to preserve throughout the analogy with the classical theory of the pendulum model. So far, however, as the results are concerned, the r' states of the same energy H' can be represented equally well by two systems of r' pendulums whose oscillations are determined either by equations (178) or (178 a).

Taking equations (178 a), we can first of all obtain the normal vibrations (i.e. the K-stationary states) by putting $c_n = a_n\,e^{-i2\pi\Delta H't/h}$ [or $C_n = a_n\,e^{-i2\pi K't/h}$ in the case of equations (178)], whereby it reduces to the system of equations (154 b), which was obtained by another method in § 19. After this, the general solution of (178 a) can be written in the form

$$c_n = \sum_{s=1}^{r'} \gamma_s\,a_{ns}\,e^{-i2\pi(\Delta H')_s t/h}, \tag{178b}$$

where the $(\Delta H')_s$ are the solutions of (154 c) and the a_{ns} are the corresponding normalized solutions of (154 b), while the γ_s denote arbitrary constants. As already mentioned, these constants can be adjusted in such a way as to make all the c_m vanish at the initial instant $t = 0$ with the exception of one of them, c_m say. This particular set of γ_s can conveniently be denoted by γ_{sm}.

We have, for their determination, the system of equations

$$\sum_s a_{ns}\gamma_{sm} = \delta_{nm}, \tag{179}$$

which shows that the matrix γ is identical with a^{-1} or $a^\dagger$. We thus get, writing c_{nm} instead of c_n,

$$c_{nm} = \sum_s a_{ns}a_{ms}^* e^{-i2\pi(\Delta H')_s t/h}, \tag{179 a}$$

or

$$C_{nm} = \sum_s a_{ns}a_{ms}^* e^{-i2\pi K_s' t/h}. \tag{179 b}$$

Multiplying these expressions by their conjugate complex, we get

$$N_m = \sum_s \sum_{s'} \rho_{ss'}^{nm} \cos\frac{2\pi}{h}(K_s' - K_{s'}')t, \tag{179 c}$$

where ρ_{ss}^{nm} is the real part of the product $a_{ns}a_{ms}^* a_{ns'}^* a_{ms'}$.

We thus see that N_m is represented as a function of the time as a sum of constant terms ($s' = s$) and terms oscillating with the 'difference-' or 'beat'-frequencies $\nu_{ss'} = (K_s' - K_{s'}')/h = (\Delta H_s' - \Delta H_{s'}')/h$. So long as the product of the time t with these frequencies (which are the reciprocals of the 'beat periods') is small compared with 1, we can put

$$\cos\frac{2\pi}{h}\nu_{ss'}t \cong 1 - \frac{1}{2}\left(\frac{2\pi}{h}\nu_{ss'}t\right)^2,$$

which gives, since N_m vanishes for $t = 0$ (unless $m = n$),

$$N_n \cong -\frac{4\pi^2}{h^2}\left(\sum_{s<s'}\sum \rho_{ss'}^{nm}\nu_{ss'}^2\right)t^2.$$

This expression coincides with (177 b) if

$$\sum_{s<s'}\sum \rho_{ss'}^{nm}\nu_{ss'}^2 = -|S_{nm}^0|^2.$$

It can easily be shown, with the help of equations (154 b) and (154 c), that this relation actually holds. We shall not, however, give the proof of it here.

It may be remarked that equation (179) reduces, subject to the same condition or rather subject to the condition $\Delta H_s' t/h \ll 1$ (for all s), to

$$c_{nm} \cong -\frac{i2\pi}{h}\left(\sum_s a_{ns}a_{ms}^*(\Delta H')_s\right)t,$$

while equation (177) gives, in the case of resonance,

$$\Delta_1 c_{H''H'} = c_{nm} \cong \frac{i2\pi}{h}S_{nm}^0 t.$$

from which, by the way, it follows that

$$S^0_{nm} = \sum_s a_{ns} a^*_{ms} (\Delta H')_s.$$

This relation can be derived from the equations

$$\sum_{n} S^0_{mn} a_{ns} = \Delta H'_s a_{ms}$$

by multiplying them by $a^*_{n's}$ and summing over s. We thus get

$$\sum_s \Delta H'_s a_{ms} a^*_{n's} = \sum_n S^0_{mn} \sum_s a_{ns} a^*_{n's} = \sum_n S^0_{mn} \delta_{nn'} = S^0_{mn'}.$$

Further, it should be mentioned that an expansion of the same type as that for the coefficients $c_{H'm}$ is not possible for the coefficients $C_{H'm}$, as determined by (179 b), on account of the large value of the frequencies K'_s/h. More exactly, the approximate expression $C_{nm} \sim t$ would be valid for exceedingly short times only (small compared with the reciprocal of K'/h), which hardly come into consideration.

The resonance between the r' states we have just considered corresponds to an absolute degeneracy between these states in the sense of the perturbation theory not involving the time. In the present theory we need not, however, distinguish between this case and that of a 'relative degeneracy' (§ 20), so long as the energy-differences $(H'-H'')$ between the states under consideration are small compared with the corresponding matrix elements of the perturbation energy $S_{H'H''}$. If the ratios $S_{H'H''}/(H'-H'')$ are large compared with 1 we can still use the expression (177 b) for the probability of the transition $H' \to H''$ provided the time t is small compared with the reciprocal of the 'beat frequency' $(H''-H')/h$. In the contrary case we must limit ourselves to the expression (177 a) for the average value of the probability of finding the system in the new state H''.

We have, hitherto, confined ourselves exclusively to the case of a discrete H-spectrum. The modifications of the general theory which are necessary in order to allow for the presence of a continuous or mixed spectrum in a limited or unlimited range have already been indicated in the preceding section. They necessitate, however, an important revision of the approximate theory for the case of resonance between states belonging to a discrete set, on the one hand, and states belonging to a continuous set on the other (and also between states belonging to two different continuous sets). The essence of this revision consists in the replacement of the idea of *sharp resonance*, referring to two *exactly* determined states, by that of *unsharp resonance* for a narrow range or 'band' of final states belonging to a continuous set.

Let us consider transitions which are produced by a perturbing force vibrating harmonically with the frequency ν. The initial state will be supposed to belong to a discrete set and to have the energy H'. If the energy $H'+h\nu$ lies in the region of the continuous spectrum (as can happen in the case of a hydrogen-like atom if $H' < 0$ while $H'+h\nu > 0$), then transitions will be produced not only to the state with the energy $H''_\nu = H'+h\nu$, but also to the neighbouring states whose energy H'' is slightly different from H''_ν. This follows from two considerations. Firstly, the resonance condition $H'' = H'+h\nu$ need not be exactly satisfied even when the final state belongs to a discrete set. Secondly, the neighbouring states of a continuous set are themselves approximately in resonance with each other and cannot therefore be considered separately. We must consider instead a 'band' of neighbouring states or, in other words, a 'wave group' formed by the superposition of the harmonic waves representing them.

According to the general theory, we obtain for the coefficient $c_{H''}$ of the functions $\psi_{H''}$ belonging to a continuous set exactly the same differential equations as for the coefficients of the functions belonging to a discrete state. If the particle were supposed to be initially in the (discrete) state H', then we have in both cases the same expression for $c_{H''} = c_{H''H'}$, namely, (175). Limiting ourselves to states in the neighbourhood of the resonance state with the energy $H'' = H''_\nu = H'+h\nu$, we can drop the first term in (175) on account of its relative smallness, so that

$$\Delta_1 c_{H''H'} = -\tfrac{1}{2}T^0_{H''H'}\,e^{-i\beta}\frac{e^{i2\pi(H''-H'-h\nu)t/h}-1}{H''-H'-h\nu}. \qquad (180)$$

If the functions $\psi_{H''}$ are duly normalized, the number of copies of the particles that have passed during the time t from the state H' into a range $\Delta H''$ about the resonance value H''_ν is given by the expression

$$N_{\Delta H''_\nu} = \int_{\Delta H''} |\Delta_1 c_{H''H'}|^2\, dH''. \qquad (180\,\text{a})$$

Before carrying out the integration over H'' we must notice that this integration actually refers to the energy alone if the other two parameters specifying the wave functions $\psi_{H''}$ remain discrete (as, for example, in the case of the hydrogen-like atom). If one or both of these parameters are continuously variable, dH'' must be replaced by the product of dH'' with the element or elements of these continuously variable parameters. Leaving this case aside, we can calculate (180 a) by integrating over the energy alone.

Since the last factor in (180) has, for not too small values of t, a very sharp maximum at the resonance point $H'' = H''_\nu$ and comparatively very small values outside the immediate vicinity of this point, we can replace the first factor by its value for $H'' = H''_\nu$ and extend the integration over the difference $H'' - H''_\nu$ from $-\infty$ to $+\infty$.

Putting, for brevity, $2\pi(H'' - H' - h\nu)t/h = \xi$, we then get

$$N_{\Delta H''_\nu} = \tfrac{1}{4}|T^0_{H''_\nu H'}|^2 \frac{2\pi}{h} \int_{-\infty}^{+\infty} \left|\frac{e^{i\xi}-1}{\xi}\right|^2 d\xi.$$

Since $|e^{i\xi}-1|^2 = 2(1-\cos\xi) = 4\sin^2\tfrac{1}{2}\xi$ and

$$\int_{-\infty}^{+\infty} \frac{4\sin^2\tfrac{1}{2}\xi}{\xi^2}\, d\xi = 2\int_{-\infty}^{+\infty}\left(\frac{\sin\tfrac{1}{2}\xi}{\tfrac{1}{2}\xi}\right)^2 d(\tfrac{1}{2}\xi) = 2\pi,$$

this gives
$$N_{\Delta H''_\nu} = \frac{\pi^2}{h}|T^0_{H''_\nu H'}|^2 t. \tag{181}$$

The probability of a transition from the state H' into the band $\Delta H''_\nu$ per unit time is thus equal to

$$\Gamma_{H''_\nu H'} = \frac{\pi^2}{h}|T^0_{H''_\nu H'}|^2. \tag{181 a}$$

The same result could be obtained with the help of the quasi-discrete functions

$$\bar\psi_{H''} = \lim \frac{1}{\sqrt{(\Delta H'')}} \int_{\Delta H''} \psi_{H''}\, dH''.$$

We must first consider the intervals $\Delta H''$ as finite and calculate the coefficients $\bar c_{H''H'} = \Delta_1 \bar c_{H''H'}$ according to formula (180) with the matrix elements $T^0_{H''H'}$ replaced by

$$\bar T^0_{H''H'} = \int \bar\psi^{0*}_{H''}\, T\psi^0_{H'}\, dV \cong \frac{1}{\sqrt{(\Delta H'')}} \int dV \int_{\Delta H''} \psi^{0*}_{H''}\, T\psi^0_{H'}\, dH''$$

$$\cong \sqrt{(\Delta H'')} \int \psi^0_{H''}\, T\psi^0_{H'}\, dV = \sqrt{(\Delta H'')}\, T^0_{H''H'}.$$

This formula is the more accurate the smaller the interval $\Delta H''$. We can therefore use it in the calculation of the limiting value of the sum $\sum_{H''} |\Delta\bar c_{H''H'}|^2 = \sum_{H''} |\Delta c_{H''H'}|^2 \Delta H''$ extended over a large number of infinitely small intervals containing the resonance value H''_ν. This limiting value is obviously nothing else but the integral (180 a).

An important example of transitions of the mixed type just considered is the *ionization* of an atom by the action of light, i.e. the *photoelectric effect*. In this case we can put

$$S = -eE_0 \cos(2\pi\nu t + \beta),$$

where E_0 is the amplitude of the electric vector of the light waves, supposed to be parallel to the x-axis, and e is the charge of the electron. This gives

$$\Gamma_{H''_\nu H'} = \frac{\pi^2 e^2 E_0^2}{h} |x_{H''_\nu H'}|^2. \tag{181 b}$$

Let us now turn to the case $\nu = 0$ corresponding to a perturbation which does not depend upon the time. The transition being again from a discrete state H' to a continuous range of states H'' belonging to approximately the same value of the energy, we can determine its probability per unit time by the formula (181 a), putting $T = S$ and introducing the factor 4, for the same reason as in the formula (177 b) [in contradistinction from (176 a)]. We thus get

$$\Gamma_{H''H'} = \frac{4\pi^2}{h} |S^0_{H''H'}|^2 \qquad (H'' = H'). \tag{182}$$

Another—purely formal—modification which must be introduced for the case $\nu = 0$ refers to the notation. If the continuous spectrum overlaps the discrete spectrum (which is necessary for the resonance condition $H'' = H'$ to be satisfied), we must introduce explicitly one or two parameters in order to distinguish the different states (continuous and discrete) which have the same energy. Denoting this parameter by Q, we can rewrite (182) in the form

$$\Gamma_{Q''Q'} = \frac{4\pi^2}{h} |S^0_{H'Q'';H'Q'}|^2. \tag{182 a}$$

If, finally, the parameter Q'' is continuously variable and if a range of the continuous spectrum is specified by the product

$$\sigma(H'', Q'') \, dH'' dQ'',$$

where σ is a certain function of H'' and Q'' such that the probability of finding the particle in the above range is equal to

$$|c_{H'Q'}|^2 \sigma(H'', Q'') \, dH'' dQ'',$$

then the probability of a resonance transition from the sharply defined state $H'Q'$ into a band corresponding to the interval dQ'' is given by

$$\Gamma_{dQ'',Q'} = \frac{4\pi^2}{h} |S^0_{H'Q'',H'Q'}|^2 \sigma(H', Q'') \, dQ''. \tag{182 b}$$

The same modification applies to a resonance transition produced by a harmonically vibrating perturbation. Instead of (181 a) we then get

$$\Gamma_{dQ'',Q'} = \frac{\pi^2}{h} |T^0_{H''_{\nu}Q'';H'Q'}|^2 \sigma(H''_{\nu}, Q'')\, dQ''. \qquad (182\,c)$$

It can easily be shown that these formulae remain valid when both the final *and the initial* states belong to a continuous set. We come upon this case in *collision problems* of the simplest type such as the deflexion of a particle by some field of force practically limited to a finite region of space, the initial and final states ('before' and 'after' the collision with the source of the perturbing field) being described by wave functions corresponding to the motion in the absence of this field.

If, however, the final state belongs to a discrete set, then the initial state must be specified unsharply, i.e. by a certain range of H' (and eventually also of Q').

In conclusion the following circumstance must be pointed out. From the corpuscular point of view resonance means the *conservation of energy*. The fact that perturbing forces practically produce only those transitions which satisfy the resonance condition can be regarded from this point of view as the natural consequence of the law of conservation of energy. As we have seen, however, the resonance condition is not strictly obeyed in wave mechanics. First of all, transitions of a non-systematic character are produced from the initial state to states with an entirely different energy, the average probability of finding the particle in these 'stray' states being given by the formula (183 a). Further, in the case of a continuous spectrum, the systematic transitions are governed by the condition of *unsharp* resonance, implying slight deviations from the law of conservation of energy. It thus seems that the latter does not strictly hold in wave mechanics.

This conclusion is, however, wrong, for the simple reason that H does not represent the actual energy of the particle, this energy, if the perturbation S does not depend upon the time, being specified by the characteristic values of the operator $K = H + S$. The resonance equation $H'' = H'$ is therefore merely an *approximate* expression of the law of conservation of energy which in reality should be expressed by $K'' = K'$.

As a matter of fact, if the motion of the particle is described from the point of view of K, i.e. by means of the characteristic functions of this operator, then a set of stationary states is obtained between which no transitions are possible, irrespective of whether $K'' = K'$ or $K'' \neq K'$. It is only when the motion of the particle is described from the point of view of H that transitions appear, produced by the neglected part S of the total energy K. It is precisely this 'misuse' of the energy S which is the cause of the apparent violation of the law of conservation of energy. From the point of view of H, S is not a constant—unless it commutes with H, which, in general, is not so—and therefore has no definite value. It can therefore be regarded as the 'goat' responsible for the deviations from the conservation law $H'' = H'$ in the transitions for which this equation is not satisfied.

A similar consideration applies even more strongly to the general case in which S does depend upon the time, for in this case the values of the total energy K remain undetermined.

23. Second Approximation; Theory of Combined Transitions

The preceding considerations pave the way to an understanding of transitions the probability of which vanishes when derived from the equations of the first approximation but does not vanish when estimated with the help of the second approximation.

According to equations (173) and (173 a), we have this case if the matrix component $S_{H''H'}$ vanishes, while there is one or several states H''' such that the components $S_{H'H'''}$ and $S_{H'''H'}$ are both different from zero.

For the sake of simplicity we shall first consider the case of discrete states together with a perturbation independent of the time. If there is no resonance between the initial and final states, i.e. if $H'' \neq H'$, then the probability amplitude, $c_{H''H'} = \Delta_2 c_{H''H'}$, of finding the particle in the state H'' will remain a small quantity of the second order, and the square of its modulus $N_{H''}$ will oscillate about an average value of the fourth order of smallness. If, however, $H'' = H'$, $c_{H''H'}$ will increase linearly and $N_{H''}$ will increase quadratically with the time, which means that there are systematic transitions from the initial state H' to the final H'' via one or several intermediate states H'''. For these intermediate states the resonance condition with the end states need not (and in general cannot) be satisfied; the fact, however, that in the combined transitions $H' \to H''' \to H''$ the particle has to pass through a state with an energy H''' different from the initial (and final) value does not in the least prevent it from making such transitions. The apparent violation of the energy law for each of the two 'legs' of the jump from H' to H'' can obviously be straightened out by taking into account the perturbation energy S not only as the cause of the transition but also as an invisible factor in the energy balance. If, for instance,

$H''' > H'$, then we can imagine that the energy $H''' - H'$, which is required for the first step of the transition, is 'borrowed' from the perturbation energy S and restored to it during the second step. The probability amplitude $c_{H'''H'} = \Delta_1 c_{H'''H'}$, of the state H''', will remain small, the corresponding probability (or number of copies in the state H''') $N_{H'''} = |\Delta_1 c_{H'''H'}|^2$ oscillating about the constant value $2|S_{H'''H'}|^2/(H''' - H')^2$, while the number $N_{H''}$, though initially much smaller, increases with the time, and may finally become very large. We can visualize this process by imagining each state as a vessel which may be filled with a liquid representing the probability or the number of copies. This liquid is initially concentrated in the vessel H' and is pumped by the perturbation to the vessel H'' with which it is connected indirectly through a set of vessels H'''; the liquid does not, however, accumulate in the latter—just passing through them and accumulating in H''. A still better picture of this transition process is provided by our pendulum model, the probability or number of copies being represented by the energy flowing from the pendulum H' to the pendulum H'' which is coupled with it through the pendulums H'''. The lack of resonance between the latter and H' results in these pendulums performing steady oscillations of small amplitude and functioning simply as carriers of energy from H' to H''.

After these preliminary considerations of a qualitative character, we can pass to the quantitative theory of the double transitions. Putting in (173 a)

$$S_{H''H'''} = S^0_{H''H'''} e^{i2\pi(H'' - H''')t/h}$$

and

$$S_{H'''H'} = S^0_{H'''H'} e^{i2\pi(H''' - H')t/h},$$

we get

$$\Delta_2 c_{H''H'} = \sum_{H'''} S^0_{H''H'''} S^0_{H'''H'} f_{H''H'''H'}(t), \tag{183}$$

where

$$f_{H''H'''H'}(t) = -\frac{4\pi^2}{h^2} \int_0^t dt' \, e^{i2\pi(H'' - H''')t'/h} \int_0^{t'} dt'' \, e^{i2\pi(H''' - H')t''/h}$$

$$= \frac{2\pi i}{h} \int_0^t dt' \, e^{i2\pi(H'' - H''')t'/h} \frac{e^{i2\pi(H''' - H')t'/h} - 1}{H''' - H'},$$

that is,

$$f_{H''H'''H'}(t) = \frac{e^{i2\pi(H'' - H')t/h} - 1}{(H'' - H')(H''' - H')} - \frac{e^{i2\pi(H'' - H''')t/h} - 1}{(H'' - H''')(H''' - H')}. \tag{183 a}$$

In the case of resonance $H'' = H'$ this expression reduces to

$$f_{H''H'''H'}(t) = \frac{i2\pi t}{h(H''' - H')} + \frac{e^{i2\pi(H' - H''')t/h} - 1}{(H''' - H')^2}. \tag{183 b}$$

Dropping the second term on account of its smallness, we thus get

$$\Delta_2 c_{H''H'} = \frac{2\pi it}{h} \sum_{H'''} \frac{S^0_{H''H'''} S^0_{H'''H'}}{H''' - H'}. \qquad (183\,c)$$

We did not replace $S^0_{H'H'''}$ by $S^0_{H'H''''}$ in spite of the fact that $H'' = H'$ in order to indicate somehow that the final state is different from the initial one. This can be done in a clearer way by introducing the additional suffix Q and writing $S^0_{H'Q'',H'''Q'''} S^0_{H'''Q''',H'Q'}$ instead of $S^0_{H''H'''} S^0_{H'''H'}$.

In the case of double transitions, just as in the case of simple transitions, one usually has to do with an unsharp resonance between the initial state and a band of continuously variable final states. If the energy is the only continuously variable parameter, the probability of transition from $H'Q'$ to $H'Q''$ in the time t is expressed by the integral

$$N_{\Delta H'} = \int |\Delta_2 c_{H''H'}(t)|^2 \, dH''$$

extended over the neighbourhood of the resonance value $H'' = H'$. In carrying out the integration we can drop the second term in the expression (183 a). With this condition we must obviously get the same result as for the simple resonance transition $H' \to H''$, *with the matrix element $S^0_{H''H'}$ replaced by the expression*

$$\sum_{H'''} \frac{S^0_{H''H'''} S^0_{H'''H'}}{H''' - H'}.$$

We thus obtain for the probability per unit time of the transition $H' \to H''$ the following formula [cf. eq. (182 a)]:

$$\Gamma_{H''H'} = \frac{4\pi^2}{h} \left| \sum_{H'''} \frac{S^0_{H''H'''} S^0_{H'''H'}}{H''' - H'} \right|^2 \qquad (H'' = H'). \qquad (184)$$

This formula is not complete in two respects. Firstly, it does not take into account other parameters (Q) in addition to the energy. Secondly, it neglects intermediate states belonging to the continuous energy spectrum. If the parameter Q is discretely variable, we get, instead of (184), the expression

$$\Gamma_{H'Q'',H'Q'} = \frac{4\pi^2}{h} \left| \sum_{H'''} \sum_{Q'''} \frac{S^0_{H'Q'',H'''Q'''} S_{H'''Q''',H'Q'}}{H''' - H'} + \right.$$

$$\left. + \sum_{Q'''} \int dH'''' \frac{S^0_{H'Q'',H''''Q'''} S^0_{H''''Q''',H'Q'}}{H'''' - H'} \right|^2. \qquad (184\,a)$$

If Q is itself continuously variable, then the summation over Q''' must be replaced by an integration, the element dQ''' being multiplied by the factor $\sigma(H''', Q''')$, and Q'' being replaced by the element dQ'' with the factor $\sigma(H', Q'')$ on the right side of (184 a).

If there is a slight direct coupling between the states H' and H'', then the transition probability is determined by the sum of $\Delta_1 c_{H''H'}$ and $\Delta_2 c_{H''H'}$, so that instead of (184) we get

$$\Gamma_{H''H'} = \frac{4\pi^2}{h} \left| S^0_{H''H'} + \sum_{H'''} \frac{S^0_{H''H'''} S^0_{H'''H'}}{H''' - H'} \right|^2. \tag{184 b}$$

It often happens that the perturbation is due to the simultaneous action of two different forces—which are *incoherent* with regard to each other—in the sense that they involve independent phase-factors, over which one must average, with the result that all quantities containing odd powers of these factors vanish.

We thus get $\qquad\qquad S = F + G, \qquad\qquad\qquad$ (185)

and $\qquad\qquad |S^0_{H''H'}|^2 = |F^0_{H''H'}|^2 + |G^0_{H''H'}|^2,$ (185 a)

the average value of the product of $F^0_{H''H'}$ with $G^{0*}_{H''H'}$ being equal to zero.

If we consider simple transitions $H' \to H''$ produced by the simultaneous action of two such perturbations, we get for the transition probability the sum of the two probabilities, corresponding to the action of each of the two perturbations taken separately.

However, in the case of combined transitions, we get, according to (184), the following expression for the transition probability

$$\Gamma_{H''H'} = (F, F)_{H''H'} + (F, G)_{H''H'} + (G, G)_{H''H'}, \tag{186}$$

the first and last terms being obtained from (184) by replacing S by F or G. They represent the 'solo' action of the two perturbing forces, while the middle term represents their combined action, one of the perturbing forces producing the first and the other the second step of the transition. This combination term

$$(F, G)_{H''H'} = \frac{4\pi^2}{h^2} \left| \sum_{H'''} \frac{F^0_{H''H'''} G^0_{H'''H'} + G^0_{H''H'''} F^0_{H'''H'}}{H''' - H'} \right|^2 \qquad (H'' = H') \tag{186 a}$$

turns out to be, in many cases, more important than the two 'pure' terms.

These considerations acquire a particular importance in the generalization of the preceding results for the case of a perturbation depending upon the time.

Let us first assume that S reduces to a simple harmonic vibration without a constant term. We then have, as before,

$$S = T(x, y, z)\cos(2\pi\nu t + \beta).$$

Substituting this in equation (173a), we get the former expression (183) for $\Delta_2 c_{H'H'}$ with

$$f_{H''H'''H'} = -\frac{\pi^2}{h^2}\int\limits_0^t dt' \{e^{i[2\pi(\nu_{H''H'''}+\nu)t'+\beta]}+$$

$$+ e^{i[2\pi(\nu_{H''H'''}-\nu)t'-\beta]}\}\int\limits_0^{t'} dt'' \{e^{i[2\pi(\nu_{H'''H'}+\nu)t''+\beta]}+e^{i[2\pi(\nu_{H'''H'}-\nu)t''-\beta]}\}$$

i.e.

$$f_{H''H'''H'} = \frac{1}{4h^2}\Big\{e^{i2\beta}\frac{e^{i[2\pi(\nu_{H''H'}+2\nu)t]}-1}{(\nu_{H''H'}+2\nu)(\nu_{H'''H'}+\nu)} - e^{i2\beta}\frac{e^{i[2\pi(\nu_{H''H'''}+\nu)t]}-1}{(\nu_{H''H'''}+\nu)(\nu_{H'''H'}+\nu)}+$$

$$+\frac{e^{i2\pi\nu_{H''H'}t}-1}{\nu_{H''H'}(\nu_{H'''H'}-\nu)} - \frac{e^{i2\pi(\nu_{H''H'''}+\nu)t}-1}{(\nu_{H''H'''}+\nu)(\nu_{H'''H'}-\nu)}+$$

$$+\frac{e^{i2\pi\nu_{H''H'}t}-1}{\nu_{H''H'}(\nu_{H'''H'}+\nu)} - \frac{e^{i2\pi(\nu_{H''H'''}-\nu)t}-1}{(\nu_{H''H'''}-\nu)(\nu_{H'''H'}+\nu)}+$$

$$+e^{-i2\beta}\frac{e^{i2\pi(\nu_{H''H'}-2\nu)t}-1}{(\nu_{H''H'}-2\nu)(\nu_{H'''H'}-\nu)} - e^{-i2\beta}\frac{e^{i2\pi(\nu_{H''H'''}-\nu)t}-1}{(\nu_{H''H'''}-\nu)(\nu_{H'''H'}-\nu)}\Big\}.$$

This expression clearly shows that the resonance condition $\nu_{H''H'} = \pm\nu$ (i.e. $H''-H' = \pm h\nu$) of the theory of simple transitions has to be replaced in the case of double transitions by the condition

$$\nu_{H''H'} = \pm 2\nu \quad \text{or} \quad 0,$$

that is,
$$H''-H' = \pm 2h\nu \quad \text{or} \quad 0,$$

giving respectively

$$f_{H''H'''H'} = \frac{i\pi}{h}\frac{e^{\pm i2\beta}t}{H'''-H'\pm h\nu} \quad \text{or} \quad \frac{i\pi}{h}\Big[\frac{1}{H'''-H'+h\nu}+\frac{1}{H'''-H'-h\nu}\Big]t.$$

These results can easily be interpreted by assuming that *each step of the double transition* $H' \to H''' \to H''$ *consists either in the absorption or in the (forced) emission of one quantum $h\nu$ of light*—if, for the sake of concreteness, the perturbation S is regarded as due to monochromatic light of frequency ν.

This interpretation is supported by the fact that the transition probability as determined by the square of $\Delta_2 c_{H'H'}$ turns out to be proportional to the *square of the intensity of the light* (i.e. to the fourth power of the electric force E_0, to which S must be proportional in the case under consideration). This is just what would be expected if the probability of each of the two steps of the transition is proportional to the intensity of the light.

It must be emphasized, however, that for each of these two steps the usual resonance condition $\nu_{H'''H'} = \pm\nu$ is, in general, *not* satisfied.

We have here the same situation as in the case $\nu = 0$ discussed above—an apparent violation of the energy principle, straightened out by the perturbation energy whose value is actually indeterminate.

It is, in principle, quite possible for light to induce transitions whose probability is proportional not to the first but to the second or even to a higher power of its intensity. In order that such effects could be observed, however, the intensity of the light must be extremely high, in fact much higher than that with which we usually have to do in our laboratory experiments. For, according to these experiments, the transition probability, as measured by the rate of photo-ionization for example, turns out to be exactly proportional to the light intensity.

We are thus entitled to conclude that double transitions produced by the action of *light alone* practically do not occur—on the surface of the earth at least.

There is, however, a great variety of phenomena which can be described as double transitions under the *combined* action of light and some other perturbation which does not depend upon the time.

Such combined perturbations are represented by a function of the type

$$S = T(x,y,z)\cos(2\pi\nu t + \beta) + G(x,y,z). \tag{187}$$

If, in the calculation of $\Delta_2 c_{H''H'}$, only those terms are preserved which are bilinear in T and G, i.e. proportional to their product, then, instead of (183), we get

$$\Delta_2 c_{H''H'} = \sum_{H'''} [T^0_{H''H'''} G^0_{H'''H'} f_{H''H'''H'}(t) + G^0_{H''H'''} T^0_{H'''H'} g_{H''H'''H'}(t)], \tag{187 a}$$

with

$$f_{H''H'''H'}(t)$$
$$= -\frac{2\pi^2}{h^2} \int_0^t dt' \left\{ e^{i[2\pi(\nu_{H''H'''}+\nu)t'+\beta]} + e^{i[2\pi(\nu_{H''H'''}-\nu)t'-\beta]} \right\} \int_0^{t'} dt'' \, e^{i2\pi\nu_{H'''H'}t''},$$

and

$$g_{H''H'''H'}(t)$$
$$= -\frac{2\pi^2}{h^2} \int_0^t dt' \, e^{i2\pi\nu_{H''H'''}t'} \int_0^{t'} dt'' \left\{ e^{i[2\pi(\nu_{H'''H'}+\nu)t''+\beta]} + e^{i[2\pi(\nu_{H'''H'}-\nu)t''-\beta]} \right\},$$

that is

$$f_{H''H'''H'}(t) = \frac{1}{2h^2} \left\{ e^{i\beta} \frac{e^{i2\pi(\nu_{H''H'}+\nu)t}-1}{(\nu_{H''H'}+\nu)\nu_{H'''H'}} - e^{i\beta} \frac{e^{i2\pi(\nu_{H''H'''}+\nu)t}-1}{(\nu_{H''H'''}+\nu)\nu_{H'''H'}} + \right.$$
$$\left. + e^{-i\beta} \frac{e^{i2\pi(\nu_{H''H'}-\nu)t}-1}{(\nu_{H''H'}-\nu)\nu_{H'''H'}} - e^{-i\beta} \frac{e^{i2\pi(\nu_{H''H'''}-\nu)t}-1}{(\nu_{H''H'''}-\nu)\nu_{H'''H'}} \right\},$$

and

$$g_{H''H'''H'}(t) = \frac{1}{2h^2}\left\{e^{i\beta}\frac{e^{i2\pi(\nu_{H''H'}+\nu)t}-1}{(\nu_{H''H'}+\nu)(\nu_{H'''H'}+\nu)} - e^{i\beta}\frac{e^{i2\pi\nu_{H''H'''}}-1}{\nu_{H''H'''}(\nu_{H'''H'}+\nu)}+\right.$$
$$\left. +e^{-i\beta}\frac{e^{i2\pi(\nu_{H''H'}-\nu)t}-1}{(\nu_{H''H'}-\nu)(\nu_{H'''H'}-\nu)} - e^{-i\beta}\frac{e^{i2\pi\nu_{H''H'''}t}-1}{\nu_{H''H'''}(\nu_{H'''H'}-\nu)}\right\}.$$

The two expressions define the resonance condition in the same way as for a simple transition produced by the action of the light alone.

In the case of an unsharp resonance in the neighbourhood of the value $H''_\nu = H' \pm h\nu$, these expressions practically reduce to

$$\left. \begin{aligned} f_{H''H'''H'}(t) &= \frac{1}{2h^2}e^{\mp i\beta}\frac{e^{i2\pi(\nu_{H''H'}\mp\nu)t}-1}{(\nu_{H'''H'}\mp\nu)\nu_{H'''H'}} \\ g_{H''H'''H'}(t) &= \frac{1}{2h^2}e^{\mp i\beta}\frac{e^{i2\pi(\nu_{H''H'}\mp\nu)t}-1}{(\nu_{H''H'}\mp\nu)(\nu_{H'''H'}\mp\nu)} \end{aligned} \right\}, \qquad (187\,b)$$

so that we get

$$\Delta_2 c_{H''H'} = \tfrac{1}{2}\,e^{\mp i\beta}\sum_{H'''}\left(\frac{T^0_{H''H'''}G^0_{H'''H'}}{H'''-H'} + \frac{G^0_{H''H'''}T^0_{H'''H'}}{H'''-H'\mp h\nu}\right)\frac{e^{i2\pi\left(\frac{H''-H'}{h}\mp\nu\right)t}-1}{H''-H'\mp h\nu},$$

and consequently

$$\Gamma_{H''H'} = \frac{\pi^2}{h}\left|\sum_{H'''}\left(\frac{T^0_{H''H'''}G^0_{H'''H'}}{H'''-H'} + \frac{G^0_{H''H'''}T^0_{H'''H'}}{H'''-H'\mp h\nu}\right)\right|^2, \qquad (187\,c)$$

instead of (184). This formula should be completed to allow for transitions through states belonging to the continuous H-spectrum, and also for other parameters (Q) besides the energy, in the same way as (184).

It must be mentioned that those terms—quadratic in T or G—which have been dropped in formula (187a) have no importance so long as we restrict ourselves to resonance transitions of the above type. As shown above, they would become predominant only for transitions of the type $H'' = H' \pm 2h\nu$ or $H'' = H'$.

An interesting feature of the expression (187 c) is the non-symmetrical character of the two terms in the brackets with regard to the frequency ν. The latter affects the second term only, which corresponds to the action of light in the first step of the transition, while in the first term, which corresponds to the action of light in the second step, the frequency ν appears only through the subscript H''_ν.

As an example of the application of the formula (187 c) we could cite the problem of the *transformation of light into heat* in gaseous bodies. In this case G must represent the perturbing force experienced by the atom under consideration due to other atoms with which it is supposed to come into collision. The complete treatment of this problem requires, however, the generalization of the preceding theory to allow for the motion of all the particles which act on each other (see Part III).

Another example of double transitions of the above kind is provided by the phenomenon of the *scattering* of light which can be considered as a combination of two elementary acts (simple transitions)—namely, the absorption of a light quantum $h\nu$ and the *spontaneous* emission of another light quantum $h\nu'$ corresponding, in general, to a different frequency. The two acts may take place in either order—since the law of the conservation of energy need not be satisfied in the intermediate state (if the perturbation energy is left out of account).

The application of formula (187 c) to the case of the scattering of light necessitates, however, two important amendments both in the underlying principles and in the form of the result.

First of all it is necessary to visualize a 'spontaneous' transition, associated with light emission, as caused by some perturbation G—the reaction of the electron's radiation field on itself, for example (see Part I, § 18). This question has, however, no practical significance, since in formula (187 c) we have to do not with the perturbation energy G itself—which cannot be specified in the usual way, i.e. as a function of the coordinates or as an operator $G(x)$—but with its matrix elements only. The latter, however, can be regarded as known, since they define the emission probability for which the expression (93), § 17, Part I, can be used. Identifying this expression with the expression $4\pi^2|G_{H'''H'}|^2\sigma(H''')/h$, we can determine the matrix elements of G provided the function $\sigma(H''')$ is known.

We shall not investigate this question here, for it will be considered in detail later in connexion with a more direct theory of light-scattering It must be mentioned, however, that this theory leads to a formula for $\Gamma_{H''_\nu H'}$ which differs from (187 c) in two respects.

Firstly, the resonance condition $H''_\nu = H' \pm h\nu$ is replaced by

$$H''_\nu = H' + h\nu - h\nu'; \qquad (188)$$

where ν is the frequency of the absorbed and ν' the frequency of the emitted ('scattered') light. This result can be considered as the direct consequence of the energy principle.

Secondly, taking the sign $-$ in the denominator of the second term in (187 c) (which corresponds to absorption of light), we must replace the denominator of the first term, i.e. the difference $H'''-H'$, by $H'''-H'+h\nu'$ (which corresponds to the emission of light of frequency ν' in the first step of the double transition). We thus get for the probability of scattering, instead of (187 c), the expression

$$\Gamma_{H'_r H'} = \frac{\pi^2}{h} \left| \sum_{H'''} \left(\frac{T^0_{H'_r H'''} G^0_{H''' H'}}{H''' - H' + h\nu} + \frac{G^0_{H'_r H'''} T^0_{H''' H'}}{H''' - H' - h\nu} \right) \right|^2. \qquad (188\,a)$$

If the incident light is polarized in the direction of the unit vector $\mathbf{q}$ and that part of the scattered radiation is considered which corresponds to vibrations of the electron in the direction $\mathbf{q}'$, then we must put

$$T = -e(\mathbf{r} \cdot \mathbf{q})E_0 \quad \text{and} \quad G = -e(\mathbf{r} \cdot \mathbf{q}')E_0', \qquad (188\,b)$$

where $\mathbf{r}$ is the radius vector of the electron (with respect to the nucleus of the atom) and E_0' is a certain 'effective amplitude'. G is thus obtained from T by replacing the amplitude of the external electric force by a certain constant, which will be determined later.

These results can be derived from the general perturbation theory by replacing the *spontaneous* emission forming one of the two steps of the scattering process by an *induced emission*, i.e. an emission due to the action of a secondary light wave with the frequency ν' and the amplitude E_0'.

Assuming the electron to be exposed simultaneously to the action of these two light waves, we have for the total perturbation energy an expression of the form

$$S = T(x,y,z)\cos(2\pi\nu t + \beta) + T'(x,y,z)\cos(2\pi\nu' t + \beta'). \qquad (189)$$

This gives for the bilinear part of $\Delta_2 c_{H''H'}$ the previous expression (187 a) with $G = T'$ but with somewhat different values for the factors f and g.

Limiting ourselves to the case of an approximate resonance in the neighbourhood of the value (188) and dropping relatively small terms, we get

$$\left. \begin{aligned} f_{H'H'''H'}(t) &= \frac{1}{4h^2} e^{i(\beta'-\beta)} \frac{e^{i2\pi(\nu_{H''H'} - \nu + \nu')t} - 1}{(\nu_{H''H'} - \nu + \nu')(\nu_{H'''H'} + \nu')} \\ g_{H'H'''H'}(t) &= \frac{1}{4\pi^2} e^{i(\beta'-\beta)} \frac{e^{i2\pi(\nu_{H''H'} - \nu + \nu')t} - 1}{(\nu_{H'H'} - \nu + \nu')(\nu_{H'''H'} - \nu)} \end{aligned} \right\}, \qquad (189\,a)$$

which gives

$$\Delta_2 c_{H''H'}$$

$$= \frac{1}{4h^2} e^{i(\beta'-\beta)} \sum_{H'''} \left(\frac{T^0_{H''H'''} T'^0_{H'''H'}}{\nu_{H'''H'} + \nu'} + \frac{T'^0_{H''H'''} T^0_{H'''H'}}{\nu_{H'''H'} - \nu} \right) \frac{e^{i2\pi(\nu_{H''H'} - \nu + \nu')t} - 1}{\nu_{H''H'} - \nu + \nu'} \qquad (189\,b)$$

and consequently

$$\Gamma_{H''H'} = \frac{\pi^2}{h} \left| \sum_{H'''} \left(\frac{T^0_{H''H'''} T'_{H'''H'}}{H''' - H' + h\nu'} + \frac{T'^0_{H''H'''} T^0_{H'''H'}}{H''' - H' - h\nu} \right) \right|^2, \qquad (189\,c)$$

i.e. exactly formula (188 a) with G replaced by T'. All that remains is to assume a fixed effective value for E_0' in order to obtain the probability of scattering.

This value can be determined in the following way:

The unsharpness of the resonance implied in the preceding calculations can be realized either by a transition of the particle into a 'band' $\Delta H''$ of a continuous spectrum, with exactly specified values both of ν and ν', or by a transition into a perfectly definite state H'' belonging to a discrete set, the unsharpness of the resonance being due in this case to a variation of ν' in a small interval $\Delta\nu'$ about the value $(H''-H'-h\nu)/h$ or, in other words, to the emission of a spectral line ν' of finite width.

From the latter point of view, which we shall adopt for the present, we must consider instead of $S' = T'\cos(2\pi\nu't+\beta')$, a superposition of a set of harmonic vibrations with different frequencies contained in the small interval $\Delta\nu'$ and with completely independent phase constants, i.e. incoherent with regard to each other.

This means that $|T^{'0}_{H''H'''}|^2$ must be proportional not to the square of the sum of the amplitudes of the component vibrations, but to the sum of the squares of these elementary amplitudes. Denoting the value of this sum for all the frequencies contained within the interval $d\nu'$ by $E^{'2}_{\nu'}d\nu'$, we get

$$|T^{'0}_{H''H'''}|^2 = e^2|(\mathbf{r}\cdot\mathbf{q}')_{H''H'''}|^2 E^{'2}_{\nu'}$$

or if—as has been done above—the integration is extended over the values of the energy and not over the frequency,

$$|T^{'0}_{H''H'''}|^2 = \frac{e^2}{h}|(\mathbf{r}\cdot\mathbf{q}')_{H''H'''}|^2 E^{'2}_{\nu'}. \qquad (190)$$

The corresponding transition probability is equal to

$$\frac{\pi^2}{h}|T^{'0}_{H''H'''}|^2 = \frac{\pi^2 e^2}{h^2}|(\mathbf{r}\cdot\mathbf{q}')_{H''H'''}|^2 E^{'2}_{\nu'}.$$

This quantity must obviously be identified with the probability of spontaneous emission (see Part I, eq. (93), § 17)

$$A = \frac{64\pi^4}{3c^3}\frac{e^2\nu'^3}{h}|(\mathbf{r}\cdot\mathbf{q}')_{H''H'''}|^2,$$

whence it follows that
$$E^{'2}_{\nu'} = \frac{64\pi^2}{3c^3}h\nu'^3. \qquad (190\,\text{a})$$

Putting further
$$T = -e\mathbf{r}\cdot\mathbf{q}E_0$$

(q being the direction of the vector $\mathbf{E}_0$), we get, according to (189 c),

$\Gamma_{H''H'}$

$$= \frac{64\pi^4}{3c^3}\nu'^3 E_0^2 e^2 \left|\sum_{H'''}\left[\frac{(\mathbf{r}_{H''H'''}\cdot\mathbf{q})(\mathbf{r}_{H'''H'}\cdot\mathbf{q}')}{H'''-H'+h\nu'} + \frac{(\mathbf{r}_{H''H'''}\cdot\mathbf{q}')(\mathbf{r}_{H'''H'}\cdot\mathbf{q})}{H'''-H'-h\nu}\right]\right|^2.$$

$$(190\,\text{b})$$

The intensity of the scattered radiation is equal to the product of $\Gamma_{H''H'}$ and $h\nu'$.

If ν'.is different from ν, and if a direct transition from the state H' to the (discrete) state H'' is impossible—as assumed hitherto—formula (190 b) describes, in conjunction with the resonance condition (188), the so-called *Raman effect* or incoherent scattering of light. If the state H'' belongs to a continuous set, corresponding to an ionized state of the atom, we get the *Compton effect* instead of the Raman effect. In this case it is necessary, however, to modify formula (190 b), *firstly* by allowing for transitions through intermediate states belonging to the continuous spectrum, and *secondly* by allowing for the finite speed of light both in absorption and emission. These corrections will be introduced later in Part III where an exact theory of the Compton effect will be given.

24. Theory of Transitions for an Undefined Initial State

The coefficients $c_{H'}$—or in particular $c_{H''H'}$—are complex quantities, whose modulus determines the probability of the corresponding states —or the number of copies associated with the latter—while their phases have no direct physical significance.

We shall see later that these phases can be used for the building up of a theory, in which the copies of the particle appear as a number of particles of the same sort (cf. Part I, § 20). So long, however, as we confine ourselves to one particle only, the phases of the quantities $c_{H'}$ are devoid of all meaning and must therefore not appear in the final equations. This means that the latter must contain only the moduli or the squares of the moduli of the coefficients $c_{H'}$.

We shall apply this principle to the problem (first treated by Dirac) of the change in the distributon of the copies of a particle among different states due to a perturbation of any kind when the state of the particle at the initial instant was not exactly specified, so that only the initial values of the probabilities $N^0_{H'}$ were known. Our problem will consist in the determination of these probabilities $N_{H'}(t)$ as functions of the time (for sufficiently small values of the latter).

In this form the problem is indeterminate, for the equations of the perturbation theory involve not the probabilities $N_{H'}$, but the probability amplitudes $c_{H'}$, whose values, both with respect to modulus and phase, are determined by the values of their moduli $\sqrt{N^0_{H'}}$ and phases $\gamma^0_{H'}$ at the initial moment. In order to get rid of these phases, which are completely irrelevant so far as the probabilities are concerned, we can average the results over them—*assuming all the values of these phases to be equally probable.*

Taking the case of a discrete set of states, we have, according to (161),

$$-\frac{h}{2\pi i}\frac{dc_{H'}}{dt} = \sum_{H''} S_{H'H''} c_{H''}.$$

To these equations we shall add the conjugate complex equations

$$\frac{h}{2\pi i}\frac{dc_{H'}^*}{dt} = \sum_{H''} S_{H'H''}^* c_{H''}^* = \sum_{H''} S_{H''H'} c_{H''}^*.$$

Multiplying the former by $c_{H'}^*$ and the latter by $c_{H'}$ and subtracting one from the other, we get

$$-\frac{h}{2\pi i}\frac{d}{dt}(c_{H'} c_{H'}^*) = \sum_{H''} (S_{H'H''} c_{H'}^* c_{H''} - S_{H''H'} c_{H'}^* c_{H''}),$$

i.e.

$$\frac{d}{dt} N_{H'} = \frac{2\pi i}{h} \sum_{H''} (S_{H''H'} c_{H''}^* c_{H'} - S_{H'H''} c_{H'}^* c_{H''}). \qquad (191)$$

We see that the right side of these equations cannot be expressed as a function of the numbers $N_{H''}$.

One might be tempted to put

$$c_{H''} = \sqrt{N_{H''}}\, e^{i\gamma_{H''}}$$

and average over the phases $\gamma_{H''}$ (and $\gamma_{H'}$), considering all their values as equally probable. This would, however, reduce the right side of (191) to zero. In fact, we are not allowed to assume the equal probability of all the values of the phases $\gamma_{H'}$ at any time; if they were equally probable at the instant $t = 0$ they will no longer be so later on.

We shall therefore, in the right side of (191), substitute for the probability amplitudes $c_{H'}$ approximate expressions in terms of their initial values—up to the first approximation, so as to obtain the second-order approximation for the time derivatives of the numbers $N_{H'}$ (it should be remembered that the matrix components of S by which the coefficients c are multiplied are regarded as small quantities of the first order).

We thus get

$$c_{H''}^* c_{H'} \cong c_{H''}^{0*} c_{H'}^0 + c_{H'}^0 \Delta_1 c_{H''}^* + c_{H''}^{0*} \Delta_1 c_{H'}.$$

Now we obviously have

$$\Delta_1 c_{H''} = \sum_{H'''} \Delta_1 c_{H''H'''} c_{H'''}^0, \qquad (191\,a)$$

so that

$$c_{H''}^* c_{H'} = c_{H''}^{0*} c_{H'}^0 + \sum_{H'''} (\Delta_1 c_{H''H'''}^* c_{H''}^{0*} c_{H'}^0 + \Delta_1 c_{H'H'''} c_{H'''}^0 c_{H''}^{0*}).$$

If now we put

$$c_{H'}^0 = \sqrt{N_{H'}^0}\, e^{i\gamma_{H'}^0} \qquad (191\,b)$$

and average over the values of the initial phases $\gamma_{H'}^0$, $\gamma_{H''}^0$, etc., regarding them as independent of each other and equally probable, we get

$$\overline{c_{H''}^* \, c_{H'}} = \delta_{H''H'} + \Delta_1 c_{H''H'}^* \, N_{H'}^0 + \Delta_1 c_{H'H''} \, N_{H''}^0,$$

or since
$$\Delta_1 c_{H''H'}^* = -\Delta_1 c_{H'H''},$$

$$\overline{c_{H''}^* \, c_{H'}} = \delta_{H''H'} + \Delta_1 c_{H'H''}(N_{H''}^0 - N_{H'}^0). \tag{192}$$

Substituting this in (191) and remembering that

$$\Delta_1 c_{H'H''} = -\frac{2\pi i}{h} \int_0^t S_{H'H''} \, dt,$$

we get

$$\frac{dN_{H'}}{dt}$$
$$= \frac{4\pi^2}{h^2} \sum \left(S_{H'H''}(t) \int_0^t S_{H''H'}(t') \, dt' + S_{H''H'}(t) \int_0^t S_{H'H''}(t') \, dt' \right)(N_{H''}^0 - N_{H'}^0),$$

that is,
$$\frac{dN_{H'}}{dt} = \sum_{H''} \Gamma_{H'H''}(N_{H''}^0 - N_{H'}^0), \tag{192a}$$

with
$$\Gamma_{H'H''} = \frac{d}{dt} \frac{4\pi^2}{h^2} \left| \int_0^t S_{H'H''}(t') \, dt' \right|^2, \tag{192b}$$

which is obviously nothing else but the probability (per unit time) of a direct transition from the state H' into H'' or vice versa. Equation (192a) could be obtained directly from the symmetry relation $\Gamma_{H'H''} = \Gamma_{H''H'}$. It is easy to obtain higher approximations for $dN_{H'}/dt$, taking account of combined transitions. This would not affect the form of equations (192a). Instead of (192b) we should, however, obtain the following expression for the transition probability:

$$\Gamma_{H'H''} = \frac{d}{dt} \frac{4\pi^2}{h^2} \left| \int_0^t S_{H'H''}(t') \, dt' + \sum_{H'''} \int_0^t dt' \, S_{H'H'''}(t') \int_0^{t'} dt'' \, S_{H'''H''}(t'') \right|^2. \tag{192c}$$

VI

RELATIVISTIC REMODELLING AND MAGNETIC GENERALIZATION OF THE WAVE MECHANICS OF A SINGLE ELECTRON

25. Simplest Form of Relativistic Wave Mechanics

All the developments of the preceding chapters were based on Schrö-dinger's wave equation for a single particle moving in an external field of force with a given potential-energy function $U(x, y, z, t)$.

This equation, as we have seen in Chap. I, corresponds to the pre-relativistic classical mechanics, which neglects the *variation of the mass of a particle with its velocity*. In addition it does not take into account *magnetic* forces, which depend not only upon the position of a particle but also upon its velocity (being in fact proportional to the latter).

Our next problem will be to find the improved form of the funda-mental equation of wave mechanics for a single particle—which we shall think of as an electron—that will take account both of the variability of mass and of the magnetic forces.

It turns out that the two parts of this problem can be solved simul-taneously—at one stroke as it were—if in reforming the Schrödinger equation we let ourselves be guided by the basic principle of the relativity theory, namely, the equivalence of the space coordinates and the time (multiplied by ic), which must be expressed by the symmetry of all the fundamental equations of physics with respect to both, and which entails the four-dimensional character of all physical quantities.

It should be mentioned that the same principle can be applied to the problem of improving the equations of the classical pre-relativistic theory and finding their relativistically correct pre-quantum form.

The formal correspondence between the energy-momentum relation of Newtonian mechanics

$$\frac{1}{2m}(g_x^2 + g_y^2 + g_z^2) + U - W = 0 \tag{193}$$

and the Schrödinger equation written in the form

$$\left[\frac{1}{2m}(p_x^2 + p_y^2 + p_z^2) + U + p_t\right]\psi = 0, \tag{193a}$$

with

$$p_x = \frac{h}{2\pi i}\frac{\partial}{\partial x}, \qquad p_y = \frac{h}{2\pi i}\frac{\partial}{\partial y}, \qquad p_z = \frac{h}{2\pi i}\frac{\partial}{\partial z}, \qquad p_t = \frac{h}{2\pi i}\frac{\partial}{\partial t}, \tag{193b}$$

leads us straight back to that four-dimensional representation of physical quantities, which is the formal content of the relativity theory. We must, therefore, so modify our original equations that they assume a symmetrical form with respect to the components of four-dimensional vectors appearing therein.

If, as will be done in future, the time is specified in the usual way, i.e. by the real quantity t without the imaginary factor ic, this symmetry will be slightly distorted by the appearance of the factor $-c^2$ or $-1/c^2$ in the product of the fourth components of any two vectors.

To begin with, we must fill up an important gap in the usual definition of the momentum-energy vector

$$g_x = mv_x, \qquad g_y = mv_y, \qquad g_z = mv_z, \qquad -g_t = W \qquad (193\,\mathrm{c})$$

—a gap which makes this definition inconsistent from the point of view of the relativity theory and which limits its correspondence with the operator-vector (193 b).

In Einstein's mechanics of a particle with rest mass m_0 we have, corresponding to the components of the momentum, i.e.

$$mv_x = \frac{m_0 v_x}{\sqrt{(1-v^2/c^2)}}, \qquad mv_y = \frac{m_0 v_y}{\sqrt{(1-v^2/c^2)}}, \qquad mv_z = \frac{m_0 v_z}{\sqrt{(1-v^2/c^2)}}$$

as fourth component of the four-vector concerned, the 'proper energy'

$$mc^2 = \frac{m_0 c^2}{\sqrt{(1-v^2/c^2)}} \qquad \left(\text{or} \qquad imc = \frac{m_0 ic}{\sqrt{(1-v^2/c^2)}} \right).$$

Now the quantity p_t in (193 b) represents, not this proper energy, but the total energy $E = mc^2 + U$ diminished by the constant rest-energy $m_0 c^2$. For the relativistic formulation of the laws of corpuscular mechanics we must clearly add this constant to the energy W, i.e. we must put

$$-g_t = E = W + m_0 c^2 = mc^2 + U.$$

In addition to this, we must regard the potential energy U as the fourth component, i.e. as the 'time-projection', of a certain four-vector and also take into account its space projection. This space projection $\mathbf{G}$, which obviously corresponds to the momentum and which, just as U, can be an arbitrary function of the coordinates and the time, will be called the potential momentum. In the—so far exclusively considered— special case $\mathbf{G} = 0$ the components of the force acting on the particle reduce to the usual expressions $-\dfrac{\partial U}{\partial x}, \; -\dfrac{\partial U}{\partial y}, \; -\dfrac{\partial U}{\partial z}$. The question as to the nature and the mathematical expression of the force due to the vector function $\mathbf{G}$ will be considered later on. We are at present only interested in the fact that, by the introduction of the 'potential momentum', the quantities g_x, g_y, g_z appearing in formulae (193 c) must be defined as the components of the *total momentum* $m\mathbf{v}+\mathbf{G}$ just as the quantity $-g_t$ denotes the total energy mc^2+U.

We obtain, therefore, instead of (193 c), the formulae

$$g_x = mv_x+G_x, \qquad g_y = mv_y+G_y, \qquad g_z = mv_z+G_z \;\Big\}. \qquad (194)$$
$$-g_t = mc^2+U$$

The components of the 'proper energy momentum vector' are related to one another, according to definition, by the relation

$$(mv_x)^2+(mv_y)^2+(mv_z)^2-\frac{1}{c^2}(mc^2)^2 = -m_0^2 c^2 \qquad (194\,\text{a})$$

$\Big($which is equivalent to the formula $m = \dfrac{m_0}{\sqrt{(1-v^2/c^2)}}\Big)$. In the case $\mathbf{G} = 0$ this relation can be written in the form

$$(mv_x)^2+(mv_y)^2+(mv_z)^2-\frac{1}{c^2}(E-U)^2 = -m_0^2 c^2.$$

In the limiting case of small velocities $(v/c \ll 1)$ we can put approximately
$$(mv)^2 \cong (m_0 v)^2$$

and $\quad \dfrac{1}{c^2}(E-U)^2 = \dfrac{1}{c^2}(m_0 c^2+W-U)^2 \cong m_0^2 c^2+2m_0(W-U).$

Thus the previous equation reduces to

$$(m_0 v_x)^2+(m_0 v_y)^2+(m_0 v_z)^2+2m_0(U-W) = 0,$$

which is the classical energy-momentum equation (193). It should be noticed that it expresses the 'law of the conservation of energy' when W (or E) is constant, which can only be the case when the function U is independent of the time (static field).

We see therefore that the equation

$$(g_x-G_x)^2+(g_y-G_y)^2+(g_z-G_z)^2-\frac{1}{c^2}(g_t+U)^2+m_0^2 c^2 = 0, \quad (194\,\text{b})$$

which results from (194), and (194 a) represents the relativistic generalization and refinement of the Newtonian relation (193).

From this equation we can go over to the corresponding fundamental equation of the relativistic wave mechanics in the same way as in the non-relativistic case—namely, by replacing the vector $\mathbf{g}$ in (194 b) by the corresponding operator-vector $\mathbf{p}$ and equating to zero the result obtained by the application of the resulting operator to a wave function

ψ. We thus get
$$D\psi = 0, \qquad (195)$$
with
$$D = \left(\frac{h}{2\pi i}\frac{\partial}{\partial x} - G_x\right)^2 + \left(\frac{h}{2\pi i}\frac{\partial}{\partial y} - G_y\right)^2 +$$
$$+ \left(\frac{h}{2\pi i}\frac{\partial}{\partial z} - G_z\right)^2 - \frac{1}{c^2}\left(\frac{h}{2\pi i}\frac{\partial}{\partial t} + U\right)^2 + m_0 c^2. \qquad (195\,a)$$

In the case of 'multiplication' of expressions which, besides ordinary quantities, also contain differential operators, the order of the factors must remain unaltered. Thus the 'product' $\frac{\partial}{\partial x}G_x\psi$ where the operator $\partial/\partial x$ is to be applied to the function $G_x\psi$ standing on its right side differs from the 'product' $G_x\frac{\partial}{\partial x}\psi$ by the additional term $\psi\frac{\partial G_x}{\partial x}$.

If we take this into consideration we obtain
$$\left(\frac{h}{2\pi i}\frac{\partial}{\partial x} - G_x\right)^2\psi = \left(\frac{h}{2\pi i}\frac{\partial}{\partial x} - G_x\right)\left(\frac{h}{2\pi i}\frac{\partial}{\partial x} - G_x\right)\psi$$
$$= -\frac{h^2}{4\pi^2}\frac{\partial^2\psi}{\partial x^2} - \frac{h}{2\pi i}G_x\frac{\partial}{\partial x}\psi - \frac{h}{2\pi i}\frac{\partial}{\partial x}G_x\psi + G_x^2\psi$$
$$= -\frac{h^2}{4\pi^2}\frac{\partial^2\psi}{\partial x^2} - \frac{h}{\pi i}G_x\frac{\partial\psi}{\partial x} - \frac{h}{2\pi i}\psi\frac{\partial G_x}{\partial x} + G_x^2\psi,$$

and similar expressions for the other terms in the equation. Written out in detail it runs, therefore, as follows:

$$\left.\begin{aligned}
&\frac{\partial^2\psi}{\partial x^2} + \frac{\partial^2\psi}{\partial y^2} + \frac{\partial^2\psi}{\partial z^2} - \frac{1}{c^2}\frac{\partial^2\psi}{\partial t^2} - \\
&- \frac{4\pi i}{h}\left(G_x\frac{\partial\psi}{\partial x} + G_y\frac{\partial\psi}{\partial y} + G_z\frac{\partial\psi}{\partial z} + \frac{U}{c^2}\frac{\partial\psi}{\partial t}\right) - \\
&- \frac{2\pi i}{h}\left(\frac{\partial G_x}{\partial x} + \frac{\partial G_y}{\partial y} + \frac{\partial G_z}{\partial z} + \frac{1}{c^2}\frac{\partial U}{\partial t}\right)\psi - \\
&- \frac{4\pi^2}{h}\left(G_x^2 + G_y^2 + G_z^2 - \frac{1}{c^2}U^2 + m_0^2 c^2\right)\psi = 0
\end{aligned}\right\} \qquad (196)$$

If the rest-mass vanishes ($m_0 = 0$), and if there are no external forces, i.e. in the case of an Einstein photon, this equation reduces to the equation
$$\frac{\partial^2\psi}{\partial x^2} + \frac{\partial^2\psi}{\partial y^2} + \frac{\partial^2\psi}{\partial z^2} - \frac{1}{c^2}\frac{\partial^2\psi}{\partial t^2} = 0$$

for electromagnetic waves. Further, it can easily be shown that when $m_0 \neq 0$ and $\mathbf{G} = 0$ the relativistic wave equation (196) for the special case of a harmonic vibration process (i.e. motion with a given constant energy) agrees with the relativistic equation (48 b), § 13, Part I. In fact, if we put $\partial U/\partial t = 0$ and $\psi = \psi^0(x, y, z)e^{-2\pi i \nu t}$, equation (196) reduces to the form

$$\nabla^2\psi + \left(\frac{4\pi\nu^2}{c^2} - \frac{8\pi^2\nu}{hc^2}U + \frac{4\pi^2}{h^2c^2}U^2 - \frac{4\pi^2}{h^2}m_0^2c^2\right)\psi = 0,$$

or, with $\nu = \epsilon/h$,

$$\nabla^2\psi + \frac{4\pi^2}{h^2c^2}[(E-U)^2 - m_0^2c^4]\psi = 0, \qquad (196\,\text{a})$$

which is identical with (48 b), Part I.

We shall now investigate the relation of equation (196) to the equation of motion of Einstein's mechanics. For this purpose we shall put in (196)

$$\psi = \text{const.}\, e^{2\pi i S/h}. \qquad (197)$$

After dividing the result by $(2\pi i/h)^2 e^{i2\pi S/h}$ and dropping the terms which contain the small factor $h/2\pi i$ we obtain the equation

$$\left(\frac{\partial S}{\partial x}\right)^2 + \left(\frac{\partial S}{\partial y}\right)^2 + \left(\frac{\partial S}{\partial z}\right)^2 - \frac{1}{c^2}\left(\frac{\partial S}{\partial t}\right)^2 - 2\left(G_x\frac{\partial S}{\partial x} + G_y\frac{\partial S}{\partial y} + G_z\frac{\partial S}{\partial z} + \frac{U}{c^2}\frac{\partial S}{\partial t}\right) +$$
$$+ G_x^2 + G_y^2 + G_z^2 - \frac{1}{c^2}U^2 + m_0^2c^2 = 0,$$

which must obviously be the relativity form of the Hamilton-Jacobi equation. It can be written more briefly in the form

$$\left(\frac{\partial S}{\partial x} - G_x\right)^2 + \left(\frac{\partial S}{\partial y} - G_y\right)^2 + \left(\frac{\partial S}{\partial z} - G_z\right)^2 - \frac{1}{c^2}\left(\frac{\partial S}{\partial t} + U\right)^2 + m_0^2c^2 = 0,$$
$$(197\,\text{a})$$

and can be obtained directly from (195) if we replace the vector **p** in D by the vector **g** defined according to the equations

$$g_x = \frac{\partial S}{\partial x}, \qquad g_y = \frac{\partial S}{\partial y}, \qquad g_z = \frac{\partial S}{\partial z}, \qquad g_t = \frac{\partial S}{\partial t}. \qquad (197\,\text{b})$$

From these equations, which refer to the copy continuum of one particle, one can easily go over to the relativistic equations of motion of a given copy and, indeed, just as in the non-relativity theory, by differentiation of equation (197 a) with regard to the coordinates and the time, bearing in mind the following relations resulting from (194) and (197 b),

$$\frac{\partial S}{\partial x} - G_x = mv_x, \quad ..., \quad \frac{\partial S}{\partial t} + U = -mc^2.$$

If we differentiate (197 a) with regard to x and divide by m, we get

$$\left(\frac{\partial^2 S}{\partial x^2} - \frac{\partial G_x}{\partial x}\right)v_x + \left(\frac{\partial^2 S}{\partial x\partial y} - \frac{\partial G_y}{\partial x}\right)v_y + \left(\frac{\partial^2 S}{\partial x\partial z} - \frac{\partial G_z}{\partial x}\right)v_z + \frac{\partial^2 S}{\partial x\partial t} + \frac{\partial U}{\partial x} = 0,$$

or, by (197 b),

$$\frac{\partial g_x}{\partial x}\frac{dx}{dt}+\frac{\partial g_y}{\partial y}\frac{dy}{dt}+\frac{\partial g_z}{\partial z}\frac{dz}{dt}+\frac{\partial g_x}{\partial t}=v_x\frac{\partial G_x}{\partial x}+v_y\frac{\partial G_y}{\partial x}+v_z\frac{\partial G_z}{\partial x}-\frac{\partial U}{\partial x}=0,$$

i.e.
$$\frac{dg_x}{dt}=\frac{\partial}{\partial x}(\mathbf{v}\cdot\mathbf{G}-U). \tag{198}$$

The three-dimensional velocity vector $\mathbf{v}$ referring to a *definite* particle is here no longer considered as an explicit function of the coordinates and the time. Therefore, its *partial* derivatives with regard to x, y, z, t must be put equal to zero.

The equations for g_y and g_z analogous to (198) will not be written down here. The fourth equation runs

$$\frac{dg_t}{dt}=\frac{\partial}{\partial t}(\mathbf{v}\cdot\mathbf{G}-U).$$

If the potential functions $\mathbf{G}$ and U are independent of the time (static field of force) this equation reduces to $dg_t/dt=0$, i.e. $-g_t=E$ = const. (law of the conservation of energy).

If we split up g_x in (198) into the sum of mv_x and G_x, we then get

$$\frac{dg_x}{dt}=\frac{d}{dt}(mv_x)+\frac{\partial G_x}{\partial t}+\frac{\partial G_x}{\partial x}\frac{dx}{dt}+\frac{\partial G_x}{\partial y}\frac{dy}{dt}+\frac{\partial G_x}{\partial z}\frac{dz}{dt}$$

$$=\frac{d}{dt}(mv_x)+\frac{\partial G_x}{\partial t}+v_x\frac{\partial G_x}{\partial x}+v_y\frac{\partial G_x}{\partial y}+v_z\frac{\partial G_x}{\partial z},$$

and consequently,

$$\frac{d}{dt}(mv_x)=-\frac{\partial U}{\partial x}-\frac{\partial G_x}{\partial t}+v_y\left(\frac{\partial G_y}{\partial x}-\frac{\partial G_x}{\partial y}\right)-v_z\left(\frac{\partial G_x}{\partial z}-\frac{\partial G_z}{\partial x}\right). \tag{198 a}$$

The right side of this equation must obviously represent the x-component of the force $\mathbf{f}$ acting on the particle.

If we put

$$U=e\phi,\qquad \mathbf{G}=\frac{e}{c}\mathbf{A} \tag{199}$$

with

$$E_x=-\frac{\partial\phi}{\partial x}-\frac{\partial A_x}{c\partial t},\quad E_y=-\frac{\partial\phi}{\partial y}-\frac{\partial A_y}{c\partial t},\quad E_z=-\frac{\partial\phi}{\partial z}-\frac{\partial A_z}{c\partial t},$$

$$\left(\mathbf{E}=-\operatorname{grad}\phi-\frac{1}{c}\frac{\partial A}{\partial t}\right)$$

$$\tag{199 a}$$

$$H=\frac{\partial A_z}{\partial y}-\frac{\partial A_y}{\partial z},\quad H_y=\frac{\partial A_x}{\partial z}-\frac{\partial A_z}{\partial x},\quad H_z=\frac{\partial A_y}{\partial x}-\frac{\partial A_x}{\partial y},$$

$$(\mathbf{H}=\operatorname{curl}\mathbf{A})$$

$$\tag{199 b}$$

we obtain $\qquad f_x = e\left(E_x + \dfrac{v_y}{c}H_z - \dfrac{v_z}{c}H_y\right),$

or in vector notation $\qquad \mathbf{f} = e\left(\mathbf{E} + \dfrac{\mathbf{v}}{c}\times\mathbf{H}\right),$ $\qquad\qquad$ (200)

and $\qquad\qquad\qquad \dfrac{d}{dt}(m\mathbf{v}) = \mathbf{f}.$ $\qquad\qquad\qquad$ (200 a)

Here ϕ and $\mathbf{A}$ are the scalar (electric) and the vector (magnetic) potentials, $\mathbf{E}$ and $\mathbf{H}$ the electric and magnetic field strengths respectively, while e is the electric charge of the particle. A point-like corpuscle can thus be defined by *two constants* only—its rest-mass and its charge.

The vector defined by (200) represents, therefore, the external force (so-called 'Lorentz force') acting on an electron or a proton which is moving in an arbitrary electromagnetic field.

The time projection of the four-dimensional equation of motion, of which (200 a) is the space projection, has the form

$$\frac{d(mc^2)}{dt} = e\mathbf{E}\cdot\mathbf{v} = e(E_x v_x + E_y v_y + E_z v_z).$$ $\qquad$ (200 b)

We thus obtain the relation

$$\frac{d}{dt}(mc^2) = \mathbf{f}\cdot\mathbf{v} = \mathbf{v}\cdot\frac{d}{dt}(m\mathbf{v}),$$

from which at once follows the well-known formula

$$m = \frac{m_0}{\sqrt{(1-v^2/c^2)}}.$$

It still remains to find out the expressions, corresponding to the relativity wave equation just considered, for the quantities ρ (probability density) and $\mathbf{j}$ (probability current density). This is done most simply as follows (according to W. Gordon). We first introduce the operators:

$$\left.\begin{aligned} u_x &= \frac{h}{2\pi i}\frac{\partial}{\partial x} - \frac{e}{c}A_x, & u_y &= \frac{h}{2\pi i}\frac{\partial}{\partial y} - \frac{e}{c}A_y \\[2mm] u_z &= \frac{h}{2\pi i}\frac{\partial}{\partial z} - \frac{e}{c}A_z, & u_t &= \frac{1}{c}\left(\frac{h}{2\pi i}\frac{\partial}{\partial t} + e\phi\right) \end{aligned}\right\}$$ $\qquad$ (201)

by means of which we can write the relativistic wave equation (195) in the form

$$(u_x^2 + u_y^2 + u_z^2 - u_t^2 + m_0^2 c^2)\psi = 0.$$ $\qquad$ (201 a)

We multiply this equation on the left by ψ^* and subtract from it the conjugate equation for ψ^* multiplied by ψ. We then get, bearing in mind (196), the formula:

$$\frac{\partial}{\partial x}\left(\psi^*\frac{\partial\psi}{\partial x}-\psi\frac{\partial\psi^*}{\partial x}-\frac{4\pi i}{h}G_x\psi\psi^*\right)+\frac{\partial}{\partial y}\left(\psi^*\frac{\partial\psi}{\partial y}-\psi\frac{\partial\psi^*}{\partial y}-\frac{4\pi i}{h}G_y\psi\psi^*\right)+$$

$$+\frac{\partial}{\partial z}\left(\psi^*\frac{\partial\psi}{\partial z}-\psi\frac{\partial\psi^*}{\partial z}-\frac{4\pi i}{h}G_z\psi\psi^*\right)-$$

$$-\frac{1}{c^2}\frac{\partial}{\partial t}\left(\psi^*\frac{\partial\psi}{\partial t}-\psi\frac{\partial\psi^*}{\partial t}+\frac{4\pi i}{h}U\psi\psi^*\right)=0,$$

or
$$\frac{\partial}{\partial x}(\psi^*u_x\psi+\psi u_x^*\psi^*)+\frac{\partial}{\partial y}(\psi^*u_y\psi+\psi u_y^*\psi^*)+$$

$$+\frac{\partial}{\partial z}(\psi^*u_z\psi+\psi u_z^*\psi^*)-\frac{\partial}{c\partial t}(\psi^*u_t\psi+\psi u_t^*\psi^*)=0.$$

This formula can be regarded as the *equation of continuity* if we define the quantities

$$j_x=\frac{1}{2m_0}(\psi^*u_x\psi+\psi u_x^*\psi^*)$$

$$\cdots\cdots\cdots\cdots\cdots\cdots \tag{201 b}$$

$$\rho=-\frac{1}{2m_0c}(\psi^*u_t\psi+\psi u_t^*\psi^*)$$

as the components of the current-density vector and the copy density respectively. With regard to the first, this definition is the immediate generalization of that given earlier. The expression for ρ, on the other hand, seems to be completely different from $\psi\psi^*$ which has been used so far. We can easily convince ourselves, however, by the example of a conservative motion, that this difference is, in practice, quite unimportant. Putting

$$\frac{h}{2\pi i}\frac{\partial\psi}{\partial t}=-E\psi, \quad \text{and} \quad \frac{h}{2\pi i}\frac{\partial\psi^*}{\partial t}=E\psi^*,$$

we obtain

$$\psi^*u_t\psi+\psi u_t^*\psi^*=-\frac{2}{c}\psi\psi^*(E-U)=-\frac{2}{c}\psi\psi^*(m_0c^2+W-U),$$

and hence
$$\rho=\psi\psi^*\left(1+\frac{W-U}{m_0c^2}\right), \tag{201 c}$$

i.e., in so far as the kinetic energy $W-U$ is small compared with m_0c^2, $\rho\cong\psi\psi^*$.

With regard to the exact meaning of $\psi\psi^*$, one can easily show that it corresponds to the *rest density*. This can be seen, for example, from the relation $\rho/(\psi\psi^*)=m/m_0$ which is obtained from (201 c) if the mass

m is introduced by means of the usual formula

$$m = m_0 + \frac{W - U}{c^2}.$$

26. Magnetic Forces in the Approximate Non-Relativistic Wave Mechanics

If in reducing equation (196) to the form corresponding to conservative motion the potential momentum is supposed to be different from zero, we get instead of (196 a) an equation which in vector form can be written as follows:

$$\left\{ \left(\frac{h}{2\pi i} \nabla - \mathbf{G} \right)^2 - \frac{1}{c^2} [(E - U)^2 - m_0^2 c^4] \right\} \psi = 0. \qquad (202)$$

If the energy $W = E - m_0 c^2$ is small compared with the rest-energy $E_0 = m_0 c^2$, which classically corresponds to motion with a velocity v small compared with the velocity of light, then we can put with sufficiently good approximation

$$(E - U)^2 = (E_0 + W - U)^2 = E_0^2 + 2E_0(W - U),$$

neglecting the relatively small term $(W - U)^2$, and thus replace equation (202), which is supposed to be exact, by the approximate equation

$$\left\{ \left(\frac{h}{2\pi i} \nabla - \mathbf{G} \right)^2 - 2m_0(W - U) \right\} \psi = 0. \qquad (202 a)$$

This equation corresponds to the classical equation of motion allowing for the presence of magnetic forces (derived from the *constant* potential $\mathbf{G}$) but neglecting the relativistic variation of the mass with velocity.

As a rule, the magnetic forces are relatively weak, so that the terms of (202 a) which are quadratic in $\mathbf{G}$ can be neglected compared with the linear terms. With this condition, equation (202 a) reduces to the still simpler form

$$\left\{ \left(\frac{h}{2\pi i} \nabla \right)^2 - \frac{h}{2\pi i} \nabla \cdot \mathbf{G} - \mathbf{G} \cdot \frac{h}{2\pi i} \nabla - 2m_0(W - U) \right\} \psi = 0.$$

Now we have $\nabla \cdot \mathbf{G}\psi = \operatorname{div} \mathbf{G}\psi = \mathbf{G} \cdot \nabla \psi + \psi \operatorname{div} \mathbf{G}.$

It is well known further that in the case of a static field the divergence of the magnetic potential A vanishes, so that we have $\operatorname{div} \mathbf{G} = 0$. The preceding equation can therefore be written in the form

$$\left\{ \frac{1}{2m_0} \left(\frac{h}{2\pi i} \nabla \right)^2 - \frac{h}{2\pi m_0 i} \mathbf{G} \cdot \nabla + U - W \right\} \psi = 0. \qquad (202 b)$$

So far we have been making perfectly permissible approximations. We are now going to generalize the preceding approximate equations for the case of *non-conservative* motion (in a static or non-static field)—in the same way as was done before with $\mathbf{G} = 0$, namely, by replacing the energy W by the operator $-p_t$ (or $-p_t - m_0 c^2$; the constant term $m_0 c^2$ is immaterial in this case because it is absorbed by the potential energy).

We thus obtain the equations

$$\left[\frac{1}{2m_0} \left(\frac{h}{2\pi i} \nabla \right)^2 - \frac{h}{2\pi m_0 i} \mathbf{G} \cdot \nabla + U + p_t \right] \psi = 0 \tag{203}$$

for weak magnetic fields or

$$\left[\frac{1}{2m_0} \left(\frac{h}{2\pi i} \nabla - \mathbf{G} \right)^2 + U + p_t \right] \psi = 0 \tag{203 a}$$

for strong fields; these can be considered as the generalization of Schrödinger's equation (193 a) for the case of the presence of magnetic forces, with neglect of the relativistic variation of mass with velocity.

The transition from equations (202 a) and (202 b) to (203) and (203 a) is certainly an illogical step, which, moreover, is in contradiction with the results arrived at in the preceding section. For if equations (202 a) and (202 b) are permissible approximations of equation (202), which is supposed to be exact, referring to the case of motion with a definite energy, equations (203) or (203 a) cannot be considered as an approximation, in the strict sense of the word, to the general equation (196). In fact, the latter involves a *second* derivative of ψ with regard to the time, which we are not entitled to drop or to replace by a first derivative multiplied by a constant factor—unless the dependence of ψ upon the time is given by the factor $e^{-i2\pi Et/h}$—corresponding to a motion with the constant energy E.

We have here an approximation of a kind similar to that which is constituted by the Hamilton-Jacobi equation with respect to Schrödinger's equation for the function $S = (h/2\pi i)\log\psi$: in the latter case, however, it is the second derivatives with regard to the space coordinates and not to the time which have to be dropped.

The preceding consideration does not, however, invalidate equations (203) and (203 a) as good approximations to the truth within a certain range corresponding to a negligible variation of the mass with velocity. Apart from the fact that the validity of the relativistic equation (196) still remains to be proved (and we shall see later that, as a matter of fact, the contrary can be proved)—equations (203), and (203 a) represent a very natural generalization of Schrödinger's equation for the presence of magnetic forces, and must therefore describe the motion affected by such forces just as well as Schrödinger's equation describes a motion unaffected by the latter.

An important advantage of the 'approximate' equations (203) and (203 a) over the 'exact' equation (196) consists in the fact that they fit into the general scheme of the operator theory developed on the basis of Schrödinger's equation, since they can be written in the same form, namely,

$$(H+p_t)\psi = 0, \tag{204}$$

where the Hamiltonian or energy operator H must be defined by the generalized formula

$$H = \frac{1}{2m_0}\left(\frac{h}{2\pi i}\nabla - \mathbf{G}\right)^2 + U, \tag{204a}$$

or
$$H = \frac{1}{2m_0}\left(\frac{h}{2\pi i}\nabla\right)^2 - \frac{h}{2\pi m_0 i}\mathbf{G}\cdot\nabla + U. \tag{204b}$$

Equation (196), since it contains the square of the operator p_t, cannot be written in the form (204)—unless we assume that it is possible to extract square roots of operators in the same way as of ordinary numbers and succeed in finding an equation linear with regard to p_t and actually equivalent to (196).

Leaving this question till a later section, we shall now indicate briefly the principal modifications of the general theory, developed in the preceding chapters, which are necessitated by the generalized form of the Hamiltonian operator (204) or (204 a).

First of all, we must notice that this operator is *complex* (which does not prevent it from representing a real quantity, just as the operator $\mathbf{p} = \frac{h}{2\pi i}\nabla$ does). We must distinguish therefore the operator H from the conjugate complex operator H^*, which determines the conjugate complex wave function ψ^* by the equation

$$(H^* - p_t)\psi^* = 0. \tag{204c}$$

Multiplying this equation by ψ and subtracting it from equation (204) multiplied by ψ^*, we get

$$\frac{\partial\rho}{\partial t} + \operatorname{div}\mathbf{j} = 0,$$

with the old—non-relativistic—expression $\psi\psi^*$ for ρ and the expression

$$\mathbf{j} = \frac{1}{2m_0}\left[\psi^*\left(\frac{h}{2\pi i}\nabla - \mathbf{G}\right)\psi + \psi\left(-\frac{h}{2\pi i}\nabla - \mathbf{G}\right)\psi^*\right] \tag{205}$$

for the current density. This expression turns out to be the same for the two Hamiltonians (204 a) and (204 b), and coincides with the expression derived above from the 'exact' relativistic theory [cf. the first equation (201 b)].

Equation (205) can obviously be rewritten in the form

$$j = \frac{1}{m_0}\rho R(\nabla S - G) = \frac{1}{m_0}\rho\{\nabla R(S) - G\}, \tag{205 a}$$

where

$$S = \frac{h}{2\pi i}\log\psi,$$

and $R(S)$ is its real part. In the approximation corresponding to the classical (Newtonian) theory of the motion of an electron in an electromagnetic field, S is the action function and its gradient ∇S is the total momentum $\mathfrak{g}$. The difference $\nabla S - G$ thus reduces to the proper momentum $m_0 v$ and the vector j reduces to the product ρv—just as in the absence of magnetic forces—as, of course, is to be expected.

The complex character of the operator H necessitates the revision of some of the properties of its characteristic functions, which were established on the assumption that H was real. This refers, in the first place, to the orthogonality property which was deduced from the self-adjointness of H, i.e. from the formula

$$\int (f_1 H f_2 - f_2 H f_1)\, dV = 0.$$

Now in the general case of a complex H defined by (204 a) or (204 b), this formula does not hold and must be replaced by

$$\int (f_1 H f_2 - f_2 H^* f_1)\, dV = 0. \tag{206}$$

We have, in fact, according to either one of the two definitions of H,

$$f_1 H f_2 - f_2 H^* f_1$$

$$= -\frac{h^2}{8\pi^2 m_0}(f_1\nabla^2 f_2 - f_2\nabla^2 f_1) - \frac{h}{4\pi m_0 i}(f_1 G\cdot\nabla f_2 + f_2 G\cdot\nabla f_1)$$

$$= -\frac{h^2}{8\pi^2 m_0}\operatorname{div}(f_1\nabla f_2 - f_2\nabla f_1) - \frac{h}{4\pi m_0 i}G\cdot\nabla(f_1 f_2),$$

or, so long as $\operatorname{div}G = 0$,

$$f_1 H f_2 - f_2 H^* f_1 = \operatorname{div}\mathbf{f}_{12}, \tag{206 a}$$

where

$$\mathbf{f}_{12} = -(f_1\nabla f_2 - f_2\nabla f_1) - \frac{h}{4\pi m_0 i}G f_1 f_2. \tag{206 b}$$

If, therefore, the functions f_1 and f_2 vanish sufficiently rapidly at infinity (so that the integral $\int f_1 f_2\, dV$ converges), we must have equation (206).

Putting, in particular, $f_1 = \psi_{H'}^*$ and $f_2 = \psi_{H''}$, where H' and H'' are two different (real) characteristic values of H, we get

$$\int (\psi_{H'}^* H \psi_{H''} - \psi_{H''} H^* \psi_{H'}^*)\, dV = (H'' - H') \int \psi_{H'}^* \psi_{H''}\, dV = 0,$$

whence $\qquad\qquad \int \psi_{H'}^* \psi_{H''}\, dV = 0 \qquad (H'' \neq H'),$

as before.

It should be mentioned that in the case of a real H (i.e. in the absence of magnetic forces), the characteristic functions $\psi_{H'}$, neglecting the time-factor $e^{-i2\pi H't/h}$, can always be defined to be real, i.e. *to have real amplitudes* $\psi_{H'}^0(x, y, z)$, while in the case of a complex H these *amplitudes are complex*. The orthogonality relation holds therefore only in the above form, and not in the form

$$\int \psi_{H'} \psi_{H''}\, dV = 0 \quad \text{or} \quad \int \psi_{H'}^* \psi_{H''}^*\, dV = 0$$

in which it can be expressed if H is real.

It should also be mentioned that the property of self-adjointness expressed by equation (206 a), refers not only to the operator H but to *any* operator which represents a real quantity, i.e. which is a real function of the coordinates and the elementary operators p_x, p_y, p_z— or of the vector-operator $\mathbf{p} = \dfrac{h}{2\pi i}.\nabla$. This can easily be shown with the help of the relations

$$f_1 p_x^{2n} f_2 - f_2 p_x^{2n} f_1 = \left(\frac{h}{2\pi i}\right)^{2n}\left(f_1 \frac{\partial^{2n}}{\partial x^{2n}} f_2 - f_2 \frac{\partial^{2n}}{\partial x^{2n}} f_1\right) = \left(-\frac{h^2}{4\pi^2}\right)^n \frac{\partial}{\partial x} f_{12},$$

where

$$f_{12} = f_1 \frac{\partial^{2n-1} f_2}{\partial x^{2n-1}} - \frac{\partial f_1}{\partial x}\frac{\partial^{2n-2} f_2}{\partial x^{2n-2}} + \frac{\partial^2 f_1}{\partial x^2}\frac{\partial^{2n-3} f_2}{\partial x^{2n-3}} + \cdots - \frac{\partial^{2n-1} f_1}{\partial x^{2n-1}} f_2,$$

and $\qquad\qquad f_1 p^{2n+1} f_2 + f_2 p^{2n+1} f_1 = \dfrac{\partial}{\partial x} f_{12},$

with $\qquad f_{12} = f_1 \dfrac{\partial^{2n} f_2}{\partial x^{2n}} - \dfrac{\partial f_1}{\partial x}\dfrac{\partial^{2n-1} f_2}{\partial x^{2n-1}} + \dfrac{\partial^2 f_1}{\partial x^2}\dfrac{\partial^{2n-2} f_2}{\partial x^{2n-2}} + \cdots + \dfrac{\partial^{2n} f_1}{\partial x^{2n}} f_2,$

in conjunction with

$$(p^{2n})^* = p^{2n}, \qquad (p^{2n+1})^* = -p^{2n+1}.$$

We can thus say that not only the energy operator, but any operator F representing a real physical quantity is self-adjoint in the sense of the equation $\qquad\qquad f_1 F f_2 - f_2 F^* f_1 = \operatorname{div} \mathbf{f}_{12},$

and that the characteristic functions of this operator are orthogonal with regard to each other in the same sense as the characteristic functions of the energy operator.

Another result which was associated with the reality of H and its self-adjointness in the old sense was the possibility of replacing the differential equation for its characteristic functions and values

$$(H-H')\psi_{H'} = 0$$

by the variational equation

$$\delta \int \psi^* H \psi \, dV = 0,$$

with the condition $\int \psi^* \psi \, dV = \text{const.} (= 1)$.

Since, in the case of a complex H, the function ψ^* no longer satisfies the same equation as ψ, the preceding results seem to require a modification.

As a matter of fact, however, no such modification is needed, for we have

$$\delta \int \psi^* H \psi \, dV = \int \delta\psi^* H \psi \, dV + \int \psi^* H \delta\psi \, dV$$

and, with the help of (206),

$$\int \psi^* H \delta\psi \, dV = \int \delta\psi H^* \psi^* \, dV,$$

that is,

$$\delta \int \psi^* H \psi \, dV = \int \delta\psi^* H \psi \, dV + \int \delta\psi H^* \psi^* \, dV = \delta \int \psi H^* \psi^* \, dV.$$

The variational principle thus preserves its usual form

$$\delta\overline{H} = 0, \qquad E = \text{const.} (= 1)$$

with

$$\overline{H} = \int \psi^* H \psi \, dV = \int \psi H^* \psi^* \, dV,$$

and

$$E = \int \psi^* \psi \, dV.$$

As has been already pointed out, the two equations $\delta H = 0$, $\delta E = 0$ can be replaced by the single one $\delta\overline{H} = 0$ if $\overline{H}$ is defined by the formula

$$\overline{H} = \int \psi^* H \psi \, dV \Big/ \int \psi^* \psi \, dV \quad \left(\text{or} \quad \int \psi H^* \psi^* \, dV \Big/ \int \psi^* \psi \, dV\right),$$

without any normalizing condition for the function ψ.

It should be noticed further that the two equations $\delta\overline{H} = 0$, $\delta E = 0$ can be split up, as it were, into the following two pairs of equations:

$$\int \delta\psi^* H \psi \, dV = 0, \qquad \int \delta\psi^* \psi \, dV = 0 \qquad (207)$$

and

$$\int \delta\psi H^* \psi^* \, dV = 0, \qquad \int \psi^* \delta\psi \, dV = 0,$$

the first pair being equivalent to the equation $(H-H')\psi = 0$ and the second to the equation $(H^*-H')\psi^* = 0$.

The preceding result can easily be generalized for non-stationary motion, the equation $\left(H+\dfrac{h}{2\pi i}\dfrac{\partial}{\partial t}\right)\psi = 0$ being equivalent to

$$\int \delta\psi^*\left(H+\frac{h}{2\pi i}\frac{\partial}{\partial t}\right)\psi\, dV = 0, \qquad (207\,\text{a})$$

and the conjugate complex equation $\left(H^*-\dfrac{h}{2\pi i}\dfrac{\partial}{\partial t}\right)\psi^* = 0$, to

$$\int \delta\psi\left(H^*-\frac{h}{2\pi i}\frac{\partial}{\partial t}\right)\psi^*\, dV = 0.$$

So long as ψ is the exact solution of the equation $\left(H+\dfrac{h}{2\pi i}\dfrac{\partial}{\partial t}\right)\psi = 0$ and $\delta\psi^*$ is quite arbitrary, the variational equation (207 a) is nothing but a transcription of the ordinary differential equation of motion. The same variational equation is obtained, however, as the condition for the error involved to be *permanently small*,† when ψ is replaced by an *approximate* function of some relatively simple form ψ_1.

At some initial moment $t = t_0$ the form of the function ψ can be fixed quite arbitrarily. We can accordingly identify $\psi(t_0)$ with $\psi_1(t_0)$. Now $\psi_1(t)$ does *not* satisfy the equation $\left(H+\dfrac{h}{2\pi i}\dfrac{\partial}{\partial t}\right)\psi = 0$ but an equation of the form

$$\left(H+\frac{h}{2\pi i}\frac{\partial}{\partial t}\right)\psi_1+\psi_2 = 0. \qquad (207\,\text{b})$$

Our problem is thus reduced to that of making the additional term $\psi_2(t)$ as small as possible for any time t. Taking $t = t_0+dt$, we get from the preceding equation

$$\psi_1(t_0+dt) = \psi_1(t_0) - \frac{2\pi i}{h}H\psi_1(t_0)dt - \frac{2\pi i}{h}\psi_2(t_0)dt.$$

Now if the function $\psi_1(t_0+dt)$ is altered by a small amount $\delta\psi_1(t_0+dt)$, the function $\psi_1(t_0)$ remaining the same as before, the corresponding variation of the correction term $\psi_2(t_0)$ will be

$$\delta\psi_2(t_0) = -\frac{h}{2\pi i}\delta\psi_1(t_0+dt).$$

The condition that $\psi_2(t_0)$ should be as small as possible for all values of the coordinates can be stated as the minimum condition for the integral $\int \psi_2^*(t_0)\psi_2(t_0)\, dV$ and is equivalent accordingly to the equation

$$\int \delta\psi_2^*(t_0)\psi_2(t_0)\, dV = 0.$$

---

† The argument presented below is taken from Dirac's appendix to the Russian edition of his book, *The Principles of Quantum Mechanics*.

Replacing here $\delta\psi_2^*(t_0)$ by $\dfrac{h}{2\pi i}\delta\psi_1^*(t_0+dt)$, we get

$$\int \delta\psi_1^*(t_0+dt)\psi_2(t_0)\, dV = 0,$$

or passing to the limit $dt \to 0$ and dropping the index 0 (since the above results must hold for all values of t)

$$\int \delta\psi_1^*(t)\psi_2(t)\, dV = 0.$$

This equation means that the correction $\psi_2(t)$ must be orthogonal to any variation of the approximate function $\psi_1(t)$. Hence ψ_2 can be eliminated from the equation (207 b) if the latter is multiplied by $\delta\psi_1^*$ and integrated over the coordinates, thus giving equation (207 a) with the exact function ψ replaced by the approximate one ψ_1.

The expressions $\int \psi^* H\psi\, dV$ and $\int \psi H^*\psi^*\, dV$ for $\bar{H}$ can easily be put in the symmetrical form

$$\bar{H} = \int \left[\frac{1}{2m_0}\left(\frac{h}{2\pi i}\nabla - \mathbf{G}\right)\psi\left(-\frac{h}{2\pi i}\nabla - \mathbf{G}\right)\psi^* + U\psi\psi^* \right] dV, \qquad (208)$$

if H is defined by (204 a), that is

$$\bar{H} = \int \left[\frac{1}{2m_0}\left(\frac{h}{2\pi i}\nabla\psi\right)\left(-\frac{h}{2\pi i}\nabla\psi^*\right) - \mathbf{G}\cdot\mathbf{j} + U\rho \right] dV, \qquad (208\,a)$$

where $\rho = \psi\psi^*$ is the density of probability and $\mathbf{j}$ the probability current density as defined by (205). Using the approximate expression (204 b) for H, we get, instead of (208),

$$\bar{H} = \int \left[\frac{1}{2m_0}\left|\frac{h}{2\pi i}\nabla\psi\right|^2 - \frac{h}{4\pi i m_0}\mathbf{G}(\psi^*\nabla\psi - \psi\nabla\psi^*) + U|\psi|^2 \right] dV, \tag{208\,b}$$

which coincides with (208 a) if, in the above definition of $\mathbf{j}$, we put $\mathbf{G} = 0$, thus coming back to the old definition of the current density

$$\mathbf{j} = \frac{h}{4\pi i m_0}(\psi^*\nabla\psi - \psi\nabla\psi^*).$$

So long as the reality of the characteristic values of the operator H and the mutual orthogonality of its characteristic functions is unaffected by that change of it which corresponds to the presence of a magnetic field, we can preserve, without any modification, all the results of the preceding chapters concerning the matrix representation of physical quantities 'from the point of view' of H, the transformation theory and the perturbation theory.

If the magnetic (or, in general, the electromagnetic) field specified by the vector $\mathbf{G}$ is relatively weak (compared with the field of force defined by the potential energy U), then it can itself be treated as a perturbation. Subtracting from the Hamiltonian (204 b), which in future may be denoted by K, the usual Hamiltonian

$$H = \frac{1}{2m_0}\left(\frac{h}{2\pi i}\nabla\right)^2 + U,$$

which corresponds to the absence of the 'perturbing' forces specified by $\mathbf{G}$, we get the following expression for the perturbation energy:

$$S = -\frac{h}{2\pi m_0 i}\mathbf{G}\cdot\nabla \qquad (209)$$

or

$$S = \frac{ieh}{2\pi m_0 c}\mathbf{A}\cdot\nabla, \qquad (209\,\mathrm{a})$$

where $\mathbf{A}$ is the vector potential corresponding to $\mathbf{G}$ ($= e\mathbf{A}/c$) and e the electric charge of the particle under consideration. Putting $\frac{h}{2\pi i}\nabla = \mathbf{p}$, we can rewrite (209) in the form

$$S = -\frac{e}{m_0 c}\mathbf{A}\cdot\mathbf{p}. \qquad (209\,\mathrm{b})$$

The simplest application of this formula is provided by the special case of the action of a permanent *homogeneous* magnetic field (Zeeman effect). Denoting the field strength by $\mathfrak{H}$, we can, in this case, put

$$\mathbf{A} = \tfrac{1}{2}\mathfrak{H}\times\mathbf{r}, \qquad (210)$$

where $\mathbf{r}$ is the radius vector of the particle. This gives in fact

$$\mathrm{curl}\,\mathbf{A} = \mathfrak{H},$$

as can be verified most simply with the help of the coordinate representation.

Substituting (210) in (209 b), we get

$$S = -\frac{e}{2m_0 c}(\mathfrak{H}\times\mathbf{r})\cdot\mathbf{p},$$

which can be rewritten in the form

$$S = -\frac{e}{2m_0 c}\mathfrak{H}\cdot(\mathbf{r}\times\mathbf{p}).$$

Now the operator $\mathbf{r}\times\mathbf{p} = \mathbf{M}$
obviously represents the angular momentum of the electron about the central point (nucleus), from which the radius vector $\mathbf{r}$ is supposed to be drawn. We thus get

$$S = -\frac{e}{2m_0 c}\mathfrak{H}\cdot\mathbf{M},$$

or
$$S = -\mathfrak{H} \cdot \boldsymbol{\mu}, \tag{210a}$$

where
$$\boldsymbol{\mu} = \frac{e}{2m_0 c} \mathbf{M}, \tag{210b}$$

can be defined as the operator representing the *magnetic moment* due to the rotation of the electron about the (fixed) nucleus.

This definition follows from the fact that (210 a) has exactly the same form as the classical expression for the energy of a particle with a (constant) magnetic moment $\boldsymbol{\mu}$ in a homogeneous magnetic field $\mathfrak{H}$.

If the unperturbed motion is a motion in a central field of force, so that the vector $\mathbf{M}$ is constant, the vector $\boldsymbol{\mu}$ will also be a constant. Its characteristic values are equal to those of $\mathbf{M}$ multiplied by $e/2m_0 c$. Taking the z-component of $\mathbf{M}$ and remembering that, with suitably chosen characteristic functions $Y_{lm}(\theta, \phi) = P_{lm} e^{im\phi}$, the characteristic values of M_z are equal to integral multiples of $h/2\pi$, we get for the characteristic values of μ_z integral multiples of the quantity

$$\mu_1 = \frac{eh}{4\pi m_0 c},$$

which is called the *Bohr magneton* (since it is equal to the magnetic momentum of a one-quantum Bohr orbit).

If the magnetic field is parallel to the z-axis, or rather if the latter is chosen in the direction of the magnetic field, then the change of the additional energy of the perturbed states of motion compared with that of the corresponding unperturbed states can easily be shown to be equal to the product of $\mathfrak{H}$ by the characteristic values of μ_z. In fact the non-diagonal matrix elements of the perturbation energy

$$S_{nlm;n'l'm'} = -\mathfrak{H}(\mu_z)_{nlm;n'l'm'}$$

with regard to the functions ψ_{nlm}^0 and $\psi_{n'l'm'}^0$ all vanish (which means that the perturbation is of such a kind as to introduce no coupling forces between the pendulums representing different states), so that the additional values of the energy $\Delta H'$ reduce to the diagonal elements of the perturbation matrix. We thus have, in the first approximation,

$$\Delta_1 H' = \Delta_1 H_{nlm} = S_{nlm;nlm} = -\mathfrak{H}(\mu_z)_{nlm},$$

or
$$\Delta_1 H' = -\frac{\mathfrak{H}eh}{4\pi m_0 c} m. \tag{211}$$

This splitting up of the energy-levels by the magnetic field—or rather the corresponding splitting of the spectral lines due to transitions between energy-levels with different values of the axial quantum number m is called the 'normal' Zeeman effect. Since only such transitions occur for which $\Delta m = 0, +1,$ or $-1,$ the normal Zeeman effect consists in the splitting up of each line into three lines, one of which coincides with the original line (corresponding to the absence of the magnetic field), while the other two are displaced in opposite directions by the amount

$$\Delta \nu = -\frac{e\mathfrak{H}}{4\pi m_0 c}. \qquad (211\,\text{a})$$

The undisplaced line corresponds to harmonic oscillations of the electron parallel to the magnetic field, while the displaced ones correspond to circular motion in the one or the other sense about the direction of this field. The relative intensities of these three lines for the case $\Delta l = +1$ and $\Delta l = -1$ have been determined in § 13, Chap. III.

We shall not discuss the Zeeman effect in greater detail here, but shall postpone this question until a later section where it will be dealt with in connexion with the complications arising as a consequence of the hitherto ignored 'intrinsic' magnetic moment of the electron ('anomalous' Zeeman effect).

Although the preceding results have been obtained to a first approximation by the perturbation method, they can easily be shown to hold *exactly*—so long as the action of the magnetic field is represented by the (approximate) operator (209) or (210 a).

We have, in fact, denoting by ϕ the azimuthal angle about the z-axis (supposed to coincide with the direction of the magnetic field),

$$M_z = \frac{h}{2\pi i}\frac{\partial}{\partial \phi},$$

and consequently

$$S = \frac{h\Delta \nu}{i}\frac{\partial}{\partial \phi}, \qquad (211\,\text{b})$$

where $\Delta \nu$ is given by (211 a).

If we now compare the exact equation of the electron's motion

$$(H + S - K')\chi^0_{K'} = 0,$$

with the equation

$$(H - H')\psi^0_{H'} = 0,$$

corresponding to the absence of the magnetic field, we easily find that they can be satisfied by *the same functions*

$$\chi^0_{K'} = \psi^0_{H'} = f_{nl}(r)P_{lm}(\theta)e^{im\phi},$$

if we put

$$K' - H' = \Delta H' = h\Delta \nu\, m$$

in accordance with (211). Thus, in the present case, we have

$$\Delta H' = \Delta_1 H'.$$

We shall consider, in conclusion, another method of dealing with the effect of a homogeneous magnetic field which is very instructive in that it brings to light the similarity between the wave-mechanical and the classical theory.

We shall write the equation of the electron's motion in the general form

$$\left(H+S+\frac{h}{2\pi i}\frac{\partial}{\partial t}\right)\chi = 0, \tag{212}$$

and shall introduce, instead of the original coordinate system x, y, z, another system, $x', y', z'(=z)$, rotating about the common (fixed) z-axis with a constant angular velocity ω. The azimuthal angle ϕ' with respect to this rotating system is thus connected with ϕ by the formula

$$\phi' = \phi - \omega t, \tag{212a}$$

whence it follows that

$$\left(\frac{\partial\chi}{\partial t}\right)_\phi = \left(\frac{\partial\chi}{\partial t}\right)_{\phi'} + \frac{\partial\chi}{\partial\phi'}\frac{d\phi'}{dt} = \left(\frac{\partial\chi}{\partial t}\right)_{\phi'} - \frac{\partial\chi}{\partial\phi}\omega. \tag{212b}$$

Now the partial derivative with respect to t in equation (212) obviously refers to a constant value of ϕ. Taking account of (212b), we can therefore rewrite this equation in the form

$$\left(H+S-\frac{h\omega}{2\pi i}\frac{\partial}{\partial\phi'}+\frac{h}{2\pi i}\frac{\partial'}{\partial t}\right)\chi = 0, \tag{213}$$

where $\partial'\chi/\partial t$ denotes the value of the partial derivative with respect to t, taken for a constant value of ϕ'. This equation can obviously be regarded as describing the motion of the electron with respect to the rotating coordinate system.

Substituting in it the expression (211b) for S, we get, since

$$\left(\frac{\partial}{\partial\phi'}\right)_t = \left(\frac{\partial}{\partial\phi}\right)_t,$$

$$\left\{H+\frac{h}{i}\left(\Delta\nu-\frac{\omega}{2\pi}\right)\frac{\partial}{\partial\phi'}+\frac{h}{2\pi i}\frac{\partial'}{\partial t}\right\}\chi = 0. \tag{213a}$$

This equation reduces to that which describes the motion of the electron with respect to the fixed axes in the absence of the magnetic field— with the fixed axes replaced by the rotating ones—if the angular velocity ω is defined by

$$\omega = 2\pi\Delta\nu, \tag{213b}$$

i.e. if the frequency of revolution is just equal to $\Delta\nu$.

This result is identical with that which is obtained with the help of classical mechanics, where it is interpreted as a *precession of the electron's orbit about the direction of the magnetic field with the angular velocity* $\omega = 2\pi\Delta\nu$ *(Larmor's precession)*.

The particular solutions of the equation

$$\left(H + \frac{h}{2\pi i}\frac{\partial'}{\partial t}\right)\chi = 0,$$

corresponding to a conservative motion of the electron with respect to the rotating axes, are obviously the same as those of the equation $\left(H + \frac{h}{2\pi i}\frac{\partial}{\partial t}\right)\psi = 0$, with ϕ replaced by ϕ'. We thus have

$$\chi = \chi_{H'} = f_{nl}(r)P_{lm}(\theta)e^{im\phi'}e^{-i2\pi H't/h},$$

where H' is a characteristic value of H, i.e.

$$\chi_{H'} = \psi_{H'}e^{-im\omega t} = \psi^0_{H'}e^{-i2\pi(H'+h\omega m/2\pi)t/h}.$$

This is another expression of the result $\chi^0_{K'} = \psi^0_{H'}$, $K'-H' = h\Delta\nu m$ found by the preceding method.

27. Relativistic Wave Mechanics as a Formal Generalization of Maxwell's Electromagnetic Theory of Light

Coming back to the relativistic theory of the motion of an electron in an external electromagnetic field, we have to face the following situation. If the relativistic equation (196) established in § 25 is assumed to be correct, we must give up the theory of the preceding chapters, so far as the introduction of the energy operator H is concerned. If, on the other hand, we wish to preserve this theory and express the wavemechanical law of motion by an equation of the type $\left(H + \frac{h}{2\pi i}\frac{\partial}{\partial t}\right)\psi = 0$, we must replace the relativistic equation (196) by an equation or system of equations which are *linear* and not quadratic with respect to the operator $p_t = \frac{h}{2\pi i}\frac{\partial}{\partial t}$.

We shall now try the second alternative, not only because it fits in better with our previous ideas, but also because it is more general than the first alternative. In fact, the order of a differential equation can always be increased by repeated differentiation, so that, in particular, from an equation of the type $(H + p_t)\psi = 0$ we can always pass to an equation containing the square of p_t. This can be done, for instance, by applying to the preceding equation the operator $H + p_t$ or $H - p_t$ giving $(H^2 + 2Hp_t + p_t^2)\psi = 0$ in the first case and $(H^2 - p_t^2)\psi = 0$ in the second.

Of course we must be prepared to find that the equation of the second order (with regard to p_t), obtained in this way, will be somewhat different from our original equation (196). Which one is chosen will ultimately be decided by comparing theory with experiment.

It can easily be shown that a single equation of the first order with one unknown function ψ, satisfying the space-time symmetry requirements of the relativity theory and giving by repeated differentiation anything like equation (196) is a thing utterly impossible. It is, however, possible to replace equation (196) by a *system* of several equations of the first order with as many unknown functions, which would satisfy the space-time symmetry condition and with the help of a second differentiation would assume a form similar to and, in the special case of free motion, identical with equation (196). We shall see, moreover, that this system of equations can be written in the form of a single equation of the type $(H+p_t)\psi = 0$, where H, p_t, and ψ are treated as four-dimensional matrices, or similarly, in one of the following three equivalent forms $(P_x-p_x)\psi = 0$, $(P_y-p_y)\psi = 0$, $(P_z-p_z)\psi = 0$, where P_x, P_y, P_z are matrix operators representing the components of the electron's momentum in the same sense as $H = P_t$ represents its energy. The possibility of writing the equation of motion in these four equivalent forms is the direct expression of the equivalence of the space coordinates and the time, which forms the essence of the relativity theory.

The first part of our problem, namely, the establishment of a system of first-order equations satisfying the space-time symmetry condition, can be solved in a very simple way, with the help of the analogy between mechanics and optics, which was the starting-point for the development of wave mechanics and which can still be used—with certain reservations—as a source of inspiration.

Equation (201 a)

$$(u_x^2+u_y^2+u_z^2-u_t^2+m_0^2c^2)\psi = 0$$

in the case of a particle with vanishing charge and rest-mass, reduces to

$$\left(\frac{\partial^2}{\partial x^2}+\frac{\partial^2}{\partial y^2}+\frac{\partial^2}{\partial z^2}-\frac{1}{c^2}\frac{\partial^2}{\partial t^2}\right)\psi = 0, \tag{214}$$

i.e. to the equation of the propagation of light-waves (in empty space) with the true velocity c. If the wave velocity is equal to c, then the velocity of the associated particles must also be equal to c, so that these particles can be identified with *photons*.

Now, according to the electromagnetic theory of light, equation (214), usually denoted as d'Alembert's equation, does not give a complete description of the electromagnetic field of the light waves. This field is specified by six quantities, namely, the three components E_x, E_y, E_z

of the electric field and the three components† H_x, H_y, H_z of the magnetic field, these quantities satisfying the well-known *equations of Maxwell*:

$$\left.\begin{aligned}
\frac{\partial H_z}{\partial y} - \frac{\partial H_y}{\partial z} - \frac{1}{c}\frac{\partial E_x}{\partial t} &= 0 \\[2mm]
\frac{\partial H_x}{\partial z} - \frac{\partial H_z}{\partial x} - \frac{1}{c}\frac{\partial E_y}{\partial t} &= 0 \\[2mm]
\frac{\partial H_y}{\partial x} - \frac{\partial H_x}{\partial y} - \frac{1}{c}\frac{\partial E_z}{\partial t} &= 0
\end{aligned}\right\} \qquad \left(\operatorname{curl}\mathbf{H} - \frac{1}{c}\frac{\partial \mathbf{E}}{\partial t} = 0\right), \qquad (215)$$

and

$$\left.\begin{aligned}
\frac{\partial E_z}{\partial y} - \frac{\partial E_y}{\partial z} + \frac{1}{c}\frac{\partial H_x}{\partial t} &= 0 \\[2mm]
\frac{\partial E_x}{\partial z} - \frac{\partial E_z}{\partial x} + \frac{1}{c}\frac{\partial H_y}{\partial t} &= 0 \\[2mm]
\frac{\partial E_y}{\partial x} - \frac{\partial E_x}{\partial y} + \frac{1}{c}\frac{\partial H_z}{\partial t} &= 0
\end{aligned}\right\} \qquad \left(\operatorname{curl}\mathbf{E} + \frac{1}{c}\frac{\partial \mathbf{H}}{\partial t} = 0\right). \qquad (215\,\mathrm{a})$$

To these six equations we may add the following two:

$$\operatorname{div}\mathbf{E} = \frac{\partial E_x}{\partial x} + \frac{\partial E_y}{\partial y} + \frac{\partial E_z}{\partial z} = 0, \qquad (216)$$

$$\operatorname{div}\mathbf{H} = \frac{\partial H_x}{\partial x} + \frac{\partial H_y}{\partial y} + \frac{\partial H_z}{\partial z} = 0. \qquad (216\,\mathrm{a})$$

The latter equations can, however, for vibrational processes, be regarded as a consequence of (215) and (215 a) respectively. Thus, if we differentiate equations (215) with regard to x, y, z, and add them, we get $\frac{\partial}{\partial t}\operatorname{div}\mathbf{E} = 0$. From this it follows—in so far as we reject purely static fields—that $\operatorname{div}\mathbf{E}=0$. In the same way we can derive (216 a) from (215 a).

If we differentiate the left side of the first equation (215) with respect to the time t, we obtain, using (215 a),

$$\frac{\partial}{\partial y}\frac{1}{c}\frac{\partial}{\partial t}H_z - \frac{\partial}{\partial z}\frac{1}{c}\frac{\partial}{\partial t}H_y - \frac{1}{c^2}\frac{\partial^2 E_x}{\partial t^2}$$

$$= \frac{\partial}{\partial y}\left(\frac{\partial E_x}{\partial y} - \frac{\partial E_y}{\partial x}\right) - \frac{\partial}{\partial z}\left(\frac{\partial E_z}{\partial x} - \frac{\partial E_x}{\partial z}\right) - \frac{1}{c^2}\frac{\partial^2 E_x}{\partial t^2}$$

$$= \frac{\partial^2 E_x}{\partial y^2} + \frac{\partial^2 E_x}{\partial z^2} - \frac{\partial}{\partial x}\left(\frac{\partial E_y}{\partial y} + \frac{\partial E_z}{\partial z}\right) - \frac{1}{c^2}\frac{\partial^2 E_x}{\partial t^2},$$

i.e., by (216),

$$\frac{\partial^2 E_x}{\partial x^2} + \frac{\partial^2 E_x}{\partial y^2} + \frac{\partial^2 E_x}{\partial z^2} - \frac{1}{c^2}\frac{\partial^2 E_x}{\partial t^2} = 0,$$

---

† The reader will easily distinguish between the symbol H in the combinations H_x, H_y, H_z used here for the components of $\mathbf{H}$ and the simple H used *passim* for the Hamiltonian energy.

which is merely equation (214) with $\psi = E_x$. In the same way we obtain similar equations for the other five components of the electromagnetic field. We see, therefore, that d'Alembert's equation must be regarded as the result of the elimination, with the help of a second differentiation, of the different field-components from Maxwell's equations.

This elimination is usually carried out with the help of the potentials A_x, A_y, A_z, ϕ which are introduced by means of the formulae

$$\mathbf{E} = -\nabla\phi - \frac{1}{c}\frac{\partial}{\partial t}\mathbf{A}, \qquad \mathbf{H} = \operatorname{curl}\mathbf{A}.$$

Thereby equations (215 a) and (216 a) turn themselves into identities, while equations (215) and (216), with the additional condition

$$\frac{\partial A_x}{\partial x} + \frac{\partial A_y}{\partial y} + \frac{\partial A_z}{\partial z} + \frac{1}{c}\frac{\partial \phi}{\partial t} = 0,$$

yield four d'Alembert equations of the type (214) for the components of the potential.

The preceding relation leads to a simplification of the wave equation (196), which assumes the following form:

$$\left.\begin{aligned}
&\frac{\partial^2\psi}{\partial x^2} + \frac{\partial^2\psi}{\partial y^2} + \frac{\partial^2\psi}{\partial z^2} - \frac{1}{c^2}\frac{\partial^2\psi}{\partial t^2} - \\
&\quad - \frac{4\pi i e}{hc}\left(A_x\frac{\partial\psi}{\partial x} + A_y\frac{\partial\psi}{\partial y} + A_z\frac{\partial\psi}{\partial z} + \frac{\phi}{c}\frac{\partial\psi}{\partial t}\right) - \\
&\quad - \frac{4\pi^2 e^2}{h^2 c^2}\left(A_x^2 + A_y^2 + A_z^2 - \phi^2 + \frac{m_0^2 c^4}{e^2}\right)\psi = 0
\end{aligned}\right\}, \qquad (217)$$

or, in vector notation,

$$\left.\begin{aligned}
&\nabla^2\psi - \frac{1}{c^2}\frac{\partial^2\psi}{\partial t^2} - \frac{4\pi i e}{hc}\left(A\cdot\operatorname{grad}\psi + \frac{\phi}{c}\frac{\partial\psi}{\partial t}\right) - \\
&\quad - \frac{4\pi^2 e^2}{h^2 c^2}\left(A^2 - \phi^2 + \frac{m_0^2 c^4}{e^2}\right)\psi = 0
\end{aligned}\right\}. \qquad (217\,\text{a})$$

This equation, written in the form (201 a), can be regarded as the simplest generalization of d'Alembert's equation (214) for material particles (electrons) with a non-vanishing charge e and rest-mass m_0 — a generalization obtained by replacing the operators

$$\frac{h}{2\pi i}\frac{\partial}{\partial x}, \qquad \frac{h}{2\pi i}\frac{\partial}{\partial y}, \qquad \frac{h}{2\pi i}\frac{\partial}{\partial z}, \qquad \frac{h}{2\pi i}\frac{1}{c}\frac{\partial}{\partial t},$$

by the operators $u_x = \dfrac{h}{2\pi i}\dfrac{\partial}{\partial x} - \dfrac{e}{c}A_x$, etc., and further by adding to the left side of (214) the term $\left(\dfrac{2\pi i}{h}\right)^2 m_0 c^2\psi$.

Now Maxwell's equations form a system of equations of the first order satisfying the space-time symmetry condition and implying d'Alembert's equation as a corollary. We are thus naturally led to the conclusion that the first-order equations of the relativistic wave mechanics, which must replace the second-order equation (201 a), can be obtained as a generalization of Maxwell's equations, in a way similar to that which leads from d'Alembert's equation (214) to the wave-mechanical equation (201 a).

We shall assume, therefore, that the electron (or proton) waves can be described not, as so far assumed, by a scalar quantity ψ but by two vector quantities $\mathbf{M}$ and $\mathbf{N}$ which are analogous to the magnetic and electric field strength ($\mathbf{H}$ and $\mathbf{E}$) respectively, and we shall seek to generalize Maxwell's equations by introducing the operators u_x instead of $\dfrac{h}{2\pi i}\dfrac{\partial}{\partial x}$, etc. The second part of this generalization, i.e. the introduction of the rest-mass, we shall at first disregard, i.e. we shall put $m_0 = 0$.

To begin with, we must notice that the generalized operators $u_x,\dots$, unlike the original, are *non-commutative*, i.e. we obtain different results if we apply to any function ψ two such operators in a different order. For example, if we form the difference of the expressions $u_x u_y \psi$ and $u_y u_x \psi$ we obtain

$$\left[\left(\frac{h}{2\pi i}\right)^2 \frac{\partial^2\psi}{\partial x\partial y} - \frac{h}{2\pi i}\frac{\partial}{\partial x}\left(\frac{e}{c}A_y\psi\right) - \frac{e}{c}A_x\frac{h}{2\pi i}\frac{\partial\psi}{\partial y} + \frac{e^2}{c^2}A_x A_y\psi\right] -$$

$$- \left[\left(\frac{h}{2\pi i}\right)^2 \frac{\partial^2\psi}{\partial y\partial x} - \frac{h}{2\pi i}\frac{\partial}{\partial y}\left(\frac{e}{c}A_x\psi\right) - \frac{e}{c}A_y\frac{h}{2\pi i}\frac{\partial\psi}{\partial x} + \frac{e^2}{c^2}A_y A_x\psi\right],$$

i.e.
$$(u_x u_y - u_y u_x)\psi = \frac{he}{2\pi i c}\left(\frac{\partial A_x}{\partial y} - \frac{\partial A_y}{\partial x}\right)\psi,$$

or, by (199 b),
$$u_x u_y - u_y u_x = -\frac{he}{2\pi i c}H_z, \qquad (218)$$

if we omit the factor ψ operated upon. In a similar way we get the formulae

$$u_y u_z - u_z u_y = -\frac{he}{2\pi i c}H_x, \qquad u_z u_x - u_x u_z = -\frac{he}{2\pi i c}H_y,$$

and also
$$u_x u_t - u_t u_x = -\frac{he}{2\pi i c}E_x, \qquad (218\,\mathrm{a})$$

and two analogous formulae for the combinations (y, t) and (z, t).

Because the operators u are not commutative, their introduction into the eight Maxwell equations [multiplied by $h/(2\pi i)$] in place of the operators $\dfrac{h}{2\pi i}\dfrac{\partial}{\partial x}$, etc., necessitates a further modification. We must, namely, add to the right side of these equations extra terms of the form uM_0 or uN_0 where M_0 and N_0 are two new scalars; otherwise (i.e. when $M_0 = N_0 = 0$) the eight equations obtained for the six quantities M_x, M_y, M_z, N_x, N_y, N_z would be, *in general, incompatible with one another*. In fact, if we limited ourselves to a replacement of the operators $\dfrac{h}{2\pi i}\dfrac{\partial}{\partial x}$,.... by u_x,..., the equations obtained from (216) and (216a) would no longer be a corollary of the equations obtained from (215) and (215a) and would therefore contradict the latter.

In writing down the generalized 'Maxwell-like' equations, the following circumstances should be noticed:

(1) The extra terms uM_0 and uN_0 on the right side must represent the space-time components of two four-dimensional vectors analogous respectively to the vector of *electric* current and charge density in the case of equations (215) and (216)—which will be referred to as the I group of Maxwell's equations—and to the vector of '*magnetic* current and charge density' in the case of the II group, formed by equations (215a) and (216a).

Treating M_0 and N_0 as scalar quantities, we can define the components of the first vector by $u_x M_0$, $u_y M_0$, $u_z M_0$, $\pm u_t M_0$, and that of the second by $u_x N_0$, $u_y N_0$, $u_z N_0$, $\pm u_t N_0$.

(2) The ambiguity of sign $(\pm)$ arising in this connexion can be removed with the help of the fact that the two groups of Maxwell's equations can be derived from each other if $\mathbf{E}$ is replaced by $\mathbf{H}$ and $\mathbf{H}$ by $-\mathbf{E}$.

We must therefore require that one of the two groups of the generalized Maxwell-like equations be obtained from the other by replacing N_x, N_y, N_z, N_0 by M_x, M_y, M_z, M_0 and M_x, M_y, M_z, M_0 by $-N_x$, $-N_y$, $-N_z$, $-N_0$. Taking this into consideration, we obtain, as the first step in our generalization of Maxwell's equations, leaving the rest-mass out of account, the following system of equations:

$$\left.\begin{aligned}
u_y M_z - u_z M_y - u_t N_x &= u_x M_0 \\
u_z M_x - u_x M_z - u_t N_y &= u_y M_0 \\
u_x M_y - u_y M_x - u_t N_z &= u_z M_0
\end{aligned}\right\} \qquad (219)$$

$$\left.\begin{aligned}
u_y N_z - u_z N_y + u_t M_x &= u_x N_0 \\
u_z N_x - u_x N_z + u_t M_y &= u_y N_0 \\
u_x N_y - u_y N_x + u_t M_z &= u_z N_0
\end{aligned}\right\} \qquad (219\,\mathrm{a})$$

$$u_x N_x + u_y N_y + u_z N_z = -u_t M_0 \qquad (220)$$

$$u_x M_x + u_y M_y + u_z M_z = +u_t N_0. \qquad (220\,a)$$

From these equations we will now by 'generalized differentiation', i.e. by repeated application of the operators u, obtain eight differential equations of the second order which correspond to d'Alembert's differential equation.

If we apply the operators u_x, u_y, u_z to the equations (219) and the operator u_t to equation (220), we obtain by addition, using (218) and (218 a):

$$-\frac{he}{2\pi i c}[H_x M_x + H_y M_y + H_z M_z - E_x N_x - E_y N_y - E_z N_z]$$
$$= (u_x^2 + u_y^2 + u_z^2 - u_t^2)M_0,$$

or, if we put for shortness

$$D_0 \equiv u_x^2 + u_y^2 + u^2 - u_t^2 \qquad (221)$$

and use the vector notation:

$$D_0 M_0 = \frac{he}{2\pi i c}(-\mathbf{H \cdot M} + \mathbf{E \cdot N}). \qquad (221\,a)$$

Similarly we get from (219 a) and (220 a) the equation

$$D_0 N_0 = \frac{he}{2\pi i c}(-\mathbf{H \cdot N} - \mathbf{E \cdot M}). \qquad (221\,b)$$

With $e = 0$ these equations can be satisfied *identically* if we put $M_0 = N_0 = 0$. In the general case, however, the scalar functions M_0 and N_0 must be different from zero.

If we apply the operator u_t to the first equation (219) and interchange the order of the different operators u, we get, taking account of (218 a),

$$\frac{he}{2\pi i c}(E_y M_z - E_z M_y - E_x M_0) + u_y u_t M_z - u_z u_t M_y -$$
$$- u_x u_t M_0 - u_t^2 N_x = 0.$$

Now by (219 a) and (220):

$$u_y u_t M_z = u_y u_z N_0 - u_y u_x N_y + u_y^2 N_x,$$
$$-u_z u_t M_y = -u_z u_y N_0 + u_z^2 N_x - u_z u_x N_z,$$
$$-u_x u_t M_0 = u_x^2 N_x + u_x u_y N_y + u_x u_z N_z.$$

By repeated application of the relations (218) and (218 a), we thus obtain

$$(u_x^2 + u_y^2 + u_z^2 - u_t^2)N_x +$$
$$+ \frac{he}{2\pi i c}(E_y M_z - E_z M_y - E_x M_0 + H_y N_z - H_z N_y - H_x N_0) = 0.$$

This equation and the two others which result from it by cyclic interchange of the indices x, y, z can be summarized in the following vector equation:

$$D_0 \mathbf{N} + \frac{he}{2\pi i c}[(\mathbf{E} \times \mathbf{M} - \mathbf{E}M_0) + (\mathbf{H} \times \mathbf{N} - \mathbf{H}N_0)] = 0. \qquad (222)$$

Similarly, by application of the same method to equations (219 a), we obtain the second vector equation,

$$D_0 \mathbf{M} + \frac{he}{2\pi i c}[(\mathbf{H} \times \mathbf{M} - \mathbf{H}M_0) - (\mathbf{E} \times \mathbf{N} - \mathbf{E}N_0)] = 0. \qquad (222\,\text{a})$$

Equations (221 a), (221 b), (222), and (222 a) are the required generalization of d'Alembert's equation. They differ, however, from the latter, not only by the differential operators u appearing in D_0 instead of $\frac{h}{2\pi i}\frac{\partial}{\partial x}$, etc., but also by additional terms which are proportional to the electromagnetic field components and which for each equation have a special form.

If we omit these additional terms (whose physical meaning will be explained later) we obtain, for all the eight functions $M_x, ..., N_z, M_0, N_0$, identical equations of the d'Alembert type—equations which differ from the relativity wave equation (201 a) or (217 a) found earlier only by the absence of the 'mass term' $m_0^2 c^2$ in the operator D_0. This shows that the second step of our generalization of Maxwell's equations—in so far as it is a question of the resulting generalized d'Alembert equations—must consist in replacing the operator D_0 by the operator introduced earlier, namely,

$$D = D_0 + m_0^2 c^2. \qquad (223)$$

The corresponding introduction of the parameter $m_0 c$ into the equations of the first order (219) to (220) is done most simply as follows: In equations (219) and (219 a), which contain the time derivatives of the quantities N_x, N_y, N_z, N_0, we replace the operator u_t by

$$u_t' = u_t - m_0 c, \qquad (223\,\text{a})$$

and in equations (219 a) and (220) by

$$u_t'' = u_t + m_0 c. \qquad (223\,\text{b})$$

Taking into account the relation $u_t' u_t'' = u_t'' u_t' = u_t^2 - m_0^2 c^2$, we can easily convince ourselves that from these generalized Maxwell's equations

$$\left.\begin{array}{l} u_y M_z - u_z M_y - u_t' N_x = u_x M_0 \\ u_z M_x - u_x M_z - u_t' N_y = u_y M_0 \\ u_x M_y - u_y M_x - u_t' N_z = u_z M_0 \end{array}\right\} \qquad (224)$$

$$u_y N_z - u_z N_y + u''_t M_x = u_x N_0 \left.\begin{array}{c}\\\\\end{array}\right\}$$
$$u_z N_x - u_x N_z + u''_t M_y = u_y N_0$$
$$u_x N_y - u_y N_x + u''_t M_z = u_z N_0 \qquad (224\,\text{a})$$

$$u_x N_x + u_y N_y + u_z N_z = -u''_t M_0 \qquad (225)$$

$$u_x M_x + u_y M_y + u_z M_z = +u'_t N_0, \qquad (225\,\text{a})$$

there follow the generalized d'Alembert's equations:

$$DM_0 + \frac{he}{2\pi i c}(\mathbf{H}\cdot\mathbf{M} - \mathbf{E}\cdot\mathbf{N}) = 0 \left.\begin{array}{c}\\\\\\\end{array}\right\},$$
$$DN_0 + \frac{he}{2\pi i c}(\mathbf{H}\cdot\mathbf{N} + \mathbf{E}\cdot\mathbf{M}) = 0 \qquad (226)$$

$$DM + \frac{he}{2\pi i c}[(\mathbf{H}\times\mathbf{M} - \mathbf{H}M_0) - (\mathbf{E}\times\mathbf{N} - \mathbf{E}N_0)] = 0 \left.\begin{array}{c}\\\\\\\end{array}\right\}.$$
$$DN + \frac{he}{2\pi i c}[(\mathbf{E}\times\mathbf{M} - \mathbf{E}M_0) + (\mathbf{H}\times\mathbf{N} - \mathbf{H}N_0)] = 0 \qquad (226\,\text{a})$$

Equations (226) and (226 a) become identical if we put either

$$\mathbf{N} = i\mathbf{M}, \qquad N_0 = iM_0 \qquad (227)$$

or
$$\mathbf{N} = -i\mathbf{M}, \qquad N_0 = -iM_0. \qquad (227\,\text{a})$$

Thereby they assume the following simple form:

$$DM_0 + \frac{he}{2\pi i c}(\mathbf{H}\mp i\mathbf{E})\cdot\mathbf{M} = 0, \qquad (228)$$

$$DM + \frac{he}{2\pi i c}[(\mathbf{H}\mp i\mathbf{E})\times\mathbf{M} - (\mathbf{H}\mp i\mathbf{E})M_0] = 0. \qquad (228\,\text{a})$$

Let that solution of these equations which corresponds to the upper sign be denoted by M^+ and the other by M^-. The general solution of equations (226) and (226 a), therefore, can obviously be written in the form

$$\mathbf{M} = c_1 \mathbf{M}^+ + c_2 \mathbf{M}^-, \qquad M_0 = c_1 M_0^+ + c_2 M_0^- \left.\begin{array}{c}\\\\\end{array}\right\},$$
$$\mathbf{N} = i(c_1 \mathbf{M}^+ - c_2 \mathbf{M}^-), \qquad N_0 = i(c_1 M_0^+ - c_2 M_0^-) \qquad (228\,\text{b})$$

where c_1 and c_2 are two arbitrary constants (which must be introduced if the solutions M^+ and M^- are normalized in some way).

It must be mentioned, however, that the first-order equations (224)–(225 a) do *not* admit solutions of the type (227) and (227 a), because of the appearance of the two different operators u'_t and u''_t. These solutions do not have, therefore, any real significance.

28. Alternative Form of the Wave Equations; Duplicity and Quadruplicity Phenomenon

There is another possibility of halving the number both of the second-order equations (226)–(226 a) and of the first-order equations (224)–(225 a), as well as of the wave functions M, N, defined by them.

We must notice, first, that equations (224)–(225 a) can be naturally regrouped by associating (225 a) not with (224 a), as has been done before, but with (224), and (225) with (224 a). The two groups of four equations thus formed will be denoted by I' and II" respectively.

It is now easily seen that the equations of each group can be compounded in pairs and, as it were, folded up together, in such a way as to form two groups of two equations involving four unknown wave functions. Taking the group I' we can, for example, compound the first two equations (224) to form one pair and the third with equation (225 a) to form the second pair. If we multiply the first equation of the second pair by i and add it to the other, we get

$$(u_x - iu_y)M_x + (iu_x + u_y)M_y + u_z(M_z - iM_0) + u_i'(-iN_z - N_0)$$
$$= (u_x - iu_y)(M_x + iM_y) + u_z(M_z - iM_0) + u_i'(-iN_z - N_0) = 0.$$

Likewise we obtain, by subtracting the second equation (224) from the first equation multiplied by i,

$$(u_x + iu_y)M_z + u_z(-M_x - iM_y) + u_i'(-iN_x + N_y) - (iu_x - u_y)M_0$$
$$= (u_x + iu_y)(M_z - iM_0) - u_z(M_x + iM_y) + u_i'(-iN_x + N_y) = 0.$$

If we put, therefore,

$$\left. \begin{aligned} \psi_1 &= M_x + iM_y, & \psi_2 &= M_z - iM_0 \\ \psi_3 &= -i(N_x + iN_y), & \psi_4 &= -i(N_z - iN_0) \end{aligned} \right\}, \tag{229}$$

we can reduce the four equations under consideration to the following two:

$$\left. \begin{aligned} (u_x - iu_y)\psi_1 + u_z\psi_2 + u_i'\psi_4 &= 0 \\ (u_x + iu_y)\psi_2 - u_z\psi_1 + u_i'\psi_3 &= 0 \end{aligned} \right\}, \tag{229 a}$$

In a similar way the four equations of the group II", (224 a) and (225), can be folded up into the two equations

$$\left. \begin{aligned} (u_x - iu_y)\psi_3 + u_z\psi_4 + u_i''\psi_2 &= 0 \\ (u_x + iu_y)\psi_4 - u_z\psi_3 + u_i''\psi_1 &= 0 \end{aligned} \right\}, \tag{229 b}$$

with the same four unknown wave functions (229). The equations (229 a, b) were first derived by Dirac.

The process just described can be applied to the second-order equations which are obtained from (226) and (226 a) by taking their components along the coordinate axes. We have, for instance, according to the first equation (226 a),

$$D(M_x + iM_y) +$$
$$+ \frac{he}{2\pi ic} \{[(H_y M_z - H_z M_y - H_x M_0) + i(H_z M_x - H_x M_z - H_y M_0)] -$$
$$- [(E_y N_z - E_z N_y - E_x N_0) + i(E_z N_x - E_x N_z - E_y N_0)]\} = 0,$$

that is,

$$D(M_x + iM_y) + \frac{he}{2\pi ic} \{[iH_z(M_x + iM_y) - i(H_x + iH_y)(M_z - iM_0)] -$$
$$- [iE_z(N_x + iN_y) - i(E_x + iE_y)(N_z - iN_0)]\} = 0;$$

and similarly,

$$D(M_z - iM_0) +$$
$$\frac{he}{2\pi ic} \{[(H_x M_y - H_y M_x - H_z M_0) - i(H_x M_x + H_y M_y + H_z M_z)] -$$
$$- [(E_x N_y - E_y N_x - E_z N_0) - i(E_x N_x + E_y N_y + E_z N_z)]\} = 0,$$

that is,

$$D(M_z - iM_0) + \frac{he}{2\pi ic} \{[-i(H_x - iH_y)(M_x + iM_y) - iH_z(M_z - iM_0)] -$$
$$- [-i(E_x - iE_y)(N_x + iN_y) - iE_z(N_z - iN_0)]\} = 0,$$

or, according to (229),

$$\left. \begin{aligned} D\psi_1 + \frac{he}{2\pi c} \{[H_z \psi_1 - (H_x + iH_y)\psi_2] - i[E_z \psi_3 - (E_x + iE_y)\psi_4]\} = 0 \\ D\psi_2 + \frac{he}{2\pi c} \{-[(H_x - iH_y)\psi_1 + H_z \psi_2] + i[(E_x - iE_y)\psi_3 + E_z \psi_4]\} = 0 \end{aligned} \right\}. \tag{230}$$

In the same way the four remaining equations (226)–(226 a) are folded up into

$$\left. \begin{aligned} D\psi_3 + \frac{he}{2\pi c} \{-i[E_z \psi_1 - (E_x + iE_y)\psi_2] + [H_z \psi_3 - (H_x + iH_y)\psi_4]\} = 0 \\ D\psi_4 + \frac{he}{2\pi c} \{+i[(E_x - iE_y)\psi_1 + E_z \psi_2] - [(H_x - iH_y)\psi_3 + H_z \psi_4]\} = 0 \end{aligned} \right\}. \tag{230 a}$$

They can be derived from (230) if ψ_1 and ψ_2 are replaced by ψ_3 and ψ_4, and the latter by ψ_1 and ψ_2. Both the equations (230) and (230 a) can be obtained, of course, directly from equations (229 a, b) in the same way as the equations (226)–(226 a) are obtained from (224)–(225 a), i.e. by the application of the operators u to the left side of (229 a, b). The latter equations were established by Dirac in an externally different form and by a different method, which will be indicated later and which does not make use of the formal analogy between wave mechanics and the electromagnetic theory of light. We shall see that this analogy is actually not so deep as it seems at first sight, and that the regrouping of the equations (224)–(225a), which is necessary for their folding up into the Dirac equations, is a formal expression of a drastic divergence between the wave-mechanical functions M, N and the electromagnetic functions H, E.

It is interesting to notice that a similar regrouping and folding up can be carried out with regard to Maxwell's equations. These 'disguised' Maxwell's equations can be obtained from equations (229a) and (229b) by putting $e = m_0 = 0$, and further by replacing the vectors M and N in the definition (229) of the functions ψ by H and E, dropping the terms M_0, N_0.

In fact, it can be directly verified that if we put

$$H_x + iH_y = \psi_1, \qquad H_z = \psi_2 \atop -i(E_x + iE_y) = \psi_3, \qquad -iE_z = \psi_4,} \tag{231}$$

we obtain, instead of the eight equations (215)–(216a), the following four equations:

$$\left.\begin{aligned}
\left(\frac{\partial}{\partial x} - i\frac{\partial}{\partial y}\right)\psi_1 + \frac{\partial}{\partial z}\psi_2 + \frac{1}{c}\frac{\partial}{\partial t}\psi_4 &= 0 \\
\left(\frac{\partial}{\partial x} + i\frac{\partial}{\partial y}\right)\psi_2 - \frac{\partial}{\partial z}\psi_1 + \frac{1}{c}\frac{\partial}{\partial t}\psi_3 &= 0 \\
\left(\frac{\partial}{\partial x} - i\frac{\partial}{\partial y}\right)\psi_3 + \frac{\partial}{\partial z}\psi_4 + \frac{1}{c}\frac{\partial}{\partial t}\psi_2 &= 0 \\
\left(\frac{\partial}{\partial x} + i\frac{\partial}{\partial y}\right)\psi_4 - \frac{\partial}{\partial z}\psi_3 + \frac{1}{c}\frac{\partial}{\partial t}\psi_1 &= 0
\end{aligned}\right\} \tag{231a}$$

Another well-known possibility of reducing the eight Maxwell equations to four consists in combining the electric and the magnetic field strengths to form a complex vector

$$\mathbf{K} = \mathbf{H} \pm i\mathbf{E}.$$

We then obtain, instead of (215)–(216a), four equations of a similar type, namely,

$$\operatorname{curl}\mathbf{K} \pm \frac{i}{c}\frac{\partial}{\partial t}\mathbf{K} = 0, \qquad \operatorname{div}\mathbf{K} = 0.$$

This method is not applicable to the generalized Maxwell equations (224)–(225a).

The formulae (230) and (230a) correspond to the union of the variables x and y as well as of the corresponding components of various *real* vectors to form *complex* quantities $w = x+iy$, $H_x+iH_y = \psi_1$, $E_x+iE_y = i\psi_3$, etc. The operators $\partial/\partial x-i\partial/\partial y$ and $\partial/\partial x+i\partial/\partial y$ can thereby be regarded as the differential operators $\partial/\partial w$ and $\partial/\partial w^*$ corresponding to the complex variable w and the complex conjugate variable $w^* = x-iy$ respectively.

While we can regard the formulae (230) as a decomposition of the complex functions $\psi_1,..., \psi_4$ into real and imaginary parts, this is not so in the case of the analogous formulae (229). The fact that all the eight quantities M, N must in general assume *complex* values follows immediately from the complex nature of the operators u in the equations (224)–(225 a) determining them.

The reduction of these eight equations to the four equations (229 a, b) is, therefore, an actual halving of the number of unknowns, while in the case of the Maxwell equations we have simply a union of real quantities —as the components of the electromagnetic field are—to form complex quantities.

If the four complex quantities $\psi_1,..., \psi_4$ actually suffice for the complete determination of the electron waves it must be possible by means of these functions to express the statistical quantities, i.e. the probability density ρ and the components of the probability current density j_x, j_y, j_z which we have determined earlier by means of the scalar ψ. In the new determination of these quantities we shall at first be guided by the same analogy as that which led us to the generalized Maxwell equations—or to the Dirac equations equivalent to them. From this point of view the quantities ρ and $\mathbf{j}$ must correspond respectively to the electromagnetic energy density

$$P = \frac{1}{8\pi}(E^2+H^2)$$

and the energy-current density (i.e. to Poynting's vector)

$$\mathbf{J} = \frac{c}{4\pi}\mathbf{E}\times\mathbf{H}.$$

If we put here, instead of the components of $\mathbf{E}$ and $\mathbf{H}$, their expressions obtained from (231):

$$H_x = \tfrac{1}{2}(\psi_1+\psi_1^*), \qquad H_y = \frac{1}{2i}(\psi_1-\psi_1^*), \qquad H_z = \psi_2 = \psi_2^*,$$

$$E_x = \frac{i}{2}(\psi_3-\psi_3^*), \qquad E_y = \tfrac{1}{2}(\psi_3+\psi_3^*), \qquad E_z = i\psi_4 = -i\psi_4^*,$$

we obtain $$P = \frac{1}{8\pi}(\psi_1\psi_1^*+\psi_2\psi_2^*+\psi_3\psi_3^*+\psi_4\psi_4^*);$$

and further,

$$J_x = \frac{c}{4\pi}(E_y H_z - E_z H_y) = \frac{c}{8\pi}[(\psi_3 + \psi_3^*)\psi_2 + \psi_4^*(\psi_1 - \psi_1^*)]$$

$$= \frac{c}{8\pi}(\psi_3\psi_2^* + \psi_3^*\psi_2 + \psi_4^*\psi_1 + \psi_4\psi_1^*),$$

and similar formulae for J_y and J_z.

These quadratic expressions are clearly real and also remain real when all the four quantities $\psi_1,\ldots, \psi_4$ are complex. We are led, therefore, to use them for the representation of the quantities ρ and $\mathbf{j}$. Omitting the common factor $1/8\pi$, we obtain

$$\rho = \psi_1\psi_1^* + \psi_2\psi_2^* + \psi_3\psi_3^* + \psi_4\psi_4^* \tag{232}$$

$$\left.\begin{array}{l} j_x = c(\psi_1\psi_4^* + \psi_4\psi_1^* + \psi_2\psi_3^* + \psi_3\psi_2^*) \\ j_y = -ic(\psi_1\psi_4^* - \psi_4\psi_1^* + \psi_2\psi_3^* - \psi_3\psi_2^*) \\ j_z = -c(\psi_1\psi_3^* + \psi_3\psi_1^* + \psi_2\psi_4^* + \psi_4\psi_2^*) \end{array}\right\} . \tag{232 a}$$

If these expressions are correct they must, like the expressions obtained earlier for ρ and j, satisfy the equation

$$\frac{\partial\rho}{\partial x} + \frac{\partial j_x}{\partial x} + \frac{\partial j_y}{\partial y} + \frac{\partial j_z}{\partial z} = 0, \tag{232 b}$$

expressing the law of the conservation of probability (or of the number of copies). It can easily be shown by means of equations (229 a, b) that this is indeed the case.

Multiplying these equations successively by ψ_4^*, ψ_3^*, ψ_2^*, ψ_1^*, subtracting from them the corresponding conjugate equations

$$(u_x^* + iu_y^*)\psi_1^* + u_z^*\psi_2^* + u_t'^*\psi_4^* = 0,$$

$$(u_x^* - iu_y^*)\psi_2^* - u_z^*\psi_2^* + u_t'^*\psi_3^* = 0,$$

etc., multiplied by ψ_4, ψ_3, etc., and finally adding the results, we get:

$$[\psi_4^*(u_x - iu_y)\psi_1 - \psi_1(u_x^* - iu_y^*)\psi_4^*] + [\psi_3^*(u_x + iu_y)\psi_2 - \psi_2(u_x^* + iu_y^*)\psi_3^*] +$$
$$+ [\psi_2^*(u_x - iu_y)\psi_3 - \psi_3(u_x^* - iu_y^*)\psi_2^*] + [\psi_1^*(u_x + iu_y)\psi_4 - \psi_4(u_x^* + iu_y^*)\psi_1^*] +$$
$$+ (\psi_4^* u_z \psi_2 - \psi_2 u_z^* \psi_4^*) - (\psi_3^* u_z \psi_1 - \psi_1 u_z^* \psi_3^*) + (\psi_2^* u_z \psi_4 - \psi_4 u_z^* \psi_2^*) -$$
$$- (\psi_1^* u_z \psi_3 - \psi_3 u_z^* \psi_1^*) + (\psi_4^* u_t' \psi_4 - \psi_4 u_t'^* \psi_4^*) + (\psi_3^* u_t' \psi_3 - \psi_3 u_t'^* \psi_3^*) +$$
$$+ (\psi_2^* u_t'' \psi_2 - \psi_2 u_t''^* \psi_2^*) + (\psi_1^* u_t'' \psi_1 - \psi_1 u_t''^* \psi_1^*) = 0,$$

which, by the definition of the operators u, easily reduces to (232 b) with the expressions (232) and (232 a) for ρ and j_x, j_y, j_z.

Formula (232) is the immediate generalization of the formula $\rho = \psi\psi^*$ of the original non-relativistic Schrödinger theory. On the other hand,

the expressions (232 a) have a form entirely different from the original
expressions for the current density

$$j_x = \frac{h}{4\pi m_0 i}\left(\psi^* \frac{\partial \psi}{\partial x} - \psi \frac{\partial \psi^*}{\partial x}\right).$$

A more accurate investigation of equations (229 a, b) shows, however,
that this difference is not so great as it seems. With harmonically
vibrating waves, corresponding to a motion with a definite energy ϵ,
the dependence of the functions $\psi_1, ..., \psi_4$ on the time is described by the
common factor $e^{-i2\pi \epsilon t/h}$, so that the operators u'_t and u''_t reduce to the
ordinary factors

$$\left. \begin{aligned}
u'_t &= -\frac{1}{c}(\epsilon - U + m_0 c^2) = -\frac{1}{c}(W - U + 2m_0 c^2) \\
u''_t &= -\frac{1}{c}(\epsilon - U - m_0 c^2) = -\frac{1}{c}(W - U)
\end{aligned} \right\}, \tag{233}$$

where $U = e\phi$ is the potential energy of the electron and $W - U$ is its
kinetic energy. In general (so far as we restrict ourselves to positive
values of ϵ, see below), the first factor is enormously large compared
with the second; therefore the functions ψ_3 and ψ_4 which are multiplied
by it in equations (229 a) must, with regard to their absolute magnitude, be very small compared with the functions ψ_1 and ψ_2. If, moreover, we restrict ourselves to the case of motion with a kinetic energy
$W - U$, which is small compared with the rest-energy $m_0 c^2$, i.e. with
a velocity v whose square is small compared with c^2, we can put
approximately, according to (229 a),

$$\left. \begin{aligned}
2m_0 c\psi_3 &= (u_x + iu_y)\psi_2 - u_z\psi_1 \\
2m_0 c\psi_4 &= (u_x - iu_y)\psi_1 + u_z\psi_2
\end{aligned} \right\}. \tag{233 a}$$

Since these relations no longer contain the energy ϵ, they may be
regarded as approximately valid in the general case of non-conservative
motion.

It should be mentioned that, according to (233 a), the ratio of the
functions ψ_3, ψ_4 to the functions ψ_1, ψ_2 is of the order of magnitude
$g/(m_0 c) \cong v/c$, where v is the velocity of the electron, and g is its proper
momentum estimated roughly by the ratio $u\psi_{1,2}/\psi_{1,2}$. It follows from
this that, to the first approximation with regard to small quantities of
the order v/c, we can put, instead of (232),

$$\rho = \psi_1^*\psi_1 + \psi_2^*\psi_2 \tag{234}$$

neglecting the squares of ψ_3 and ψ_4. Substituting the expressions

(233 a) in (232 a), we get further,

$$j_x = \frac{1}{2m_0}\{[\psi_1^*(u_x - iu_y)\psi_1 + \psi_1^* u_z \psi_2] + [\psi_1(u_x^* + iu_y^*)\psi_1^* + \psi_1 u_z^* \psi_2^*] +$$

$$+ [\psi_2^*(u_x + iu_y)\psi_2 - \psi_2^* u_z \psi_1] + [\psi_2(u_x^* - iu_y^*)\psi_2^* + \psi_2 u_z^* \psi_1^*]\}$$

$$= \frac{1}{2m_0}\{[(\psi_1^* u_x \psi_1 + \psi_2^* u_x \psi_2) + (\psi_1 u_x^* \psi_1^* + \psi_2 u_x^* \psi_2^*)] +$$

$$+ i[(\psi_2^* u_y \psi_2 - \psi_1^* u_y \psi_1) - (\psi_2 u_y^* \psi_2^* - \psi_1 u_y^* \psi_1^*)] +$$

$$+ [(\psi_1^* u_z \psi_2 - \psi_2^* u_z \psi_1) + (\psi_1 u_z^* \psi_2^* - \psi_2 u_z^* \psi_1^*)]\}.$$

If we put $A_1 = A_2 = A_3 = 0$ (i.e. if we neglect the potential momentum —if any—compared with the proper momentum), we obtain the following formula:

$$j_x = \frac{h}{4\pi m_0 i}\left\{\left[\psi_1^* \frac{\partial \psi_1}{\partial x} + \psi_2^* \frac{\partial \psi_2}{\partial x} - \psi_1 \frac{\partial \psi_1^*}{\partial x} - \psi_2 \frac{\partial \psi_2^*}{\partial x}\right] + \right.$$

$$\left. + i\frac{\partial}{\partial y}(\psi_2^* \psi_2 - \psi_1^* \psi_1) + \frac{\partial}{\partial z}(\psi_1^* \psi_2 - \psi_2^* \psi_1)\right\},$$

the first term of which (in square brackets) is the same generalization of the original expression

$$j_x = \frac{h}{4\pi m_0 i}\left(\psi^* \frac{\partial}{\partial x}\psi - \psi \frac{\partial}{\partial x}\psi^*\right)$$

as (234) is of the original expression $\psi^*\psi$ for ρ. The physical meaning of the two additional terms will be cleared up in the next section. From the purely formal point of view, these two terms, as well as the corresponding terms in j_y and j_z, can be regarded as the x-, y-, and z-components of the *curl* of a certain vector $c\mathfrak{M}$, defined by the formulae

$$\mathfrak{M}_x = \frac{h}{4\pi m_0 c}(\psi_1^* \psi_2 + \psi_2^* \psi_1), \qquad \mathfrak{M}_y = \frac{h}{4\pi m_0 ci}(\psi_1^* \psi_2 - \psi_2^* \psi_1) \left.\right\}$$

$$\left.\mathfrak{M}_z = \frac{h}{4\pi m_0 c}(\psi_2^* \psi_2 - \psi_1^* \psi_1)\right\} \quad (234\,a)$$

so that the approximate expression for the current density in vector form is:

$$\mathbf{j} = \frac{h}{4\pi m_0 i}(\psi_1^* \nabla \psi_1 + \psi_2^* \nabla \psi_2 - \psi_1 \nabla \psi_1^* - \psi_2 \nabla \psi_2^*) + c\,\mathrm{curl}\,\mathfrak{M}. \quad (234\,b)$$

If, further, we substitute the approximate expressions (233 a) in equations (229 b), the latter assume the following form:

$$(u_x - iu_y)(u_x + iu_y)\psi_2 - (u_x - iu_y)u_z \psi_1 + u_z(u_x - iu_y)\psi_1 +$$

$$+ u_z^2 \psi_2 + 2m_0 cu_t''\psi_2 = 0,$$

$$(u_x + iu_y)(u_x - iu_y)\psi_1 + (u_x + iu_y)u_z \psi_2 - u_z(u_x + iu_y)\psi_2 +$$

$$+ u_z^2 \psi_1 + 2m_0 cu_t''\psi_1 = 0.$$

Now according to the relations (218) and (218 a), we have

$$(u_x - iu_y)(u_x + iu_y) = u_x^2 + u_y^2 + i(u_x u_y - u_y u_x) = u_x^2 + u_y^2 - \frac{he}{2\pi c} H_z,$$

$$(u_x + iu_y)(u_x - iu_y) = u_x^2 + u_y^2 + \frac{he}{2\pi c} H_z,$$

$$u_z(u_x - iu_y) - (u_x - iu_y)u_z = \frac{he}{2\pi c}(-H_x + iH_y),$$

$$(u_x + iu_y)u_z - u_z(u_x + iu_y) = -\frac{he}{2\pi c}(H_x + iH_y).$$

We have further

$$2m_0 c u_t'' = 2m_0\left[\left(\frac{h}{2\pi i}\frac{\partial}{\partial t} + e\phi\right) + m_0 c^2\right].$$

which reduces to $-2m_0(W - U)$ for conservative motion. We can drop the constant term $m_0 c^2$ if $\frac{h}{2\pi i}\frac{\partial}{\partial t}$ is assumed to reduce in the latter case to $-W$ and not to $-\epsilon$ (this constant term entails an irrelevant factor $e^{-i2\pi m_0 c^2 t/h}$ in the expression of the functions ψ_1, ψ_2). With this condition, the preceding equations can be written down in the following form:

$$\left.\begin{array}{l}\left(\dfrac{1}{2m_0}\mathbf{u}^2 + p_t + U\right)\psi_1 + \dfrac{he}{4\pi m_0 c}[H_z\psi_1 - (H_x + iH_y)\psi_2] = 0 \\[2mm] \left(\dfrac{1}{2m_0}\mathbf{u}^2 + p_t + U\right)\psi_2 + \dfrac{he}{4\pi m_0 c}[-(H_x - iH_y)\psi_1 - H_z\psi_2] = 0\end{array}\right\}, \quad (235)$$

where $\mathbf{u}$ is the (three-dimensional) vector with the components u_x, u_y, u_z.

These equations represent the approximate form of the relativistic second-order equations (230) and can indeed be obtained from them by dropping the small quantities ψ_3, ψ_4. The approximation involved corresponds to neglecting terms of the second and higher orders in v/c, including those which represent the variation of mass with velocity. It must be mentioned that, although the functions ψ_3, ψ_4 are themselves small of the first order with regard to ψ_1, ψ_2, they are multiplied, in equations (230), by the factor $he/2\pi c$, which can be regarded as a small quantity of the first order (in $1/c$).

If, in equations (235), we drop the additional terms, proportional to the magnetic intensity (putting either $\mathbf{H} = 0$ or $c = \infty$), they reduce to equation (203 a), § 26, the two functions ψ_1 and ψ_2 becoming identical with the single function ψ of the previous theory. Equations (235) thus give a more complete description of the motion than equation (203 a). In fact they exhibit the *duplicity phenomenon* which has already been indicated in Part I, § 19, and traced to the electron's *'spin'* or *'intrinsic magnetic moment'.* To these properties correspond additional forces, which are represented by the additional terms, proportional to the magnetic field in equation (235), and also to the electric field in the exact equations (230).

The duplicity phenomenon, as explained in Part I, in its simplest form consists in the splitting-up of each quantized state, as determined by Bohr's theory, into two states which in general have slightly different energies. So far as the number of states is concerned, Bohr's theory gives the same results as the ordinary Schrödinger equation with one wave function ψ. Now to each solution of this equation, $\psi_{H'}$ say, there corresponds a set of *two* solutions of the system of equations (235) or rather of the equations obtained from them, if the operator $-p_t$ is replaced by the energy constant.

This means that to each energy-value H' of the ordinary Schrödinger equation there correspond two slightly different energy values, H'_+ and H'_- say, of the system of equations (235). Each of these energy values is associated with a set of two functions $\psi_{1H'+}$, $\psi_{2H'+}$ and $\psi_{1H'-}$, $\psi_{2H'-}$; these four functions replace the single function $\psi_{H'}$ of the Schrödinger theory.

If, instead of the approximate equations (235), we take the system of four exact equations (230) and (230a), then by a similar argument it seems to follow that to each state of the ordinary Schrödinger theory there corresponds, according to the exact theory, four states, whose energies, if the magnetic and electric field strengths are not too large, lie close to the energy H' of the single Schrödinger state.

This conclusion is, however, fallacious, for the four second-order equations (230)–(230a) are not independent of each other, being in fact derived from the four first-order equations (229a)–(229b). So far as the number of solutions (i.e. states) is concerned, the latter are equivalent to *two* of the four second-order equations derived from them. We get, therefore, with the exact equations (230)–(230a), a duplicity phenomenon of the same type as with the approximate equations (235), the value of the energy being, of course, somewhat different in the exact theory from what it is in the approximate theory.

The exact theory, when compared with the approximate theory or with the original non-relativistic Schrödinger theory, leads, however, to an additional duplicity phenomenon of an entirely different type, which is not connected with the 'spin' property, but can be referred to as due to the variation of the mass with velocity. This type of duplicity is already implied in the relativistic equation with the single function ψ, which was derived at the beginning of this chapter. We come upon it in its simplest form in the case of *free* motion, when the operators u_x, u_y, u_z, u_t can be replaced by ordinary numbers (multipliers) $g_x, g_y, g_z, \epsilon/c$ representing respectively the components of the momentum and the energy, *including the rest-energy* $m_0 c^2$, divided by c. Equations (230) reduce in this case to the same form as equation (196), namely,

$$\left(g_x^2 + g_y^2 + g_z^2 - \frac{\epsilon^2}{c^2} + m_0^2 c^2\right)\psi = 0,$$

which is equivalent to the ordinary relativistic relation between momentum and energy

$$g^2 - \frac{\epsilon^2}{c^2} + m_0^2 c^2 = 0.$$

Now since this relation contains the square of the energy, it leads to two numerically equal values of the latter, one positive and the other *negative*,

$$\epsilon = \pm c\sqrt{(m_0^2 c^2 + g^2)}.$$

In Einstein's mechanics, the negative value was rejected as having no physical meaning. It has, however, been explained already in Part I, § 19, that this rejection is *not* justified in wave mechanics, because of the possibility of a continuous transition from a state of positive to that of negative energy ϵ through imaginary values of the velocity or because of a 'jump' produced by some perturbing forces.

In the case of non-relativistic wave mechanics, we have, under the same conditions (free motion),

$$g^2 - 2m_0 W = 0,$$

where W is the ordinary (kinetic) energy, not including the rest-energy $m_0 c^2$. This non-relativistic energy is related to the *positive* energy ϵ of relativity mechanics by the equation

$$W = \epsilon - m_0 c^2,$$

whereas the negative energy ϵ has no counterpart in non-relativity mechanics. The appearance of the negative energy ϵ in addition to the positive energy forms the essence of the duplicity phenomenon of the second kind. The situation is not substantially changed in the general case of motion in a conservative field of force, the only difference being that the positive and negative energies of the corresponding states are not numerically equal.

Combining the two duplicity phenomena—that due to the spin and that due to the relativistic variation of the mass—we get a *quadruplicity pheno-menon* which can conveniently (though not quite correctly) be associated with the replacement of the single ψ-function of the Schrödinger theory by the four ψ-functions of Dirac's theory.—This association is not quite correct, for the same quadruplicity phenomenon would result from Pauli's theory, based on the use of two functions ψ_1 and ψ_2, if, in the approximate equations (235) defining them, the non-relativistic operator $u^2/2m_0+p_t+U$ were replaced by the corresponding relativistic operator of the second order, $D = (u^2-u_t^2+m_0^2c^2)/2m_0$. It must be mentioned, however, that in doing this we should be guilty of inconsistency, because, having dropped additional terms of the second order proportional to the electric field strength in deriving the approximate equations (235) from the exact equations (230), we must also drop second- and higher-order terms, representing the dependence of mass upon velocity, in the main operator D.

In the case of free motion (represented by plane waves), there exists a very simple relation between the four functions ψ referring to the positive energy and the corresponding negative energy solution of the Dirac equations (299 a)–(299 b). Putting

$$\psi_k = a_k e^{i2\pi(g_x x+g_y y+g_z z-\epsilon t)/h}, \tag{236}$$

where the a_k are constants ($k = 1, 2, 3, 4$), we can replace them by the following algebraic system:

$$\left.\begin{aligned}(g_x-ig_y)a_1+g_z a_2+\frac{1}{c}(\epsilon+m_0 c^2)a_4 = 0 \\[2mm](g_x+ig_y)a_2-g_z a_1+\frac{1}{c}(\epsilon+m_0 c^2)a_3 = 0\end{aligned}\right\}, \tag{236 a}$$

$$\left.\begin{aligned}(g_x-ig_y)a_3+g_z a_4+\frac{1}{c}(\epsilon-m_0 c^2)a_2 = 0 \\[2mm](g_x+ig_y)a_4-g_z a_3+\frac{1}{c}(\epsilon-m_0 c^2)a_1 = 0\end{aligned}\right\}. \tag{236 b}$$

If, in these equations, the energy ϵ is replaced by $-\epsilon$, then the first two become identical with the second two and the latter with the former if simultaneously a_1, a_2 are replaced by a_3, a_4 and a_3, a_4 by $-a_1$, $-a_2$. This means that, with

$$\psi_1 = \psi_1', \qquad \psi_2 = \psi_2', \qquad \psi_3 = \psi_3', \qquad \psi_4 = \psi_4',$$

corresponding to $\epsilon = \epsilon' > 0$, we have

$$\psi_1 = \psi_3', \qquad \psi_2 = \psi_4', \qquad \psi_3 = -\psi_1', \qquad \psi_4 = -\psi_2',$$

for $\epsilon = -\epsilon'$.

It has been assumed, hitherto, that the functions ψ_3, ψ_4 were small (of the first order in v/c) compared with ψ_1, ψ_2. We now see that this is only true if we restrict ourselves to positive energy solutions; the converse is true in the case of negative energy solutions—both for free motion and for a motion in a conservative field of force.

From the point of view of the old relativity mechanics, the reversal of the sign of the energy $\epsilon = c^2 m_0/\sqrt{(1-v^2/c^2)}$ is equivalent to the reversal of the sign of the rest-mass m_0. This is not exactly true, however, in the wave-mechanical theory. For a reversal of the sign of m_0 in equations (236 a)–(236 b) leads to the replacement of ψ_1, ψ_2 by ψ_3, ψ_4 and ψ_3, ψ_4 by ψ_1, ψ_2 *without reversal of the sign of the latter.* The two solutions have nothing to do with each other, since they refer to particles of different kinds (particles with negative rest-mass being in reality non-existent), whereas the two solutions corresponding to $\epsilon = \pm\epsilon'$ refer to the same particle with a positive rest-mass m_0, the values of the energy being due to the ambiguity of sign in the radical of the expression $\epsilon = c^2 m_0/\sqrt{(1-v^2/c^2)}$.

It is important to notice that the states of negative energy, as determined by relativity wave mechanics, *are not directly observable.* According to Dirac's theory of the duality of matter and electricity, outlined in Part I, § 19, nearly all these states are occupied by electrons, the vacant states ('holes') being observed as protons. According to the revised version of this theory, the holes in question represent not protons but positive electrons, which have been recently discovered by Anderson in America (1932) and by Blackett and Occhialini in England (1933).

29. The Approximate Pauli Theory in the Two-dimensional Matrix Form; Electron's Magnetic Moment and Angular Momentum

The approximate (non-relativistic) equations (235) were initially obtained by W. Pauli in 1927, not as an approximation to the Dirac theory, which was published a year later, but as the result of a semi-empirical attempt to interpret wave-mechanically the duplicity phenomenon, which a year before had been incorporated by Uhlenbeck and Goudsmit into the Bohr theory on the assumption that the electron possesses a spin motion, with an angular momentum equal to half of the Bohr unit $h/2\pi$ and a magnetic moment equal to Bohr's magneton $\mu = eh/(4\pi m_0 c)$.

Pauli's equations (235) can actually be put in a form corresponding to this assumption, i.e. giving a wave-mechanical interpretation of the electron's 'spin', and, indeed, by using a matrix notation, based upon the representation of the two functions ψ_1, ψ_2 as the elements of a one-column matrix

$$\psi = \begin{Bmatrix} \psi_1 \\ \psi_2 \end{Bmatrix}, \tag{237}$$

the conjugate complex functions ψ_1^*, ψ_2^* forming the adjoint one-row matrix

$$\psi^\dagger = \{\psi_1, \psi_2\}. \tag{237 a}$$

Under this condition, the two equations (235) can be written in the form

$$P\psi = 0, \tag{238}$$

where P is a square 'operator-matrix' of the second rank

$$P = \begin{Bmatrix} P_{11}, P_{12} \\ P_{21}, P_{22} \end{Bmatrix}, \tag{238 a}$$

with suitably defined elements. These elements must be defined in such a way that the two equations (235) assume the form

$$\left. \begin{aligned} (P\psi)_1 &= P_{11}\psi_1 + P_{12}\psi_2 = 0 \\ (P\psi)_2 &= P_{21}\psi_1 + P_{22}\psi_2 = 0 \end{aligned} \right\}. \tag{238 b}$$

Hence it follows that

$$P = \frac{1}{2m_0}(\mathbf{u}^2 + p_t + U)\delta - \mu\mathbf{H}\cdot\boldsymbol{\sigma}, \tag{239}$$

where

$$\delta = \begin{Bmatrix} 1 & 0 \\ 0 & 1 \end{Bmatrix}, \tag{239 a}$$

is the unit matrix of the second rank and $\boldsymbol{\sigma}$ is a vector matrix with the following rectangular components:

$$\sigma_x = \begin{Bmatrix} 0 & 1 \\ 1 & 0 \end{Bmatrix}, \qquad \sigma_y = \begin{Bmatrix} 0 & i \\ -i & 0 \end{Bmatrix}, \qquad \sigma_z = \begin{Bmatrix} -1 & 0 \\ 0 & +1 \end{Bmatrix}. \tag{239 b}$$

The scalar product $\mathbf{H}\cdot\boldsymbol{\sigma}$ denotes, as usual, the sum $H_x\sigma_x + H_y\sigma_y + H_z\sigma_z$. This is a matrix with the elements

$$\left. \begin{aligned} (\mathbf{H}\cdot\boldsymbol{\sigma})_{11} &= -H_z, & (\mathbf{H}\cdot\boldsymbol{\sigma})_{12} &= H_x + iH_y \\ (\mathbf{H}\cdot\boldsymbol{\sigma})_{21} &= H_x - iH_y, & (\mathbf{H}\cdot\boldsymbol{\sigma})_{22} &= +H_z \end{aligned} \right\}. \tag{239 c}$$

The matrix $\boldsymbol{\sigma}$ was introduced by Pauli for the wave-mechanical representation of the electron's magnetic moment which was supposed to be due to its spin. This 'intrinsic' magnetic moment can be defined as the operator or matrix

$$\boldsymbol{\mu} = \mu\boldsymbol{\sigma},$$

where $\mu = eh/(4\pi m_0 c)$ is the value of the Bohr magneton.

The reason for this is that equation (238) can be written in the usual form

$$(K + p_t)\psi = 0 \tag{240}$$

if p_t is defined as the matrix-operator

$$p_t = \delta \frac{h}{2\pi i} \frac{\partial}{\partial t}, \tag{240 a}$$

and K as the energy matrix-operator

$$K = \left(\frac{1}{2m_0} \mathbf{u}^2 + U \right) \delta - \mathbf{\mu} \cdot \mathbf{H}, \tag{240 b}$$

the additional term $-\mathbf{\mu} \cdot \mathbf{H}$ having exactly the same form as the energy of an elementary magnet with a moment $\mathbf{\mu}$ in the given external magnetic field $\mathbf{H}$.

We thus see that the generalization of the Schrödinger theory which is necessary to account for the spin phenomenon consists in adding to the energy operator the extra term $-\mathbf{\mu} \cdot \mathbf{H}$ and in replacing ordinary operators by operator-matrices of the second rank, the function ψ being replaced accordingly by the one-column matrix (237). The old operators of the Schrödinger theory, such as $\frac{1}{2m_0} \mathbf{u}^2 + U$ and $\frac{h}{2\pi i} \frac{\partial}{\partial t}$, are replaced by their products with the unit matrix of the second rank δ.

In future we shall usually omit the unit matrix, its presence as a factor being understood whenever we have to deal with an ordinary operator—like $\mathbf{u}^2$ or U, etc.—of the old theory. With this convention, the old theory can be preserved without any change of form whatsoever —except for the addition of the extra term $-\mathbf{\mu} \cdot \mathbf{H}$ to the energy operator and the corresponding modification of other expressions connected with the resulting operator K.

Thus, for instance, if the characteristic values of K, which will be denoted by K', K'', etc., as before, are imagined to be multiplied by the unit matrix δ, we may write, omitting the latter, in the same way as in the old theory:

$$(K - K')\psi_{K'} = 0, \tag{241}$$

which is actually equivalent to the system of equations

$$\left. \begin{aligned} (K_{11} - K')\psi_{K'1} + K_{12}\psi_{K'2} &= 0 \\ K_{21}\psi_{K'1} + (K_{22} - K')\psi_{K'2} &= 0 \end{aligned} \right\}. \tag{241 a}$$

It should be mentioned that Schrödinger's theory can be regarded as a particular (or rather limiting) case of Pauli's theory, obtained by putting $\mu = 0$, i.e. by dropping the extra term $-\mathbf{\mu} \cdot \mathbf{H}$ in K, but preserving the matrix form of the resulting operator H, which can be defined as the product of the ordinary operator $\frac{1}{2m_0} \mathbf{u}^2 + U$ and the unit matrix δ. The two functions ψ_1 and ψ_2 become identical in this case except for a constant factor ψ_2/ψ_1, which remains arbitrary, and which, without loss of generality, can be put equal to zero, the function ψ_2 thus vanishing and ψ_1 reducing to the ordinary Schrödinger function ψ.

Before proceeding further, we must consider the equation which is satisfied by the function-matrix $\psi^\dagger$, adjoint to ψ.

The conjugate complex of equation (240) satisfied by ψ^* is

$$(K^* + p_t^*)\psi^* = 0, \tag{242}$$

where

$$\psi^* = \begin{Bmatrix} \psi_1^* \\ \psi_2^* \end{Bmatrix}$$

is the conjugate complex of ψ. We shall not, however, in future need this matrix, but the transposed matrix $\psi^\dagger = \{\psi_1^*, \psi_2^*\}$. If the matrix elements of K and p_t were ordinary numbers (and not operators), we could, instead of the preceding equation, write

$$\psi^\dagger(K^\dagger + p_t^\dagger) = 0. \tag{243}$$

We shall preserve this equation in the general case, with the convention that the operators $K^\dagger$ and $p_t^\dagger$—contrary to the rule assumed hitherto—act not on their right but *on their left*. The same refers to matrix operators of any type. Thus, if

$$F = \begin{Bmatrix} F_{11} & F_{12} \\ F_{21} & F_{22} \end{Bmatrix}$$

is a matrix operator acting on ψ and $F\psi$ the one-column matrix

$$F\psi = \begin{Bmatrix} F_{11}\psi_1 + F_{12}\psi_2 \\ F_{21}\psi_1 + F_{22}\psi_2 \end{Bmatrix}$$

resulting therefrom, then the adjoint matrix $(F\psi)^\dagger$ will be defined by

$$\psi^\dagger F^\dagger = \{\psi_1^\dagger F_{11}^\dagger + \psi_2^\dagger F_{21}^\dagger, \psi_1^\dagger F_{12}^\dagger + \psi_2^\dagger F_{22}^\dagger\}$$
$$= \{F_{11}^* \psi_1^* + F_{12}^* \psi_2^*, F_{21}^* \psi_1^* + F_{22}^* \psi_2^*\},$$

which is in accordance with the usual definition of adjoint matrices. The necessity for reversing the direction of the action of an operator from right to left in a transition from F to $F^\dagger$ is due to the fact that $\psi^\dagger$, being a one-row matrix, must always stand as the first factor in a matrix product involving it (while ψ, being defined as a one-column matrix, must always stand in the second place).

With this convention, the equation for the matrix-function $\psi_{K'}^\dagger$ can be written in the form

$$\psi_{K'}^\dagger(K^\dagger - K'^\dagger) = 0$$

or, since $K'^\dagger = K'$,

$$\psi_{K'}^\dagger(K^\dagger - K') = 0. \tag{243a}$$

This is equivalent to the ordinary equations

$$\psi_{K'1}^\dagger(K_{11}^\dagger - K') + \psi_{K'2}^\dagger K_{21}^\dagger = (K_{11}^* - K')\psi_{K'1}^* + K_{12}^* \psi_{K'2}^* = 0,$$
$$\psi_{K'1}^\dagger K_{21}^\dagger + \psi_{K'2}^\dagger(K_{22}^\dagger - K') = K_{12}^* \psi_{K'1}^* + (K_{22}^* - K')\psi_{K'2}^* = 0,$$

which are the conjugate complex of the equations (241 a) (K' being real).

The product of the matrices $\psi^\dagger$ and ψ is a matrix consisting of one row and one column only; it can be treated accordingly as a simple number. This number

$$\psi^\dagger \psi = \psi_1^* \psi_1 + \psi_2^* \psi_2 \tag{244}$$

can also be regarded as the scalar product of the two-component vectors ψ and ψ^* (or $\psi^\dagger$). It measures, as we know, the probability-density for finding the electron at a given point in a state of motion specified by the matrix or vector ψ. If the latter is 'quadratically integrable', i.e. if the integral $\int \psi^\dagger \psi \, dV$ extended over the whole space converges, then ψ can be normalized by setting this integral equal to 1. This refers, in particular, to functions $\psi_{K'}$ belonging to a discrete energy spectrum, in which case we can put

$$\int \psi_{K'}^\dagger \psi_K \, dV = 1. \tag{244 a}$$

It can in addition easily be shown in practically the same way as in the old theory that functions ψ belonging to different energy values, K' and K'' say, satisfy the orthogonality relation

$$\int \psi_{K''}^\dagger \psi_{K'} \, dV = 0 \qquad (K' \neq K''), \tag{244 b}$$

where $\qquad \psi_{K''}^\dagger \psi_{K'} = \psi_{K''1}^* \psi_{K'1} + \psi_{K''2}^* \psi_{K'2}$

is the product of the matrices (or vectors) $\psi_{K''}^\dagger$ and $\psi_{K'}$.

We have in fact, multiplying the equation $(K - K')\psi_{K'} = 0$ (on the left) by $\psi_{K''}^\dagger$ and the equation $\psi_{K''}^\dagger(K - K'') = 0$ (on the right) by $\psi_{K'}$ and subtracting one from the other,

$$\psi_{K''}^\dagger(K\psi_{K'}) - (\psi_{K''}^\dagger K^\dagger)\psi_{K'} = (K' - K'')\psi_{K''}^\dagger \psi_{K'}. \tag{244 c}$$

The two sides of this equation can be considered as ordinary numbers.

If K were not a differential operator but an ordinary matrix of Hermitian character, i.e. satisfying the condition $K_{\alpha\beta} = K_{\beta\alpha}^* = K_{\alpha\beta}^\dagger$ or $K = K^\dagger$, then the left side of (244 c) would vanish identically. In reality, the matrix K, as defined by formula (240 b), has two component parts of the above type—namely, the potential energy $U\delta$ and the additional magnetic energy $-\boldsymbol{\mu} \cdot \mathbf{H} = -\mu \boldsymbol{\sigma} \cdot \mathbf{H}$. In fact, it can be directly seen from the expressions (239 b) for the rectangular components of Pauli's 'spin matrix' $\boldsymbol{\sigma}$ that

$$\boldsymbol{\sigma}^\dagger = \boldsymbol{\sigma}. \tag{245}$$

The left side of equation (244 c) thus reduces to

$$\frac{1}{2m_0}\left[\psi_{K''}^\dagger(\mathbf{u}^2 \psi_{K'}) - (\psi_{K''}^\dagger \mathbf{u}^{2\dagger})\psi_{K'}\right] = \frac{1}{2m_0}\sum_{\alpha=1}^{2}(\psi_{K''\alpha}^* \mathbf{u}^2 \psi_{K'\alpha} - \psi_{K'\alpha}\mathbf{u}^{2*}\psi_{K''\alpha}^*)$$

$$= \operatorname{div}\frac{h}{4\pi i m_0}\sum_{\alpha}(\psi_{K''\alpha}^* \mathbf{u}\psi_{K'\alpha'} + \psi_{K'\alpha}\mathbf{u}^* \psi_{K''\alpha}^*).$$

It should be mentioned that in the case $\psi_{K'} = \psi_{K''}$ we obtain under the div-sign an approximate expression for the current density $\mathbf{j}$. [Cf. the derivation of the expressions (201 b) in § 25.]

Multiplying equation (244 c) by the volume-element dV and integrating over all space, we thus get

$$(K' - K'') \int \psi_{K''}^\dagger \psi_{K'} \, dV = 0,$$

whence the orthogonality relation (244 b) follows, unless $K' = K''$. The case of degeneracy, i.e. $\psi_{K'} \neq \psi_{K''}$ when $K' = K''$, can be dealt with in the new theory in exactly the same way as in the old theory, the Schrödinger 'scalar' function ψ being replaced by the Pauli two-component vector (or matrix) ψ.

The present theory in the above form is a combination of the ordinary operator theory and the matrix theory, as developed in the preceding chapters on the basis of Schrödinger's equation. It can be reduced, however, to the usual matrix form by introducing the matrix-components of the various (two-dimensional) operators F by means of the formula

$$F_{K''K'} = \int \psi_{K''}^\dagger F \psi_{K'} \, dV, \tag{246}$$

where

$$\psi_{K''}^\dagger F \psi_{K'} = \sum_{\alpha=1}^{2} \sum_{\beta=1}^{2} \psi_{K''\alpha}^* F_{\alpha\beta} \psi_{K'\beta}, \tag{246 a}$$

is an ordinary number (the 'scalar product' of the two-dimensional vectors $\psi_{K''}^\dagger$ and $F\psi_{K'}$; the latter can be regarded as the product of the vector $\psi_{K'}$ and the two-dimensional 'tensor' F).

Replacing the functions $\psi_{K'}$ by their 'amplitudes' $\psi_{K'}^0$, with which they are connected by the same relation

$$\psi_{K'} = \psi_{K'}^0(x, y, z) e^{-i2\pi K't/h},$$

as in the Schrödinger theory, we obtain the matrix-elements of F

$$F_{K''K'}^0 = \int \psi_{K''}^{0\dagger} F \psi_{K'}^0 \, dV.$$

They are connected with the matrix-components by the usual relations

$$F_{K''K'} = F_{K''K'}^0 e^{i2\pi(K''-K')t/h}. \tag{246 b}$$

All the theorems which have been established in Chap. III with regard to the matrix representation of physical quantities 'from the point of view' of the energy K, remain valid if the latter, as well as the operators representing other physical quantities, are defined as two-dimensional tensors (or square matrices of the second rank). We have, for instance, the usual expansion formula

$$F \psi_{K'}^0 = \sum_{K''} F_{K''K'}^0 \psi_{K''}^0, \tag{247}$$

which is a direct consequence of the orthogonality and normalizing relations for the vector-functions $\psi_{K'}^0$ and which is equivalent to the following two component-equations:

$$\sum_{\beta=1}^{2} F_{\alpha\beta} \psi_{K'\beta}^0 = \sum_{K''} F_{K''K'}^0 \psi_{K''\alpha}^0 \qquad (\alpha = 1, 2), \qquad (247\,a)$$

that is,

$$F_{11} \psi_{K'1}^0 + F_{12} \psi_{K'2}^0 = \sum_{K''} F_{K''K'}^0 \psi_{K''1}^0,$$

$$F_{21} \psi_{K'1}^0 + F_{22} \psi_{K'2}^0 = \sum_{K''} F_{K''K'}^0 \psi_{K''2}^0.$$

The transformation theory, i.e. the transformation of the matrices of various physical quantities from the point of view of K (original energy matrix) to the point of view of some other quantity L, as developed in Chap. IV on the basis of Schrödinger's 'one-dimensional' theory, can be applied without any formal modification to Pauli's two-dimensional theory. Introducing the transformation coefficients $a_{K''L'}$, we have, for example, the usual equation

$$\psi_{L'}^0 = \sum_{K''} a_{K''L'} \psi_{K''}^0 \qquad (248)$$

which is equivalent to the two equations

$$\psi_{L'\alpha}^0 = \sum_{K''} a_{K''L'} \psi_{K''\alpha}^0 \qquad (\alpha = 1, 2). \qquad (248\,a)$$

To make the result expressed by these transformation equations unambiguous, we must affix to the functions ψ the index x (short for x, y, z, i.e. the rectangular coordinates of the point to which these functions refer). We thus get

$$\psi_{L'\alpha x} = \sum_{K''} a_{K''L'} \psi_{K''\alpha x}. \qquad (248\,b)$$

This equation clearly shows that the index α (which is supposed to assume the two values 1 and 2) plays exactly the same role as the space coordinates x, y, z. It can be considered accordingly as an additional 'fourth' coordinate, which is usually referred to as the 'spin coordinate'. With this condition, the two functions $\psi_1(x, y, z)$ and $\psi_2(x, y, z)$, forming the components of the Pauli vector (or matrix) ψ, can be considered as the two values of the same function $\psi(\alpha, x, y, z)$ referring to the same values of x, y, z and to the two different values $\alpha = 1$ and $\alpha = 2$ of the spin coordinate. The addition of the latter to the usual three coordinates x, y, z enables one to reduce the two-dimensional Pauli theory to the old uni-dimensional form—with one modification only concerning the operators $F_{(\alpha x)}$ as defined 'from the point of view' of the basic quantities α, x, y, z. These operators can be defined as ordinary functions of the continuously variable quantities x, y, z and of the elementary differential operators $p_x = \dfrac{h}{2\pi i}\dfrac{\partial}{\partial x}$, $p_y = \dfrac{h}{2\pi i}\dfrac{\partial}{\partial y}$, $p_z = \dfrac{h}{2\pi i}\dfrac{\partial}{\partial z}$; they must, however, be defined as *matrices* with regard to the discrete variable α. In fact, the result of the application of an operator F to a function of the type $\psi(\alpha, x, y, z)$ must be another function of the same type $\phi(\beta, x, y, z)$, referring to the same values of x, y, z but *not necessarily to the same value of* α. Assuming β to be independent of α, we see that the most general type of *linear* operator satisfying the condition

$$F\psi(\alpha, x) = \phi(\beta, x)$$

can be defined by putting

$$F\psi(\alpha, x) = \sum_{\alpha=1}^{2} F_{\beta\alpha}\psi(\alpha, x),$$

where the $F_{\beta\alpha}$ are ordinary operators involving the space coordinates only.

It is possible and sometimes convenient to modify the preceding notation in the opposite way, namely, by preserving α as a duplicity index and introducing similar indices for the two values of all the other quantities which are derived from a single value through the action of the spin term $-\mu\boldsymbol{\sigma}\cdot\mathbf{H}$ in the energy operator K. This refers in the first place to the characteristic values of the energy itself. The two values of K', which are obtained by the splitting up of a certain characteristic value of the Schrödinger energy operator H' and which, in general, lie very close to each other, could be denoted by adding to one of them a subsidiary index, κ say, assuming the two values 1 and 2, the combination $(1, K')$ being equivalent to K'_+, say, and $(2, K')$ being equivalent to K'_-, where $K'_\pm$ are the two values of K' corresponding to the given value of H'. With this notation, the transformation equation (248 b) can be rewritten in the form

$$\psi_{\lambda'L';\,\alpha'x'} = \sum_{K''}\sum_{\kappa''=1}^{2} a_{\kappa''K'';\,\lambda'L'}\psi_{\kappa''K'';\,\alpha'x'},$$

where K'' and L' are the single values of the energy operators K or L unperturbed by the spin term $-\boldsymbol{\mu}\cdot\mathbf{H}$.

From this point of view, the matrix components of an operator F:

$$F_{\kappa''K'';\,\kappa'K'} = \int \psi^{\dagger}_{\kappa''K''} F\psi_{\kappa'K'}\,dV, \tag{249}$$

can be grouped together into two-dimensional matrices

$$F_{K''K'} = \begin{pmatrix} F_{1K'';\,1K'}, & F_{1K'';\,2K'} \\ F_{2K'';\,1K'}, & F_{2K'';\,2K'} \end{pmatrix}, \tag{249 a}$$

which correspond to the ordinary components of the matrix F_K, defined from the point of view of the Schrödinger energy operator K without the spin term.

The matrix $F_{\kappa K}$ considered in this way—i.e. as formed by elements which are themselves matrices—is called a 'super-matrix'.

We shall not consider the further development of these formal considerations. The preceding outline will be sufficient for handling various problems connected with Pauli's theory in any one of the three equivalent forms, which have just been indicated. The simplest and most important of these problems is the approximate solution of Pauli's equation, considering the spin term $-\mu\boldsymbol{\sigma}\cdot\mathbf{H}$ as a small perturbation. The energy operator resulting from K by the omission of this term will be denoted by H; it is equal to the Schrödinger operator $\mathbf{u}^2/(2m_0)+U$ multiplied by the two-dimensional unit matrix δ. In order to avoid confusion between this operator and the magnetic field strength, we shall denote the latter by $\mathfrak{H}$.

The change of the energy values H' produced by this perturbation can be calculated, to the first approximation, by means of the same equations as in the case of the Schrödinger perturbation theory. In doing this we must, however, keep in mind the fact that the unperturbed problem is *degenerate*, each value of H' corresponding to at least two different states. It is just this latent duplicity which must be revealed by taking into account the spin energy

$$S = -\mu\mathfrak{H}\cdot\boldsymbol{\sigma}. \tag{250}$$

Assuming no other degeneracy to take place (or the matrix elements of the perturbation energy S with regard to other states of equal unperturbed energy to vanish), we obtain the following equation for the first-order correction $\Delta H'$ of the unperturbed energy

$$\begin{vmatrix} S^{1,1}-\Delta H' & S^{1,2} \\ S^{2,1} & S^{2,2}-\Delta H' \end{vmatrix} = 0, \tag{250 a}$$

where
$$S^{\kappa,\lambda} \equiv S_{\kappa H';\,\lambda H'} = \int \psi^{\dagger}_{\kappa H'}\, S\psi_{\lambda H'}\, dV, \tag{250 b}$$

the indices κ, λ ($= 1, 2$) specifying the two degenerate states in question. They are used as superscripts in the matrix elements of S in order to distinguish the latter from the matrix elements with regard to the spin-index

$$S_{\alpha\beta} = -\mu\mathfrak{H}\cdot\boldsymbol{\sigma}_{\alpha\beta} = -\mu(\mathfrak{H}_x\,\sigma_{x\alpha\beta}+\mathfrak{H}_y\,\sigma_{y\alpha\beta}+\mathfrak{H}_z\,\sigma_{z\alpha\beta}).$$

The two functions $\psi_{\kappa H'}$ ($\kappa = 1, 2$), or rather function-pairs $\psi_{\kappa H';\,\alpha x}$ ($\alpha = 1, 2$) describing these degenerate states must be defined with the help of the ordinary Schrödinger function $\psi_{H'x} = \psi$ in such a way as to satisfy the orthogonality and normalizing relations. The simplest way to do this is to put

$$\left.\begin{array}{ll} \psi_{1H';\,1x} = \psi_{H'x}, & \psi_{1H';\,2x} = 0 \\ \psi_{2H';\,1x} = 0, & \psi_{2H';\,2x} = \psi_{H'x} \end{array}\right\} \tag{251}$$

(supposing the function $\psi_{H'x}$ to be normalized).

By the definition of the spin matrix $\boldsymbol{\sigma}$ [cf. equations (239 b)] we have, dropping the indices H' and x,

$$(S\psi_\lambda)_1 = S_{11}\psi_{\lambda 1} + S_{12}\psi_{\lambda 2} = +\mu[\mathfrak{H}_z\psi_{\lambda 1} - (\mathfrak{H}_x + i\mathfrak{H}_y)\psi_{\lambda 2}],$$
$$(S\psi_\lambda)_2 = S_{21}\psi_{\lambda 1} + S_{22}\psi_{\lambda 2} = \mu[(-\mathfrak{H}_x + i\mathfrak{H}_y)\psi_{\lambda 1} - \mathfrak{H}_z\psi_{\lambda 2}].$$

In the present case these expressions reduce to

$$(S\psi_1)_1 = \mu\mathfrak{H}_z\psi, \qquad (S\psi_1)_2 = \mu(-\mathfrak{H}_x + i\mathfrak{H}_y)\psi,$$

for $\lambda = 1$, and

$$(S\psi_2)_1 = -\mu(\mathfrak{H}_x + i\mathfrak{H}_y)\psi, \qquad (S\psi_2)_2 = -\mu\mathfrak{H}_z\psi,$$

for $\lambda = 2$. We thus get, with the help of (250 b) or

$$S^{\kappa,\lambda} = \int \sum_\alpha \sum_\beta \psi_{\kappa\alpha}^* S_{\alpha\beta}\psi_{\lambda\beta}\ dV:$$

$$\left.\begin{aligned} S^{1,1} &= \mu \int \mathfrak{H}_z \psi^* \psi\ dV \\ S^{1,2} &= -\mu \int (\mathfrak{H}_x + i\mathfrak{H}_y)\psi^* \psi\ dV \\ S^{2,1} &= -\mu \int (\mathfrak{H}_x - i\mathfrak{H}_y)\psi^* \psi\ dV \\ S^{2,2} &= -\mu \int \mathfrak{H}_z \psi^* \psi\ dV \end{aligned}\right\}, \tag{251 a}$$

whence, according to (250 a)

$$(\Delta H')^2 = (S^{1,1})^2 + |S^{1,2}|^2,$$

since $S^{2,2} = -S^{1,1}$ and $S^{2,1} = S^{1,2*}$, or

$$\Delta H' = \pm\sqrt{\{(S^{1,1})^2 + |S^{1,2}|^2\}}. \tag{251 b}$$

This formula solves our problem so far as the splitting of the original 'unperturbed' energy-level is concerned. The fact that the two sublevels have an additional energy of the same magnitude and of opposite sign can be interpreted by assuming that the intrinsic magnetic moment of the electron has in both cases opposite orientations varying, in general, from one place to another according to the direction of the magnetic field. In the simplest case of a *homogeneous* field, the two orientations can be shown to be parallel to the latter.

We have, in fact, in this case

$$S^{1,1} = \mu \mathfrak{H}_z \int \psi^* \psi \, dV = \mu \mathfrak{H}_z,$$

$$S^{1,2} = -\mu(\mathfrak{H}_z + i\mathfrak{H}_y),$$

so that $$\Delta H' = \pm\mu\mathfrak{H}, \qquad\qquad (251\,c)$$

where $\mathfrak{H} = \sqrt{\{\mathfrak{H}_x^2 + \mathfrak{H}_y^2 + \mathfrak{H}_z^2\}}$ is the magnitude of the magnetic field strength. This formula is in full agreement with the assumption that the electron has an intrinsic magnetic moment of magnitude μ (Bohr's magneton), which in a homogeneous magnetic field is oriented either in the same or in the opposite direction to the magnetic lines of force.

It can in addition easily be shown that, in the case under consideration, formula (251 c), which has been derived as the first approximation, holds exactly.

For the sake of simplicity, we shall imagine the magnetic field to be parallel to the z-axis. Pauli's equation then reduces to the form

$$(H - \mu \mathfrak{H} \sigma_z - K')\psi = 0,$$

which is equivalent to the two equations (cf. (235)):

$$(H + \mu\mathfrak{H} - K')\psi_1 = 0,$$

$$(H - \mu\mathfrak{H} - K')\psi_2 = 0.$$

If $\psi_{H'}$ is the solution of the Schrödinger equation $(H - H')\psi_{H'} = 0$ corresponding to the unsplit energy-level H', then the solution of the preceding system can be put in the form

(1) $K' = H' + \mu\mathfrak{H}, \qquad \psi_1 = \psi_{H'}, \qquad \psi_2 = 0,$

(2) $K' = H' - \mu\mathfrak{H}, \qquad \psi_1 = 0, \qquad \psi_2 = \psi_{H'}.$

The first case obviously corresponds to an orientation in the direction opposite to that of the magnetic field, and the second to an orientation in a direction coinciding with it (i.e. in the direction of the positive z-axis).

This indicates, incidentally, that the functions ψ_1 and ψ_2 can be considered as the probability amplitudes for finding the electron at a given point with its intrinsic magnetic moment pointing in the negative and positive directions of the z-axis respectively. In the general case, both of them are different from zero. It is perfectly natural that, under this condition, the probability of finding the electron at a given point *irrespective of its orientation* should be measured by the sum $|\psi_1|^2 + |\psi_2|^2$. We see, further, that the index α which distinguishes the two components of the 'vector' ψ fully deserves the title of a fourth 'spin-coordinate'; it must be borne in mind, however, that it specifies not the orientation of the 'spin' or magnetic axis *in space,* but only its orientation in one of the two senses *parallel to a given direction*—namely, that of the z-axis.

This interpretation is supported by the form of the expression for the average or *probable* value of the z-component of the electron's magnetic moment, as defined in the usual way by the formula

$$\bar{\mu}_z = \int \psi^\dagger \mu_z \psi \, dV.$$

We have, namely, with $\mu_z = \mu \sigma_z$ and $(\sigma_z \psi)_1 = \sigma_{z11} \psi_1 + \sigma_{z12} \psi_2 = -\psi_1$, $(\sigma_z \psi)_2 = \sigma_{z21} \psi_1 + \sigma_{z22} \psi_2 = +\psi_2$,

$$\bar{\mu}_z = \mu \int (\psi_2^* \psi_2 - \psi_1^* \psi_1) \, dV. \tag{252}$$

In a similar way we find

$$\left. \begin{aligned} \bar{\mu}_x &= \mu \int (\psi_1^* \psi_2 + \psi_2^* \psi_1) \, dV \\ \bar{\mu}_y &= i\mu \int (\psi_1^* \psi_2 - \psi_2^* \psi_1) \, dV \end{aligned} \right\}. \tag{252 a}$$

We thus see that the direct relation of the functions ψ_1 and ψ_2 to the orientation of the electron's magnetic moment is limited to the z-axis. The two functions $\psi_1^* \psi_2$ and $\psi_2^* \psi_1$ have complex conjugate values, and cannot be associated with a definite direction of the electron's moment parallel to the x- or to the y-axis.

The quantities

$$\mathfrak{M}_x = \mu(\psi_1^* \psi_2 + \psi_2^* \psi_1), \quad \mathfrak{M}_y = i\mu(\psi_1^* \psi_2 - \psi_2^* \psi_1), \quad \mathfrak{M}_z = \mu(\psi_2^* \psi_2 - \psi_1^* \psi_1) \tag{252 b}$$

are the components of a certain vector $\mathfrak{M}$, which can be defined as the *probable magnetization,* i.e. the probable value per unit volume of the magnetic moment of the 'electron cloud' distributed with the density $\psi_1^* \psi_1 + \psi_2^* \psi_2 = \rho$. The vector $\mathfrak{M}/\rho$ can be regarded accordingly as defining, both with respect to magnitude and direction, the probable value of the intrinsic magnetic moment of the electron, supposed to be situated at a given point. The magnitude of $\mathfrak{M}$ must, of course, be expected to be equal to μ. This is easily seen to be actually the case. We have in fact,

$$\mathfrak{M}^2 = \mathfrak{M}_x^2 + \mathfrak{M}_y^2 + \mathfrak{M}_z^2 = (\mathfrak{M}_x + i\mathfrak{M}_y)(\mathfrak{M}_x - i\mathfrak{M}_y) + \mathfrak{M}_z^2$$
$$= \mu^2 [4\psi_2^* \psi_1 \psi_1^* \psi_2 + (\psi_2 \psi_2^*)^2 + (\psi_1 \psi_1^*)^2 - 2\psi_2 \psi_2^* \psi_1 \psi_1^*] = \mu^2 (\psi_2^* \psi_2 + \psi_1^* \psi_1)^2,$$

so that $\mathfrak{M}/\rho = \mu$. The unit vector $\mathfrak{M}/\mu\rho$ thus determines the probable direction of the electron's moment at a given point.

The physical meaning of the vector $\mathfrak{M}$ is in agreement with the expression c curl $\mathfrak{M}$ in formula (234 a) for the additional current density (cf., for instance, my *Lehrbuch der Elektrodynamik*, vol. ii, Chap. I).

In contradistinction to the electron's position, its orientation cannot be specified exactly, so that we must confine ourselves to the determination of the *probable* orientation or of the probability of a certain orientation (under given circumstances). The formal reason for this difference is that the matrices μ_x, μ_y, μ_z or σ_x, σ_y, σ_z, whose characteristic values should specify the orientation in the same way as the values of the coordinates x, y, z specify the position, *are not independent of each other*.

In fact, multiplying them according to the usual rule of matrix multiplication, we get

$$\left.\begin{aligned}
\sigma_x \sigma_y &= \begin{Bmatrix} 0 & 1 \\ 1 & 0 \end{Bmatrix}\begin{Bmatrix} 0 & i \\ -i & 0 \end{Bmatrix} = \begin{Bmatrix} -i & 0 \\ 0 & i \end{Bmatrix} = i\begin{Bmatrix} -1 & 0 \\ 0 & 1 \end{Bmatrix} = i\sigma_z \\
\sigma_y \sigma_z &= \begin{Bmatrix} 0 & i \\ -i & 0 \end{Bmatrix}\begin{Bmatrix} -1 & 0 \\ 0 & 1 \end{Bmatrix} = \begin{Bmatrix} 0 & i \\ i & 0 \end{Bmatrix} = i\begin{Bmatrix} 0 & 1 \\ 1 & 0 \end{Bmatrix} = i\sigma_x \\
\sigma_z \sigma_x &= \begin{Bmatrix} -1 & 0 \\ 0 & 1 \end{Bmatrix}\begin{Bmatrix} 0 & 1 \\ 1 & 0 \end{Bmatrix} = \begin{Bmatrix} 0 & -1 \\ 1 & 0 \end{Bmatrix} = i\begin{Bmatrix} 0 & i \\ -i & 0 \end{Bmatrix} = i\sigma_y
\end{aligned}\right\} . \quad (253)$$

If the multiplication is effected in the opposite order, the same results are obtained but with the *opposite sign*, so that

$$\sigma_y \sigma_x = -\sigma_x \sigma_y, \qquad \sigma_z \sigma_y = -\sigma_y \sigma_z, \qquad \sigma_x \sigma_z = -\sigma_z \sigma_x. \qquad (253\,a)$$

These equations express the fact that the matrices σ_x, σ_y, σ_z *do not commute* with each other—in contradistinction to the coordinates x, y, z; according to Dirac's terminology they are said to 'anticommute'. Combining equations (253) and (253 a), we get

$$\sigma_x \sigma_y - \sigma_y \sigma_x = 2i\sigma_z,$$

etc., or in vector notation

$$\boldsymbol{\sigma} \times \boldsymbol{\sigma} = 2i\boldsymbol{\sigma}. \qquad (253\,b)$$

The non-commutability of the matrices σ_x, σ_y, σ_z means that the values of the quantities represented by them *cannot be determined* ('observed' or 'measured') *simultaneously*. It should be mentioned that these values are to be defined in the usual way, namely, as the *characteristic values* of the corresponding matrices, regarded as linear operators, acting on a two-component function of the type ψ. Denoting these values by dashes, we have for their determination the equations

$$\sigma_x \psi_x = \sigma'_x \psi_x, \qquad \sigma_y \psi_y = \sigma'_y \psi_y, \qquad \sigma_z \psi_z = \sigma'_z \psi_z,$$

or in components

$$\sigma_{x11}\psi_{x1}+\sigma_{x12}\psi_{x2} = \sigma'_x\psi_{x1}, \qquad \sigma_{x21}\psi_{x1}+\sigma_{x22}\psi_{x2} = \sigma'_x\psi_{x2},$$

etc., that is,

$$\left.\begin{array}{ll} \psi_{x2} = \sigma'_x\psi_{x1}, & \psi_{x1} = \sigma'_x\psi_{x2} \\ i\psi_{y2} = \sigma'_y\psi_{y1}, & -i\psi_{y1} = \sigma'_y\psi_{y2} \\ -\psi_{z1} = \sigma'_z\psi_{z1}, & \psi_{z2} = \sigma'_z\psi_{z2} \end{array}\right\}, \qquad (254)$$

whence it follows that

$$\left.\begin{array}{ll} \sigma'_x = \pm 1, & \psi_{x2} = \pm\psi_{x1} \\ \sigma'_y = \pm 1, & \psi_{y2} = \mp i\psi_{y1} \\ \sigma'_z = \pm 1, & \psi_{z2} = \mp\psi_{z1} \end{array}\right\}. \qquad (254\,a)$$

The characteristic values of the rectangular components of the electron's magnetic moment $\boldsymbol{\mu} = \mu\boldsymbol{\sigma}$ are equal accordingly to $\pm\mu$. This means that, in determining the orientation of this moment with respect to some axis, we have to assume beforehand that it is parallel to this axis, the question to be decided reducing to the choice between the positive and the negative direction. In other words, we have to assume that the electron's magnetic moment is *quantized about some* (arbitrarily chosen) *axis*, the two possible values of its projection on this axis being $+\mu$ and $-\mu$, while its projection on any other axis remains undetermined. In the preceding theory this role of quantization or reference axis has been conferred on the z-axis. The theory can easily be generalized for the case when this reference axis has any direction whatsoever with regard to the coordinate axes.

These results appear quite natural from the point of view of the general transformation theory, developed in Chapter IV. Since the matrices σ_x, σ_y, σ_z do not commute with each other, one of them only can be used as a basic quantity, not only for the determination of the two others, but also for the determination of the matrix σ_n representing the projection of $\boldsymbol{\sigma}$ on any other direction n. In the preceding theory, this basic role has been conferred on σ_z, which appears accordingly as a diagonal matrix, while σ_x and σ_y are not diagonal.

The present case can serve as a very simple illustration of the transformation theory, since we have to do with two states only, the state-space thus reducing to a plane in which the two states are represented by two mutually perpendicular axes, z_+ and z_- say. Replacing z as a reference axis (in ordinary space) by some other axis z', we obtain two other states (in which the electron's magnetic moment is oriented parallel to z'), which are represented on the 'state-plane' by two other mutually perpendicular axes z'_+ and z'_- (with the same origin as the axes $z_\pm$). If the angle between z and z' is equal to θ, then the angle between the axes z_+ and z'_+ in the state-plane must obviously be equal to $\frac{1}{2}\theta$—since to an angle of 180° between the direction of the positive and negative z (or z') axis there corresponds an angle of 90° between the axes z_+ and z_- (or z'_+ and z'_-) on the state diagram. Now, as we know from the general theory, the square of the cosine of the angle between two axes in the state-space is equal to the relative probability of the state represented by one of them subject to the assumption that the probability of the other is equal to unity. Hence it follows that if the magnetic moment of the electron is known to be pointing in a certain direction (that of $+z$, say), there is a probability equal to $\cos^2 \frac{1}{2}\theta$ that it will be found pointing in another direction (that of $+z'$) making an angle θ with the former. The probability that it will be found pointing in the direction opposite to the latter (i.e. that of $-z'$) is equal to $\cos^2 \frac{1}{2}(\pi-\theta) = \sin^2 \frac{1}{2}\theta$. We thus see that if the electron's moment is known to point in a certain direction $(+z)$, there is a probability equal to $\cos^2 \frac{1}{2}\theta + \sin^2 \frac{1}{2}\theta = 1$ that it will be parallel to any other direction (in the positive *or* the negative sense). This means, as stated above, that the direction of the reference-axis to which the electron's moment must be assumed to be parallel can be chosen quite arbitrarily.

All these results can be considered as a particular case of those holding for the magnetic moment—or the mechanical angular momentum—due to the orbital motion of a (non-spinning) electron in a radially symmetrical (central) field of force. As shown in Chapter II, the z-component of this orbital angular momentum M_z can be assumed to be quantized, i.e. to take a discrete set of (characteristic) values $mh/2\pi$ the axial quantum number m varying from $-l$ to $+l$, where l is the angular quantum number determining the total angular momentum according to the formula $M^2 = h^2 l(l+1)/4\pi^2$, while the x- and y-components of $\mathbf{M}$ do not have definite values. The present case can be obtained from the general case by taking l equal to $\frac{1}{2}$—i.e. by ascribing to the electron, irrespective of its orbital motion, a spin motion of a 'half-quantum' magnitude. We have seen in Chapter III that the matrix representation of physical quantities, being more general than the operator representation, leaves room both for integral and half-integral values of the angular quantum number, subject to the condition that the axial quantum number should vary by elementary steps $\Delta m = 1$ from $-l$ to $+l$. This vacant place, or rather the lowest vacant step on the l-staircase, can now be filled by the electron's spin angular momentum. The other—higher—steps can be represented by combining the latter with the orbital angular momentum—if any (see below).

The possibility of attributing to the electron, in addition to an intrinsic magnetic moment μ, an intrinsic angular momentum **s** proportional to it, i.e. represented by the same matrix $\boldsymbol{\sigma}$ with a certain numerical factor, follows also from the fact that this matrix satisfies the commutation relation (253 b) which is quite similar to the commutation relation $\mathbf{M} \times \mathbf{M} = -h\mathbf{M}/2\pi i$ satisfied by the orbital angular momentum **M**. Assuming the electron to possess an intrinsic angular momentum

$$\mathbf{s} = \kappa\boldsymbol{\sigma} \tag{255}$$

satisfying the preceding relation, we get

$$\kappa^2\boldsymbol{\sigma} \times \boldsymbol{\sigma} = -\frac{h}{2\pi i}\kappa\boldsymbol{\sigma},$$

or, according to (253 b), $\kappa = \dfrac{1}{2}\dfrac{h}{2\pi},$ (255 a)

which means that the magnitude of this momentum corresponds to $l = \frac{1}{2}$, as was deduced above from the fact that the electron's magnetic moment can only assume two (opposite) orientations parallel to a quantization axis.

It should be noticed that the formula $\mathbf{M} = \kappa\boldsymbol{\sigma}$, with the above half-quantum value of κ, does not contradict the result that the characteristic value of the square of M must be equal not to $\frac{1}{4}h^2/4\pi^2$, but to $\frac{3}{4}h^2/4\pi^2$, where $\frac{3}{4} = l(l+1)$ with $l = \frac{1}{2}$. In fact, squaring the equation $\mathbf{s} = \kappa\boldsymbol{\sigma}$, we get

$$s^2 = \kappa^2\sigma^2 = \kappa^2(\sigma_x^2 + \sigma_y^2 + \sigma_z^2).$$

The characteristic values of s^2 are obtained by substituting the characteristic values of σ_x^2, σ_y^2, σ_z^2. Now from the definition of the matrices $\sigma_x, \sigma_y, \sigma_z$, it follows that their squares are equal to the unit matrix $\delta = \begin{pmatrix} 1 & 0 \\ 0 & 1 \end{pmatrix}$:

$$\sigma_x^2 = \sigma_y^2 = \sigma_z^2 = \delta. \tag{255 b}$$

The characteristic values of the latter being equal to 1, we thus get

$$\text{char. value of } M^2 = 3\kappa^2 = \frac{3}{4}\frac{h^2}{4\pi^2}.$$

While the electron's intrinsic angular momentum κ has a half-quantum value, its magnetic moment $\mu = he/4\pi m_0 c$ has a whole-quantum value, i.e. the same value as the magnetic moment due to the orbital motion with the angular quantum number $l = 1$. The ratio of the magnetic moment to the angular momentum

$$\frac{\mu}{\kappa} = \frac{e}{m_0 c}$$

is thus twice as large in the case of spin as it is in the case of the orbital motion.

This difference may be reduced formally to the fact that the spin matrix satisfies the relations (253) and (253 a), which are responsible for the factor 2 in (253 b) and consequently for the factor $\frac{1}{2}$ in (255 a) (these relations have no parallel in the case of the matrices representing the orbital angular momentum). It is the fundamental cause of the complications in the action of a magnetic field on a spinning electron, moving in a central field of force, which are usually referred to as the 'anomalous' Zeeman effect.

Postponing the detailed consideration of the latter till a later section, we shall calculate here the rate of change of the total angular momentum of the electron due to the couple produced by the magnetic field. If the preceding assumptions about the electron's spin are correct, then we must have (so long as the electrostatic field can be supposed to produce no couple), according to the classical mechanics,

$$\frac{d}{dt}(\mathbf{L}+\kappa\boldsymbol{\sigma}) = \frac{e}{2m_0 c}(\mathbf{L}+2\kappa\boldsymbol{\sigma})\times\mathfrak{H}, \qquad (256)$$

where $\mathbf{L}$ is that part of the angular momentum which is due to the orbital motion. The same equation must hold in wave mechanics if $\mathbf{L}$ and $\boldsymbol{\sigma}$ are considered as operators and if the time derivative of an operator F is defined with the help of the energy operator K by means of the formula

$$\frac{dF}{dt} = [K, F] = \frac{2\pi i}{h}(KF - FK). \qquad (256 a)$$

In equation (256), the operator (or operator-matrix) $\mathbf{M} = \mathbf{L}+\kappa\boldsymbol{\sigma}$ represents the total angular momentum of the electron and the operator-matrix

$$\frac{e}{2m_0 c}\mathbf{L} + \frac{e}{m_0 c}\kappa\boldsymbol{\sigma} = \frac{e}{2m_0 c}(\mathbf{L}+2\mathbf{s})$$

the total magnetic moment, due both to its motion about the nucleus and the supposed 'spinning' about its own axis.

Neglecting the terms proportional to the square of the magnetic field, we can put $K = H - \mu\mathfrak{H}\cdot\boldsymbol{\sigma}$,

where H is the Schrödinger energy operator,

$$H = \frac{1}{2m_0}\left(\frac{h}{2\pi i}\nabla\right)^2 + U - \frac{e}{2m_0 c}\mathfrak{H}\cdot\mathbf{L}$$

[cf. (210 a, b), § 26], supposed to be multiplied by the two-dimensional unit matrix δ [$eL/(2m_0 c)$ is the magnetic moment of the orbital motion].

The sum of the first two terms of this operator, representing the kinetic energy and the potential energy of the radially symmetrical electric field, commute both with $\mathbf{L}$ and $\boldsymbol{\sigma}$, so that in the formula (256 a), with $F = \mathbf{M}$, we can put simply

$$K = -\mathfrak{H}\cdot\left(\frac{e}{2m_0 c}\mathbf{L} + \mu\boldsymbol{\sigma}\right), \tag{256 b}$$

it being understood that $\mathbf{L}$ is multiplied by the unit matrix δ.

Now we have, since $\boldsymbol{\sigma}$ obviously commutes with $\mathbf{L}$,

$$[K, \mathbf{L}] = -\frac{e}{2m_0 c}[(\mathfrak{H}\cdot\mathbf{L}), \mathbf{L}]$$

$$[K, \kappa\boldsymbol{\sigma}] = -\kappa\mu[(\mathfrak{H}\cdot\boldsymbol{\sigma}), \boldsymbol{\sigma}].$$

For the sake of simplicity, we shall assume the magnetic field to be parallel to the z-axis (this does not, of course, involve any loss of generality). Taking the rectangular components of the bracket expressions on the right side of the preceding equations, we get, with the help of the equations $\mathbf{L}\times\mathbf{L} = -h\mathbf{L}/2\pi i$ and $\boldsymbol{\sigma}\times\boldsymbol{\sigma} = 2i\boldsymbol{\sigma}$,

$$[\mathfrak{H}L_z, L_x] = \mathfrak{H}[L_z, L_x] = \frac{2\pi i}{h}\mathfrak{H}(\mathbf{L}\times\mathbf{L})_y = -\mathfrak{H}L_y = -(\mathbf{L}\times\mathfrak{H})_x$$

$$[\mathfrak{H}L_z, L_y] = \mathfrak{H}[L_z, L_y] = -\frac{2\pi i}{h}\mathfrak{H}(\mathbf{L}\times\mathbf{L})_x = \mathfrak{H}L_x = -(\mathbf{L}\times\mathfrak{H})_y$$

$$[\mathfrak{H}L_z, L_z] = 0,$$

$$[\mathfrak{H}\sigma_z, \sigma_x] = \frac{2\pi i}{h}\mathfrak{H}(\boldsymbol{\sigma}\times\boldsymbol{\sigma})_y = -\frac{4\pi}{h}\mathfrak{H}\sigma_y = -\frac{4\pi}{h}(\boldsymbol{\sigma}\times\mathfrak{H})_x$$

$$[\mathfrak{H}\sigma_z, \sigma_y] = -\frac{2\pi i}{h}\mathfrak{H}(\boldsymbol{\sigma}\times\boldsymbol{\sigma})_x = \frac{4\pi}{h}\mathfrak{H}\sigma_x = -\frac{4\pi}{h}(\boldsymbol{\sigma}\times\mathfrak{H})_y$$

$$[\mathfrak{H}\sigma_z, \sigma_z] = 0.$$

We thus have, returning to the vector notation,

$$[(\mathfrak{H}\cdot\mathbf{L}), \mathbf{L}] = -\mathbf{L}\times\mathfrak{H}, \qquad [(\mathfrak{H}\cdot\boldsymbol{\sigma}), \boldsymbol{\sigma}] = -\frac{4\pi}{h}\boldsymbol{\sigma}\times\mathfrak{H},$$

and consequently

$$[K, (\mathbf{L}+\kappa\boldsymbol{\sigma})] = \left(\frac{e}{2m_0 c}\mathbf{L} + \frac{4\pi}{h}\kappa\mu\boldsymbol{\sigma}\right)\times\mathfrak{H},$$

or, since $\kappa = h/4\pi$,

$$[K, (\mathbf{L}+\kappa\boldsymbol{\sigma})] = \left(\frac{e}{2m_0 c}\mathbf{L} + \mu\boldsymbol{\sigma}\right)\times\mathfrak{H},$$

which is nothing else but equation (256).

Our interpretation of the matrix σ as representing a spin motion of the electron with an angular momentum $\kappa = h/4\pi$ and a magnetic moment $\mu = eh/4\pi m_0 c$ is thus fully checked—at least from the formal point of view. One may argue that it cannot have an actual physical significance since the electron in the Pauli theory, just as in that of Schrödinger, is dealt with as a *point*, with definite coordinates x, y, z, and a point-like particle cannot be imagined to be spinning. To this one can retort firstly, that Pauli's theory amounts to the addition of a fourth 'spin' coordinate, giving a schematical representation of the spin motion; and secondly, that the translational motion—in particular the revolution about a fixed centre—in wave mechanics is also represented in a schematical way only.

30. More Exact Form of the Two-dimensional Matrix Theory; Electron's Electric Moment

Pauli's theory, discussed in the preceding section, accounts for the duplicity phenomenon in the presence of a magnetic field only, whereas, in reality, this phenomenon is observed just as well without such a field. A full account of the experimental facts is given by the theory of Dirac which we are now going to examine on the same lines. The preceding analysis of Pauli's theory will prove very helpful in the discussion of the mathematical form and physical meaning of Dirac's exact theory.

If we put
$$\psi_3 = \chi_1, \qquad \psi_4 = \chi_2, \tag{257}$$
then equations (229 a) and (229 b) of Dirac's theory can be written in the following form:
$$\left. \begin{array}{l} \sigma \cdot u\psi + (u_t - m_0 c)\chi = 0 \\ \sigma \cdot u\chi + (u_t + m_0 c)\psi = 0 \end{array} \right\}, \tag{257 a}$$
where σ is Pauli's spin matrix, while the operators $u_t \mp m_0 c$ are understood to be multiplied by the unit matrix $\delta = \begin{Bmatrix} 1 & 0 \\ 0 & 1 \end{Bmatrix}$; ψ denotes here the two-dimensional matrix $\begin{Bmatrix} \psi_1 \\ \psi_2 \end{Bmatrix}$ and χ denotes the matrix $\begin{Bmatrix} \chi_1 \\ \chi_2 \end{Bmatrix}$.

Applying to the first of equations (257 a) the operation $\sigma \cdot u$, we get, with the help of the second equation,
$$(\sigma \cdot u)^2 \psi + [(\sigma \cdot u)u_t - u_t(\sigma \cdot u)]\chi + (u_t - m_0 c)\sigma \cdot u\chi$$
$$= (\sigma \cdot u)^2 \psi + [(\sigma \cdot u)u_t - u_t(\sigma \cdot u)]\chi - (u_t - m_0 c)(u_t + m_0 c)\psi = 0.$$
Now $(u_t - m_0 c)(u_t + m_0 c) = u_t^2 - m_0^2 c^2$; we have further, according to (218 a),
$$uu_t - u_t u = -\frac{he}{2\pi ic} E;$$

and
$$(\mathbf{\sigma}\cdot\mathbf{u})^2 = \sigma_x^2 u_x^2 + \ldots + \sigma_x \sigma_y u_x u_y + \ldots$$
$$= (u_x^2 + u_y^2 + u_z^2) + i\sigma_z(u_x u_y - u_y u_x) + \ldots,$$

i.e., according to (218),

$$(\mathbf{\sigma}\cdot\mathbf{u})^2 = \mathbf{u}^2 - i\mathbf{\sigma}\frac{he}{2\pi ic}\mathbf{H} = \mathbf{u}^2 - \frac{he}{2\pi c}\mathbf{\sigma}\cdot\mathbf{H}.$$

Putting, for the sake of brevity, $\mathbf{u}^2 - u_t^2 + m_0^2 c^2 = D$, we thus get

$$D\psi - \frac{he}{2\pi c}\mathbf{\sigma}(\mathbf{H}\psi - i\mathbf{E}\chi) = 0. \qquad (258)$$

In a similar way we obtain the equation

$$D\chi - \frac{he}{2\pi c}\mathbf{\sigma}(\mathbf{H}\chi - i\mathbf{E}\psi) = 0. \qquad (258\,\mathrm{a})$$

These equations are equivalent respectively to the second-order equations (230) and (230 a) of the Dirac theory and could, of course, be derived directly from the latter.

The expressions (232) and (232 a) for the probability density and the probability current-density can be written in the form

$$\rho = \psi^\dagger \psi + \chi^\dagger \chi, \qquad (259)$$
$$\mathbf{j} = c(\psi^\dagger \mathbf{\sigma}\chi + \chi^\dagger \mathbf{\sigma}\psi). \qquad (259\,\mathrm{a})$$

In the case of a conservative motion with a positive energy ϵ which differs relatively little from the rest energy $m_0 c^2$, the functions χ can be expressed in terms of ψ with the help of the relations (233 a) or

$$\chi = \frac{1}{2m_0 c}\mathbf{\sigma}\cdot\mathbf{u}\psi, \qquad (260)$$

which is the approximate form of the first of equations (257 a).

Using the relation

$$\sigma_x(\mathbf{\sigma}\cdot\mathbf{u}) = \sigma_x\sigma_x u_x + \sigma_x\sigma_y u_y + \sigma_x\sigma_z u_z = u_x + i\sigma_z u_y - i\sigma_y u_z,$$

that is,
$$\mathbf{\sigma}(\mathbf{\sigma}\cdot\mathbf{u}) = \mathbf{u} + i\mathbf{u}\times\mathbf{\sigma}, \qquad (260\,\mathrm{a})$$

we get, substituting the expression (260) in (259 a),

$$\mathbf{j} = \frac{1}{2m_0}\psi^\dagger\mathbf{u}\psi + \frac{i}{2m_0}\psi^\dagger\mathbf{u}\times\mathbf{\sigma}\psi + \text{conjugate complex},$$

which is easily reduced to the approximate form (234 b) with $\mathfrak{M} = \mu\psi^\dagger\mathbf{\sigma}\psi$, in agreement with (252 b). As a matter of fact, we have merely repeated the argument of § 28, using the new matrix notation to illustrate its convenience.

The equation of Pauli's theory was obtained from (258) by neglecting the last term (proportional to χ) and replacing the two terms $-u_t^2 + m_0^2 c^2$ in the relativistic operator D by $2m_0(p_t + U)$. We shall get a better approximation if we substitute in (258) the expression (260) for χ—which gives an additional term of the second order in $1/c$—and introduce a correction term of the same order in the expression for D. Limiting ourselves, for the sake of simplicity, to the case of conservative motion, and putting $\epsilon = m_0 c^2 + K$ and $\epsilon' = m_0 c^2 + K'$, we have

$$u_t = -\frac{1}{c}(\epsilon' - U) = -\frac{1}{c}(m_0 c^2 + K' - U).$$

This gives $D = \mathbf{u}^2 - 2m_0(K' - U) - (K' - U)^2/c^2$, so that equation (258) assumes the form

$$[\mathbf{u}^2 - 2m_0(K' - U) - \frac{1}{c^2}(K' - U)^2]\psi - \frac{he}{2\pi c}\boldsymbol{\sigma}\cdot(\mathbf{H}\psi - i\mathbf{E}\chi) = 0.$$

Neglecting the relativistic corrections, i.e. putting $c = \infty$, we obtain the ordinary Schrödinger equation

$$[\mathbf{u}^2 - 2m_0(K' - U)]\psi = 0,$$

whence it follows that, with an accuracy of the order of $1/c^2$, we can replace the operator $(K' - U)^2/c^2$ by $\mathbf{u}^4/(2m_0 c)^2 = (u_x^2 + u_y^2 + u_z^2)^2/(2m_0 c)^2$. The preceding equation thus reduces to the standard form

$$(K - K')\psi = 0,$$

with the energy operator

$$K = U + \frac{1}{2m_0}\mathbf{u}^2 - \frac{1}{(2m_0)^3 c^2}\mathbf{u}^4 - \mu\boldsymbol{\sigma}\cdot\left[\mathbf{H} - \frac{i}{2m_0 c}\mathbf{E}(\boldsymbol{\sigma}\cdot\mathbf{u})\right].$$

With the help of the formula (260a) the last term in this expression can be rewritten in the form

$$-\mu\left[\mathbf{H}\cdot\boldsymbol{\sigma} + \mathbf{E}\cdot\frac{1}{2m_0 c}(\mathbf{u}\times\boldsymbol{\sigma} - i\mathbf{u})\right].$$

The operator $i\mu\mathbf{E}\cdot\mathbf{u}$ represents a purely imaginary quantity whose average value vanishes and which can therefore be left out of account.[†] Putting $\mu\boldsymbol{\sigma} = \boldsymbol{\mu}$, we thus get

$$K = \left(\frac{1}{2m_0}\mathbf{u}^2 + U\right) + S, \qquad (261)$$

where the first term represents the usual (Schrödinger) energy operator (multiplied by the two-dimensional unit-matrix δ), while the operator

$$S = -\frac{1}{(2m_0)^3 c^2}\mathbf{u}^4 - \mathbf{H}\cdot\boldsymbol{\mu} - \mathbf{E}\cdot\frac{1}{2m_0 c}\mathbf{u}\times\boldsymbol{\mu} \qquad (261\,\text{a})$$

can be regarded as a kind of *perturbation energy*, which specifies, with

† In fact the product $\dfrac{e}{m_0}\mathbf{E}\cdot\mathbf{u}$ is approximately equal to the work done on the electron per unit time, i.e. to $-dU/dt$; in the case of a stationary motion its average value must obviously be equal to zero.

an accuracy of the second order in $1/c$, the influence of the relativity corrections. One of these, represented by the first term in S, refers to the variability of mass with velocity, while the other, represented by the second and third terms, corresponds to the spin phenomenon. The second term, which has been discussed already in the preceding section, can be regarded as the additional energy due to the electron's intrinsic magnetic moment μ. As to the third term, it can be interpreted in a similar way—namely, as the additional energy due to the presence of an *electric moment* represented by the operator

$$\nu = \frac{1}{2m_0 c} \mathbf{u} \times \boldsymbol{\mu}.$$

We are thus led to regard the electron as a particle combining the properties of a point charge, of an elementary magnet, and of an elementary *electric dipole*, with an electric moment proportional to the magnetic moment (μ) and to the velocity of translational motion, represented approximately by the operator $\mathbf{u}/m_0$.

It should be mentioned that the association of an electric moment with a moving particle which is known to possess, when at rest, a magnetic moment, is a direct consequence of the relativity theory as applied to the connexion between the magnetic and the electric field.

If we have, for example, in the coordinate system A only a magnetic field $\mathbf{H}$ ($\mathbf{E} = 0$), then in another system A' which is moving relatively to the first with a velocity $\mathbf{v}' = -\mathbf{v}$, we must have, in addition to a magnetic field $\mathbf{H}'$ which is slightly different from $\mathbf{H}$ (the difference being of the second order in v/c), an electric field

$$\mathbf{E}' = -\mathbf{v} \times \mathbf{H}'/c \cong -\mathbf{v} \times \mathbf{H}/c,$$

and vice versa: in the case of the presence of a pure electric field $\mathbf{E}$ ($\mathbf{H} = 0$) in the system A, there must be, in the system A', besides an electric field $\mathbf{E}'$ somewhat different from $\mathbf{E}$, also a magnetic field $\mathbf{H}' = \mathbf{v} \times \mathbf{E}'/c \cong \mathbf{v} \times \mathbf{E}/c$.

Let us consider in the latter case a particle which is moving with the system A' and which, with regard to this system, possesses a magnetic moment μ. It will have accordingly an additional magnetic energy $U' = -\boldsymbol{\mu} \cdot \mathbf{H}' = -\boldsymbol{\mu} \cdot \mathbf{v} \times \mathbf{E}'/c \cong \boldsymbol{\mu} \cdot \mathbf{v}' \times \mathbf{E}'/c$. Now this energy can be expressed in the form

$$U' = \frac{1}{c} \mathbf{E}' \cdot (\boldsymbol{\mu} \times \mathbf{v})$$

or

$$U' \cong -\frac{1}{c} \mathbf{E} \cdot (\mathbf{v}' \times \boldsymbol{\mu})$$

and interpreted as the additional electric energy with regard to the system A of an electric dipole with a moment

$$\mathbf{\nu} = \frac{1}{c}\mathbf{v}' \times \mathbf{\mu}.$$

We are thus entitled to assume that a particle which, when at rest, behaves like an elementary magnet with a moment $\mathbf{\mu}$ acquires, when moving with a velocity $\mathbf{v}'$, an electric moment $\mathbf{v}' \times \mathbf{\mu}/c$. This result can be obtained directly with the help of the spinning sphere model of the electron, if due account is taken of the redistribution of the electric current density produced by the superposition of the translatory motion on that of rotation.[†]

Replacing the velocity $\mathbf{v}'$ by the operator $\mathbf{u}/m_0$, we obtain for the representation of the electron's electric moment the operator

$$\mathbf{\nu} = \frac{1}{m_0 c}\mathbf{u} \times \mathbf{\mu}, \tag{261 b}$$

which is just double the previous expression. The additional electric energy, represented by the last term in (261 a), must be written accordingly in the form

$$U_e = -\tfrac{1}{2}\mathbf{E}\cdot\mathbf{\nu}, \tag{261 c}$$

while the magnetic energy is expressed in the usual way by

$$U_m = -\mathbf{H}\cdot\mathbf{\mu}.$$

The origin of the factor $\tfrac{1}{2}$ in (261 c) can be interpreted in different ways. It can be obtained, in the first place, by applying the relativity theory to the spin motion.[‡] It is simpler, however, to connect it with the fact that the energy U_e corresponds to a second-order effect (while U_m corresponds to a first-order effect), as in the familiar case of a particle possessing no rigid electric dipole moment, and acquiring such a moment under the influence of the electric field only. In the present case, this influence is an indirect one, proceeding through the velocity of translational motion which is maintained by the electric field.

Before discussing the exact theory of Dirac, we shall apply the preceding corrected form of the Pauli theory to the approximate calculation of the so-called 'relativity corrections', i.e. of the shift and splitting of the energy-levels of an electron moving in a spherically symmetrical electric field with or without a homogeneous magnetic field superposed upon it.

[†] See my *Lehrbuch der Elektrodynamik*, vol. i, pp. 295–6.
[‡] See L. H. Thomas, *Nature* (1926), p. 514, and *Phil. Mag.* (1927); also J. Frenkel, *Zeits. f. Phys.* **37** (1926), 273.

A. *No magnetic field*

The perturbation energy reduces in this case to

$$S = -\frac{1}{(2m_0)^3 c^2} \mathbf{p}^4 - \frac{\mu}{2m_0 c} \mathbf{E} \cdot (\mathbf{p} \times \boldsymbol{\sigma}), \qquad (262)$$

where $\mathbf{p} = h\nabla/2\pi i$ is the operator representing the electron's momentum. Putting

$$\mathbf{E} = \frac{Ze}{r^3} \mathbf{r},$$

which corresponds to a Coulomb field of force produced by a nucleus with a charge Ze, we get

$$\mathbf{E} \cdot (\mathbf{p} \times \boldsymbol{\sigma}) = \boldsymbol{\sigma} \cdot (\mathbf{E} \times \mathbf{p}) = \frac{Ze}{r^3} \boldsymbol{\sigma} \cdot (\mathbf{r} \times \mathbf{p}) = \frac{Ze}{r^3} \boldsymbol{\sigma} \cdot \mathbf{L},$$

where $\mathbf{L} = \mathbf{r} \times \mathbf{p}$ is the operator of the electron's angular momentum (without the contribution $\kappa\boldsymbol{\sigma}$ due to the spin). Substituting this expression in (262) and replacing $p^2/2m_0$ by $H' - U = H' + Ze^2/r$, where H' is the *unperturbed* energy, as given by Schrödinger's or Bohr's theory, we get

$$S = -\frac{1}{2m_0 c^2}\left[\left(H' + \frac{Ze^2}{r}\right)^2 + \frac{\alpha}{r^3}(\mathbf{L} \cdot \boldsymbol{\sigma})\right], \qquad (262\,\mathrm{a})$$

where

$$\alpha = c\mu Ze = \frac{Ze^2 h}{4\pi m_0},$$

the charge of the electron being denoted by $-e$.

The expression (262 a) is somewhat similar to the expression (150) for the magnetic perturbation energy, differing from it in the first place by the fact that the constant magnetic field $\mathfrak{H}$ is replaced by a kind of effective magnetic field

$$\mathfrak{H}_{\text{eff}} = \frac{Ze}{2m_0 cr^3} \mathbf{L}, \qquad (262\,\mathrm{b})$$

which is inversely proportional to the cube of the distance from the nucleus and parallel to the vector of the angular momentum $\mathbf{L}$, and in the second place by the appearance of the additional term

$$-\frac{1}{2m_0 c^2}\left(H' + \frac{Ze^2}{r}\right)^2,$$

which is supposed to be multiplied by the unit matrix $\delta = \begin{Bmatrix} 1 & 0 \\ 0 & 1 \end{Bmatrix}$.

The argument used for the solution of the magnetic perturbation problem in the previous section can thus be applied, practically without any modification, to the present case; it can be simplified by using from the outset a coordinate system with the z-axis parallel to the vector $\mathbf{L}$ (which is a constant of the unperturbed motion).

The result is expressed by the formula

$$\Delta H' = -\frac{1}{2m_0 c^2}\left[\overline{\left(H' + \frac{Ze^2}{r}\right)^2} \pm \alpha L\overline{\left(\frac{1}{r^3}\right)}\right], \tag{263}$$

where the averaging is to be carried out for the unperturbed motion with the help of the usual (scalar) Schrödinger function ψ specifying it, according to the formula $\overline{F} = \int F\psi\psi^* \, dV$. The preceding formula can be interpreted by assuming two types of the perturbed motion with the electron's spin axis parallel to the axis of the orbit and having either the same or the opposite direction ($\mathbf{L}\cdot\mathbf{\sigma} = \pm L$). The numerical values of $\Delta H' = \Delta H'_{\pm}$ can be computed approximately by replacing the wave-mechanical averages or probable values by the time averages of the classical (Bohr) theory. The latter gives†

$$\frac{\overline{1}}{r} = \frac{1}{a}, \qquad \frac{\overline{1}}{r^2} = \frac{1}{ab}, \qquad \frac{\overline{1}}{r^3} = \frac{1}{b^3},$$

where a is the semi-major and b is the semi-minor axis of the electron's elliptical orbit. We thus get

$$\Delta H' = -\frac{1}{2m_0 c^2}\left[H'^2 + \frac{2Ze^2 H'}{a} + \frac{Z^2 e^4}{ab} \pm \frac{\alpha L}{b^3}\right]. \tag{263 a}$$

Now according to the Bohr theory we have further:

$$a = \frac{h^2 n^2}{4\pi^2 m_0 c^2 Z}, \quad b = \frac{k}{n}a, \quad L = \frac{h}{2\pi}k, \quad H' = -\frac{Ze^2}{2a} = -\frac{2\pi^2 m_0 Z^2 e^4}{h^2 n^2},$$

where n is the principal and k the angular quantum number. Substituting these expressions in (263 a), we find

$$H'^2 + 2\frac{Ze^2}{a}H' + \frac{Z^2 e^4}{ab} = \left(-3 + \frac{4n}{k}\right)H'^2$$

and $$\frac{\alpha L}{b^3} = \frac{Ze^2 h}{4\pi m_0}\frac{hk}{2\pi}\frac{n^3}{k^3 a^3} = \frac{(Ze^2)^2}{4a^2}\frac{h^2 n^3}{2\pi^2 m_0 Ze^2}\frac{1}{k^2 a} = \frac{2n}{k^2}H'^2,$$

whence $$\Delta H' = \frac{2H'^2}{m_0 c^2}\left[\frac{3}{4} - n\left(\frac{1}{k} \pm \frac{1}{2k^2}\right)\right]. \tag{263 b}$$

This formula was originally obtained in 1925 by Uhlenbeck and Goudsmit in practically the same way as that shown above, without, however, any use of the matrix $\mathbf{\sigma}$ (the product $\mathbf{L}\cdot\mathbf{\sigma}$ being replaced by $\pm L$ on the *assumption* that the electron's axis can have only two opposite orientations parallel to the axis of the orbit).

By applying relativity mechanics to the stationary states of the Bohr

† Cf. Born, *Atommechanik*, i, p. 164 (Berlin, 1925).

theory, Sommerfeld, in 1915, derived the following formula:

$$\epsilon_{nk} = m_0 c^2 \left[1 + \frac{\gamma^2 Z^2}{(s+k')^2} \right]^{-\frac{1}{2}} \qquad (264)$$

which proved to be in exact agreement with the experimental data for the energy-levels in hydrogen and ionized helium. Here γ is a dimensionless constant

$$\gamma = \frac{2\pi e^2}{hc} = 7.10^{-3}, \qquad (264\,\text{a})$$

$s = n - k$ is the radial quantum number, and

$$k' = \sqrt{(k^2 - \gamma^2 Z^2)}. \qquad (264\,\text{b})$$

The constant γZ determines the 'relativity splitting' of the energy-levels belonging to the same value of the principal quantum number n, and so determines the 'fine structure' of the spectrum. When $\gamma Z \ll 1$, we can replace formula (264) by the approximate formula

$$\epsilon_{nk} - \epsilon_n = \frac{2W_n^2}{m_0 c^2} \left(\frac{3}{4} - \frac{n}{k} \right), \qquad (264\,\text{c})$$

where $W_n = \epsilon_n - m_0 c^2 = -\dfrac{m_0 c^2 \gamma^2 Z^2}{2n^2} = -\dfrac{2\pi^2 m_0 e^4 Z^3}{h^2 n^2}$ stands for H'.

This fine-structure formula of Sommerfeld has been brilliantly confirmed not only for hydrogen and ionized helium, but also for X-ray spectra of the heaviest atoms. The number of lines given by it in the latter case (with $k = 1, 2, \ldots, n$ and with regard to the selection rule $\Delta k = \pm 1$), or the number of energy-levels in the absorption spectrum of X-rays comes out, however, *too small*, being equal to n instead of $2n-1$, as found experimentally. Thus, for example, we have, when $n = 2$ (L-group), three energy-levels, while Sommerfeld's formula only gives two ($k = 1$ and $k = 2$); when $n = 3$ we have five levels instead of three, etc.

This difficulty was removed by Uhlenbeck and Goudsmit's theory of the spinning electron. To every orbit specified by the numbers n, k there are two possible oppositely directed orientations of the spin axis perpendicular to the plane of the orbit. Corresponding to these two orientations, we must have two different additional energies which bring about the doubling of all the energy-levels ϵ_{nk}, according to the formula (263 b).

However, some secondary difficulties remain unexplained by this theory: First, one of the levels belonging to the same principal quantum number (n) should remain undivided (since the number of different levels is equal to $2n - 1$ and not to $2n$). This can be explained at once if we ascribe to the angular quantum number the values $0, 1,..., n-1$ instead of $1, 2,..., n$, i.e. if we introduce straight-line orbits instead of circular ones—because obviously for such straight-line orbits all orientations perpendicular to the direction of motion are equivalent. It should be noticed, however, that the approximate formulae (263 b) and (264 c), as well as the exact formula (264), cannot be applied to the case $k = 0$.

Secondly, for hydrogen and ionized helium—briefly in the case of atomic systems with a single electron—the experimental data fit *exactly* with Sommerfeld's formula both with regard to the number and the position of the levels, if k is assumed to take the values $1, 2,..., n$.

This difficulty can also be overcome by a more exact analysis of the 'splitting due to spin' and its comparison with that due to the variability of mass ('relativity splitting' in the sense of Sommerfeld's theory).

Formula (263 b) is not valid for $k = 0$. In general, it is so much the more accurate the larger k is. In this limiting case we have

$$\frac{1}{k} \mp \frac{1}{2k^2} = \frac{1}{k \pm \frac{1}{2}},$$

so that formula (263 b) becomes identical with Sommerfeld's formula (264 c), provided k ($= n$, $n-1$, $n-2$,...) is replaced by $k-\frac{1}{2}$, each energy-level appearing twice for two consecutive values of k (the one increased and the other diminished by $\frac{1}{2}$).

The appearance of half-integral values of k ($= n-\frac{1}{2}$, $n-\frac{3}{2}$, etc.) can be explained by the fact that on the wave-mechanical theory the angular momentum L is equal to $\sqrt{\{l(l+1)\}}h/2\pi$, and not to $hk/2\pi$. Now since $l(l+1) = (l+\frac{1}{2})^2 - \frac{1}{4}$, we can put, for large values of l,

$$L = \frac{h}{2\pi}(l+\tfrac{1}{2}) = \frac{h}{2\pi}(k-\tfrac{1}{2}),$$

where $l = k-1$ is the angular quantum number of the Schrödinger theory.[†]

The average values of $1/r$, $1/r^2$, and $1/r^3$ have been calculated above, for the sake of simplicity, with the help of the old quantum theory; it can be shown, however, that the results obtained are not substantially altered on the Schrödinger theory if Bohr's k is replaced everywhere by $l+\frac{1}{2}$.

We shall see in a later section that the exact wave-mechanical theory based on Dirac's equation leads, in the case of a one-electron atomic system, to precisely the same results as the old theory of Sommerfeld,

† Cf. *infra*, § 33.

the spin-doubling remaining unrevealed. It becomes manifest, however, as soon as we turn to more complicated atoms in which the motion of each electron takes place in a field of force deviating (owing to the action of the other electrons) from the purely Coulomb one. This follows immediately from the expression (263) in which $1/r^3$ must be replaced by some other (more rapidly decreasing) function of the distance, with the result that the two terms of (263)—corresponding to the relativistic variation of the mass and to the spin effect—can no longer be combined into a single term, corresponding on the old theory to the mass effect alone.

The two states resulting from a single state of the Schrödinger theory and specified by the orientation of the electron's spin angular momentum in the direction of the orbital angular momentum or in the opposite direction are distinguished with the help of a special quantum number (formerly called the 'inner' quantum number) j, assuming the value $j = l + \frac{1}{2}$ for the former state and the value $j = l - \frac{1}{2}$ for the latter; the product of j with $h/2\pi$ can be regarded accordingly as the resulting angular momentum of the electron. This interpretation corresponds rather to the old quantum theory; it can be shown, however, that in wave mechanics the number j plays, in regard to the total angular momentum $\mathbf{M}$, exactly the same role as the angular quantum number l in regard to the orbital angular momentum L. We have, for instance, for the characteristic values of M^2

$$M^2 = \frac{h^2}{4\pi^2} j(j+1),$$

which can be obtained from the formula $M^2 = (\mathbf{L}+\mathbf{s})^2 = L^2 + 2\mathbf{L}\cdot\mathbf{s} + s^2$, where s denotes the spin angular momentum, if we put $s^2 = \frac{3}{4}h^2/4\pi^2$, $L^2 = h^2 l(l+1)/4\pi^2$, and $2\mathbf{L}\cdot\mathbf{s} = h^2 l/4\pi^2$ in the case $j = l + \frac{1}{2}$ (in the case $j = l - \frac{1}{2}$, l must be replaced by $l-1$).

As has been shown above, for a motion in a Coulomb field of force the inner quantum number j also plays the same role as l—in the absence of spin—with regard to the energy.

We shall presently see that this correspondence between j and l can be further extended in describing the splitting of the energy-levels produced by a weak magnetic field.

B. *Influence of a magnetic field* (*Zeeman effect*)

The preceding theory can easily be generalized to allow for the presence of a homogeneous magnetic field $\mathfrak{H}$. The radially symmetrical electric field will be represented by the vector $\mathbf{E} = f(r)\cdot\mathbf{r}$.

If the unperturbed motion is defined as that corresponding to the absence of the magnetic field and to the neglect of the relativity (mass-spin) corrections, i.e. if it is specified by the ordinary energy operator $H = \dfrac{1}{2m_0}\mathbf{p}^2 + U(r)$ $\left(\text{multiplied by } \delta = \begin{pmatrix} 1 & 0 \\ 0 & 1 \end{pmatrix}\right)$, then neglecting terms of the second order in $\mathfrak{H}$ we can represent the complete energy operator K as the sum of H and of the perturbation energy

$$S = -\frac{1}{2m_0 c^2}[(H'-U)^2 + c\mu f \mathbf{L}\cdot\boldsymbol{\sigma}] + \mathfrak{H}\cdot\left(\frac{e}{2m_0 c}\mathbf{L} + \mu\boldsymbol{\sigma}\right),$$

where $\mu = he/(4\pi m_0 c)$ is the absolute value of the electron's intrinsic moment, the electronic charge being denoted by $-e$ so that

$$-e\mathbf{E} = -\nabla U, \quad \text{or} \quad f(r) = -\frac{1}{r}\frac{dU}{dr}.$$

This can be written in the form

$$S = A + \mathbf{B}\cdot\boldsymbol{\sigma} \tag{265}$$

with

$$A = -\frac{1}{2m_0 c^2}(H'-U)^2 + \frac{e}{2m_0 c}\mathfrak{H}\cdot\mathbf{L} \tag{265a}$$

and

$$\mathbf{B} = -\beta\mathbf{L} + \mu\mathfrak{H}, \tag{265b}$$

where $\beta = \mu f/(2m_0 c)$.

The determination of the energy-levels of the two perturbed states resulting from a single unperturbed one can be carried out with the help of the general method outlined in the preceding section in connexion with a perturbation due to the magnetic field alone [see equations (250)–(251 b)]. We thus get

$$\Delta H' = \bar{A} \pm \bar{B}, \tag{266}$$

where $A = \int \psi^* A \psi \, dV$ and $\bar{B} = \sqrt{\{(\bar{B}_x)^2 + (\bar{B}_y)^2 + (\bar{B}_z)^2\}}$ is the quadratic average of the vector $\mathbf{B}$. If $\mathbf{L}$ is dealt with as a constant vector (which is quite exact for the unperturbed motion), we have

$$\bar{B} = \sqrt{\{(\bar{\beta})^2 L^2 - 2\bar{\beta}\mu\mathfrak{H}\cdot\mathbf{L} + \mu^2\mathfrak{H}^2\}}. \tag{266a}$$

In the extreme case of a very strong magnetic field—such that $\mu\mathfrak{H} \gg \bar{\beta}L$ —this expression reduces to $\mu\mathfrak{H}$. Putting, further, $\mathfrak{H}\cdot\mathbf{L} = h\mathfrak{H}m_l/2\pi$, where m_l is the axial (magnetic) quantum number for the orbital motion, and neglecting the first terms in (265a) and (265b) compared with the second ones, we get

$$\Delta H' = \mu\mathfrak{H}(m_l \pm 1), \tag{266b}$$

i.e. the same result as in the case of the 'normal' Zeeman effect, corresponding to the absence of spin; the influence of the latter is expressed in the replacement of the axial quantum number m_l by $m = m_l \pm 1$, both numbers being integers.

In the opposite case of a very weak magnetic field ($\mu \mathfrak{H} \ll \bar{\beta}L$) we obtain a splitting of a different type, usually denoted as the 'anomalous' Zeeman effect. Expanding the exact expression (266 a), and neglecting the terms of the second and higher orders in $\mathfrak{H}$, we get

$$\bar{B} = \bar{\beta}L(1 - \bar{\beta}\mu\mathfrak{H}\cdot\mathbf{L}/\bar{\beta}^2L^2) = \bar{\beta}L - \mu\mathfrak{H}\cdot\mathbf{L}/L = \bar{\beta}L - \mu\mathfrak{H}m_l h/2\pi L$$

or, putting $L = h(l + \tfrac{1}{2})/2\pi$ and neglecting the 'relativity correction' (represented by the first term in (265 a)),

$$\Delta H = \pm\bar{\beta}L + \mu\mathfrak{H}m_l\left(1 \pm \frac{1}{l + \tfrac{1}{2}}\right), \qquad (266\,\mathrm{c})$$

where the upper and lower signs refer to the values $j = l + \tfrac{1}{2}$ and $j = l - \tfrac{1}{2}$ of the 'inner quantum number' which determines the total angular momentum $\mathbf{M}$.

This result in a somewhat different external form involving the axial quantum number m_j which determines the component of $\mathbf{M}$ along the magnetic field, so long as the latter is supposed to be weak, can be obtained by the following simple argument.

We have seen above that in the absence of a magnetic field the vectors $\mathbf{L}$ and $\mathbf{s}$ (spin angular momentum) are not constants of the motion, even if the latter takes place in a radially symmetrical electrical field; the sum $\mathbf{L} + \mathbf{s} = \mathbf{M}$ (total angular momentum) is, however, constant in this case. Further, it can easily be shown that the *squares* of s and L remain constant, so that the perturbation produced by the spin alone can be pictured as the rotation (precession) of the two vectors $\mathbf{L}$ and $\mathbf{s}$ of constant magnitude about their resultant $\mathbf{M}$ (Fig. 3). The

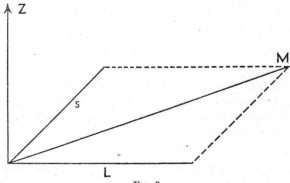

FIG. 3.

average values of **s** and **L** must therefore be parallel to **M**, and can be expressed accordingly by the equations

$$\bar{\mathbf{s}} = (g-1)\mathbf{M}, \qquad \bar{\mathbf{L}} = (2-g)\mathbf{M}, \tag{267}$$

where g is a certain numerical coefficient ($\bar{\mathbf{s}} + \bar{\mathbf{L}} = \mathbf{s} + \mathbf{L} = \mathbf{M}$).

It should be mentioned that this 'graphical' representation of the spin perturbation does not give correct results if we assume at the outset that the vectors **s** and **L** are parallel to each other (in the same or opposite directions), as has been concluded previously from equation (263).

The coefficient g can be determined with the help of the formula $L^2 = (\mathbf{M} - \mathbf{s})^2 = M^2 - 2\mathbf{M} \cdot \mathbf{s} + s^2$ if we put $L^2 = h^2 l(l+1)/4\pi^2$, $M^2 = h^2 j(j+1)/4\pi^2$, $s^2 = \frac{3}{4}h^2/4\pi^2$ and replace the scalar product $\mathbf{M} \cdot \mathbf{s}$ by $(g-1)M^2$. This gives

$$g - 1 = \frac{j(j+1) - l(l+1) + \frac{3}{4}}{2j(j+1)}, \tag{267 a}$$

that is

$$g - 1 = \pm \frac{1}{2l+1} \qquad (j = l \pm \tfrac{1}{2}). \tag{267 b}$$

The perturbation produced by a sufficiently weak magnetic field can be pictured in the same graphical way as the rotation (precession) of the parallelogram, formed by the vectors **s**, **L**, **M**, as a rigid body about the direction of the magnetic field, the magnitude of all the three vectors remaining thus constant as before.

The additional magnetic energy can be determined to the first approximation as the average value of the magnetic perturbation energy

$$S_m = \frac{e}{2m_0 c} \mathfrak{H} \cdot (\mathbf{L} + 2\mathbf{s}) = \frac{e}{2m_0 c} \mathfrak{H} \cdot (\mathbf{M} + \mathbf{s})$$

for the unperturbed motion. Replacing **s** by $(g-1)\mathbf{M}$, we get

$$\bar{S}_m = \Delta H' = \frac{e}{2m_0 c} g(\mathfrak{H} \cdot \mathbf{M}). \tag{268}$$

The factor g was introduced for the first time by Landé (in 1922). It can be interpreted as the ratio of the angular velocity of precession of the $(\mathbf{s}, \mathbf{L})$ parallelogram about the direction of $\mathfrak{H}$ to the classical or 'Larmor' angular velocity $\omega = e\mathfrak{H}/(2m_0 c)$, which corresponds to the absence of spin.

The projection of the vector **M** on $\mathfrak{H}$ preserves a constant quantized value which can be shown to be given by the formula

$$M_{\mathfrak{H}} = \frac{h}{2\pi} m_j, \tag{268 a}$$

where m_j is the axial quantum number. For a state with a given j it can assume the $2j+1$ half-integral values lying between $+j$ and $-j$. It thus plays, with regard to j, exactly the same role as the ordinary axial quantum number m_l with regard to l in the theory of the spinless electron.

With the help of (268a) the expression (268) can be rewritten in the form

$$\Delta H' = \mu \mathfrak{H} m_j g = \mu \mathfrak{H} m_j \left(1 \pm \frac{1}{2l+1} \right). \tag{268 b}$$

It differs from (266c) (without the term $\bar{\beta}L$ not involving the magnetic field) by the fact that m_l is replaced by m_j and $\frac{1}{l+\frac{1}{2}}$ by $\frac{1}{2(l+\frac{1}{2})}$. This difference is, however, easily seen to correspond to the connexion between the projections of the vectors $\mathbf{L}$ and $\mathbf{M}$ on the magnetic field. Replacing the vector $\mathbf{L}$ in (266a) by its average value according to (267), we get

$$\mathfrak{H} \cdot \bar{\mathbf{L}} = (2-g) \mathfrak{H} \cdot \mathbf{M} = (2-g) \frac{h}{2\pi} m_j \, \mathfrak{H},$$

and consequently

$$\Delta H' = \mu \mathfrak{H} m_j (2-g) \left(1 \pm \frac{1}{l+\frac{1}{2}} \right)$$

instead of the expression (266c)—or that part of it which is proportional to $\mathfrak{H}$. Equating this to $\mu \mathfrak{H} g m_j$, we obtain the following equation for the factor g:

$$g = (2-g) \left(1 \pm \frac{1}{l+\frac{1}{2}} \right),$$

whence approximately

$$2(g-1) = \pm \frac{1}{l+\frac{1}{2}},$$

which coincides with (267b).

Each level, specified by the quantum numbers n, l, j, is split up in a weak magnetic field into $2j+1$ equidistant levels with the spacing

$$\Delta H'_1 = \frac{eh}{4\pi m_0 c} g \mathfrak{H} = g \mu \mathfrak{H} = \left(1 \pm \frac{1}{2l+1} \right) \mu \mathfrak{H},$$

where the plus sign refers to the case $j = l+\frac{1}{2}$ and the minus sign to the case $j = l-\frac{1}{2}$.

We have assumed above that the magnetic field was 'sufficiently small'. The standard field with which it has to be compared in this sense is the 'effective' magnetic field which determines the spin perturbation in the case $\mathfrak{H} = 0$. This field is parallel and proportional to $\mathbf{L}$, as has been shown above [cf. eq. (262b)], and can therefore be defined by the formula $\mathfrak{H}_{\mathrm{eff}} = \beta \mathbf{L}$.

If $\mathfrak{H}$ is much larger than $\mathfrak{H}_{\text{eff}}$, the vectors $\mathbf{L}$ and $\mathbf{s}$ are no longer held together in the rigid parallelogram (Fig. 2), but must be imagined to precess independently about the direction of $\mathfrak{H}$, the former with the normal Larmor frequency and the latter with twice this frequency. We get in this case, instead of (268),

$$\bar{S}_m = \frac{e}{2m_0 c}\mathfrak{H}(L_H + 2s_H) = \mu \mathfrak{H}(m_l \pm 1),$$

in agreement with (266 b). The modification of the Zeeman effect which takes place in a transition from a weak magnetic field to a strong one is known as the Paschen-Back effect.

The preceding results will be established in a more rigorous and complete way in a later section on the basis of Dirac's exact theory.

31. The Exact Four-dimensional Matrix Theory of Dirac

The four equations of the Dirac theory, which in the last section were written in the form of two matrix equations of the Pauli type, can be put in the form of a single matrix equation (they were actually first given by Dirac in this form), in a way perfectly similar to that which has been applied for the same purpose to the Pauli equations.

The four functions of Dirac, ψ_1, ψ_2, ψ_3, ψ_4, will be considered accordingly as the four elements of a one-column matrix:

$$\psi = \begin{Bmatrix} \psi_1 \\ \psi_2 \\ \psi_3 \\ \psi_4 \end{Bmatrix} \tag{269}$$

(or the components of a four-dimensional vector), the adjoint matrix (complex conjugate vector) being

$$\psi^\dagger = \{\psi_1^*, \psi_2^*, \psi_3^*, \psi_4^*\}. \tag{269 a}$$

Introducing a suitably defined square matrix of the fourth rank (four-dimensional tensor) A we can represent the four first-order equations (229 a)–(229 b) as the four components of the matrix (or vector) equation

$$A\psi = 0, \tag{270}$$

writing them in the form

$$\left. \begin{aligned} (A\psi)_1 &\equiv A_{11}\psi_1 + A_{12}\psi_2 + A_{13}\psi_3 + A_{14}\psi_4 = 0 \\ (A\psi)_2 &\equiv A_{21}\psi_1 + A_{22}\psi_2 + A_{23}\psi_3 + A_{24}\psi_4 = 0 \\ (A\psi)_3 &\equiv A_{31}\psi_1 + A_{32}\psi_2 + A_{33}\psi_3 + A_{34}\psi_4 = 0 \\ (A\psi)_4 &\equiv A_{41}\psi_1 + A_{42}\psi_2 + A_{43}\psi_3 + A_{44}\psi_4 = 0 \end{aligned} \right\}. \tag{270 a}$$

Identifying these equations respectively with the first, second, third, and fourth equations (229 a)–(229 b), we get the following definition of the matrix A:

$$A = \alpha_x u_x + \alpha_y u_y + \alpha_z u_z + \alpha_t u_t + \alpha_0 m_0 c \tag{271}$$

with

$$\alpha_x = \begin{pmatrix} 1 & 0 & 0 & 0 \\ 0 & 1 & 0 & 0 \\ 0 & 0 & 1 & 0 \\ 0 & 0 & 0 & 1 \end{pmatrix}, \quad \alpha_y = \begin{pmatrix} -i & 0 & 0 & 0 \\ 0 & i & 0 & 0 \\ 0 & 0 & -i & 0 \\ 0 & 0 & 0 & i \end{pmatrix}, \quad \alpha_z = \begin{pmatrix} 0 & 1 & 0 & 0 \\ -1 & 0 & 0 & 0 \\ 0 & 0 & 0 & 1 \\ 0 & 0 & -1 & 0 \end{pmatrix}$$
$$\alpha_t = \begin{pmatrix} 0 & 0 & 0 & 1 \\ 0 & 0 & 1 & 0 \\ 0 & 1 & 0 & 0 \\ 1 & 0 & 0 & 0 \end{pmatrix}, \quad \alpha_0 = \begin{pmatrix} 0 & 0 & 0 & -1 \\ 0 & 0 & -1 & 0 \\ 0 & 1 & 0 & 0 \\ 1 & 0 & 0 & 0 \end{pmatrix} \tag{271a}$$

This form of the Dirac equations corresponds to a privileged role of the coordinate x, the associated matrix α_x reducing to the four-dimensional unit-matrix δ. It is possible, however, to rewrite them in four other equivalent forms, corresponding to the shifting of this privilege to one of the other four matrices α. This can be done in the simplest way by rearranging the original equations (229 a)–(229 b) and eventually multiplying them by -1. For instance, to reduce the matrix α_0 to δ we multiply the two equations (229 a) by -1, and rewrite the four equations in the reverse order. We thus get

$$(u_x + i u_y)\psi_4 - u_z \psi_3 + (u_t + m_0 c)\psi_1 = 0,$$
$$(u_x - i u_y)\psi_3 + u_z \psi_4 + (u_t + m_0 c)\psi_2 = 0,$$
$$-(u_x + i u_y)\psi_2 + u_z \psi_1 + (-u_t + m_0 c)\psi_3 = 0,$$
$$-(u_x - i u_y)\psi_1 - u_z \psi_2 + (-u_t + m_0 c)\psi_4 = 0,$$

which can be written in the form

$$B\psi = 0, \tag{272}$$

with

$$B = \beta_x u_x + \beta_y u_y + \beta_z u_z + \beta_t u_t + \beta_0 m_0 c, \tag{272a}$$

where

$$\beta_x = \begin{pmatrix} 0 & 0 & 0 & 1 \\ 0 & 0 & 1 & 0 \\ 0 & -1 & 0 & 0 \\ -1 & 0 & 0 & 0 \end{pmatrix}, \quad \beta_y = \begin{pmatrix} 0 & 0 & 0 & i \\ 0 & 0 & -i & 0 \\ 0 & -i & 0 & 0 \\ i & 0 & 0 & 0 \end{pmatrix}, \quad \beta_z = \begin{pmatrix} 0 & 0 & -1 & 0 \\ 0 & 0 & 0 & 1 \\ 1 & 0 & 0 & 0 \\ 0 & -1 & 0 & 0 \end{pmatrix}$$
$$\beta_t = \begin{pmatrix} 1 & 0 & 0 & 0 \\ 0 & 1 & 0 & 0 \\ 0 & 0 & -1 & 0 \\ 0 & 0 & 0 & -1 \end{pmatrix}, \quad \beta_0 = \begin{pmatrix} 1 & 0 & 0 & 0 \\ 0 & 1 & 0 & 0 \\ 0 & 0 & 1 & 0 \\ 0 & 0 & 0 & 1 \end{pmatrix} \tag{272b}$$

Rewriting equations (229 a)–(229 b) in the inverse order without multiplying (229 a) by -1, we get in a similar way

$$\Gamma\psi = 0, \tag{273}$$

with
$$\Gamma = \gamma_x u_x + \gamma_y u_y + \gamma_z u_z + \gamma_t u_t + \gamma_0 m_0 c, \tag{273 a}$$

where

$$\gamma_x = \begin{Bmatrix} 0 & 0 & 0 & 1 \\ 0 & 0 & 1 & 0 \\ 0 & 1 & 0 & 0 \\ 1 & 0 & 0 & 0 \end{Bmatrix}, \ \gamma_y = \begin{Bmatrix} 0 & 0 & 0 & i \\ 0 & 0 & -i & 0 \\ 0 & i & 0 & 0 \\ -i & 0 & 0 & 0 \end{Bmatrix}, \ \gamma_z = \begin{Bmatrix} 0 & 0 & -1 & 0 \\ 0 & 0 & 0 & 1 \\ -1 & 0 & 0 & 0 \\ 0 & 1 & 0 & 0 \end{Bmatrix}$$

$$\gamma_t = \begin{Bmatrix} 1 & 0 & 0 & 0 \\ 0 & 1 & 0 & 0 \\ 0 & 0 & 1 & 0 \\ 0 & 0 & 0 & 1 \end{Bmatrix}, \ \gamma_0 = \begin{Bmatrix} 1 & 0 & 0 & 0 \\ 0 & 1 & 0 & 0 \\ 0 & 0 & -1 & 0 \\ 0 & 0 & 0 & -1 \end{Bmatrix} = \beta_t$$

$$\left. \right\} . \tag{273 b}$$

This last form of the Dirac equations is especially useful because the *matrices γ are all Hermitian*, while the matrices α and β are not. There is, moreover, a very simple relationship between the Dirac matrices $\gamma_x, \gamma_y, \gamma_z$ and the Pauli 'spin' matrices $\sigma_x, \sigma_y, \sigma_z$ which can be expressed by the equations

$$\gamma_x = \begin{Bmatrix} 0 & \sigma_x \\ \sigma_x & 0 \end{Bmatrix}, \qquad \gamma_y = \begin{Bmatrix} 0 & \sigma_y \\ \sigma_y & 0 \end{Bmatrix}, \qquad \gamma_z = \begin{Bmatrix} 0 & \sigma_z \\ \sigma_z & 0 \end{Bmatrix}, \tag{274}$$

with 0 meaning the two-dimensional zero matrix $\begin{Bmatrix} 0 & 0 \\ 0 & 0 \end{Bmatrix}$. The Dirac matrices $\gamma_x, \gamma_y, \gamma_z$ can be thus defined as 'supermatrices' of the second rank, whose elements are constituted by the corresponding Pauli matrices and the two-dimensional zero matrices.

Further, it can easily be shown that the matrices $\gamma_x, \gamma_y, \gamma_z$, just like the Pauli matrices $\sigma_x, \sigma_y, \sigma_z$, anticommute with each other and with the matrix γ_0, so that putting for the sake of brevity

$$\gamma_x = \gamma_1, \qquad \gamma_y = \gamma_2, \qquad \gamma_z = \gamma_3, \qquad \gamma_0 = \gamma_4$$

(γ_t must be left aside, since it is equal to the unit matrix δ), we have

$$\gamma_\mu \gamma_\nu = -\gamma_\nu \gamma_\mu \qquad (\mu \neq \nu). \tag{274 a}$$

A relation of the type $\sigma_x \sigma_y = i\sigma_z$, etc., does not hold, however, for the matrices $\gamma_x, \gamma_y, \gamma_z$. We have, for instance, according to (273 b),

$$\gamma_x \gamma_y = \begin{Bmatrix} -i & 0 & 0 & 0 \\ 0 & i & 0 & 0 \\ 0 & 0 & -i & 0 \\ 0 & 0 & 0 & i \end{Bmatrix} = i \begin{Bmatrix} -1 & 0 & 0 & 0 \\ 0 & 1 & 0 & 0 \\ 0 & 0 & -1 & 0 \\ 0 & 0 & 0 & 1 \end{Bmatrix} = i \begin{Bmatrix} \sigma_z & 0 \\ 0 & \sigma_z \end{Bmatrix},$$

which is different from γ_z.

To equations (274 a) we may add the equations

$$\gamma_\mu^2 = \delta \qquad (274\,b)$$

which are easily verified.

It should be mentioned that the four matrices α or β (which are different from δ) also satisfy anticommutative relations of the type (274 a), while their squares are equal to $\pm\delta$. We have, namely,

$$\left.\begin{array}{ll} \beta_x^2 = \beta_y^2 = \beta_z^2 = -\delta, & \beta_t^2 = \delta \\ \alpha_y^2 = \alpha_z^2 = \alpha_0^2 = -\delta, & \alpha_t^2 = \delta \end{array}\right\}, \qquad (274\,c)$$

and, of course, $\beta_0^2 = \alpha_x^2 = \delta$ (since $\beta_0 = \alpha_x = \delta$).

With the help of these relations the transition from one form of Dirac's equations to some other equivalent form can be carried out by the multiplication of the former by that matrix which must be replaced by δ (with the $+$ or $-$ sign as the case may be). We have, for example,

$$A = \gamma_x\Gamma,\; B = \gamma_0\Gamma,\; A = -\beta_x B,\; \Gamma = \alpha_t A = \beta_t B,$$

which means that

$$\alpha_x = \gamma_x^2,\; \alpha_y = \gamma_x\gamma_y,\; \alpha_z = \gamma_x\gamma_z,\; \alpha_t = \gamma_x\gamma_t = \gamma_x,\; \alpha_0 = \gamma_x\gamma_0;\; \beta_t = \gamma_0,$$

etc.; these relations can be verified directly.

We can further easily derive from the first-order equations the second-order equations of Dirac's theory in a similar matrix form. This can be done in the simplest way by applying to the equation $B\psi = 0$ the operator

$$\bar{B} = -(\beta_x u_x + \beta_y u_y + \beta_z u_z + \beta_t u_t) + \beta_0 m_0 c.$$

We thus get $\bar{B}B\psi = 0$, or, carrying out the multiplication and taking account of the relations (274 a) and (274 b):

$$\begin{aligned} \{(u_x^2 + u_y^2 + u_z^2 - u_t^2 + m_0^2 c^2) &- [\beta_y\beta_z(u_y u_z - u_z u_y) + \beta_z\beta_x(u_z u_x - u_x u_z) + \\ &+ \beta_x\beta_y(u_x u_y - u_y u_x) + \beta_x\beta_t(u_x u_t - u_t u_x) + \\ &+ \beta_y\beta_t(u_y u_t - u_t u_y) + \beta_z\beta_t(u_z u_t - u_t u_z)]\}\psi = 0. \end{aligned}$$

This equation can be written in the form

$$Q\psi = 0 \qquad (275)$$

with the matrix operator

$$Q = D\delta - \frac{he}{2\pi c}(\mathbf{H}\cdot\boldsymbol{\xi} + \mathbf{E}\cdot\boldsymbol{\eta}), \qquad (275\,a)$$

where

$$D = u_x^2 + u_y^2 + u_z^2 - u_t^2 + m_0^2 c^2,$$

as before, while $\boldsymbol{\xi}$ and $\boldsymbol{\eta}$ are vector-matrices with the rectangular components

$$\xi_x = \begin{Bmatrix} 0 & 1 & 0 & 0 \\ 1 & 0 & 0 & 0 \\ 0 & 0 & 0 & 1 \\ 0 & 0 & 1 & 0 \end{Bmatrix}, \quad \xi_y = \begin{Bmatrix} 0 & i & 0 & 0 \\ -i & 0 & 0 & 0 \\ 0 & 0 & 0 & i \\ 0 & 0 & -i & 0 \end{Bmatrix}, \quad \xi_z = \begin{Bmatrix} -1 & 0 & 0 & 0 \\ 0 & 1 & 0 & 0 \\ 0 & 0 & -1 & 0 \\ 0 & 0 & 0 & 1 \end{Bmatrix} \quad (275\,\text{b})$$

$$\eta_x = \begin{Bmatrix} 0 & 0 & 0 & -i \\ 0 & 0 & -i & 0 \\ 0 & -i & 0 & 0 \\ -i & 0 & 0 & 0 \end{Bmatrix}, \quad \eta_y = \begin{Bmatrix} 0 & 0 & 0 & 1 \\ 0 & 0 & -1 & 0 \\ 0 & 1 & 0 & 0 \\ -1 & 0 & 0 & 0 \end{Bmatrix}, \quad \eta_z = \begin{Bmatrix} 0 & 0 & i & 0 \\ 0 & 0 & 0 & -i \\ i & 0 & 0 & 0 \\ 0 & -i & 0 & 0 \end{Bmatrix}.$$

$$(275\,\text{c})$$

We can also write down the relations

$$\begin{aligned} \xi_x = i\beta_y\beta_z, && \xi_y = i\beta_z\beta_x, && \xi_z = i\beta_x\beta_y \\ \eta_x = i\beta_x\beta_t, && \eta_y = i\beta_y\beta_t, && \eta_z = i\beta_z\beta_t \end{aligned} \Bigg\}, \qquad (276)$$

or in vector notation

$$\boldsymbol{\xi} = \tfrac{1}{2}i\boldsymbol{\beta}\times\boldsymbol{\beta}, \qquad \boldsymbol{\eta} = i\boldsymbol{\beta}\beta_t = -i\boldsymbol{\gamma}. \qquad (276\,\text{a})$$

The identity of equation (275) with the four equations (230)–(230 a) is easily verified.

It should be mentioned that the actual way in which Dirac first obtained his first-order equation $B\psi = 0$ was to some extent the reverse of the preceding derivation *for the particular case of the free motion when the matrix Q reduces to the operator D (multiplied by* δ). Assuming the possibility of representing Q *in this case* in the form $\bar{B}B$ one can easily obtain the conditions $\beta_x^2 = \beta_y^2 = \beta_z^2 = -\beta_t^2 = -\delta$ and $\beta_\mu\beta_\nu = -\beta_\nu\beta_\mu$ $(\mu \neq \nu)$ for the matrices β; after this the first-order equation $B\psi = 0$ is naturally generalized for the motion of the electron in an arbitrary field of force (by replacing p by u), and finally the corresponding generalized expression for the second-order operator Q is obtained in the way shown above.

We have preferred to this straightforward method of Dirac the somewhat more lengthy and complicated path starting with Maxwell's equations, because of the resulting gain in the comprehensiveness of the theory. Moreover, the determination of the matrices β from the properties above stated is an ambiguous problem, which can be solved only after some assumption has been made as to their rank, i.e. the number of wave functions ψ, whereas in our derivation this number is settled from the beginning with the help of the analogy between d'Alembert's equation and Maxwell's equations on the one hand, and the wave-mechanical equations of the second and first order on the other.

The four-dimensional second-order equation (275) is equivalent to the two equations (258) and (258 a) involving the two-dimensional Pauli spin matrix $\boldsymbol{\sigma}$. The Dirac matrix $\boldsymbol{\xi}$ can be defined as a duplication of the latter according to the formula

$$\boldsymbol{\xi} = \begin{pmatrix} \boldsymbol{\sigma} & 0 \\ 0 & \boldsymbol{\sigma} \end{pmatrix}, \tag{277}$$

where 0 is short for the two-dimensional zero-matrix $\begin{pmatrix} 0 & 0 \\ 0 & 0 \end{pmatrix}$. This formula is equivalent to the following three:

$$\xi_x = \begin{pmatrix} \sigma_x & 0 \\ 0 & \sigma_x \end{pmatrix}, \qquad \xi_y = \begin{pmatrix} \sigma_y & 0 \\ 0 & \sigma_y \end{pmatrix}, \qquad \xi_z = \begin{pmatrix} \sigma_z & 0 \\ 0 & \sigma_z \end{pmatrix},$$

which differ from the formulae (274) for $\gamma_x,\ \gamma_y,\ \gamma_z$ by the fact that the duplication is carried out in the direction of the right diagonal and not of the left one. The formulae (274) can be replaced by the single vector formula

$$\boldsymbol{\gamma} = \begin{pmatrix} 0 & \boldsymbol{\sigma} \\ \boldsymbol{\sigma} & 0 \end{pmatrix}.$$

The vectors $\boldsymbol{\gamma}$ and $\boldsymbol{\xi}$ are easily seen to be connected with each other by the relations

$$\boldsymbol{\gamma} = \rho\boldsymbol{\xi} = \boldsymbol{\xi}\rho, \qquad \boldsymbol{\xi} = \rho\boldsymbol{\gamma} = \boldsymbol{\gamma}\rho, \tag{277 a}$$

where ρ is the scalar matrix

$$\rho = \begin{pmatrix} 0 & 0 & 1 & 0 \\ 0 & 0 & 0 & 1 \\ 1 & 0 & 0 & 0 \\ 0 & 1 & 0 & 0 \end{pmatrix} = \begin{pmatrix} 0 & \delta \\ \delta & 0 \end{pmatrix} \qquad (\rho^2 = 1), \tag{277 b}$$

which commutes with $\boldsymbol{\xi}$, $\boldsymbol{\gamma}$ and anticommutes with γ_0:

$$\rho\gamma_0 = -\gamma_0\rho.$$

It should be mentioned that γ_0 commutes with $\boldsymbol{\xi}$ (since it anticommutes both with $\boldsymbol{\gamma}$ and with ρ). We have further, from comparing (273 b) and (273 c):

$$\boldsymbol{\eta} = -i\rho\boldsymbol{\xi}. \tag{277 c}$$

The expression (275 a) for the matrix operator Q can thus be rewritten in the form

$$Q = D - \frac{he}{2\pi c}(\mathbf{H} - i\rho\mathbf{E})\cdot\boldsymbol{\xi},$$

where the factor δ is to be understood in D.

It is clear that the matrix $\boldsymbol{\xi}$ must have in the Dirac theory a similar physical meaning to that of the matrix $\boldsymbol{\sigma}$ in the Pauli theory, i.e. it must represent, with a suitable numerical factor, the spin angular momentum or the magnetic moment. The matrix $\boldsymbol{\eta}$ must represent accordingly, when multiplied by μ, the *electric moment* of the electron. An important distinction between the matrices $\boldsymbol{\xi}$ and $\boldsymbol{\eta}$ consists in the fact that the former is Hermitian and therefore represents a real quantity (with the characteristic values ± 1), while the latter is anti-Hermitian and therefore represents an imaginary quantity (with the characteristic values $\pm i$).

This result seems at first sight to contradict the conclusion arrived at in the preceding section, namely, that a moving electron possesses a *real* electric moment represented approximately (in the corrected Pauli theory) by the matrix $\mathbf{u} \times \boldsymbol{\sigma}/(2m_0 c)$. As a matter of fact such a contradiction does not exist, for the matrices $\mu\boldsymbol{\xi}$ and $\mu\boldsymbol{\eta}$ represent the 'rest-values' of the magnetic and electric moments, i.e. their values in a system of coordinates with respect to which the electron is at rest. In a coordinate system with respect to which it is in motion, the electron has an *additional* imaginary magnetic moment and an additional real electric moment, these additional moments being numerically equal and to a first approximation proportional to the velocity.

From the point of view of the classical theory, if $\boldsymbol{\mu}$ and $\boldsymbol{\nu}$ are the rest-values of the magnetic and electric moments of a particle, then in a coordinate system with respect to which this particle is moving with a velocity $\mathbf{v}$ it will have an additional magnetic moment $\Delta\boldsymbol{\mu}$ equal, to a first approximation, to $\dfrac{\mathbf{v}}{c} \times \boldsymbol{\nu}$ and an additional electric moment $\Delta\boldsymbol{\nu}$ equal (to the same approximation) to $\dfrac{\mathbf{v}}{c} \times \boldsymbol{\mu}$. Putting $\boldsymbol{\nu} = i\boldsymbol{\mu}$ we get $\Delta\boldsymbol{\mu} = i\Delta\boldsymbol{\nu}$. The numerical equality of the two moments is thus maintained for a moving electron (it can easily be shown to hold exactly), the imaginary electric moment giving rise to an imaginary magnetic one and the real magnetic moment to a real electric one. This real electric moment is represented wave-mechanically by the operator $\mu\mathbf{u} \times \boldsymbol{\sigma}/(m_0 c)$.

We can now turn to the discussion of the physical meaning of Dirac's first-order equation $\Gamma\psi = 0$. We shall note first of all that it can be written in the standard form

$$(\epsilon + p_t)\psi = 0, \tag{278}$$

where p_t denotes the operator $\dfrac{h}{2\pi i}\dfrac{\partial}{\partial t}$ multiplied by the four-dimensional matrix δ, and ϵ the first-order energy operator defined as the four-dimensional matrix

$$\epsilon = U + c(\gamma_x u_x + \gamma_y u_y + \gamma_z u_z) + m_0 c^2 \gamma_0 = U + c\boldsymbol{\gamma}\cdot\mathbf{u} + m_0 c^2 \gamma_0. \tag{278a}$$

The important point about Dirac's equation—namely, its relativistic symmetry with regard to time and space—is revealed by the possibility of writing it in one of the three other equivalent forms:

$$(P_x-p_x)\psi = 0, \qquad (P_y-p_y)\psi = 0, \qquad (P_z-p_z)\psi = 0,$$

corresponding to the election of one of the space coordinates to the presidential role played in the usual form of the theory by the time. Replacing the latter by the coordinate x, for example, we get for the corresponding 'momentum operator matrix', with the help of the equation $A\psi = 0$, the following expression:

$$P_x = G_x-\alpha_y u_y-\alpha_z u_z-\alpha_t u_t-\alpha_0 m_0 c,$$

where G_x, the x-component of the 'potential momentum' eA_x/c, is supposed to be multiplied by the unit matrix δ. The same refers, of course, to the operator $p_x = \dfrac{h}{2\pi i}\dfrac{\partial}{\partial x}$ in the equation $(P_x-p_x)\psi = 0$ (as well as to the operators p_y and p_z in the two other momentum equations).

If the operator ϵ does not contain the time explicitly, then equation (278) admits particular solutions $\psi_{\epsilon'} = \psi_{\epsilon'}^0 e^{-i2\pi\epsilon't/h}$ for which it reduces to the form $(\epsilon-\epsilon')\psi_{\epsilon'} = 0$. These solutions represent different stationary states of the electron moving in a constant electromagnetic field.

It can easily be shown in exactly the same way as in Pauli's theory that functions $\psi = \psi_{\epsilon'}$ and $\psi_{\epsilon''}$, belonging to different energy values which form a discrete spectrum, satisfy the orthogonality relation

$$\int \psi_{\epsilon'}^\dagger \psi_{\epsilon''} \, dV = 0,$$

where $\psi_{\epsilon'}^\dagger \psi_{\epsilon''} = \sum_{\alpha=1}^{4} \psi_{\epsilon'\alpha}^* \psi_{\epsilon''\alpha}$. This enables us to build up a matrix representation of physical quantities and a transformation theory which differs from that based on Pauli's equation by the fact that the additional 'spin-index' α assumes four values instead of two. Another important difference consists in the fact that Dirac's equation $(\epsilon-\epsilon')\psi_{\epsilon'} = 0$ admits solutions corresponding to *negative* values of the energy ϵ'. This circumstance will be discussed in more detail later on (§ 34).

It may seem at first sight that the wave-mechanical expression (278 a), because it is linear in the operators u_x, u_y, u_z, representing the components of the electron's proper momentum, has no parallel in the classical relativistic mechanics. A similar expression is obtained, however, on the Einstein theory if the proper energy $mc^2 = m_0 c^2/\sqrt{(1-v^2/c^2)}$

is rewritten in the form

$$mc^2 = \frac{m_0 c^2}{\sqrt{(1-v^2/c^2)}}\left(1-\frac{v^2}{c^2}\right) + \frac{m_0 v^2}{\sqrt{(1-v^2/c^2)}} = m_0 c^2 \sqrt{(1-v^2/c^2)} + \mathbf{g} \cdot \mathbf{v},$$

where $\mathbf{g} = m\mathbf{v}$ is the proper momentum. Putting $\epsilon = mc^2 + U$ and $\mathbf{g} \cdot \mathbf{v} = v_x g_x + v_y g_y + v_z g_z$, we get

$$\epsilon = U + v_x g_x + v_y g_y + v_z g_z + m_0 c^2 \sqrt{(1-v^2/c^2)}, \tag{279}$$

which becomes identical with the expression (277 a) if we replace the proper momentum vector $\mathbf{g}$ by the operator $\mathbf{u}$, the velocity vector $\mathbf{v}$ by the vector-matrix $c\boldsymbol{\gamma}$, and the expression $\sqrt{(1-v^2/c^2)}$ by the matrix γ_0. We shall write this symbolically in the form of ordinary equations:

$$\mathbf{g} = \mathbf{u}, \qquad \mathbf{v} = c\boldsymbol{\gamma}, \qquad \sqrt{(1-v^2/c^2)} = \gamma_0. \tag{279 a}$$

The startling point about these relations is the fact that the classical momentum and velocity are replaced by operators of an entirely different type. This may be due partially to the variation of the mass—which is the proportionality coefficient between momentum and velocity—as a function of the latter. If, however, this were the only reason for the difference, we should expect the relation

$$\gamma_0 \mathbf{u} = m_0 c\boldsymbol{\gamma}$$

to hold—which of course is not the case (see below).

The fact that the operators $\mathbf{u}$ and $c\boldsymbol{\gamma}$ are the wave-mechanical representatives of the momentum and velocity vectors respectively can be established in a more direct and convincing way than has been done above. Let us consider the classical equation of motion of the relativity theory in the Lorentz-Einstein form

$$\frac{d}{dt}\mathbf{g} = e\left(\mathbf{E} + \frac{1}{c}\mathbf{v} \times \mathbf{H}\right). \tag{280}$$

Replacing the classical time derivative of $\mathbf{g}$ by the wave-mechanical expression

$$\frac{d}{dt}\mathbf{u} = \frac{\partial}{\partial t}\mathbf{u} + [\epsilon, \mathbf{u}], \tag{280 a}$$

we get, since $\mathbf{u} = \mathbf{p} - \mathbf{G} = \mathbf{p} - e\mathbf{A}/c$,

$$\frac{\partial}{\partial t}\mathbf{u} = -\frac{e}{c}\frac{\partial}{\partial t}\mathbf{A},$$

and further, with the help of the expression (278 a), for the energy operator

$$[\epsilon, \mathbf{u}] = c[(\boldsymbol{\gamma} \cdot \mathbf{u}), \mathbf{u}] + [U, \mathbf{u}]$$

(since γ_0 commutes with $\mathbf{u}$). Now

$$[U, u_x] = [U, p_x] = -\frac{\partial U}{\partial x} = -e\frac{\partial \phi}{\partial x}$$

and

$$[(\boldsymbol{\gamma}\cdot\mathbf{u}), u_x] = \gamma_x[u_x, u_x] + \gamma_y[u_y, u_x] + \gamma_z[u_z, u_x]$$

$$= \frac{2\pi i}{h}[\gamma_y(u_y u_x - u_x u_y) + \gamma_z(u_z u_x - u_x u_z)]$$

$$= \frac{e}{c}(\gamma_y H_z - \gamma_z H_y) = \frac{c}{e}(\boldsymbol{\gamma}\times\mathbf{H})_x,$$

according to (218). We thus have

$$[\epsilon, \mathbf{u}] = e[-\nabla\phi + \boldsymbol{\gamma}\times\mathbf{H}],$$

and consequently

$$\frac{d}{dt}\mathbf{u} = e\left[-\frac{1}{c}\frac{\partial \mathbf{A}}{\partial t} - \nabla\phi + \boldsymbol{\gamma}\times\mathbf{H}\right],$$

or finally
$$\frac{d}{dt}\mathbf{u} = e(\mathbf{E} + \boldsymbol{\gamma}\times\mathbf{H}). \qquad (280\,\mathrm{b})$$

This equation is of exactly the same form as the classical equation (280) with $\mathbf{g}$ replaced by $\mathbf{u}$ and $\mathbf{v}/c$ by $\boldsymbol{\gamma}$ in agreement with (279 a).

Another still more direct and conclusive proof that the operator $c\boldsymbol{\gamma}$ is the wave-mechanical equivalent for the velocity is obtained by calculating the operators dx/dt, dy/dt, dz/dt which obviously represent the components of the vector $\mathbf{v}$. We thus get

$$\frac{dx}{dt} = [\epsilon, x] = c[\gamma_x u_x, x]$$

(since all the other elementary operators constituting ϵ commute with x), that is

$$\frac{dx}{dt} = c\gamma_x[u_x, x] = c\gamma_x[p_x, x] = c\gamma_x,$$

or
$$\frac{d}{dt}\mathbf{r} = c\boldsymbol{\gamma}, \qquad (280\,\mathrm{c})$$

which is the desired relation.

The physical meaning of the operator $c\boldsymbol{\gamma}$ as the representative of the velocity can be finally recognized from the fact that, with the expression

$$\rho = \psi^\dagger\psi \qquad (281)$$

for the density of probability, following from (232), the expressions (232 a) for the probability current-density can be written in the form

$$\mathbf{j} = c\psi^\dagger\boldsymbol{\gamma}\psi = c\psi^\dagger\boldsymbol{\gamma}^\dagger\psi, \qquad (281\,\mathrm{a})$$

corresponding to the classical relation $\mathbf{j} = \rho\mathbf{v}$. We have, for instance, according to (271 b), taking the x-component of $\mathbf{j}$,

$$j_x = c\psi^\dagger\gamma_x\psi = c[\psi_1^*(\gamma_x\psi)_1 + \psi_2^*(\gamma_x\psi)_2 + \psi_3^*(\gamma\psi)_3 + \psi_4^*(\gamma\psi)_4]$$
$$= c[\psi_1^*\psi_4 + \psi_2^*\psi_3 + \psi_3^*\psi_2 + \psi_4^*\psi_1],$$

which coincides with the expression (232 a) for j_x. Since all the three matrices $\gamma_x, \gamma_y, \gamma_z$ are Hermitian, we have $\boldsymbol{\gamma}^\dagger = \boldsymbol{\gamma}$, so that the two forms (281 a) for $\mathbf{j}$ (with $\boldsymbol{\gamma}$ acting on ψ and $\boldsymbol{\gamma}^\dagger$ on $\psi^\dagger$) are equivalent, being actually obtained from each other by the associative law of multiplication.

The expressions (281) and (281 a) can be derived directly from Dirac's equation $\Gamma\psi = 0$, and this in a much simpler way than without the use of the matrix notation. Multiplying, namely, this equation (on the left) by $\psi^\dagger$ and subtracting from it the product of the adjoint equation $\psi^\dagger \Gamma^\dagger = 0$ by ψ (on the right), we get

$$\psi^\dagger(\Gamma\psi) - (\psi^\dagger\Gamma^\dagger)\psi = 0,$$

that is, since $\gamma_0^\dagger = \gamma_0$ and $\boldsymbol{\gamma}^\dagger = \boldsymbol{\gamma}$,

$$\psi^\dagger(u_t\psi) - (u_t^*\psi^\dagger)\psi + \psi^\dagger\mathbf{u}\cdot\boldsymbol{\gamma}\psi - (\mathbf{u}^*\psi^\dagger)\boldsymbol{\gamma}\psi = 0,$$

or finally
$$\frac{\partial}{\partial t}(\psi^\dagger\psi) + \operatorname{div} c\psi^\dagger\boldsymbol{\gamma}\psi = 0. \tag{281 b}$$

This is the equation of continuity for the probability density and current density as defined by (281) and (281 a).

The expression (281 a) for the probability current-density can be transformed (according to Gordon) in the following way. Replacing ψ by the expression $-(\boldsymbol{\beta}\cdot\mathbf{u} + \beta_t u_t)\psi/m_0 c$, with the help of equation (272 a) we have

$$\mathbf{j} = c\psi^\dagger\boldsymbol{\gamma}\psi = -\frac{1}{m_0}\psi^\dagger[\boldsymbol{\gamma}(\boldsymbol{\beta}\cdot\mathbf{u}) + \boldsymbol{\gamma}\beta_t u_t]\psi,$$

or, since $\boldsymbol{\gamma} = \beta_t\boldsymbol{\beta}$,

$$m_0\mathbf{j} = -\psi^\dagger\beta_t\boldsymbol{\beta}(\boldsymbol{\beta}\cdot\mathbf{u})\psi - \psi^\dagger\beta_t\boldsymbol{\beta}\beta_t u_t\psi.$$

We have further, according to (276),

$$\beta_x\boldsymbol{\beta}\cdot\mathbf{u} = \beta_x\beta_x u_x + \beta_x\beta_y u_y + \beta_x\beta_z u_z = -u_x + i(\xi_y u_z - \xi_z u_y),$$

that is,
$$\boldsymbol{\beta}(\boldsymbol{\beta}\cdot\mathbf{u}) = -\mathbf{u} - i\mathbf{u}\times\boldsymbol{\xi}$$

and $\boldsymbol{\beta}\beta_t = -i\boldsymbol{\eta}$. We thus get

$$\mathbf{j} = \frac{1}{m_0}\psi^\dagger\beta_t\mathbf{u}\psi + \frac{i}{m_0}[\psi^\dagger\beta_t(\mathbf{u}\times\boldsymbol{\xi} + \boldsymbol{\eta}u_t)\psi]. \tag{282}$$

Transforming in a similar way the factor $\psi^\dagger$ (instead of ψ) in the expression $\mathbf{j} = \psi^\dagger\boldsymbol{\gamma}^\dagger\psi$ and adding the result to the previous one, we get finally, remembering that

$$\beta_t^\dagger = \beta_t = \gamma_0, \quad \boldsymbol{\xi}^\dagger = \boldsymbol{\xi}, \quad \boldsymbol{\eta}^\dagger = -\boldsymbol{\eta} = i\boldsymbol{\gamma},$$

$$\mathbf{j} = \frac{1}{m_0}\mathrm{R}(\psi^\dagger\gamma_0\mathbf{u}\psi) + \operatorname{curl}\left(\frac{h}{4\pi m_0}\psi^\dagger\gamma_0\boldsymbol{\xi}\psi\right) + \frac{\partial}{\partial t}\left(\frac{h}{4\pi m_0 c}\psi^\dagger\gamma_0\boldsymbol{\eta}\psi\right). \tag{282 a}$$

This expression multiplied by e/c (e = charge of the electron) gives the density of the electric current (in e.m. units). The latter can accordingly be written in the form

$$\frac{e}{c}\mathbf{j} = \mu\left\{\frac{1}{i}[\psi^\dagger\gamma_0(\nabla\psi)-(\psi^\dagger\nabla^\dagger)\gamma_0\psi]-\frac{2e}{c}\mathbf{A}\psi^\dagger\gamma_0\psi\right\} + \operatorname{curl}\mathfrak{M} + \frac{1}{c}\frac{\partial}{\partial t}\mathfrak{P},$$

(282 b)

where
$$\mathfrak{M} = \mu\psi^\dagger\gamma_0\,\boldsymbol{\xi}\psi$$

and
$$\mathfrak{P} = \mu\psi^\dagger\gamma_0\,\boldsymbol{\eta}\psi$$

(283)

The vector $\mathfrak{M}$ must obviously be interpreted as the 'magnetization', i.e. the probable value per unit volume of the magnetic moment due to the electron's spin. Its components are expressed by the formulae

$$\begin{aligned}
\mathfrak{M}_x &= \mu[(\psi_1^*\psi_2+\psi_2^*\psi_1)-(\psi_3^*\psi_4+\psi_4^*\psi_3)] \\
\mathfrak{M}_y &= i\mu[(\psi_1^*\psi_2-\psi_2^*\psi_1)-(\psi_3^*\psi_4-\psi_4^*\psi_3)] \\
\mathfrak{M}_z &= \mu[(-\psi_1^*\psi_1+\psi_2^*\psi_2)-(-\psi_3^*\psi_3+\psi_4^*\psi_4)]
\end{aligned}$$

(283 a)

If in these expressions we neglect the products of ψ_3 with ψ_4 (which are small quantities of the second order in $1/c$) they reduce to the expressions (252 b) of Pauli's theory. Splitting up the matrix ψ into two two-dimensional matrices ψ, χ, we can rewrite (283 a) in the form

$$\mathfrak{M} = \mu(\psi^\dagger\boldsymbol{\sigma}\psi-\chi^\dagger\boldsymbol{\sigma}\chi).$$

(283 b)

The vector $\mathfrak{P}$ represents the 'electric polarization', i.e. the probable value per unit volume of the electric moment due to the electron's spin. In spite of its imaginary appearance it is easily seen to be a real quantity. We have, namely,

$$\begin{aligned}
\mathfrak{P}_x &= -i\mu[(\psi_1^*\psi_4-\psi_1\psi_4^*)+(\psi_2^*\psi_3-\psi_2\psi_3^*)] \\
\mathfrak{P}_y &= \mu[\psi_1^*\psi_4+\psi_1\psi_4^*-\psi_2^*\psi_3-\psi_2\psi_3^*] \\
\mathfrak{P}_z &= i\mu[(\psi_1^*\psi_3-\psi_1\psi_3^*)-(\psi_2^*\psi_4-\psi_2\psi_4^*)]
\end{aligned}$$

(283 c)

which can also be written in the form

$$\mathfrak{P} = -i\mu(\psi^\dagger\boldsymbol{\sigma}\chi-\chi^\dagger\boldsymbol{\sigma}\psi)$$

(283 d)

corresponding to (283 b). If χ is replaced here by its approximate expression in terms of ψ according to (260) we get, with the help of (260 a),

$$\mathfrak{P} = \frac{\mu}{m_0 c}\psi^\dagger\mathbf{u}\times\boldsymbol{\sigma}\psi$$

in agreement with our previous interpretation of the operator

$$\boldsymbol{\nu} = \frac{\mu}{m_0 c}\mathbf{u}\times\boldsymbol{\sigma}$$

as the electron's real electric moment [cf. (261 b)].

It is interesting to note that the magnetic moment is in Dirac's theory specified by the matrix $\gamma_0 \boldsymbol{\xi}$ and not by the matrix $\boldsymbol{\xi}$ which was assumed to specify the mechanical angular momentum due to spin. This difference can be interpreted as the expression of the fact that in the classical theory the ratio of the magnetic moment to the angular momentum is equal to $e/(2cm)$ for orbital motion or $e/(cm)$ for the spin motion, where m is not the rest-mass, but the actual mass $m_0/\sqrt{(1-v^2/c^2)}$. If, therefore, in wave mechanics the spin angular momentum is represented by the matrix $h\boldsymbol{\xi}/4\pi$, then the magnetic moment must be represented by the matrix $eh\gamma_0\boldsymbol{\xi}/(4\pi m_0) = \mu\gamma_0\boldsymbol{\xi}$ since the classical quantity $\sqrt{(1-v^2/c^2)}$ is represented by the matrix γ_0 [cf. (279 a)].

32. General Treatment of the Spin Effect; Angular Momentum and Magnetic Moment

The fact that the spin angular momentum must be represented by the vector $\mathbf{s} = h\boldsymbol{\xi}/4\pi$ can be proved in the same way as in the case of the Pauli theory (where $\boldsymbol{\xi}$ is replaced by $\boldsymbol{\sigma}$).

We have, to begin with, according to (275 b), the following relations:

$$\xi_x\xi_y = -\xi_y\xi_x = i\xi_z, \ \xi_y\xi_z = -\xi_z\xi_y = i\xi_x, \ \xi_z\xi_x = -\xi_x\xi_z = i\xi_y \quad (284)$$

and consequently $\qquad\qquad \boldsymbol{\xi}\times\boldsymbol{\xi} = 2i\boldsymbol{\xi}, \qquad\qquad\qquad (284\,a)$

so that the matrix $\boldsymbol{\xi}$ satisfies the same relations as Pauli's matrix $\boldsymbol{\sigma}$, giving for the angular momentum $\mathbf{s} = \kappa\boldsymbol{\xi}$ ($\kappa = h/4\pi$) the usual commutative relation $\mathbf{s}\times\mathbf{s} = -h\mathbf{s}/(2\pi i)$.

It should be mentioned that the characteristic values of the matrices ξ_x, ξ_y, ξ_z are equal to ± 1 (each value occurring twice), while those of $\xi_x^2, \xi_y^2, \xi_z^2$ are equal to 1. The characteristic value of s^2 thus turns out to be equal to $\frac{3}{4}(h/2\pi)^2$, as before.

It can easily be verified that the matrix γ_0 commutes with $\boldsymbol{\xi}$. Since, further, its square is equal to 1, the preceding relations will hold for the matrix $\gamma_0\boldsymbol{\xi}$ just as well as for $\boldsymbol{\xi}$. The necessity of interpreting the latter and not the former as the spin angular momentum can be inferred in an unambiguous way from the fact that the sum of $\mathbf{s} = h\boldsymbol{\xi}/2\pi$ and of the orbital angular momentum

$$\mathbf{L} = \mathbf{r}\times\mathbf{u}, \qquad\qquad\qquad (285)$$

that is, the vector $\qquad\qquad \mathbf{M} = \mathbf{L}+\mathbf{s}$

satisfies the equation of motion

$$\frac{d}{dt}\mathbf{M} = \mathbf{r}\times\mathbf{F},$$

where $\mathbf{F} = e(\mathbf{E}+\boldsymbol{\gamma}\times\mathbf{H})$ is the force acting on the electron [cf. (280 b)], and can accordingly be defined as the total angular momentum, while the vector $L+\gamma_0 s$ does not satisfy this equation.

We have in fact,

$$\frac{d}{dt}L = \frac{dr}{dt} \times u + r \times \frac{du}{dt},$$

that is

$$\frac{d}{dt}L = c\gamma \times u + r \times F, \qquad (285\,a)$$

according to (280 b) and (280 c).

Replacing L by s, we get, on the other hand,

$$\frac{d}{dt}s = \kappa c[\gamma \cdot u + \gamma_0 m_0 c, \xi],$$

or, putting $\gamma = \rho\xi$, since ξ commutes both with ρ and with γ_0,

$$\frac{d}{dt}s = \kappa c \rho[(\xi \cdot u), \xi].$$

Taking the z-component of this vector, we have

$$\frac{d}{dt}s_z = \kappa c \rho(u_x[\xi_x, \xi_z] + u_y[\xi_y, \xi_z]) = \frac{4\pi}{h}\kappa c \rho(u_x \xi_y - u_y \xi_x)$$

$$= c\rho(u \times \xi)_z = cu \times \gamma$$

according to (284), that is,

$$\frac{d}{dt}s = -c\gamma \times u. \qquad (285\,b)$$

Adding (285 a) and (285 b), we get the equation

$$\frac{d}{dt}(L+s) = \frac{d}{dt}M = r \times F, \qquad (285\,c)$$

which coincides with the classical equation for the total angular momentum. In the case of a spherically symmetrical electric field and in the absence of a magnetic field the product $r \times F$ vanishes, so that the vector M is a constant of the motion.

Taking the square of M, we get the expression

$$M^2 = L^2 + 2L \cdot s + s^2 \qquad (286)$$

which is also a constant of the motion. Now since

$$s^2 = \frac{3}{4}\left(\frac{h}{2\pi}\right)^2 \delta$$

is itself a constant, we get

$$\frac{d}{dt}(L^2 + 2L \cdot s) = 0. \qquad (286\,a)$$

The two terms in the brackets taken separately are not constant; as has been shown, however, by Dirac, we obtain a new constant of the motion, characteristic of the relation between $\mathbf{L}$ and $\mathbf{s}$, if we consider the vector $\gamma_0\mathbf{L}\cdot\mathbf{s} = \mathbf{L}\cdot\mathbf{s}\gamma_0$. Taking the time derivative of this vector, we get

$$\frac{d}{dt}(\mathbf{L}\cdot\mathbf{s}\gamma_0) = \frac{d\mathbf{L}}{dt}\cdot\mathbf{s}\gamma_0 + \mathbf{L}\cdot\frac{d}{dt}(\mathbf{s}\gamma_0).$$

Replacing $d\mathbf{L}/dt$ by the expression $c\gamma\times\mathbf{p}$, according to (285a) (using $\mathbf{u} = \mathbf{p}$ and $\mathbf{r}\times\mathbf{F} = 0$) we get

$$\frac{d\mathbf{L}}{dt}\cdot\mathbf{s} = c(\gamma\times\mathbf{p})\cdot\mathbf{s} = c\kappa\rho(\boldsymbol{\xi}\times\mathbf{p})\cdot\boldsymbol{\xi} = -c\kappa\rho(\boldsymbol{\xi}\times\boldsymbol{\xi})\cdot\mathbf{p}$$

$$= -2ic\kappa\rho\boldsymbol{\xi}\cdot\mathbf{p} = -2ic\kappa(\gamma\cdot\mathbf{p}),$$

and consequently

$$\frac{d\mathbf{L}}{dt}\cdot\mathbf{s}\gamma_0 = -2ic\kappa(\gamma\cdot\mathbf{p})\gamma_0 = -c\kappa\frac{h}{2\pi}[(\gamma\cdot\mathbf{p}),\gamma_0]$$

since γ anticommutes with γ_0, or

$$\frac{d\mathbf{L}}{dt}\cdot\mathbf{s}\gamma_0 = -\kappa\frac{h}{2\pi}[\epsilon,\gamma_0] = -\frac{h^2}{8\pi^2}\frac{d\gamma_0}{dt}.$$

We have further

$$\frac{d}{dt}(\mathbf{s}\gamma_0) = -c(\gamma\times\mathbf{p})\gamma_0 + \frac{4\pi}{h}isc(\mathbf{p}\cdot\gamma)\gamma_0 = [-(\gamma\times\mathbf{p})+i\boldsymbol{\xi}(\mathbf{p}\cdot\gamma)]c\gamma_0.$$

Now $\boldsymbol{\xi}(\mathbf{p}\cdot\gamma) = \rho\boldsymbol{\xi}(\mathbf{p}\cdot\boldsymbol{\xi}) = \rho(\mathbf{p}+i\mathbf{p}\times\boldsymbol{\xi}) = \rho\mathbf{p}+i\mathbf{p}\times\gamma,$

so that $\frac{d}{dt}(\mathbf{s}\gamma_0) = i\rho\mathbf{p}c\gamma_0,$ $\mathbf{L}\cdot\frac{d}{dt}(\mathbf{s}\gamma_0) = 0,$

since $\mathbf{L}\cdot\mathbf{p} = (\mathbf{r}\times\mathbf{p})\cdot\mathbf{p} = 0$. We thus get

$$\frac{d}{dt}(\mathbf{L}\cdot\mathbf{s}\gamma_0) = -\frac{h^2}{8\pi^2}\frac{d}{dt}\gamma_0,$$

that is, $$\left(\mathbf{L}\cdot\mathbf{s}+\frac{h^2}{8\pi^2}\right)\gamma_0 = \text{const.} = \frac{h^2}{8\pi^2}k, \qquad (287)$$

where k is an ordinary number, replacing the angular quantum number of the old theory; the fact that it can assume integral values only will be shown later on.

Taking into account the identity

$$(\mathbf{L}\cdot\boldsymbol{\xi})^2 = L^2+i(\mathbf{L}\times\mathbf{L})\cdot\boldsymbol{\xi} = L^2-\frac{h}{2\pi}\mathbf{L}\cdot\boldsymbol{\xi} = L^2-2\mathbf{L}\cdot\mathbf{s}$$

and rewriting (287) in the form

$$\mathbf{L}\cdot\boldsymbol{\xi} = \frac{h}{2\pi}(\gamma_0 k-1) \qquad (\gamma_0^2 = 1),$$

we get further
$$L^2 - 2\mathbf{L}\cdot\mathbf{s} = \left(\frac{h}{2\pi}\right)^2 (\gamma_0 k - 1)^2,$$

that is,
$$L^2 = \left(\frac{h}{2\pi}\right)^2 \gamma_0 k(k\gamma_0 - 1) = \left(\frac{h}{2\pi}\right)^2 k(k - \gamma_0), \tag{287 a}$$

and
$$L^2 + 2\mathbf{L}\cdot\mathbf{s} = \left(\frac{h}{2\pi}\right)^2 (k^2 - 1) = \text{const.}, \tag{287 b}$$

in agreement with (286 a). Adding to both sides of this equation the term $s^2 = \frac{3}{4}(h/2\pi)^2$, we obtain finally

$$M^2 = \left(\frac{h}{2\pi}\right)^2 (k^2 - \tfrac{1}{4}). \tag{287 c}$$

The latter expression is usually written in the form

$$M^2 = \left(\frac{h}{2\pi}\right)^2 j(j+1),$$

where $j = |k| - \frac{1}{2}$ is the so-called 'inner' or 'total' angular quantum number.

An angular quantum number of the same character as that which in the Schrödinger theory specifies L according to the formula $L^2 = (h/2\pi)^2 l(l+1)$ does not exist in Dirac's theory, since L^2 is not a constant of the motion—as shown by the formula (287 a). It should be noticed that the number k can assume both positive and negative values (which can be interpreted as corresponding respectively to the same or to the opposite orientation of the orbit and spin axis), the value $k = 0$ being obviously excluded [as seen from (287 c)].

The preceding results, which are strictly valid for the motion in a spherically symmetrical electric field, remain approximately valid in the presence of a weak homogeneous magnetic field. Such a field $\mathfrak{H}$, which can be derived from the vector potential $\mathbf{A} = \frac{1}{2}\mathfrak{H} \times \mathbf{r}$, corresponds to the additional term $S_m = -(e/c)\mathbf{A}\cdot c\boldsymbol{\gamma} = -\frac{1}{2}e(\mathfrak{H} \times \mathbf{r})\cdot\boldsymbol{\gamma}$, that is

$$S_m = -\frac{e}{2c}\mathfrak{H}\cdot(\mathbf{r} \times c\boldsymbol{\gamma}) \tag{288}$$

in the energy operator ϵ. This additional term can be identified with the ordinary expression for the magnetic energy if the vector

$$\boldsymbol{\mu} = \frac{e}{2c}\mathbf{r} \times c\boldsymbol{\gamma} = \tfrac{1}{2}e\mathbf{r} \times \boldsymbol{\gamma} \tag{288 a}$$

is defined as the *total* magnetic moment of the electron.

We have in this case, according to (285 a) with $\mathbf{F} = e\boldsymbol{\gamma} \times \mathfrak{H}$,

$$\frac{d}{dt}\mathbf{M} = e\mathbf{r} \times (\boldsymbol{\gamma} \times \mathfrak{H}).$$

With the help of the equation

$$\frac{d}{dt}[\mathbf{r}\times(\mathbf{r}\times\mathfrak{H})] = \frac{d\mathbf{r}}{dt}\times(\mathbf{r}\times\mathfrak{H})+\mathbf{r}\times\left(\frac{d}{dt}\mathbf{r}\times\mathfrak{H}\right)$$

we get, neglecting the left-hand term (since its time-average value vanishes),

$$\boldsymbol{\gamma}\times(\mathbf{r}\times\mathfrak{H})+\mathbf{r}\times(\boldsymbol{\gamma}\times\mathfrak{H}) = 0,$$

whence, using the vector identity

$$\mathbf{r}\times(\boldsymbol{\gamma}\times\mathfrak{H})+\boldsymbol{\gamma}\times(\mathfrak{H}\times\mathbf{r})+\mathfrak{H}\times(\mathbf{r}\times\boldsymbol{\gamma}) = 0,$$

$$\frac{d}{dt}\mathbf{M} = \tfrac{1}{2}e(\mathbf{r}\times\boldsymbol{\gamma})\times\mathfrak{H} = \boldsymbol{\mu}\times\mathfrak{H} \qquad (288\,\mathrm{b})$$

in agreement with the classical theory.

Taking the scalar product of both sides with $\mathfrak{H}$, we get

$$\frac{d}{dt}(\mathbf{M}\cdot\mathfrak{H}) = 0, \qquad (288\,\mathrm{c})$$

which means that the projection of the angular momentum in the direction of the magnetic field remains constant.

The formula (288 a) corresponds to the classical formula $\boldsymbol{\mu} = \tfrac{1}{2}e\mathbf{r}\times\mathbf{v}/c$ for the orbital magnetic moment due to the electron's translational motion alone, without any spin. According to the considerations developed before in connexion with the spin magnetic moment $\mu\gamma_0\boldsymbol{\xi}$ one might expect that the total magnetic moment would be expressed as the sum

$$\frac{e}{2cm_0}\gamma_0\mathbf{r}\times\mathbf{u}+\mu\gamma_0\boldsymbol{\xi} = \frac{e}{2m_0c}\gamma_0\left(\mathbf{r}\times\mathbf{u}+\frac{h}{2\pi}\boldsymbol{\xi}\right).$$

This expression is, however, not exactly equivalent to the expression (288 a).

In order to transform the operator $\boldsymbol{\mu}$ to an equivalent form of the above type, we shall consider its probable or average value $\int\psi^\dagger\boldsymbol{\mu}\psi\,dV$, which can obviously be written in the form

$$\bar{\boldsymbol{\mu}} = \frac{e}{2c}\int\mathbf{r}\times\mathbf{j}\,dV,$$

where $\mathbf{j} = c\psi^\dagger\boldsymbol{\gamma}\psi$ is the probability current density. Using the expression (282 b) for $e\mathbf{j}/c$, we get

$$\bar{\boldsymbol{\mu}} = \frac{e}{2cm_0}\mathrm{R}\int\psi^\dagger\gamma_0\mathbf{r}\times\mathbf{u}\psi\,dV + \tfrac{1}{2}\int\mathbf{r}\times\mathrm{curl}\,\mathfrak{M}\,dV + \frac{1}{c}\int\mathbf{r}\times\frac{\partial}{\partial t}\mathfrak{P}\,dV.$$

Now the first integral is equal to the probable value of $\gamma_0\mathbf{L}$. With the help of the vector identity

$$\nabla(\mathbf{A}\cdot\mathbf{B}) = (\mathbf{A}\cdot\nabla)\mathbf{B}+(\mathbf{B}\cdot\nabla)\mathbf{A}+\mathbf{A}\times\mathrm{curl}\,\mathbf{B}+\mathbf{B}\times\mathrm{curl}\,\mathbf{A}$$

we get further

$$\mathbf{r}\times\mathrm{curl}\,\mathfrak{M} = \nabla(\mathbf{r}\cdot\mathfrak{M})-(\mathfrak{M}\cdot\nabla)\mathbf{r}-(\mathbf{r}\cdot\nabla)\mathfrak{M} = \nabla(\mathfrak{M}\cdot\mathbf{r})-\mathfrak{M}-r\frac{\partial}{\partial r}\,\mathfrak{M},$$

since

$$\mathrm{curl}\,\mathbf{r} = 0, \qquad (\mathfrak{M}\cdot\nabla)\mathbf{r} = \mathfrak{M}, \qquad (\mathbf{r}\cdot\nabla) = x\frac{\partial}{\partial x}+y\frac{\partial}{\partial y}+z\frac{\partial}{\partial z} = r\frac{\partial}{\partial r}.$$

In the latter expression $\partial/\partial r$ denotes a partial differentiation with regard to the distance from the origin of a polar coordinate system, the two angular coordinates being kept constant. Writing the volume element dV in the form $r^2\,dr\,d\omega$, where $d\omega$ denotes the element of solid angle, we have

$$\int r\frac{\partial}{\partial r}\,\mathfrak{M}\,dV = \int d\omega\int_0^\infty r^3\frac{\partial}{\partial r}\,\mathfrak{M}\,dr$$

$$= \int d\omega\int_0^\infty \frac{\partial}{\partial r}(r^3\mathfrak{M})\,dr - 3\int d\omega\int_0^\infty \mathfrak{M}r^2\,dr = -3\int\mathfrak{M}\,dV.$$

Consequently,

$$\tfrac{1}{2}\int \mathbf{r}\times\mathrm{curl}\,\mathfrak{M}\,dV = \int \mathfrak{M}\,dV = \mu\overline{\gamma_0\,\boldsymbol{\xi}} = \frac{e}{m_0 c}\,\overline{\gamma_0\,\mathbf{s}}.$$

We thus see that so far as its probable value is concerned the operator μ is equivalent, at least in the case of a stationary state when the expression

$$\frac{\partial}{\partial t}\int \mathbf{r}\times\mathfrak{P}\,dV$$

vanishes, to the following one:

$$\mu_{\mathrm{eff}} = \frac{e}{2m_0 c}\,\gamma_0(\mathbf{L}+2\mathbf{s}).$$

This 'effective' magnetic moment can be replaced approximately by the expression

$$\mu'_{\mathrm{eff}} = \frac{e}{2m_0 c}\,(\mathbf{L}+2\mathbf{s})$$

not involving the factor γ_0, which accounts for the variation of the mass with the velocity, and whose probable value differs by quantities of the second order in $1/c$ from 1.

The fact that the expression (288 a) does not contain explicitly the spin contribution to the magnetic moment shows very clearly that the 'spin-motion' has no real existence as something independent of the translational motion, but is actually a certain aspect of it. This circumstance can be regarded as a consequence of the fact that in Dirac's theory there is no direct relation between the vector $\mathbf{u} = \mathbf{p} - e\mathbf{A}/c$ representing the proper momentum of the electron ($m\mathbf{v}$) and the vector $c\gamma$ representing its velocity. These two vectors cannot be treated accordingly as parallel to each other. In fact, the lack of parallelism, as measured by the vector product $c\gamma \times \mathbf{u}$, can be considered according to equations (285 a) and (285 b) as the cause of the change of the orbital and spin components of the angular momentum in the absence of a magnetic field.

The fact that the electron's spin is not an independent kinematic property but merely an aspect of the translational motion (resulting from the divorce between the velocity and momentum) is indicated also by the relation (277 b) between the matrices γ and ξ representing respectively the translational and the 'spin' velocity. If the proportionality coefficient ρ were an ordinary number, then the relation $\gamma = \rho\xi$ would imply that the two vectors represented by γ and ξ were parallel to each other. Since, however, ρ is a matrix, such a parallelism does not necessarily exist, as may be seen from the calculation of the probable values of γ and ξ.

It should be mentioned further that the characteristic values of the matrices γ_x, γ_y, γ_z are the same as those of ξ_x, ξ_y, ξ_z, that is, $+1$ and -1 (each of them occurring twice). This means that the characteristic values of the components of the electron's velocity as defined by the vector $c\gamma$ are equal either to $+c$ or $-c$. We have here the same type of duplicity as in the case of the electron's spin. For the components of the momentum as represented by the vector $\mathbf{u}$ we get a continuous spectrum extending from $-\infty$ to $+\infty$, as in the classical theory. The same would refer to the velocity if the latter were defined not by the vector $c\gamma$ but by the vector $\gamma_0 \mathbf{u}/m_0$, corresponding to the classical relation between velocity and momentum. Such a definition is, however, inconsistent with the relations $dx/dt = c\gamma_x$, etc., derived above. It has been shown by V. Fock that, in spite of this, the two definitions of the velocity become identical in the limiting case when the quantum theory reduces to the classical one (for instance, in the case of a motion with very large energy).

The relationship between the translational and spin motion can be interpreted according to Bohr as a particular case of Heisenberg's uncertainty relation, resulting from the consideration of the magnetic force experienced or produced by a moving electrified particle *without any actual spin*.

The magnetic field produced by such a particle (electron) at a distance

r is given by the well-known Biot-Savart formula:

$$\mathfrak{H} = \frac{e}{c} \frac{\mathbf{v} \times \mathbf{r}}{r^3}.$$

Now the exact determination of $\mathfrak{H}$ according to this formula requires the simultaneous knowledge both of the position, i.e. the radius vector $\mathbf{r}$ of the electron (drawn from the point P for which $\mathfrak{H}$ is to be determined) and its velocity $\mathbf{v}$. This is, however, impossible, since it is only possible to measure both quantities at the same time with a limited accuracy, so that the products $\Delta x \Delta v_x$, etc., are at least of the order of magnitude of h/m_0. This implies an inaccuracy

$$\Delta \mathfrak{H} \cong \frac{eh}{cm_0} \frac{1}{r^3} \cong \frac{\mu}{r^3} \qquad \left(\mu = \frac{eh}{4\pi m_0 c} \right)$$

in the determination of $\mathfrak{H}$, which can be interpreted as an additional magnetic field (of unknown direction) due to a particle with a magnetic moment μ. The superposition of the magnetic field produced by the electron's spin on that due to its translational motion thus secures the validity of the uncertainty relation between position and velocity, so far as they can be determined from the electron's magnetic action.

A similar result is obtained if we consider the force $\mathbf{F} = e\mathbf{v} \times \mathfrak{H}/c$ experienced by an electron in a given external magnetic field. The inaccuracy $\Delta \mathbf{r}$ in the electron's location leads to an inaccuracy $\Delta \mathfrak{H} = (\Delta \mathbf{r} \cdot \nabla)\mathfrak{H}$ in the estimation of the field strength $\mathfrak{H}$. Replacing $\mathbf{v}$ in the preceding formula by the corresponding inaccuracy Δv, we get

$$|\Delta F| \cong \frac{e}{c} \Delta v \times \Delta r \cdot \nabla \mathfrak{H} \cong \frac{eh}{cm_0} \nabla \mathfrak{H} \cong \mu \nabla \mathfrak{H},$$

which agrees, with regard to the order of magnitude, with the force acting on a magnet with moment μ in an inhomogeneous field $[(\mu \nabla)\mathfrak{H}]$.

33. The Motion of an Electron in a Central Field of Force; Fine Structure and Zeeman Effect

We shall now turn to the more detailed discussion of the problem of the motion of an electron in a spherically symmetrical field of force according to Dirac's theory.

The function quadruplet ψ_1, ψ_2, ψ_3, ψ_4 corresponding to a definite energy-level $\epsilon = \epsilon'$ can be determined in a general way from the equation $(\epsilon - \epsilon')\psi = 0$. In the case under consideration it is, however, more advantageous to start not with the energy but with the angular constants of the motion and specify the functions ψ so as to make them the characteristic functions of the corresponding operators.

The most suitable operators for this purpose are M_z—the projection of the angular momentum operator on one of the coordinate axes—and the operator M^2; the operator L^2, although it is not an exact constant of the motion, can also serve for the determination of ψ.

Putting
$$(M_z - M_z')\psi = 0, \tag{289}$$

we get, from $M_z = L_z + s_z = \dfrac{h}{2\pi i}\dfrac{\partial}{\partial \phi} + \dfrac{h}{4\pi}\xi_z$ and the definition (275 b) of ξ_z, the following system of four ordinary equations:

$$\frac{1}{i}\frac{\partial \psi_1}{\partial \phi} - \tfrac{1}{2}\psi_1 = c'\psi_1, \qquad \frac{1}{i}\frac{\partial \psi_2}{\partial \phi} + \tfrac{1}{2}\psi_2 = c'\psi_2,$$

$$\frac{1}{i}\frac{\partial \psi_3}{\partial \phi} - \tfrac{1}{2}\psi_3 = c'\psi_3, \qquad \frac{1}{i}\frac{\partial \psi_4}{\partial \phi} + \tfrac{1}{2}\psi_4 = c'\psi_4,$$

where $c' = 2\pi M_z'/h$ is a constant. An immediate consequence of these equations is that the dependence of the functions ψ_3, ψ_4 on the longitude ϕ is the same as that of the functions ψ_1, ψ_2. This dependence is obviously given by the formulae

$$\left.\begin{aligned} \psi_1 &= A_1 e^{i(m+1)\phi}, & \psi_2 &= A_2 e^{im\phi} \\ \psi_3 &= B_1 e^{i(m+1)\phi}, & \psi_4 &= B_2 e^{im\phi} \end{aligned}\right\}, \tag{289 a}$$

where A and B are functions of the co-latitude θ, with $c' = m + \tfrac{1}{2}$, that is,

$$M_z' = \frac{h}{2\pi}(m + \tfrac{1}{2}), \tag{289 b}$$

m denoting an arbitrary integral number.

The determination of the functions A, B can be carried out in the simplest way by applying to ψ the operator L^2. This gives, according to the relation (287 a),

$$\left.\begin{aligned} L^2\psi_1 &= \left(\frac{h}{2\pi}\right)^2 k(k-1)\psi_1, & L^2\psi_2 &= \left(\frac{h}{2\pi}\right)^2 k(k-1)\psi_2 \\ L^2\psi_3 &= \left(\frac{h}{2\pi}\right)^2 k(k+1)\psi_3, & L^2\psi_4 &= \left(\frac{h}{2\pi}\right)^2 k(k+1)\psi_4 \end{aligned}\right\}, \tag{290}$$

since
$$\gamma_0 = \begin{pmatrix} 1 & 0 & 0 & 0 \\ 0 & 1 & 0 & 0 \\ 0 & 0 & -1 & 0 \\ 0 & 0 & 0 & -1 \end{pmatrix}.$$

Equations (290) show that the functions ψ, so far as their dependence on the polar angles θ, ϕ is concerned, are spherical harmonics, just as in Schrödinger's theory. (It will be remembered that $L^2 = -(h/2\pi)^2\Omega^2$, where Ω^2 is the Laplacian operator on the sphere, and that the equation

$\Omega^2\psi + l(l+1)\psi = 0$ is satisfied by spherical harmonic functions of the order $l \geqslant 0$.) They show, moreover, that the function pairs ψ_1, ψ_2 and ψ_3, ψ_4 are spherical harmonics of different orders, and that the number k which determines these orders can have integral values only. We must distinguish two cases, namely, $k > 0$ and $k < 0$. In the former case we get, putting $k = l+1$, with regard to (289 a):

$$\left.\begin{aligned}
\psi_1 &= a_1\, FY_{l,m+1}(\theta, \phi) = a_1\, FP_{l,m+1}(\theta)e^{i(m+1)\phi} \\
\psi_2 &= a_2\, FY_{l,m}(\theta, \phi) = a_2\, FP_{l,m}(\theta)e^{im\phi} \\
\psi_3 &= a_3\, GY_{l+1,m+1}(\theta, \phi) = a_3\, GP_{l+1,m+1}(\theta)e^{i(m+1)\phi} \\
\psi_4 &= a_4\, GY_{l+1,m}(\theta, \phi) = a_4\, GP_{l+1,m}(\theta)e^{im\phi}
\end{aligned}\right\}, \qquad (290\,\text{a})$$

where F and G are two unknown functions of the distance r alone, while a_1, a_2, a_3, a_4 are certain numerical coefficients. $P_{lm}(\theta)$ denotes the associated spherical harmonic function $= \sin^{|m|}\theta\, P_l^{(|m|)}(\cos\theta)$.

In the case $k < 0$ we shall put $l = -k = |k|$, which gives

$$\left.\begin{aligned}
\psi_1 &= b_1\, FY_{l,m+1} = b_1\, FP_{l,m+1}(\theta)e^{i(m+1)\phi} \\
\psi_2 &= b_2\, FY_{l,m} = b_2\, FP_{l,m}(\theta)e^{im\phi} \\
\psi_3 &= b_3\, FY_{l-1,m+1} = b_3\, FP_{l-1,m+1}(\theta)e^{i(m+1)\phi} \\
\psi_4 &= b_4\, FY_{l-1,m} = b_4\, FP_{l-1,m}(\theta)e^{im\phi}
\end{aligned}\right\}, \qquad (290\,\text{b})$$

where b_1, b_2, b_3, b_4 are another set of coefficients.

The number

$$l = k-1 \quad (k > 0) \quad \text{or} \quad l = -k \quad (k < 0),$$

i.e. the order of the spherical harmonic functions appearing in the principal pair ψ_1, ψ_2 is called the *angular quantum number* of the state in question. The two states specified by the functions (290 a) and (290 b) can be distinguished by their inner quantum number j which is equal to $l+\frac{1}{2}$ in the first case and to $l-\frac{1}{2}$ in the second (i.e. in both cases to the arithmetic mean of the orders of the spherical harmonics in ψ_1, ψ_2 and ψ_3, ψ_4). The two states belonging to the same j and to different values $j\pm\frac{1}{2}$ of l are specified by functions of the type $\psi_1, \psi_2 \sim Y_{j+\frac{1}{2}}$; $\psi_3, \psi_4 \sim Y_{j-\frac{1}{2}}$ and $\psi_1, \psi_2 \sim Y_{j-\frac{1}{2}}$; $\psi_3, \psi_4 \sim Y_{j+\frac{1}{2}}$ respectively.

The ratio between the coefficients a_1, a_2 on the one hand and a_3, a_4 on the other can be determined from the equation

$$(M^2 - M'^2)\psi = 0 \qquad \left[M'^2 = \left(\frac{h}{2\pi}\right)^2 (k^2 - \tfrac{1}{4})\right], \qquad (291)$$

which can serve for the complete determination of the angular factors in the quadruplet ψ (inasmuch as the direction of the privileged axis remains unsettled). It is somewhat simpler, however, to combine for that purpose the equations (290) and (287). Putting $L = h\Lambda/2\pi$, we can rewrite the latter in the form

$$\Lambda\cdot\xi = k\gamma_0 - 1, \tag{291a}$$

which is equivalent to the system of equations

$$\left.\begin{array}{l}
(\Lambda_x + i\Lambda_y)\psi_2 - \Lambda_z\psi_1 = (k-1)\psi_1 \\
(\Lambda_x - i\Lambda_y)\psi_1 + \Lambda_z\psi_2 = (k-1)\psi_2 \\
(\Lambda_x + i\Lambda_y)\psi_4 - \Lambda_z\psi_3 = -(k+1)\psi_3 \\
(\Lambda_x - i\Lambda_y)\psi_3 + \Lambda_z\psi_4 = -(k+1)\psi_4
\end{array}\right\}. \tag{292}$$

We have here

$$\Lambda_x = \frac{1}{i}\left(y\frac{\partial}{\partial z} - z\frac{\partial}{\partial y}\right), \qquad \Lambda_y = \frac{1}{i}\left(z\frac{\partial}{\partial x} - x\frac{\partial}{\partial z}\right), \qquad \Lambda_z = \frac{1}{i}\left(x\frac{\partial}{\partial y} - y\frac{\partial}{\partial x}\right),$$

or in polar coordinates r, θ, ϕ,

$$\Lambda_x + i\Lambda_y = e^{i\phi}\left(\frac{\partial}{\partial\theta} + i\cot\theta\frac{\partial}{\partial\phi}\right), \qquad \Lambda_x - i\Lambda_y = e^{-i\phi}\left(-\frac{\partial}{\partial\theta} + i\cot\theta\frac{\partial}{\partial\phi}\right),$$

$$\Lambda_z = \frac{1}{i}\frac{\partial}{\partial\phi}.$$

The first two expressions can be obtained as follows. We shall put for the sake of brevity $\partial/\partial x = \partial_x$, etc. We shall further introduce the complex variable $w = x + iy$ and the corresponding derivative $\partial_w = \partial_x + i\partial_y$. We get then

$$\Lambda_x + i\Lambda_y = z\partial_w - w\partial_z.$$

On the other hand, we have

$$\partial_\theta = \frac{\partial x}{\partial\theta}\partial_x + \frac{\partial y}{\partial\theta}\partial_y + \frac{\partial z}{\partial\theta}\partial_z = \cot\theta(x\partial_x + y\partial_y) - \tan\theta\, z\partial_z,$$

and

$$x\partial_x + y\partial_y = w^*\partial_w - i\partial_\phi = w\partial_w^* + i\partial_\phi,$$

whence

$$\partial_w = \frac{1}{w^*}(x\partial_x + y\partial_y - \Lambda_z) = \frac{1}{w^*\cot\theta}[(\partial_\theta + \tan\theta\, z\partial_z) - \cot\theta\,\Lambda_z],$$

and consequently

$$\Lambda_x + i\Lambda_y = \frac{zw}{|w|^2\cot\theta}[(\partial_\theta + \tan\theta\, z\partial_z) + \cot\theta\, i\partial_\phi] - w\partial_z.$$

Since

$$\frac{z}{|w|}\tan\theta = 1, \qquad \frac{w}{|w|} = e^{i\phi},$$

we find finally

$$\Lambda_x + i\Lambda_y = e^{i\phi}(\partial_\theta + i\cot\theta\,\partial_\phi).$$

We thus get in the case of the functions (290 a) $(k = l+1)$:

$$
\left.
\begin{aligned}
a_2\left(\frac{\partial}{\partial\theta} - m\cot\theta\right)P_{l,m} &= a_1(l+m+1)P_{l,m+1} \\[4pt]
a_1\left(\frac{\partial}{\partial\theta} + (m+1)\cot\theta\right)P_{l,m+1} &= -a_2(l-m)P_{l,m} \\[4pt]
a_4\left(\frac{\partial}{\partial\theta} - m\cot\theta\right)P_{l+1,m} &= -a_3(l-m+1)P_{l+1,m+1} \\[4pt]
a_3\left(\frac{\partial}{\partial\theta} + (m+1)\cot\theta\right)P_{l+1,m+1} &= a_4(l+m+2)P_{l+1,m}
\end{aligned}
\right\}.
\tag{292 a}
$$

These equations can be used not only for the definition of the ratios $a_1 : a_2$ and $a_3 : a_4$ but also for the determination of the 'associated' spherical harmonics $P_{l,m}$, etc. (supposed to be normalized in the same way for all values of l and m). Eliminating $P_{l,m+1}^{\cdot}$ between the first two equations (292 a), we find, for instance,

$$
\frac{d^2}{d\theta^2}P_{l,m} + \cot\theta\,\frac{dP_{l,m}}{d\theta} + \left[l(l+1) - \frac{m^2}{\sin^2\theta}\right]P_{l,m} = 0,
$$

which is the standard equation for the functions $P_{l,m}$.

In the case (290 b) we get with $k = -l$ a similar set of equations, namely,

$$
\left.
\begin{aligned}
b_2\left(\frac{\partial}{\partial\theta} - m\cot\theta\right)P_{l,m} &= -b_1(l-m)P_{l,m+1} \\[4pt]
b_1\left(\frac{\partial}{\partial\theta} + (m+1)\cot\theta\right)P_{l,m+1} &= b_2(l+m+1)P_{l,m} \\[4pt]
b_3\left(\frac{\partial}{\partial\theta} - m\cot\theta\right)P_{l-1,m} &= b_3(l+m)P_{l-1,m+1} \\[4pt]
b_4\left(\frac{\partial}{\partial\theta} + (m+1)\cot\theta\right)P_{l-1,m+1} &= -b_4(l-m-1)P_{l-1,m}
\end{aligned}
\right\}.
\tag{292 b}
$$

We shall not write down the explicit expressions for the coefficients a, b (which depend upon the way the functions P are normalized), and shall now turn to the investigation of the radial factors F, G and the associated question of the characteristic values of the energy ϵ.

The functions F and G can be investigated by transforming the equation $(\epsilon - \epsilon')\psi = 0$ to polar coordinates and getting rid of the angular factors in ψ with the help of the preceding expressions.

To carry out this transformation we multiply the term $\boldsymbol{\gamma\cdot u}$ in ϵ by the square of the 'radial projection' of the vector $\boldsymbol{\gamma}$:

$$
\gamma_r = \frac{1}{r}\boldsymbol{\gamma\cdot r}.
\tag{293}
$$

Taking into account the general relation,

$$(\gamma \cdot \mathbf{A})(\gamma \cdot \mathbf{B}) = (\boldsymbol{\xi} \cdot \mathbf{A})(\boldsymbol{\xi} \cdot \mathbf{B}) = \mathbf{A} \cdot \mathbf{B} + i(\mathbf{A} \times \mathbf{B}) \cdot \boldsymbol{\xi},$$

we get $\gamma_r^2 = 1$ and, further,

$$\gamma_r \gamma \cdot \mathbf{u} = \frac{1}{r}(\mathbf{r} \cdot \mathbf{u} + i \mathbf{L} \cdot \boldsymbol{\xi}),$$

whence $\qquad \gamma \cdot \mathbf{u} = \gamma_r^2 \gamma \cdot \mathbf{u} = \frac{\gamma_r}{r}(\mathbf{r} \cdot \mathbf{u} + i \mathbf{L} \cdot \boldsymbol{\xi}).$ $\qquad$ (293 a)

Now for a spherically symmetrical electric field we have $\mathbf{u} = \mathbf{p}$, and consequently

$$\frac{1}{r}\mathbf{r} \cdot \mathbf{u} = \frac{h}{2\pi i} \frac{1}{r}\left(x \frac{\partial}{\partial x} + y \frac{\partial}{\partial y} + z \frac{\partial}{\partial z}\right) = \frac{h}{2\pi i} \frac{\partial}{\partial r}.$$

We thus get, with the help of the equation $\mathbf{L} \cdot \boldsymbol{\xi} = h(k\gamma_0 - 1)/2\pi$,

$$\epsilon = \gamma_r \frac{h}{2\pi i}\left(\frac{\partial}{\partial r} - \frac{k\gamma_0 - 1}{r}\right) + m_0 c^2 \gamma_0 + U,$$

so that Dirac's equation reduces to the form

$$\left[\gamma_r\left(\frac{\partial}{\partial r} - \frac{k\gamma_0 - 1}{r}\right) + \frac{2\pi i}{h}(\epsilon_0 \gamma_0 + U - \epsilon')\right]\psi = 0,$$

where $\epsilon_0 = m_0 c^2$.

Since the operator-matrix γ_r commutes with $\partial/\partial r$ and $1/r$, and anti-commutes with γ_0,

$$\left(\frac{\partial}{\partial r} + \frac{k\gamma_0 + 1}{r}\right)\gamma_r \psi + \frac{2\pi i}{ch}(\epsilon_0 \gamma_0 - \epsilon' + U)\psi = 0. \qquad (294)$$

By the definition of the matrices γ_x, γ_y, γ_z [cf. (273 b)], we have

$$(\gamma_r \psi)_1 = \frac{1}{r}[(x + iy)\psi_4 - z\psi_3], \quad (\gamma_r \psi)_2 = \frac{1}{r}[(x - iy)\psi_3 + z\psi_4],$$

$$(\gamma_r \psi)_3 = \frac{1}{r}[(x + iy)\psi_2 - z\psi_1], \quad (\gamma_r \psi)_4 = \frac{1}{r}[(x - iy)\psi_1 + z\psi_2],$$

or, putting $\psi_1 = \phi_1$, $\psi_2 = \phi_2$, $\psi_3 = \chi_1$, $\psi_4 = \chi_2$, and

$$\sigma_r = \frac{1}{r}(\boldsymbol{\sigma} \cdot \mathbf{r}),$$

$(\gamma_r \psi)_1 = (\sigma_r \chi)_1, \ (\gamma_r \psi)_2 = (\sigma_r \chi)_2, \ (\gamma_r \psi)_3 = (\sigma_r \phi)_1, \ (\gamma_r \psi)_4 = (\sigma_r \phi)_2.$

The equation (294) is thus equivalent to the following two:

$$\left.\begin{array}{l}
\left(\dfrac{\partial}{\partial r} + \dfrac{1+k}{r}\right)(\sigma_r \chi) - \dfrac{2\pi i}{ch}(\epsilon' - \epsilon_0 - U)\phi = 0 \\[3mm]
\left(\dfrac{\partial}{\partial r} + \dfrac{1-k}{r}\right)(\sigma_r \phi) - \dfrac{2\pi i}{ch}(\epsilon' + \epsilon_0 - U)\chi = 0
\end{array}\right\} \qquad (294 a)$$

The latter equation can be multiplied by σ_r, giving, since σ_r commutes with $\partial/\partial r$ and since its square is equal to 1, just as for γ_r,

$$\left(\frac{\partial}{\partial r}+\frac{1-k}{r}\right)\phi-\frac{2\pi i}{ch}(\epsilon'+\epsilon_0-U)(\sigma_r\chi)=0. \qquad (294\,\text{b})$$

The equations (294 a) and (294 b) serve for the determination of the functions ϕ and $\sigma_r\chi$. It should be remembered that each of these functions represents a pair of ordinary functions. We thus see that the two functions of each pair have the same radial factor, in agreement with our previous results. Putting

$$\phi = F(r), \qquad \sigma_r\chi = iG(r),$$

we obtain the following system:

$$\left.\begin{array}{l}\left(\dfrac{\partial}{\partial r}+\dfrac{1-k}{r}\right)F+\dfrac{2\pi}{ch}(\epsilon'+\epsilon_0-U)G=0\\[2ex]\left(\dfrac{\partial}{\partial r}+\dfrac{1+k}{r}\right)G-\dfrac{2\pi}{ch}(\epsilon'-\epsilon_0-U)F=0\end{array}\right\}. \qquad (295)$$

Using the identity $\qquad \left(\dfrac{d}{dr}+\dfrac{1}{r}\right)F=\dfrac{1}{r}\dfrac{d}{dr}(rF),$

we have

$$\left.\begin{array}{l}\left(\dfrac{d}{dr}-\dfrac{k}{r}\right)f+\dfrac{2\pi}{ch}(\epsilon'+\epsilon_0-U)g=0\\[2ex]\left(\dfrac{d}{dr}+\dfrac{k}{r}\right)g-\dfrac{2\pi}{ch}(\epsilon'-\epsilon_0-U)f=0\end{array}\right\}, \qquad (296)$$

where $\qquad\qquad g = rG, \qquad f = rF.$

We shall solve these equations for the particular case of the hydrogen-like atom, i.e. an electron moving in a Coulomb field with a potential energy $U = -Ze^2/r$. We shall assume that $\epsilon' < \epsilon_0$, which corresponds to a bound electron ($H' < 0$) and leads to a discrete set of energy-levels. Putting, for the sake of brevity,

$$\frac{2\pi}{h}(\epsilon'+\epsilon_0) = \alpha^2, \qquad \frac{2\pi}{h}(\epsilon_0-\epsilon') = \beta^2, \qquad \frac{2\pi Ze^2}{hc} = \gamma,$$

we get for this case

$$\left.\begin{array}{l}\left(\dfrac{d}{dr}-\dfrac{k}{r}\right)f+\left(\alpha^2+\dfrac{\gamma}{r}\right)g=0\\[2ex]\left(\dfrac{d}{dr}+\dfrac{k}{r}\right)g+\left(\beta^2-\dfrac{\gamma}{r}\right)f=0\end{array}\right\}. \qquad (296\,\text{a})$$

For large values of r these equations reduce to

$$\frac{df}{dr} + \alpha^2 g = 0, \qquad \frac{dg}{dr} - \beta^2 f = 0,$$

giving the following asymptotic solution:

$$\left.\begin{array}{c} f = A e^{-\alpha\beta r}, \qquad g = B e^{-\alpha\beta r} \\ A\beta = B\alpha \end{array}\right\}, \tag{296 b}$$

where A and B are considered as constants.

To get the exact solution we replace them by polynomials

$$A = A_0 r^\mu + A_1 r^{\mu+1} + \ldots + A_s r^{\mu+s},$$
$$B = B_0 r^\mu + B_1 r^{\mu+1} + \ldots + B_s r^{\mu+s},$$

obtaining the following relations between the coefficients:

$$\left.\begin{array}{l} A_n(\mu+n-k) + \gamma B_n = \alpha\beta A_{n-1} - \alpha^2 B_{n-1} \\ B_n(\mu+n+k) - \gamma A_n = \alpha\beta B_{n-1} - \beta^2 A_{n-1} \end{array}\right\}. \tag{297}$$

Multiplying the first of these equations by β and the second by α and adding the results, we get

$$A_n[\beta(\mu+n-k) - \alpha\gamma] + B_n[\alpha(\mu+n+k) + \beta\gamma] = 0. \tag{297 a}$$

The 'boundary conditions' $A_n = B_n = 0$ for $n = -1$ and $n = s+1$ applied to (297) give

$$A_0(\mu-k) + \gamma B_1 = 0, \qquad B_1(\mu+k) - \gamma A_1 = 0;$$
$$\beta A_s = \alpha B_s.$$

Eliminating A_1 and B_1 between the first two equations, we get

$$\mu = +\sqrt{(k^2 - \gamma^2)}. \tag{297 b}$$

The ratio $\dfrac{A_0}{B_0} = \dfrac{\sqrt{(k^2-\gamma^2)}+k}{\gamma} = \dfrac{\gamma}{k - \sqrt{(k^2-\gamma^2)}}$

which follows from the preceding equation, is identical with that which is obtained from (297 a) for $n = 1$. With $n = s$ we get, on the other hand,

$$A_s[\beta(\mu+s-k) - \alpha\gamma] + B_s[\alpha(\mu+s+k) + \beta\gamma] = 0,$$

which becomes identical with $\beta A_s = \alpha B_s$ on using the condition

$$2\alpha\beta(\mu+s) = (\alpha^2 - \beta^2)\gamma. \tag{297 c}$$

With the above definitions of α, β we get

$$\sqrt{\epsilon_0^2 - \epsilon'^2}(\mu+s) = \epsilon'\gamma,$$

that is, from (297 b),

$$\epsilon' = \epsilon_0\left[1+\frac{\gamma^2}{\{s+\sqrt{(k^2-\gamma^2)}\}^2}\right]^{-\frac{1}{2}}. \qquad (298)$$

This is exactly Sommerfeld's formula (264) (with γZ replaced by γ).†
The angular quantum number k has the same meaning in both cases,
so far as the value of the energy is concerned. It must be remembered,
however, that in the previous theory it was supposed to be essentially
positive, whereas in Dirac's theory it can assume both positive and
negative values (zero excluded). With $k > 0$ we get $l = k-1$ and
$j = l+\frac{1}{2} = k-\frac{1}{2}$, i.e. a solution of the type (290 a); while in the case
$k < 0$ we obtain a solution of the type (290 b) with $l = |k|$ and
$j = |k|-\frac{1}{2}$.

It should be emphasized that the two solutions are characterized not
only by different angular factors, but also, as is plainly seen from (297),
by different radial factors $F = f/r$ and $G = g/r$; their similarity is
restricted to the value of the energy and of the z-component of the
angular momentum M_z.

The coincidence of the energy-levels corresponding to opposite values
of k is a characteristic feature of the motion in a purely Coulomb field
of force. If the motion of the electron takes place in a field even
moderately deviating from the latter, due, for instance, to the variable
shielding action of the inner electrons in an alkali atom, the energies
of the states $+k$ and $-k$ become different and we obtain what is called
a 'screening doublet'. The two levels of such a doublet state belong
to two different values of the Schrödinger angular number l, namely,
$l = |k|-1$ and $l = |k|$, and to the same value of the inner quantum
number $j = |k|-\frac{1}{2}$. It should be mentioned that in the case of small
values of j the separation between the two energy-levels in alkali atoms
or ions of a similar structure is so large that they are no longer con-

---

† If instead of Dirac's equation we used the relativity second-order equation $D\psi = 0$,
in the present case

$$\nabla^2\psi + \frac{4\pi^2}{h^2c^2}\left[\left(\epsilon'+\frac{Ze^2}{r}\right)^2-\epsilon_0^2\right]\psi = 0,$$

not involving the spin, we should have obtained a solution of the same type

$$\psi = F(r)Y_{l,m}(\theta, \phi)$$

as in Schrödinger's theory, with

$$rF = f = e^{-\alpha r}\sum_{n=0}^{s}b_n r^{\mu+n}$$

and

$$\epsilon' = \left[1+\frac{\gamma^2}{[s-\frac{1}{2}+\sqrt{\{(l+\frac{1}{2})^2-\gamma^2\}}]^2}\right]^{-\frac{1}{2}},$$

corresponding to half-integral values of the radial and angular quantum numbers ($s-\frac{1}{2}$
instead of s, and $l+\frac{1}{2}$ instead of l). This result is, however, contradicted by the experimental data, which are in agreement with Sommerfeld's formula.

sidered as forming a doublet and are referred to different series. This notion can, however, be conveniently applied to X-ray absorption levels.

The two levels corresponding to the same value of the Schrödinger angular quantum number l and to consecutive values of the inner quantum number $j = l - \frac{1}{2}$ $(k = -l)$ and $j = l + \frac{1}{2}$ $(k = l+1)$ are said to form a 'relativity doublet'. According to Sommerfeld's formula (298) they correspond to consecutive values of the old angular quantum number $|k|$ $(= l, l+1)$. Since in the Bohr-Sommerfeld theory this number determined the eccentricity of the elliptical orbits, the relativity doublets were associated with orbits of different eccentricity. From the point of view of the present theory, the relativity doublets should be associated rather with orbits of the same size and eccentricity but with opposite orientations of the spin. Such relativity or 'spin'-doublets are extremely narrow in hydrogen or ionized helium, but they become very broad in X-ray spectra, their width increasing roughly as the fourth power of the effective nuclear charge [according to the approximate formula (264 c)]. They are rather broad, too, in the spectra of alkali atoms and other complicated systems with one external electron. In this case, however, they are due not to a large effective nuclear charge, but to a rapid variation of the latter, owing to the decrease of the shielding effect of the inner electrons when the outer electron approaches the nucleus.—Sommerfeld's formula is, of course, inapplicable to this case, which is characterized by a large Δl-separation ('screening effect') and a relatively small Δj-separation ('spin' or relativity effect).

To a given value of k (i.e. of l and j) there corresponds a degenerate set of states specified by different values of the axial quantum number m or of the number $m_j = m + \frac{1}{2}$ which determines the z-component of the total angular momentum. This degeneracy is of exactly the same type as that discussed before in connexion with Schrödinger's theory; it can be pictured as due to the possibility of $2j+1 = 2|k|$ quantized orientations of the angular momentum vector with regard to the z-axis, corresponding to all half-integral values of $m + \frac{1}{2}$ between $+j$ and $-j$. We have in fact in the case $k > 0$ a set of function-quadruplets ψ with the following angular factors $Y_{k-1,m+1}$, $Y_{k-1,m}$; $Y_{k,m+1}$, $Y_{k,m}$. The maximum or minimum admissible value of m is that for which one function at least of each pair is different from zero. We thus get $m \leqslant k-1$ and $m \geqslant -k$, i.e.
$$-k+\tfrac{1}{2} < m+\tfrac{1}{2} \leqslant k-\tfrac{1}{2}.$$

A similar relation with k replaced by $|k|$ is obtained in the case $k < 0$.

Thus, for example, in the particular case $k = 1$, $l = 0$ and $j = \frac{1}{2}$, which corresponds to the normal state of the hydrogen atom ($n = 1$; it should be mentioned that the case $k = -1$, i.e. $l = 1$, corresponds to an excited state $n \geqslant 2$) we actually obtain *two* sub-states specified by the following expressions for the functions $\psi_1,..., \psi_4$:

$$\psi_\alpha = RY_\alpha \qquad (\alpha = 1, 2, 3, 4),$$

with the radial factor

$$R(r) = r^{\sqrt{(1-\gamma^2)}-1}e^{-r/a},$$

and the angular factors

$$Y_1 = 0, \quad Y_2 = 1, \quad Y_3 = -\frac{i\gamma}{1+\sqrt{(1-\gamma^2)}}\sin\theta\, e^{i\phi},$$

$$Y_4 = -\frac{i\gamma}{1+\sqrt{(1-\gamma^2)}}\cos\theta$$

in the case $m = 0$, i.e. $m_j = +\frac{1}{2}$, and

$$Y_1 = -1, \quad Y_2 = 0, \quad Y_3 = -\frac{i\gamma}{1+\sqrt{(1-\gamma^2)}}\cos\theta,$$

$$Y_4 = \frac{i\gamma}{1+\sqrt{(1-\gamma^2)}}\sin\theta\, e^{-i\phi}$$

in the case $m = -1$, i.e. $m_j = -\frac{1}{2}$. The two states correspond to the same value of the inner quantum number j, namely, $j = \frac{1}{2}$. They are associated with the same spherically symmetrical distribution of the probability density, which is proportional to the square of the radial factor $R(r)$. It should be noticed that this factor becomes infinite at $r = 0$, but in such a way that the integral $\int_0^\infty R^2 r^2\, dr$ remains convergent.

The difference between the two states consists in the fact that for the first of them the spin axis of the electron is pointing in the positive and for the second in the negative direction of the z-axis, as follows from the approximate equation for the characteristic values

$$\sigma_z \psi = \sigma_z' \psi$$

with $\psi_3 = \psi_4 = 0$.

We must consider in conclusion the modification of the states, and in particular of the energy-levels, of a hydrogen-like or an alkali-like atom in the presence of a homogeneous magnetic field $\mathfrak{H}$ (Zeeman effect). In the former case we have to deal with a twofold $(k, -k)$ degeneracy, corresponding to the absence of any screening effect. This degeneracy is to be taken into account for very weak magnetic fields only, so weak that the product $\mu\mathfrak{H}$ is very small compared with the relativistic (Δj)

separation. In the latter case, on the contrary, the relativistic splitting is as a rule much smaller than the screening ($\pm k$) separation, so that for fields of moderate strength the only degeneracy present is that which corresponds to different values of the axial quantum number m.

It can easily be shown that the characteristic functions ψ corresponding to this privileged character of the z-axis in the absence of a magnetic field are such that the non-diagonal matrix elements of the magnetic perturbation energy

$$S = \tfrac{1}{2}e\mathfrak{H}\cdot\mathbf{r}\times\mathbf{\gamma} = \tfrac{1}{2}e\mathfrak{H}(x\gamma_y - y\gamma_x) \tag{299}$$

all vanish. So long as the magnetic field is sufficiently weak the additional energy due to its action can be determined accordingly as the diagonal elements of S with regard to the corresponding unperturbed states.

The additional magnetic energy of a state specified by the quantum numbers k, m is thus given by the formula

$$\Delta\epsilon'_{km} = S_{km;km} = \int \psi^\dagger_{km} S\psi_{km}\, dV. \tag{299\,a}$$

Dropping for the sake of simplicity the indices k, m, we have, according to (299),

$$(S\psi)_1 = \tfrac{1}{2}e\mathfrak{H}i(x+iy)\psi_4, \qquad (S\psi)_2 = -\tfrac{1}{2}e\mathfrak{H}i(x-iy)\psi_3,$$
$$(S\psi)_3 = \tfrac{1}{2}e\mathfrak{H}i(x+iy)\psi_2, \qquad (S\psi)_4 = -\tfrac{1}{2}e\mathfrak{H}i(x-iy)\psi_1,$$

and consequently

$$\psi^\dagger S\psi = -e\mathfrak{H}\frac{1}{2i}[(x+iy)\psi_1^*\psi_4 - (x-iy)\psi_4^*\psi_1 + (x+iy)\psi_3^*\psi_2 - (x-iy)\psi_2^*\psi_3]$$

$$= -e\mathfrak{H}\mathrm{R}\frac{1}{i}(x+iy)(\psi_1^*\psi_4 + \psi_3^*\psi_2),$$

or

$$\psi^\dagger S\psi = -e\mathfrak{H}\mathrm{R}\frac{1}{i}r\sin\theta\, e^{i\phi}(\psi_1^*\psi_4 + \psi_3^*\psi_2). \tag{299\,b}$$

Substituting here the expressions for the functions ψ derived before and integrating, we get

$$\Delta\epsilon'_{km}$$
$$= 2\pi e\mathfrak{H} \int dr\, F(r)G(r)r^3 \int i(a_1^* a_4\, P_{l+1,m}\, P_{l,m+1} + a_3^* a_4\, P_{l+1,m+1}\, P_{l,m})\sin^2\theta\, d\theta \tag{299\,c}$$

in the case of the equations (290 a) and a similar expression in the case (290 b).

The radial factor in this expression can easily be calculated with the help of the differential equations (296) which are satisfied by the functions $rF = f$ and $rG = g$. Taking the first of these equations and putting approximately $\epsilon' + \epsilon_0 - U \cong 2\epsilon_0$, we get

$$rg = \frac{ch}{4\pi\epsilon_0}\left(kf - r\frac{df}{dr}\right),$$

whence

$$\int FGr^3\,dr = \int fgr\,dr \cong \frac{ch}{4\pi\epsilon_0}\left(k\int f^2\,dr - \int rf\frac{df}{dr}\,dr\right),$$

or since

$$\int_0^\infty rf\frac{df}{dr}\,dr = \int_0^\infty r\frac{d}{dr}\left(\frac{f^2}{2}\right)dr = -\int_0^\infty \frac{f^2}{2}\,dr,$$

$$\int FGr^3\,dr \cong \frac{ch}{4\pi\epsilon_0}(k+\tfrac{1}{2})\int_0^\infty f^2\,dr = \frac{h}{4\pi m_0 c}(k+\tfrac{1}{2})$$

if the function $f(r)$ is appropriately normalized ($\int f^2\,dr = 1$).

The angular factor in (299 c) can also be evaluated without much trouble with due regard to the normalizing conditions for the functions $P(\theta)$.

We obtain in this way (neglecting terms of the second order in $1/c$)

$$\Delta\epsilon'_{km} = -\frac{eh}{4\pi m_0 c}g\mathfrak{H}(m+\tfrac{1}{2}) = -\mu\mathfrak{H}g(m+\tfrac{1}{2}), \qquad (300)$$

with

$$g = \frac{k}{k-\tfrac{1}{2}} \quad (k>0), \qquad g = \frac{|k|}{|k|+\tfrac{1}{2}} \quad (k<0), \qquad (300\,\text{a})$$

in agreement with the results obtained at the end of § 30 (if $m+\tfrac{1}{2}$ is identified with m_j).

The integration of the expression (299 c) requires a great deal of calculation. This can be avoided, however, if we replace the operator $\mathbf{M}$ by the operators

$$\mathbf{M}_{\text{eff}} = \frac{e\gamma_0}{2m_0 c}(\mathbf{L}+2\mathbf{s}) \quad \text{or} \quad \mathbf{M}'_{\text{eff}} = \frac{e}{2m_0 c}(\mathbf{L}+2\mathbf{s}),$$

which have been shown in the preceding section to be approximately equivalent to it and to each other with an accuracy of the second order in $1/c$. To the same approximation we can replace γ_0 in the expression (287 a) by 1, with the result $L^2 = \frac{h^2}{4\pi^2}k(k-1) = \frac{h^2}{4\pi^2}l(l+1)$ when $k > 0$.

Combining it with the equation $M^2 = \left(\frac{h}{2\pi}\right)^2 j(j+1)$ and putting $\bar{\mathbf{s}} = (g-1)\overline{\mathbf{M}}$, we obtain, with the help of (267 a) and (289 b), the above approximate expression for $\Delta\epsilon'_{km}$.

The preceding theory is applicable only to a comparatively weak magnetic field. When the shift of the energy-levels produced by the magnetic field becomes of the same order of magnitude as the Δj-doublet separation, the spin perturbation to which this separation is due must be taken into account together with the magnetic perturbation.

We must start in this case with the two unperturbed states of equal energy ϵ'_{lm}, specified by the same values of l and m and belonging to the values $j = l \pm \frac{1}{2}$ of the inner quantum number. The combined spin-magnetic perturbation $S = S_{\mathrm{sp}} + S_m$ produces a splitting-up of the unperturbed energy-level into two levels $\epsilon'_{lm} + \Delta\epsilon'_{lmj}$, according to the equation

$$\begin{vmatrix} S_{11} - \Delta\epsilon' & S_{12} \\ S_{21} & S_{22} - \Delta\epsilon' \end{vmatrix} = 0,$$

where the index 1 refers to one of the two degenerate states ($j = l + \frac{1}{2}$, say), and the index 2 to the other ($j = l - \frac{1}{2}$).

The non-diagonal elements of the spin perturbation $(S_{\mathrm{sp}})_{12}$ and $(S_{\mathrm{sp}})_{21}$ must obviously vanish since the states $j = l \pm \frac{1}{2}$ are stationary in the absence of the magnetic field. The diagonal elements $(S_{\mathrm{sp}})_{11} = \Delta_1 \epsilon'$, $(S_{\mathrm{sp}})_{22} = \Delta_2 \epsilon'$ can be defined therefore as the additional energies due to the spin perturbation alone, their difference $\delta = \Delta_1 \epsilon' - \Delta_2 \epsilon'$ being equal to the Δj-doublet separation in the absence of the magnetic field. The action of the latter can thus be determined by the equation

$$\begin{vmatrix} S_{m11} - \Delta_1 \epsilon' - \Delta\epsilon' & S_{m12} \\ S_{m21} & S_{m22} - \Delta_2 \epsilon' - \Delta\epsilon' \end{vmatrix} = 0, \qquad (301)$$

where

$$\left. \begin{aligned} S_{m11} &= -\mu\mathfrak{H}\frac{l+1}{l+\frac{1}{2}}(m+\tfrac{1}{2}), \qquad S_{m22} = -\mu\mathfrak{H}\frac{l}{l+\frac{1}{2}}(m+\tfrac{1}{2}) \\ S_{m12} &= S_{m21} = \mu\mathfrak{H}\frac{\sqrt{\{(l+m+1)(l-m)\}}}{2(l+\frac{1}{2})} \end{aligned} \right\} . \quad (301\,\mathrm{a})$$

and

The first two expressions are given by (300); the expressions for S_{m12} and S_{m21} can be derived in a similar manner [see § 20, equation (155 b)].

It is customary to refer the displaced energy-levels ϵ'_1 and ϵ'_2 to the 'centre of gravity' of the doublet, i.e. to the energy ϵ'_0 determined by the formulae

$$\epsilon'_1 = \epsilon'_0 + (l+1)\beta, \qquad \epsilon'_2 = \epsilon'_0 - l\beta$$

$[\delta = (2l+1)\beta = \epsilon'_1 - \epsilon'_2]$. Putting $\Delta_1 \epsilon' = (l+1)\beta$, $\Delta_2 \epsilon' = -l\beta$, and $\epsilon' - \epsilon'_0 = \Delta\epsilon'$, we obtain from (300) the following equation for $\Delta\epsilon'$:

$$(\Delta\epsilon')^2 + [\beta + \mu\mathfrak{H}(2m+1)]\Delta\epsilon' - l(l+1)\beta^2 + (\mu\mathfrak{H})^2 m(m+1) = 0.$$

Its solution runs

$$\Delta\epsilon' = -\tfrac{1}{2}\beta - \mu\mathfrak{H}(m+\tfrac{1}{2}) \pm$$
$$\pm \sqrt{\{[\mu\mathfrak{H}(m+\tfrac{1}{2}) + \tfrac{1}{2}\beta]^2 + \beta^2(l+1)l - \mu^2\mathfrak{H}^2 m(m+1)\}}. \quad (301\,\mathrm{b})$$

If the magnetic field is very weak, we get, in the first approximation,

$$\Delta\epsilon' = -\tfrac{1}{2}\beta - \mu\mathfrak{H}(m+\tfrac{1}{2}) \pm \left[\beta(l+\tfrac{1}{2}) + \tfrac{1}{2}\mu\mathfrak{H}\frac{m+\tfrac{1}{2}}{l+\tfrac{1}{2}}\right],$$

i.e.

$$\Delta\epsilon' = -\beta(l+1) - \mu\mathfrak{H}\frac{l+1}{l+\tfrac{1}{2}}(m+\tfrac{1}{2}),$$

and

$$\Delta\epsilon' = +\beta l - \mu\mathfrak{H}\frac{l}{l+\tfrac{1}{2}}(m+\tfrac{1}{2}),$$

in agreement with (300). In the opposite case of a very strong magnetic field—so strong that the doublet distance δ is small in comparison with the splitting $\mu\mathfrak{H}$ due to the field alone (when $\delta = 0$)—the formula (301 b) reduces to

$$\Delta\epsilon' = -\mu\mathfrak{H}(m+\tfrac{1}{2}) \pm \tfrac{1}{2}\mu\mathfrak{H} = -\mu\mathfrak{H}(m\pm 1),$$

i.e. to the earlier formula (266 b) which determines the normal Zeeman effect.

34. Negative Energy States; Positive Electrons and Neutrons

We have seen above that in Pauli's theory the two values $\alpha = 1$ and $\alpha = 2$ of the spin-coordinate refer to the two opposite orientations of the electron's spin or magnetic axis parallel to the z-axis. One might be inclined to think that the values $\alpha = 1, 2, 3, 4$ of the Dirac theory refer to four different orientations of the electron. This is, however, not true. Taking the probable value of the spin angular momentum in the z direction we get, according to (275 b):

$$\bar{s}_z = \frac{h}{4\pi}\bar{\xi}_z = \frac{h}{4\pi}\int \left(-\psi_1^*\psi_1 + \psi_2^*\psi_2 - \psi_3^*\psi_3 + \psi_4^*\psi_4\right)\,dV,$$

which shows that the values $\alpha = 3$ and $\alpha = 4$ refer to the same orientations (in the negative and positive direction parallel to z) as the values $\alpha = 1$ and $\alpha = 2$ respectively.

It should be mentioned that we get exactly the opposite result as to the meaning of $\alpha = 3$ and $\alpha = 4$ if, instead of the angular (mechanical) momentum, we consider the magnetic moment due to the spin $\mu = \mu\gamma_0\,\xi$. We get, namely, in this case [cf. (283 a)]:

$$\bar{\mu}_z = \int \mathfrak{M}_z\,dV = \mu\int \left(-\psi_1^*\psi_1 + \psi_2^*\psi_2 + \psi_3^*\psi_3 - \psi_4^*\psi_4\right)\,dV.$$

This shows that in the states $\alpha = 3, 4$ the electron behaves, so far as its spin magnetic moment is concerned, as a particle with a positive charge.

As has been explained already, the quadruplicity of the Dirac theory is connected with the introduction of states of negative energy ϵ. The values $\alpha = 3, 4$ for a state of this type have the same physical meaning as the values $\alpha = 1, 2$ for the corresponding state of positive energy (the functions ψ_3, ψ_4 being large compared with ψ_1, ψ_2 in the former case and small in the latter). The quadruplicity appearing in the comparison of Schrödinger's and Dirac's theory can be pictured as the result of the reflection of a point representing a Schrödinger state in the plane $\epsilon = 0$ and further as the splitting of the two points into a Pauli doublet.

To each characteristic value of Schrödinger's energy constant H' there correspond in Dirac's theory four energy values ϵ' which can be denoted as follows:

$$m_0 c^2 + H'^+_+, \qquad m_0 c^2 + H'^+_- \qquad (> 0),$$
$$m_0 c^2 + H'^-_+, \qquad m_0 c^2 + H'^-_- \qquad (< 0),$$

the first pair lying close to each other as well as the second pair, the two pairs having approximately opposite values.

The matrix elements of any physical quantity represented by the four-dimensional matrix-operator F, as defined by the general formula

$$F_{\epsilon''\epsilon'} = \int \psi^\dagger_{\epsilon''} F \psi_{\epsilon'} \, dV = \int \sum_{\alpha=1}^{4} \sum_{\beta=1}^{4} \psi^*_{\epsilon''\alpha} F_{\alpha\beta} \psi_{\epsilon'\beta} \, dV$$

can be combined accordingly into four-dimensional matrices:

$$F_{H''H'} = \left\{ \begin{array}{cccc} F_{H''^+_+ H'^+_+} & F_{H''^+_+ H'^+_-} & F_{H''^+_+ H'^-_+} & F_{H''^+_+ H'^-_-} \\ F_{H''^+_- H'^+_+} & F_{H''^+_- H'^+_-} & F_{H''^+_- H'^-_+} & F_{H''^+_- H'^-_-} \\ F_{H''^-_+ H'^+_+} & F_{H''^-_+ H'^+_-} & F_{H''^-_+ H'^-_+} & F_{H''^-_+ H'^-_-} \\ F_{H''^-_- H'^+_+} & F_{H''^-_- H'^+_-} & F_{H''^-_- H'^-_+} & F_{H''^-_- H'^-_-} \end{array} \right\}.$$

If the function $F\psi_{\epsilon'}$ is expanded in a series of functions $\psi_{\epsilon''}$, according to the formula

$$F\psi_{\epsilon'} = \sum_{\epsilon''} F_{\epsilon''\epsilon'} \psi_{\epsilon''},$$

negative energy states must be taken into account as well as the states of positive energy unless the matrix elements $F_{\epsilon''\epsilon'}$, where $\epsilon' > 0$ and $\epsilon'' > 0$, all vanish. This circumstance is especially important in various perturbation problems; with F denoting the operator of the perturbation energy, correct results as to the probability of combined (double) transitions are obtained only if *intermediate states of negative energy are considered* along with those of positive energy. In the problem of the scattering of light by a free electron, for example, the relative importance of intermediate states of negative energy is larger the smaller the (positive) energy of the initial and final state. This result (due to Tamm) is especially startling because relativity corrections vanish in the limiting case of small velocities, so that negative energy states which form a characteristic relativity effect would be expected to become insignificant in this limiting case.

Another interesting example of the paradoxical role played in Dirac's theory by the states of negative energy is presented by the motion of an electron through a potential energy jump, as discussed by O. Klein. For the sake of simplicity we shall take the equation of the second order, $D\psi = 0$ ($D = u^2 - u_l^2 + m_0^2 c^2$), to which the four equations of the Dirac theory reduce for free motion. The continuity conditions for the four functions $\psi_1,..., \psi_4$ can be replaced in this case by the continuity condition for one of them and its derivative in the direction of the energy jump. Assuming the latter to take place in the direction of the x-axis, the potential energy being equal to 0 on the left of the plane $x = 0$ and $U = \text{const.} > 0$ on the right, and assuming further the electron to move parallel to the x-axis, we get

$$\psi = A'e^{\frac{i2\pi}{h}(g_a x - \epsilon l)} + A''e^{+\frac{i2\pi}{h}(-g_a x - \epsilon l)}$$

for $x < 0$ (incident and reflected wave), and

$$\psi = B'e^{\frac{i2\pi}{h}(g_b x - \epsilon l)}$$

for $x > 0$ (transmitted wave), where

$$g_a^2 = \epsilon^2/c^2 - m_0 c^2 \quad \text{and} \quad g_b^2 = (\epsilon - U)^2/c^2 - m_0 c^2.$$

The continuity conditions give the same relations $A' + A'' = B'$ and $A' - A'' = B'g_b/g_a$ as in the non-relativity theory [cf. Part I]. The important difference between the latter and the present theory consists in the fact that the above relativity expression for g_b remains real not only in the case when U is smaller than the kinetic energy of the incident electron $\epsilon - m_0 c^2$, but also in the case when it is larger than $m_0 c^2 + \epsilon \simeq 2m_0 c^2$ (if ϵ is not very different from $m_0 c^2$). This means that total reflection (g_b imaginary) takes place only within the range

$$\epsilon - m_0 c^2 \leqslant U \leqslant \epsilon + m_0 c^2,$$

whereas beyond it we get transmission both for small and for large values of U.

It seems hardly possible to give a reasonable interpretation of this result. It can be shown, however, that the paradoxical transmission probability for the case $U > \epsilon + m_0 c^2$ rapidly decreases when the discontinuity U in the potential energy at $x = 0$ is replaced by a *gradual* increase within an interval comparable with or larger than the wavelength of the electron $\lambda = h/g$.

The physical meaning of the states of negative energy is at present not quite certain. They were initially interpreted by Dirac in connexion with the duplicity of electricity, and served to reduce protons to a mere absence of electrons if space is assumed to be nearly saturated with electrons in states of negative energy, with due regard to Pauli's exclusion principle. It is, however, impossible to interpret in this way the difference in the *mass* of electrons and protons. According to Pauli and to Weyl the rest-mass of a proton considered as a hole in the distribution of electrons with negative energies should be exactly equal to the rest-mass m_0 of an electron.

Although Dirac's original theory has thus failed to reduce protons to electrons, yet it may perhaps be credited with predicting the existence and properties of things that have hitherto never been anticipated by the experimental physicist and that seem to reveal themselves in the Wilson chamber cloud-tracks of particles released by the penetrating rays of cosmic origin and by very hard gamma rays. These are the 'positive electrons' whose discovery has recently been announced by Anderson (1932) and also by Blackett (1933).

The experimental data are still too scarce to make it sure that positive electrons really exist. But if they do exist they fit beautifully in the scheme of Dirac's theory. The fact that they are not found under ordinary conditions is explained by the extremely large probability that a 'positive electron' will recombine with a negative one (the latter falling from a state of positive energy into the hole constituting the former), this recombination being accompanied by the emission of two photons (cf. Part I, § 19).

The visible existence of the material world around us must be guaranteed from this point of view by the fact that the total number of electrons is larger than the number of available states of negative energy, at least in that part of the world which is accessible to observation.

Assuming the existence of positive electrons, it would be natural to postulate the existence of 'negative protons' formed by holes in a practically saturated distribution of protons between states of negative energy.

It is difficult, however, to accept the idea that space is filled up with one or two sorts of particles forming a kind of infinitely dense 'ether' which is revealed in a negative way only through the occasional absence of the full quota of these particles.

Dirac's equation has served as a starting-point for the introduction—besides positive electrons—of particles devoid of electrical charge and denoted accordingly as 'neutrons'. Dirac himself attempted in 1931 to introduce neutrons as magnetic analogues of electrons, i.e. as particles possessing a *magnetic charge* instead of an electric one. Pauli on the other hand proposed (simultaneously with Dirac) a theory of neutrons devoid of charge (both electric and magnetic) but possessing a *magnetic moment* and a spin angular momentum associated with it. The necessity, or rather plausibility, of introducing neutrons in addition to protons and electrons as constituent parts of atomic nuclei was dictated by certain nuclear phenomena, like the apparent failure of the alternation principle (Bose-Einstein statistics holding for nuclei supposed to consist of an odd number of particles) and of the principle of conservation of energy (continuous β-ray spectra of radioactive substances). These difficulties could be removed by admitting the existence in the nuclei of a third sort of elementary particles in a bound state. The idea of treating these particles as 'magnetic neutrons' was suggested by the possibility of replacing Dirac's equation for the electron by a similar equation with $e = 0$ and with the mass m_0 increased by an additional term

$$L = \mu(\mathbf{H}\cdot\boldsymbol{\xi} - \mathbf{E}\cdot\boldsymbol{\eta})$$

which represents the action of the magnetic and electric field on the neutron's magnetic and electric moment ($\boldsymbol{\xi}$ and $\boldsymbol{\eta}$ being the matrices (275 b) and (275 c), and μ hypothetically Bohr's magneton). Pauli's equation for the neutron can thus be written in the usual form $\left(\epsilon + \dfrac{h}{2\pi i}\cdot\dfrac{\partial}{\partial t}\right)\psi = 0$ with

$$\epsilon = c\boldsymbol{\gamma}\cdot\mathbf{p} + \gamma_0(m_0 c^2 + L),$$

where $\mathbf{p} = \dfrac{h}{2\pi i}\nabla$; the electromagnetic potentials $\mathbf{A}$ and ϕ do not appear in ϵ since the electric charge with which they must be multiplied is supposed equal to zero.

We shall not stop here to develop Pauli's theory. The remarkable fact we are mainly concerned with is that the neutron was discovered experimentally by Chadwick, following observations by Curie and Joliot, within a year after its existence had been tentatively admitted on theoretical grounds. It made its appearance as the disintegration product of certain nuclei bombarded by protons or α-particles in the form of a particle with a mass very little different from that of a proton (while Pauli expected it to have a mass of the same order of magnitude as the electron). It is still a matter open to question whether a neutron is a simple particle like an electron and a proton, or a combination of both.† The latter alternative seems the more natural, although we are not yet in a state to substantiate it theoretically, for the present wave-mechanical theory is inadequate in treating such systems, whose linear dimensions are of the same order of magnitude as the 'size' of the electron (attributed to it on the electromagnetic theory of mass). As to the forces binding the electron and proton in a neutron more tightly than in a hydrogen atom—they may be due to the mutual attraction of the spin magnetic moments. In fact this attraction (which corresponds to a suitable orientation of the spins) increases with decrease of distance much more rapidly than the attraction due to the electric charges of the two particles, so that the Coulomb attraction becomes negligibly small (relatively) at distances of the order of 10^{-14} cm. It cannot be asserted, however, that the usual inverse fourth-power law for the mutual attraction of two elementary magnets is applicable for distances comparable with the electron's own dimensions.

35. The Invariance of the Dirac Equation with regard to Co-ordinate Transformations

We have hitherto considered the Dirac equation of motion for a particular frame of reference specified by the coordinates x, y, z and the time t. We shall now investigate the transformation properties of this equation for such transformations as correspond to a rotation of the coordinate system x, y, z in space, or more generally to a Lorentz transformation of the coordinates and the time (i.e. to a rotation of the original frame in a four-dimensional space-time manifold).

We shall first write down the Dirac equation in the form of two two-dimensional matrix equations

$$\left. \begin{array}{l} \boldsymbol{\sigma}\cdot\mathbf{u}\psi+(u_t-m_0 c)\chi = 0 \\ \boldsymbol{\sigma}\cdot\mathbf{u}\chi+(u_t+m_0 c)\psi = 0 \end{array} \right\} \qquad (302)$$

[cf. (257 a), § 30] and limit ourselves to rotations in ordinary space, which do not affect the operator u_t. The invariance of equations (302) with regard to such rotations can be achieved in two different ways:

(1) By considering the wave functions (matrices) $\psi = \begin{Bmatrix} \psi_1 \\ \psi_2 \end{Bmatrix}$ and $\chi = \begin{Bmatrix} \chi_1 \\ \chi_2 \end{Bmatrix}$ as invariant and the matrices σ_x, σ_y, σ_z as covariant, i.e.

† It might also be surmised that the proton is a complicated particle formed by the combination of a neutron with a positive electron.

transforming according to the same law as the coordinates x, y, z. Under this condition the product $\boldsymbol{\sigma} \cdot \mathbf{u} = \sigma_x u_x + \sigma_y u_y + \sigma_z u_z$ will define a scalar (invariant) operator.

(2) By considering the matrices σ_x, σ_y, σ_z as invariant numerical operators, and introducing a suitable transformation for the matrices ψ, χ.

The two methods must, of course, give equivalent results. In the first case we can define the matrix σ_n for any direction n (which may be that of one of the new coordinate axes) as the projection of the vector $\boldsymbol{\sigma}$ in this direction. Using the polar angles θ_n, ϕ_n to specify it with respect to the original coordinate system $C(x, y, z)$, we have

$$\sigma_n = \sigma_x \cos(x, n) + \sigma_y \cos(y, n) + \sigma_z \cos(z, n)$$
$$= \sin \theta_n (\sigma_x \cos \phi_n + \sigma_y \sin \phi_n) + \sigma_z \cos \theta_n,$$

which is equivalent to four equations for the matrix elements $\sigma_{n\alpha\beta}$ $(\alpha, \beta = 1, 2)$ of σ_n. With the help of the expressions $\sigma_x = \begin{Bmatrix} 0 & 1 \\ 1 & 0 \end{Bmatrix}$, $\sigma_y = \begin{Bmatrix} 0 & i \\ -i & 0 \end{Bmatrix}$, $\sigma_z = \begin{Bmatrix} -1 & 0 \\ 0 & 1 \end{Bmatrix}$, defining the rectangular components of σ in the system A, we get

$$\sigma_n = \begin{Bmatrix} -\cos \theta_n & \sin \theta_n \, e^{i\phi_n} \\ \sin \theta_n \, e^{-i\phi_n} & \cos \theta_n \end{Bmatrix}. \tag{302 a}$$

This equation can be applied for the definition of the matrices $\sigma_{x'}$, $\sigma_{y'}$, $\sigma_{z'}$ which represent the rectangular components of the vector $\boldsymbol{\sigma}$ with regard to a new coordinate system $C'(x', y', z')$.

We shall not, however, write down the explicit expressions for these matrices (which can easily be found with the help of the three Eulerian angles), but shall limit ourselves to presenting the general transformation equation in the form

$$\sigma'_{n\alpha\beta} = \sum_{m=1}^{3} a_{mn} \sigma_{m\alpha\beta}, \tag{302 b}$$

where the indices $(m, n) = 1, 2, 3$ stand for the three axes of the old and the new system respectively ($\sigma'_1 = \sigma_{x'}$, etc.), while a_{mn} is the matrix of the orthogonal transformation $C \to C'$:

$$x'_n = \sum a_{mn} x_m.$$

It should be emphasized that the indices m, n which specify the coordinate axes or the *rectangular components* of $\boldsymbol{\sigma}$, have nothing to do with the indices α, β which specify the *matrix elements* of $\boldsymbol{\sigma}$ or of its rectangular components.

The transition from the first method (of transforming σ_m) to the second method (of transforming ψ_α and χ_α) can be carried out in the following way:

We try to find a unitary two-dimensional matrix A such that the transformation defined by (302 b) shall be equivalent to the following one:

$$\sigma_n' = A^{-1}\sigma_n A \qquad (A^{-1} = A^\dagger), \tag{303}$$

that is,

$$\sigma_{n\alpha\beta}' = \sum_{\gamma=1}^{2}\sum_{\delta=1}^{2} A_{\gamma\alpha}^* A_{\delta\beta}\sigma_{n\gamma\delta} \qquad (n = 1, 2, 3)$$

involving a component of $\boldsymbol{\sigma}$ along a given new axis and along the *corresponding* axis only of the original coordinate system.

The relation between the transformation (302 b) and (303) can be stated as follows: in the former the matrices σ_m (or σ_n') appear as components of a vector in ordinary three-dimensional space, whereas in the second case they appear as tensors in the two-dimensional spin-space specified by the Greek indices α, β, etc. The transformation matrices a_{mn} and $A_{\alpha\beta}$ are both unitary and refer respectively to the ordinary space and to the state-space.

Let us suppose that we have succeeded in finding A and let us write the scalar product $\boldsymbol{\sigma\cdot u}$ in the form

$$\sum \sigma_m u_m = \sum_n \sigma_n' u_n' = \sum_n A^{-1}\sigma_n A u_n' = A^{-1}(\sum \sigma_n u_n')A.$$

(A commutes with u_n' since the latter is a scalar in the state-space.) The transformed equations (302) can be written accordingly in the form

$$A^{-1}\left(\sum_{n=1}^{3} \sigma_n u_n'\right)A\psi + (u_t - m_0 c)\chi = 0,$$

$$A^{-1}(\sum \sigma_n u_n')A\chi + (u_t + m_0 c)\psi = 0.$$

Multiplying them on the left by the matrix A, we get

$$\left.\begin{array}{l} \left(\sum_n \sigma_n u_n'\right)\psi' + (u_t - m_0 c)\chi' = 0 \\[2mm] \left(\sum_n \sigma_n u_n'\right)\chi' + (u_t + m_0 c)\psi' = 0 \end{array}\right\}, \tag{303 a}$$

with the operator-matrix $\boldsymbol{\sigma u}'$ of the same form as in the original coordinate system and with the transformed wave functions

$$\psi' = A\psi, \qquad \chi' = A\chi. \tag{303 b}$$

We shall determine the transformation matrix A for the simple case of a rotation in the (x, y)-plane through a given angle ϕ (in the direction from x to y). This gives

$$x' = x\cos\phi + y\sin\phi, \qquad y' = -x\sin\phi + y\cos\phi, \qquad z' = z,$$

and consequently

$$\sigma'_{x'} = \sigma_x \cos\phi + \sigma_y \sin\phi, \quad \sigma'_{y'} = -\sigma_x \sin\phi + \sigma_y \cos\phi, \quad \sigma'_{z'} = \sigma_z, \quad (304)$$

that is,

$$\sigma'_{x'} = \begin{Bmatrix} 0 & e^{i\phi} \\ e^{-i\phi} & 0 \end{Bmatrix}, \quad \sigma'_{y'} = \begin{Bmatrix} 0 & ie^{i\phi} \\ -ie^{-i\phi} & 0 \end{Bmatrix}, \quad \sigma'_{z'} = \begin{Bmatrix} -1 & 0 \\ 0 & 1 \end{Bmatrix}.$$

Now we must have, irrespective of the index n,

$$\sigma_n A = A\sigma'_n,$$

and in particular for $n = 3$, $\sigma_z A = A\sigma_z$, that is, since σ_z is a diagonal matrix,

$$(\sigma_{z\alpha\alpha} - \sigma_{z\beta\beta})A_{\alpha\beta} = 0,$$

whence it follows that A must also be a diagonal matrix. Putting $A = \begin{Bmatrix} A_1 & 0 \\ 0 & A_2 \end{Bmatrix}$, we get further

$$\sigma_x A = \begin{Bmatrix} 0 & A_2 \\ A_1 & 0 \end{Bmatrix} = \begin{Bmatrix} 0 & A_1 e^{i\phi} \\ A_2 e^{-i\phi} & 0 \end{Bmatrix} = A\sigma'_{x'},$$

that is, $\qquad A_2 = A_1 e^{i\phi}, \qquad A_1 = A_2 e^{-i\phi},$

or consequently $A_1 = ce^{-\frac{1}{2}i\phi}$, $A_2 = ce^{+\frac{1}{2}i\phi}$. The same result is obtained from the equation $\sigma_y A = A\sigma'_{y'}$. The constant c is determined by the condition that the determinant of A (a unitary matrix) is equal to 1. We thus get $c = 1$ and finally

$$A = \begin{Bmatrix} e^{-\frac{1}{2}i\phi} & 0 \\ 0 & e^{+\frac{1}{2}i\phi} \end{Bmatrix} = \cos\tfrac{1}{2}\phi + i\sigma_z \sin\tfrac{1}{2}\phi, \qquad (304\,a)$$

(the first term being understood to be multiplied by the unit matrix δ) which corresponds to the following transformed expressions for the functions ψ, χ:

$$\psi'_1 = \psi_1 e^{-\frac{1}{2}i\phi}, \ \psi'_2 = \psi_2 e^{+\frac{1}{2}i\phi}; \ \chi'_1 = \chi_1 e^{-\frac{1}{2}i\phi}, \ \chi'_2 = \chi_2 e^{+\frac{1}{2}i\phi}. \quad (304\,b)$$

For a rotation in the plane x, z through the angle θ (in the direction from z to x), i.e. for the transformation

$$\sigma'_{x'} = \sigma_x \cos\theta - \sigma_z \sin\theta, \ \sigma'_{y'} = \sigma_y, \ \sigma'_{z'} = \sigma_x \sin\theta + \sigma_z \cos\theta, \quad (305)$$

or $\quad \sigma'_{x'} = \begin{Bmatrix} \sin\theta & \cos\theta \\ \cos\theta & -\sin\theta \end{Bmatrix}, \quad \sigma'_{y'} = \begin{Bmatrix} 0 & i \\ -i & 0 \end{Bmatrix}, \quad \sigma'_{z'} = \begin{Bmatrix} -\cos\theta & \sin\theta \\ \sin\theta & \cos\theta \end{Bmatrix},$

we get in a similar way

$$A_{11} = A_{22}, \qquad A_{12} = -A_{21}$$

(from the equation $\sigma_y A = A\sigma_y$), and further, from $\sigma_x A = A\sigma'_x$ or $\sigma_z A = A\sigma'_z$, together with the condition $|A| = 1$:

$$A = \begin{Bmatrix} \cos\tfrac{1}{2}\theta & -\sin\tfrac{1}{2}\theta \\ \sin\tfrac{1}{2}\theta & \cos\tfrac{1}{2}\theta \end{Bmatrix} = \cos\tfrac{1}{2}\theta + i\sigma_y \sin\tfrac{1}{2}\theta, \qquad (305\,a)$$

whence

$$\psi_1' = \psi_1 \cos \tfrac{1}{2}\theta - \psi_2 \sin \tfrac{1}{2}\theta, \qquad \psi_2' = \psi_1 \sin \tfrac{1}{2}\theta + \psi_2 \cos \tfrac{1}{2}\theta,$$
$$\chi_1' = \chi_1 \cos \tfrac{1}{2}\theta - \chi_2 \sin \tfrac{1}{2}\theta, \qquad \chi_2' = \chi_1 \sin \tfrac{1}{2}\theta + \chi_2 \cos \tfrac{1}{2}\theta.$$

It should be mentioned that the transformation matrices (304 a) and (305 a) can be written in the form $e^{i\frac{1}{2}\phi\sigma_z}$ and $e^{i\frac{1}{2}\theta\sigma_y}$ respectively. We have in fact, by the definition of the exponential function

$$e^{i\mu\sigma_n} = \left(1 - \frac{\mu^2}{2!} + \frac{\mu^4}{4!} - \ldots\right) + i\sigma_n\left(\mu - \frac{\mu^3}{3!} + \ldots\right)$$
$$= \cos\mu + i\sigma_n \sin\mu,$$

since $\sigma_n^2 = \sigma_n^4 = \ldots = \delta(\,= 1), \qquad \sigma_n^3 = \sigma_n^5 = \ldots = \sigma_n.$

With $\mu = \tfrac{1}{2}\phi$ and $\sigma_n = \sigma_z$ this gives (304 a); with $\mu = \tfrac{1}{2}\theta$ and $\sigma_n = \sigma_y$, it gives (305 a).

Two successive rotations are obviously equivalent to a single one, specified by a matrix (a'' or A'') which is equal to the product of the matrices (a, a' or A, A') specifying the two component rotations. Thus, for example, by combining the two preceding rotations in the order stated, we get a rotation with the transformation matrix (in the state-space):

$$A'' = \begin{pmatrix} \cos\tfrac{1}{2}\theta & -\sin\tfrac{1}{2}\theta \\ \sin\tfrac{1}{2}\theta & \cos\tfrac{1}{2}\theta \end{pmatrix} \begin{pmatrix} e^{-i\frac{1}{2}\phi} & 0 \\ 0 & e^{i\frac{1}{2}\phi} \end{pmatrix} = \begin{pmatrix} \cos\tfrac{1}{2}\theta\, e^{-i\frac{1}{2}\phi} & -\sin\tfrac{1}{2}\theta\, e^{i\frac{1}{2}\phi} \\ \sin\tfrac{1}{2}\theta\, e^{-i\frac{1}{2}\phi} & \cos\tfrac{1}{2}\theta\, e^{i\frac{1}{2}\phi} \end{pmatrix},$$

which can be written symbolically in the form

$$A'' = e^{i\frac{1}{2}\phi\sigma_z} e^{i\frac{1}{2}\theta\sigma_y} = e^{i\frac{1}{2}(\phi\sigma_z + \theta\sigma_y)}$$

with the understanding that the order of the two factors should not be inverted.

This means that to a coordinate transformation defined by the equations

$$x'' = (x\cos\phi + y\sin\phi)\cos\theta - z\sin\theta$$
$$y'' = -x\sin\phi + y\cos\phi$$
$$z'' = x\sin\theta + z\cos\theta$$

there corresponds the following transformation of the functions ψ:

$$\psi_1'' = \psi_1 \cos\tfrac{1}{2}\theta\, e^{-i\frac{1}{2}\phi} - \psi_2 \sin\tfrac{1}{2}\theta\, e^{i\frac{1}{2}\phi}, \qquad \psi_2'' = \psi_1 \sin\tfrac{1}{2}\theta\, e^{-i\frac{1}{2}\phi} + \psi_2 \cos\tfrac{1}{2}\theta\, e^{i\frac{1}{2}\phi},$$

and a similar transformation of χ_1, χ_2.

The preceding results are easily generalized for any number of successive rotations about arbitrarily chosen axes. These rotations are always equivalent to a single rotation over an angle ω about an axis specified by a unit vector $\mathbf{n}$. The transformation matrix A corresponding to such a rotation is easily seen to be

$$A = \cos\tfrac{1}{2}\omega + i\sigma_n \sin\tfrac{1}{2}\omega = e^{i\frac{1}{2}\omega\sigma_n}, \tag{306}$$

where $\sigma_n = \boldsymbol{\sigma}\cdot\mathbf{n} = n_x\sigma_x + n_y\sigma_y + n_z\sigma_z$ is the component of $\boldsymbol{\sigma}$ along the axis of rotation. The reciprocal matrix

$$A^{-1} = \cos\tfrac{1}{2}\omega - i\sigma_n \sin\tfrac{1}{2}\omega$$

corresponds to a rotation about the same axis in the opposite direction (or to a rotation about the oppositely directed axis $-\mathbf{n}$ through the same angle); it obviously coincides with $A^\dagger$ since $\boldsymbol{\sigma}^\dagger = \boldsymbol{\sigma}$. Hence it follows that A is a *unitary* matrix, as was assumed at the beginning.

A two-dimensional unitary matrix can be represented with the help of two complex numbers α, β satisfying the condition $\alpha\alpha^* + \beta\beta^* = 1$ in the form

$$A = \begin{Bmatrix} \alpha, & \beta \\ -\beta^*, & \alpha^* \end{Bmatrix}.$$

In the present case these numbers are

$$\alpha = \cos\tfrac{1}{2}\omega + in_z\sin\tfrac{1}{2}\omega, \qquad \beta = i(n_x + in_y)\sin\tfrac{1}{2}\omega.$$

It should be mentioned that the number of real independent parameters which determine the rotation is equal to *three* (the rotation angle ω and the two angles θ, ϕ which determine the direction of the axis of rotation n, or three of the four real numbers which define α and β under the condition $\alpha\alpha^* + \beta\beta^* = 1$).

As has been shown in § 30, the probability density and the rectangular components of the probability current density are expressed, with the help of the two-dimensional matrices ψ, χ, σ, by the equations

$$\rho = \psi^\dagger\psi + \chi^\dagger\chi, \qquad j_n = c(\psi^\dagger\sigma_n\chi + \chi^\dagger\sigma_n\psi),$$

[$n = 1, 2, 3$; cf. eqs. (259) and (259 a)]. Transforming the functions ψ and χ according to the equations $\psi' = A\psi$, $\psi'^\dagger = \psi^\dagger A^\dagger$, and regarding the matrices σ_n as invariant, we obtain for the same quantities referring to the rotated system the expressions

$$\rho' = \psi^\dagger A^\dagger A\psi + \chi^\dagger A^\dagger A\chi = \psi^\dagger\psi + \chi^\dagger\chi = \rho$$

(since $A^\dagger = A^{-1}$), and

$$\begin{aligned} j_n' &= c[\psi^\dagger(A^\dagger\sigma_n A)\chi + \chi^\dagger(A^\dagger\sigma_n A)\psi] = c(\psi^\dagger\sigma_n'\chi + \chi^\dagger\sigma_n'\psi), \\ &= \sum_m a_{mn}j_m, \end{aligned}$$

in agreement with the invariant character of ρ and the covariant character of the components of the vector $\mathbf{j}$.

The preceding results are easily extended to the four-dimensional matrix form of the Dirac equation and of the associated operators. Taking, for example, the energy operator

$$\epsilon = U + \epsilon_0\gamma_0 + c\sum_{n=1}^{3}\gamma_n u_n,$$

we can consider it as an invariant with regard to rotations in ordinary space if the three four-dimensional matrices $\gamma_1 = \gamma_x$, $\gamma_2 = \gamma_y$, $\gamma_3 = \gamma_z$. are defined as covariant operators, satisfying the same transformation equations as the coordinates $x_1 = x$, $x_2 = y$, $x_3 = z$ or the components of the operator $\mathbf{u}$. The shape of the transformed matrices γ_n is easily obtained from the above expressions for the transformed matrices σ'_n with the help of the invariant relations $\gamma_n = \begin{pmatrix} 0 & \sigma_n \\ \sigma_n & 0 \end{pmatrix}$.

The same relations can serve for the determination of the unitary matrices, L say, which determine the equivalent transformation in the four-dimensional spin-space according to the 'tensor' law

$$\gamma'_n = L^{-1}\gamma_n L = L^{\dagger}\gamma_n L \qquad (n = 1, 2, 3).$$

We have, namely, $\qquad L = \begin{pmatrix} A & 0 \\ 0 & A \end{pmatrix},$ \hfill (306 a)

where $A = \begin{pmatrix} A_{11} & A_{12} \\ A_{21} & A_{22} \end{pmatrix}$ is the two-dimensional unitary matrix defining the transformation of σ_n $\left(0 = \begin{pmatrix} 0 & 0 \\ 0 & 0 \end{pmatrix} \right)$.

With the help of the matrix $\boldsymbol{\xi} = \begin{pmatrix} \sigma & 0 \\ 0 & \sigma \end{pmatrix}$ which serves to describe the electron's spin or magnetic moment [cf. (277)] we can write the matrix L corresponding to a given rotation $(\omega, \mathbf{n})$ explicitly in the form

$$L = e^{i\frac{1}{2}\omega\xi_n} = \cos\tfrac{1}{2}\omega + i\xi_n \sin\tfrac{1}{2}\omega, \qquad (306\,\text{b})$$

similar to (306) with σ replaced by $\boldsymbol{\xi}$.

The matrix γ_0 remains invariant under this transformation. Writing Dirac's equation in the form $(\epsilon + p_t)\psi = 0$ and using equation (306) for the γ'_n, we can write it for the rotated coordinate system in the form

$$\left[(p_t + U + \epsilon_0\gamma_0) + c \sum_{n=1}^{3} L^{-1}\gamma_n L u'_n \right]\psi = 0,$$

or since $(p_t + U + \epsilon_0\gamma_0) = L^{-1}(p_t + U + \epsilon_0\gamma_0)L$,

$$L^{-1}\left[p_t + U + \epsilon_0\gamma_0 + c \sum_{1}^{3} \gamma_n u'_n \right] L\psi = 0.$$

If this equation is multiplied on the left by L, it reduces to the original form, with the old matrices γ_n, the new components of $\mathbf{u}$, and a new wave function ψ' derived from the old one by means of the transformation $\qquad\qquad \psi' = L\psi.$

Putting $\psi = \begin{pmatrix} \phi \\ \chi \end{pmatrix}$, where $\phi = \begin{pmatrix} \phi_1 \\ \phi_2 \end{pmatrix}$ and $\chi = \begin{pmatrix} \chi_1 \\ \chi_2 \end{pmatrix}$, we get, with the help of (306),

$$\begin{Bmatrix} \phi' \\ \chi' \end{Bmatrix} = \begin{Bmatrix} A\phi \\ A\chi \end{Bmatrix},$$

in agreement with the results obtained before.

It can further be shown directly that under the transformation $\psi' = L\psi$ and $\psi'^\dagger = \psi^\dagger L^\dagger$ the product $\psi^\dagger \psi$ remains invariant while the quantities $c\psi^\dagger \gamma_n \psi$ transform as the rectangular components of a vector.

We can now turn to the generalization of the preceding results for rotations in the four-dimensional space-time manifold of the relativity theory, i.e. for Lorentz transformations, corresponding to a transition from a state of 'rest' to that of uniform motion.

It will be convenient in this connexion to use Dirac's equation in the form $B\psi = 0$, i.e.

$$(\beta_x u_x + \beta_y u_y + \beta_z u_z + \beta_t u_t + m_0 c)\psi = 0,$$

or

$$\left(\sum_{n=1}^{4} \beta_n u_n + m_0 c \right)\psi = 0, \tag{307}$$

where $n = 1, 2, 3$ stands for x, y, z respectively, while

$$x_4 = \sqrt{-1}\,ct, \qquad u_4 = -\sqrt{-1}\,u_t, \qquad \beta_4 = \sqrt{-1}\,\beta_t.$$

It must be emphasized that the imaginary unit $\sqrt{-1}$ is introduced here simply for the sake of formal symmetry, and that it will be treated in the sequel as an ordinary 'real' number, in the sense that its sign will not be altered in a transition to conjugate complex quantities. In order to distinguish this relativistic $\sqrt{-1}$ from that of the quantum theory, which plays an essential role, we shall denote the relativistic $\sqrt{-1}$ by the Greek letter ι ($\iota^* = \iota$, $i^* = -i$).

A Lorentz transformation is defined as a linear transformation of the form

$$x_n' = \sum_{m=1}^{4} a_{mn} x_m,$$

satisfying the orthogonality condition $\sum_{n=1}^{4} x_n'^2 = \sum_{m=1}^{4} x_m^2$ and the condition that the first three components of x' should be real and the fourth imaginary (reality condition). The components of the four-dimensional operator u are transformed in the same way as the corresponding coordinates, and if we wish to ensure the invariance of equation (307), we must either submit the matrices β_n to the same Lorentz transformation

$$\beta_n' = \sum_{m=1}^{4} a_{mn} \beta_m \qquad \left(\beta_{n;\mu\nu}' = \sum_{m=1}^{4} a_{mn} \beta_{m;\mu\nu} \right), \tag{307 a}$$

or introduce the equivalent tensor transformation in the four-dimensional state-space

$$\beta'_n = K^\dagger \beta_n K \qquad (\beta'_{n;\mu\nu} = \sum \sum K^*_{\kappa\mu} K_{\lambda\nu} \beta_{n;\kappa\lambda}). \qquad (307\,\mathrm{b})$$

With the help of the latter the transformed Dirac equation can be put in the form

$$K^\dagger \Big(\sum_{n=1}^4 \beta_n u'_n + m_0 c \Big) K \psi = 0,$$

that is,

$$\Big(\sum_{n=1}^4 \beta_n u'_n + m_0 c \Big) \psi' = 0,$$

with the same numerical matrices β_n as the original ones and with the transformed wave function

$$\psi' = K\psi. \qquad (307\,\mathrm{c})$$

The possibility of replacing (307 a) by (307 b) is proved by the fact that the transformation matrices a_{mn} (in the ordinary space-time) and $K_{\mu\nu}$ (in the four-dimensional state-space) have the same rank. They contain therefore the same number of elements.

The determination of K through a can be carried out in the same way as in the case of rotations in ordinary space, by combining rotations in different planes.

In the case of rotations in ordinary space the matrix K must obviously coincide with the matrix L considered before. This follows from the relations $\beta_n = \gamma_0 \gamma_n$ for $n = 1, 2, 3$ ($\beta_4 = \iota\gamma_0$) in conjunction with the fact that γ_0 is not affected by a spatial rotation. Now for a rotation through an angle ω in the plane (x_1, x_2) we have, as has been shown above, $L = e^{i\frac{1}{2}\omega\xi_3}$ or, since $\xi_3 = i\beta_1\beta_2$ [according to (276), § 31], $L = e^{-\frac{1}{2}\omega\beta_1\beta_2}$. Identifying this with the matrix K for the case under consideration and taking into account the relativistic symmetry of Dirac's equation in the form (307) with respect to the space coordinates and the time (ιct), we can define the matrix K corresponding to a transition from a state of rest to that of a motion in the direction of the first axis with a velocity v by the expression

$$K = e^{-\frac{1}{2}\vartheta\beta_1\beta_4}$$

corresponding to a rotation in the plane (x_1, x_4) through the imaginary angle $\vartheta = \tan^{-1} v/\iota c$. Replacing here β_1 by $\gamma_0\gamma_1$, β_4 by $\iota\gamma_0$, and putting $\vartheta = \iota\theta$, where

$$\tanh\theta = \frac{v}{c} \qquad \Big(\cosh\theta = \frac{1}{\sqrt{(1-v^2/c^2)}}, \ \sinh\theta = \frac{v/c}{\sqrt{(1-v^2/c^2)}} \Big)$$

we get, since $\gamma_0\gamma_1\gamma_0 = -\gamma_0^2\gamma_1 = -\gamma_1$,

$$K = e^{-\frac{1}{2}\theta\gamma_1}.$$

This result is easily generalized for the case of motion in any direction specified by the unit vector $\mathbf{n}'$. Denoting the corresponding component of $\boldsymbol{\gamma}$ (i.e. the scalar product $\boldsymbol{\gamma}\cdot\mathbf{n}'$) by $\gamma_{n'}$ we get

$$K = e^{-\frac{1}{2}\theta\gamma_{n'}} = \cosh \tfrac{1}{2}\theta - \gamma_{n'} \sinh \tfrac{1}{2}\theta. \tag{308}$$

In order to find the corresponding expression for the matrix L we must come back to that form of Dirac's equation which has been used hitherto, viz. $\left(\sum_{1}^{4} \gamma_n u_n + \gamma_0 m_0 c\right)\psi = 0$ with $\gamma_4 = \iota\delta$ and $u_4 = -\iota u_t$, where the factor ι is introduced in order to secure a more complete symmetry between the terms involving the space coordinates and the time. The Lorentz transformation of the components of the operator u, defined by the equations $u'_n = \sum_{m=1}^{4} a_{mn} u_m$, must be combined with an appropriate transformation of the wave function, $\psi' = L\psi$, so that the transformed equation shall reduce to the form $\left(\sum_{1}^{4} \gamma_n u'_n + \gamma_0 m_0 c\right)\psi' = 0$ with the same matrices γ_n (including γ_0) as the original one. Replacing ψ and ψ' by $\gamma_0\psi = \bar{\psi}$ and $\gamma_0\psi' = \bar{\psi}'$ respectively, we come back to the equations

$$(\textstyle\sum \beta_n u_n + m_0 c)\bar{\psi} = 0 \quad \text{and} \quad (\textstyle\sum \beta_n u'_n + m_0 c)\bar{\psi}' = 0;$$

whence it follows that $L = \gamma_0^{-1} K \gamma_0$, where K is the transformation considered before. Since $\gamma_0^2 = 1$, i.e. $\gamma_0 = \gamma_0^{-1}$, we can put $L = \gamma_0 K \gamma_0$.

Substituting here the expression (308) for K, we get

$$L = \gamma_0^2 \cosh \tfrac{1}{2}\theta - \gamma_0 \gamma_{n'} \gamma_0 \sinh \tfrac{1}{2}\theta$$

or, since $\gamma_0^2 = 1$ and $\gamma_0 \gamma_{n'} \gamma_0 = -\gamma_0^2 \gamma_{n'} = -\gamma_{n'}$,

$$L = \cosh \tfrac{1}{2}\theta + \gamma_{n'} \sinh \tfrac{1}{2}\theta = e^{\frac{1}{2}\theta\gamma_{n'}}. \tag{308 a}$$

If $\boldsymbol{\gamma}$ is replaced here by $i\boldsymbol{\eta}$, where $\boldsymbol{\eta}$ is the matrix which serves to define the electron's electric moment in the same way as $\boldsymbol{\xi}$ defines the magnetic one [cf. (276 a)], L assumes a form quite similar to that (306 a) which corresponds to an ordinary spatial rotation. It should be remembered, however, that while $\boldsymbol{\xi}$ represents a real quantity, $\boldsymbol{\eta}$ must be considered as a pure imaginary. This corresponds to an important distinction between the matrices (306 b) and (308 a), the former being unitary ($L^\dagger = L^{-1}$ defining a rotation in the opposite sense) and the latter Hermitian ($L^\dagger = L$).

In the general case of a Lorentz transformation combining an ordinary rotation $(\omega, \mathbf{n})$ with a relative motion $(\theta, \mathbf{n}')$, the matrix L can be represented as the product of the two component transformations taken in a definite order, for instance,

$$L = e^{i\frac{1}{2}\omega\xi_n} e^{\frac{1}{2}\theta\gamma_{n'}}. \tag{308 b}$$

The adjoint matrix is

$$L^\dagger = e^{\frac{1}{2}\theta\gamma_{n'}}e^{-i\frac{1}{2}\omega\xi_n},$$

so that

$$L^\dagger L = \cosh^2\tfrac{1}{2}\theta + \sinh^2\tfrac{1}{2}\theta + 2\gamma_{n'}\sinh\tfrac{1}{2}\theta\cosh\tfrac{1}{2}\theta = \cosh\theta + \gamma_{n'}\sinh\theta.$$

Substituting this expression in the formula $\rho' = \psi^\dagger L^\dagger L\psi$ for the transformed value of the probability density (in the 'moving' coordinate system), we get

$$\rho' = \psi^\dagger\psi\cosh\theta + \psi^\dagger\gamma_{n'}\psi\sinh\theta,$$

that is,

$$\rho' = \rho\cosh\theta + \gamma_{n'}\sinh\theta = \frac{\rho + j_{n'}v/c}{\sqrt{(1-v^2/c^2)}}$$

in agreement with the well-known result following directly from the Lorentz transformation equations.

If the moving axes are parallel to the original ones ($\omega = 0$) we get in a similar way from the general formula $j_n = \psi'^\dagger\gamma_n\psi' = \psi^\dagger L^\dagger\gamma_n L\psi$

$$j'_{n'} = \psi^\dagger[\gamma_{n'}(\cosh^2\tfrac{1}{2}\theta + \sinh^2\tfrac{1}{2}\theta) + 2\cosh\tfrac{1}{2}\theta\sinh\tfrac{1}{2}\theta]\psi,$$

that is,

$$j'_{n'} = j_{n'}\cosh\theta + \rho\sinh\theta = \frac{j_{n'} + \rho v/c}{\sqrt{(1-v^2/c^2)}}.$$

It should be mentioned that instead of introducing the relativistic imaginary $\iota = \sqrt{-1}$ in the definition of the fourth component of four-dimensional vectors one can distinguish two types of real components, namely, the *covariant* and the *contravariant*, the latter differing from the former by the opposite sign of the fourth components. The contravariant components are denoted by the same letters as the covariant ones with the index placed above instead of below. If, for instance, $x_1 = x$, $x_2 = y$, $x_3 = z$, $x_4 = ct$ are the covariant components of the space-time vector, then its contravariant components must be defined by $x^{(1)} = x$, $x^{(2)} = y$, $x^{(3)} = z$, $x^{(4)} = -ct$. The square of a four-dimensional vector, A say, is thus equal to the sum of the products of its covariant components with the corresponding contravariant ones:

$$A^2 = \sum_{n=1}^{4} A_k A^k.$$

In a similar way the scalar product of two vectors is defined by the sum $\sum_{k=1}^{4} A_k B^k$ or $\sum_{k=1}^{4} A^k B_k$. With this notation Dirac's equation can be written in the form

$$\left[\sum_{1}^{4} \gamma^{(k)}u_k + \gamma_0 mc\right]\psi = 0,$$

where $u_4 = u_t = \dfrac{1}{c}\left(\dfrac{h}{2\pi i}\dfrac{\partial}{\partial t} + e\phi\right)$ and $\gamma^{(4)} = \delta\ (=1)$. The covariant components of the four-dimensional velocity vector γ must be defined accordingly as

$$\gamma_1 = \gamma_x, \qquad \gamma_2 = \gamma_y, \qquad \gamma_3 = \gamma_z, \qquad \gamma_4 = -\delta \quad (=-1),$$

and the covariant components of the operator u as

$$u^{(1)} = u_x, \qquad u^{(2)} = u_y, \qquad u^{(3)} = u_z, \qquad u^{(4)} = -u_t.$$

The transformation matrix L obtained above thus refers to the contravariant components of γ. It is easily seen, however, that it can be applied just as well to the covariant ones.

Quantities of the type of Dirac's wave function quadruplet ψ_1, ψ_2, ψ_3, ψ_4 can be regarded as forming in the space-time manifold a kind of tensor of rank $\frac{1}{2}$. This means that they are related to an ordinary vector (i.e. tensor of the first rank) in the same way as the latter is related to an ordinary tensor (of the second rank). This connexion is plainly seen from the fact that an ordinary vector—like the probability current density $(\mathbf{j}, \rho)$—can be expressed with the help of the ψ's as a quadratic quantity—just as a tensor (of the second rank) can be expressed as a quadratic quantity by means of the components of a vector or of two different vectors.

It has recently been shown by various authors[‡] that each of the two pairs of functions $\psi_1, \psi_2\ (=\phi_1, \phi_2)$ and $\psi_3, \psi_4\ (=\chi_1, \chi_2)$ rather than the whole quadruplet determines a 'tensor of the rank $\frac{1}{2}$'. Any pair of such quantities, whose transformation properties in the state-space of the spin coordinate (with its two values 1 and 2) are connected with the transformation properties of vectors in the ordinary space-time manifold by the above equations, are called, following Ehrenfest, a *spinor*. The two components of a spinor, ϕ_1 and ϕ_2 say, are complex numbers; they determine therefore *four* real numbers which can serve to specify the components of an ordinary four-dimensional vector. A vector can be defined as a particular type of spinor of the second rank, i.e. as a quantity whose components (in the *spin* space!) transform like the products of the components of two ordinary spinors, or in particular of a single spinor ϕ and its adjoint quantity $\phi^\dagger$.

It can easily be shown, for example, that the expressions

$$f_k = \phi^\dagger \sigma_k \phi \qquad (k = 1, 2, 3, 4),$$

where

$$\sigma_1 = \sigma_x, \qquad \sigma_2 = \sigma_y, \qquad \sigma_3 = \sigma_z, \qquad \sigma_4 = \delta \quad (=1),$$

‡ Cf. O. Laporte and G. Uhlenbeck, *Phys. Rev.* **37** (1931), 1380.

that is, $f_1 = \phi_1^*\phi_2 + \phi_2^*\phi_1$, $f_2 = i(\phi_1^*\phi_2 - \phi_2^*\phi_1)$, $f_3 = -\phi_1^*\phi_1 + \phi_2^*\phi_2$, and $f_4 = \phi_1^*\phi_1 + \phi_2^*\phi_2$ transform like the quantities x, y, z, ct in any ordinary rotation or in a Lorentz transformation, if ϕ is transformed according to $\phi' = A\phi$ and $\phi^\dagger$ according to $\phi'^\dagger = A^\dagger\phi^\dagger$, A being a two-dimensional matrix, which reduces to the form $e^{i\frac{1}{2}\omega\sigma_n} = \cos\frac{1}{2}\omega + \sigma_n\sin\frac{1}{2}\omega$ already considered in the case of an ordinary rotation (through the angle ω about an axis $\mathbf{n}$). In the case of a relative motion in a direction n' with a velocity v specified by the angle $\theta = \tanh^{-1}(v/c)$ we have, so long as the new axes are parallel to the old ones,

$$A = e^{\frac{1}{2}\theta\sigma_{n'}} = \cosh\tfrac{1}{2}\theta + \sigma_{n'}\sinh\tfrac{1}{2}\theta \qquad (\sigma_{n'} = n_x'\sigma_x + n_y'\sigma_y + n_z'\sigma_z).$$

This gives in particular, for a motion in the z-direction,

$$A = \begin{pmatrix} e^{-\frac{1}{2}\theta} & 0 \\ 0 & e^{\frac{1}{2}\theta} \end{pmatrix}.$$

In the most general case A can be represented by the product of $e^{i\frac{1}{2}\omega\sigma_n}$ with $e^{\frac{1}{2}\theta\sigma_{n'}}$, that is,

$$A = \cos\tfrac{1}{2}\omega\cosh\tfrac{1}{2}\theta + \sigma_n\sin\tfrac{1}{2}\omega\cosh\tfrac{1}{2}\theta + \sigma_{n'}\sinh\tfrac{1}{2}\theta\cos\tfrac{1}{2}\omega +$$
$$+ \sigma_n\sigma_{n'}\sin\tfrac{1}{2}\omega\sinh\tfrac{1}{2}\theta,$$

or, since $\qquad \sigma_n\sigma_{n'} = (\boldsymbol{\sigma}\cdot\mathbf{n})(\boldsymbol{\sigma}\cdot\mathbf{n}') = \mathbf{n}\cdot\mathbf{n}' + i\boldsymbol{\sigma}\cdot(\mathbf{n}\times\mathbf{n}'),$

$$A = \cos\tfrac{1}{2}\omega\cosh\tfrac{1}{2}\theta + \mathbf{n}\cdot\mathbf{n}' + \sigma_n\sin\tfrac{1}{2}\omega\cosh\tfrac{1}{2}\theta + \sigma_{n'}\sinh\tfrac{1}{2}\theta\cos\tfrac{1}{2}\omega +$$
$$+ i\boldsymbol{\sigma}\cdot(\mathbf{n}\times\mathbf{n}')\sin\tfrac{1}{2}\omega\sinh\tfrac{1}{2}\theta.$$

The elements of this matrix are easily verified to satisfy the relation

$$|A| = A_{11}A_{22} - A_{12}A_{21} = 1.$$

Using the notation

$$\phi_1^* = \phi_{\dot{1}}, \qquad \phi_2^* = \phi_{\dot{2}},$$

i.e. replacing the conjugate complex sign by dotted indices, one can write the covariant components of a spinor of the second rank in three different forms, namely,

$$\phi_{kl}, \qquad \phi_{\dot{k}l}, \qquad \phi_{\dot{k}\dot{l}} \qquad (k, l = 1, 2),$$

these components transforming as the products $\phi_k\phi_l$, $\phi_{\dot{k}}\phi_l$, and $\phi_{\dot{k}}\phi_{\dot{l}}$ respectively.

Besides covariant components of spinors we must also distinguish contravariant ones. For a spinor of the first rank these are defined by the relations

$$\phi^{(1)} = \phi_2, \qquad \phi^{(2)} = -\phi_1,$$
$$\phi^{(\dot{1})} = \phi_{\dot{2}}, \qquad \phi^{(\dot{2})} = -\phi_{\dot{1}},$$

because this ensures the invariance of the 'scalar products' $\phi_1\chi^{(1)} + \phi_2\chi^{(2)}$ and $\phi_{\dot{1}}\chi^{(\dot{1})} + \phi_{\dot{2}}\chi^{(\dot{2})}$.

The contravariant or mixed components of spinors of higher rank are connected with the covariant ones in a similar way. We have, for example,

$$\phi^{11} = \phi_{22}, \; \phi^{12} = -\phi_{21}, \; \phi^{21} = -\phi_{12}, \; \phi^{22} = \phi_{11}, \text{ etc.}$$

The components of a (four-dimensional) vector f can be represented with the help of a spinor of the second rank by the formulae

$$f^1 = f_1 = \tfrac{1}{2}(\phi_{\dot{2}1} + \phi_{1\dot{2}}), \qquad f^2 = f_2 = \frac{1}{2i}(\phi_{\dot{2}1} - \phi_{1\dot{2}}),$$

$$f^3 = f_3 = \frac{1}{2i}(-\phi_{1\dot{1}} + \phi_{\dot{2}\dot{2}}), \qquad f^4 = -f_4 = \tfrac{1}{2}(\phi_{1\dot{1}} + \phi_{\dot{2}\dot{2}}).$$

We shall not engage in a more detailed discussion of this question and shall point out in conclusion the following important circumstance. In our derivation of Dirac's equations as a generalization of the equations of Maxwell's theory we originally introduced, instead of the quadruplet $\psi_1, \psi_2, \psi_3, \psi_4$, eight quantities M_1, M_2, M_3, M_0; N_1, N_2, N_3, N_0, visualizing the six quantities $M_1, M_2, M_3, -N_1, -N_2, -N_3$ as analogous to the electromagnetic field components $H_x, H_y, H_z, E_x, E_y, E_z$, while M_0 and N_0 were regarded as two additional scalar quantities. This point of view had to be abandoned in the sequel because of the rearrangement of the Maxwell-like equations, corresponding to the introduction of the additional terms containing the rest-mass of the electron m_0. If, however, instead of the first-order equations we consider the second-order equations only (which are a generalization of the d'Alembert equations of the electromagnetic theory), we can preserve the above point of view and treat the quantities $M_1, M_2, M_3, iN_1, iN_2, iN_3$ as the components of a four-dimensional antisymmetric tensor of the second rank $M_{kl} = -M_{lk}$ ($k, l = 1, 2, 3, 4$) transforming under a Lorentz transformation in the same way as the components of the electromagnetic field-tensor $F_{nl} = -F_{ln}$ ($F_{23} = H_1$, $F_{31} = H_2$, $F_{12} = H_3$, $F_{14} = -iE_1$, $F_{24} = -iE_2$, $F_{34} = -iE_3$). It has been shown further that in this case we can put $N = \pm iM$ which corresponds to the 'self-duality' of the tensor M_{kl} and introduce accordingly the relation $N_0 = \pm iM_0$ between the scalars (invariants) M_0 and N_0, thus reducing the eight quantities M, N to four, just as in the case of Dirac's equation.

The fallacy of this procedure is shown by the fact that *it does not permit us to define a four-dimensional vector representing the probability current* $\mathbf{j}$ *and density* ρ. The latter would appear in such a theory not as the fourth (time) component of a vector but as the (4, 4)-component of a tensor of the second rank, corresponding to the tensor of the electro-magnetic energy and momentum; the components of the vector **j** would appear likewise as the $(1, 4)$, $(2, 4)$, and $(3, 4)$ components of this tensor, corresponding to the components of the energy-stream. So long as we confine ourselves to ordinary rotations in three-dimensional space this circumstance remains irrelevant; it becomes, however, a challenge to the theory when we pass to the more general Lorentz transformation, involving the transformation of the time. In order to make $\mathbf{j}, \rho$ a regular four-dimensional vector we must consider the quantities M, N as defining a *spinor* ψ—or more exactly two spinors ϕ, χ—whose transformation properties have been studied in this section.

The above argument serves to show in a most convincing way the restricted character of the analogy between matter and light as repre-sented by the probability and the electromagnetic waves respectively. A 'wave-mechanical' theory of light similar to that of matter would necessitate the introduction of a new type of probability field, con-nected with the photons in the same way as with ordinary particles and entirely different from the electromagnetic field which has been used hitherto to describe the phenomena of light from the point of view of the wave theory. It does not seem, however, that the introduction of such a probability field with spinor properties is warranted by the experimental facts.

36. Transformation of the Dirac Equation to Curvilinear Co-ordinates

We have considered hitherto cartesian coordinates only. We shall now generalize the results obtained for a transformation from the cartesian system x, y, z to any system of *orthogonal curvilinear* coordinates q_1, q_2, q_3. Such a system can be specified by the following expression for the square of the line-element (i.e. the distance between two neighbouring points):

$$ds^2 = e_1^2\, dq_1^2 + e_2^2\, dq_2^2 + e_3^2\, dq_3^2,$$

where $\mathbf{e}_1$, $\mathbf{e}_2$, $\mathbf{e}_3$ are mutually perpendicular vectors tangential to the coordinate lines which pass through one end of ds. The products $e_i\, dq_i$ play the same role as the differentials dx_i of a local cartesian system passing through P with its axes parallel to the vectors $\mathbf{e}_i$, so that the rectangular components of the operator **p** can be written in the form

$$p_k = \frac{h}{2\pi i} \frac{1}{e_k} \frac{\partial}{\partial q_k}.$$

In transforming the expression $\boldsymbol{\gamma} \cdot \mathbf{p} \psi = \left(\sum_1^3 \gamma_k p_k \right) \psi$ to the new co-ordinates, with the help of the formula $\gamma_k = L^{-1} \gamma_k L$ we must take into account the fact that the matrix L is to be considered as a *function of the coordinates*, varying from point to point with the direction of the local cartesian axes. We thus get

$$\boldsymbol{\gamma} \cdot \mathbf{p} \psi = L^{-1} \left(\sum_1^3 \gamma_k L p_k' \right) \psi$$

$$= L^{-1} \left[\sum \gamma_k p_k' L \psi - \sum \gamma_k (p_k' L - L p_k') \psi \right],$$

or $\qquad \boldsymbol{\gamma} \cdot \mathbf{p} \psi = L^{-1} \sum_{k=1}^3 \gamma_k [p_k' - (p_k' L - L p_k') L^{-1}] L \psi.$

In order to obtain the transformed equations we must accordingly replace the components of the vector $\mathbf{p}$ by the 'covariant' operators

$$P_k' = p_k' - (p_k' L - L p_k') L^{-1}. \tag{309}$$

In the special case of orthogonal coordinates they assume the form

$$P_k' = \frac{h}{2\pi i} \frac{1}{e_k} \left(\frac{\partial}{\partial q_k} - \frac{\partial}{\partial q_k} \log L \right), \tag{309a}$$

where $\qquad \dfrac{\partial}{\partial q_k} \log L = \dfrac{\partial L}{\partial q_k} L^{-1}.$

Now, as has been shown above, the matrix L can be defined by the expression $e^{i \frac{1}{2} \omega \boldsymbol{\xi} \cdot \mathbf{n}}$, where the rotation angle ω and the axis of rotation $\mathbf{n}$ must be considered as certain functions of the coordinates. We thus have

$$\log L = i \tfrac{1}{2} \omega \boldsymbol{\xi} \cdot \mathbf{n} = \tfrac{1}{2} i \boldsymbol{\xi} \cdot \boldsymbol{\omega}, \tag{309b}$$

the vector $\boldsymbol{\omega}$ serving to determine the rotation both with respect to magnitude and direction.

Let us consider the infinitesimal rotation $d\boldsymbol{\omega}$ corresponding to a transition from a point P (with the coordinates q_k) to a neighbouring point P' (with the coordinates $q_k' = q_k + dq_k$).

Introducing three unit vectors $\mathbf{f}_k = \mathbf{e}_k / e_k$ in the direction of the coordinate lines, we can obviously put

$$d\mathbf{f}_k = d\boldsymbol{\omega} \times \mathbf{f}_k,$$

whence

$$\mathbf{f}_i \cdot d\mathbf{f}_k = \mathbf{f}_i \cdot (d\boldsymbol{\omega} \times f_k) = d\boldsymbol{\omega} \cdot (\mathbf{f}_k \times \mathbf{f}_i) = \pm (d\boldsymbol{\omega}) \cdot \mathbf{f}_j = \pm (d\boldsymbol{\omega})_j,$$

where $\mathbf{f}_j$ is the unit vector perpendicular to $\mathbf{f}_k$ and $\mathbf{f}_i$, the positive sign corresponding to an even character of the permutation $\begin{pmatrix} k\ i\ j \\ 1\ 2\ 3 \end{pmatrix}$ and the negative sign to an odd one.

We have on the other hand

$$\mathbf{f}_i \cdot d\mathbf{f}_k = (\mathbf{e}_i/e_i) \cdot d(\mathbf{e}_k/e_k) = \mathbf{e}_i \cdot d\mathbf{e}_k/(e_i\, e_k),$$

since the vectors $\mathbf{e}_i$ and $\mathbf{e}_k$ are mutually orthogonal $(i \neq k)$, whence, putting for the sake of brevity $\dfrac{\partial}{\partial q_h} = \partial_h$,

$$\pm(\partial_h \boldsymbol{\omega})_j = \mathbf{e}_i \cdot \partial_h \mathbf{e}_k/(e_i\, e_k). \tag{310}$$

It follows from the formula

$$d\mathbf{r} = \mathbf{e}_1\, dq_1 + \mathbf{e}_2\, dq_2 + \mathbf{e}_3\, dq_3,$$

which can serve for the definition of the vectors $\mathbf{e}_i$, that the latter are equal to the differential coefficients of the radius vector $\mathbf{r}$ of the point (q_1, q_2, q_3) with respect to the corresponding coordinates. We thus have

$$\partial_h \mathbf{e}_k = \partial_k \mathbf{e}_h \quad \left(= \frac{\partial^2 \mathbf{r}}{\partial q_k\, \partial q_h} \right).$$

and consequently

$$\mathbf{e}_i \cdot \partial_i \mathbf{e}_k = \mathbf{e}_i \cdot \partial_k \mathbf{e}_i = \tfrac{1}{2}\partial_k(\mathbf{e}_i \cdot \mathbf{e}_i) = \tfrac{1}{2}\partial_k e_i^2 = e_i \partial_k e_i.$$

Further, since $\mathbf{e}_i \cdot \mathbf{e}_k = 0 \; (k \neq i)$,

$$\mathbf{e}_k \cdot \partial_i \mathbf{e}_i = -\mathbf{e}_i \cdot \partial_i \mathbf{e}_k = -e_i \partial_k e_i,$$

and if h is different from both k and i,

$$\mathbf{e}_k \cdot \partial_h \mathbf{e}_i = \mathbf{e}_i \cdot \partial_h \mathbf{e}_k = 0.$$

The latter equation is easily obtained in conjunction with the fact that $\partial_h(\mathbf{e}_k \mathbf{e}_i) = 0$.

Substituting these expressions in (310) we find

$$
\left.
\begin{aligned}
&(\partial_1 \boldsymbol{\omega})_1 = 0, & &(\partial_1 \boldsymbol{\omega})_2 = \frac{1}{e_3}\, \partial_3 e_1, & &(\partial_1 \boldsymbol{\omega})_3 = -\frac{1}{e_2}\, \partial_2 e_1 \\[2mm]
&(\partial_2 \boldsymbol{\omega})_1 = -\frac{1}{e_3}\, \partial_3 e_2, & &(\partial_2 \boldsymbol{\omega})_2 = 0, & &(\partial_2 \boldsymbol{\omega})_3 = \frac{1}{e_1}\, \partial_1 e_2 \\[2mm]
&(\partial_3 \boldsymbol{\omega})_1 = \frac{1}{e_2}\, \partial_2 e_3, & &(\partial_3 \boldsymbol{\omega})_2 = -\frac{1}{e_1}\, \partial_1 e_3, & &(\partial_3 \boldsymbol{\omega})_3 = 0.
\end{aligned}
\right\} \tag{310a}
$$

Now according to (309a) and (309b)

$$\sum_1^3 \gamma_k P_k' = \sum_{k=1}^{3} \frac{h}{2\pi i}\left(\frac{1}{e_k}\gamma_k \frac{\partial}{\partial q_k}\right) - \frac{h}{4\pi}\sum_{k=1}^{3} \frac{1}{e_k}\gamma_k\left(\boldsymbol{\xi} \cdot \frac{\partial}{\partial q_k}\boldsymbol{\omega}\right),$$

that is,

$$\boldsymbol{\gamma} \cdot \mathbf{P}' = \boldsymbol{\gamma} \cdot \mathbf{p}' - \frac{h}{4\pi}\boldsymbol{\xi} \cdot \left(\sum_k \frac{\gamma_k}{e_k}\, \partial_k \boldsymbol{\omega} \right).$$

The first component of the vector $\sum \dfrac{\gamma_k}{e_k}\,\partial_k\boldsymbol{\omega}$ (i.e. its product with $\mathbf{f}_1$) is

$$\gamma_1\frac{1}{e_1}(\partial_1\boldsymbol{\omega})_1+\gamma_2\frac{1}{e_2}(\partial_2\boldsymbol{\omega})_1+\gamma_3\frac{1}{e_3}(\partial_3\boldsymbol{\omega})_1 = -\gamma_2\frac{1}{e_3}\partial_3\log e_2+\gamma_3\frac{1}{e_2}\partial_2\log e_3$$

according to (310 a). Multiplying the right-hand side by ξ_1 we get, since

$$\xi_1\gamma_2 = \rho\xi_1\xi_2 = i\rho\xi_3 = i\gamma_3 \quad\text{and}\quad \xi_1\gamma_3 = \rho\xi_1\xi_3 = -\rho\xi_2 = -\gamma_2,$$

$$-i\left[\gamma_3\frac{1}{e_3}\frac{\partial}{\partial q_3}\log e_2+\gamma_2\frac{1}{e_2}\frac{\partial}{\partial q_2}\log e_3\right].$$

We thus find

$$\boldsymbol{\xi}\cdot\sum_k\gamma_k\frac{1}{e_k}\,\partial_k\boldsymbol{\omega}$$

$$= -i\left[\gamma_1\frac{1}{e_1}\frac{\partial}{\partial q_1}\log(e_2\,e_3)+\gamma_2\frac{1}{e_2}\frac{\partial}{\partial q_2}\log(e_3\,e_1)+\gamma_3\frac{1}{e_3}\frac{\partial}{\partial q_3}\log(e_1\,e_2)\right],$$

and consequently

$$\boldsymbol{\gamma}\cdot\mathbf{P}' = \sum_{k=1}^{3}\gamma_k\cdot\left[p_k'-\tfrac{1}{2}p_k'\log\!\left(\frac{e_1\,e_2\,e_3}{e_k}\right)\right], \tag{311}$$

it being understood that the second term in the brackets represents an ordinary number and not an operator. We can also write

$$\boldsymbol{\gamma}\cdot\mathbf{P}' = \sum_{1}^{3}\gamma_k\,p_k'\left[1-\log\sqrt{\left(\frac{e_1\,e_2\,e_3}{e_k}\right)}\,p_k'^{-1}\right], \tag{311 a}$$

the transformed Dirac equation being

$$\left[p_t+e\Phi+c\boldsymbol{\gamma}\cdot\left(\mathbf{P}'-\frac{e}{c}\mathbf{A}\right)+\gamma_0 m_0 c^2\right]\psi' = 0. \tag{311 b}$$

Two special cases should be especially noted, namely, that of a *cylindrical* and of a *spherical* coordinate system. In the former case we have, putting

$$q_1 = r = \sqrt{(x^2+y^2)},\ q_2 = \phi\ \text{(angle)},\ \text{and}\ q_3 = z,$$

$$e_1 = 1,\qquad e_2 = r,\qquad e_3 = 1,$$

and consequently

$$\boldsymbol{\gamma}\cdot\mathbf{P}' = \frac{h}{2\pi i}\left[\gamma_1\!\left(\frac{\partial}{\partial r}-\frac{\partial}{\partial r}\log\sqrt r\right)+\gamma_2\frac{1}{r}\frac{\partial}{\partial\phi}+\gamma_3\!\left(\frac{\partial}{\partial z}-\frac{\partial}{\partial z}\log\sqrt r\right)\right],$$

that is,

$$\boldsymbol{\gamma}\cdot\mathbf{P}' = \frac{h}{2\pi i}\left[\gamma_1\!\left(\frac{\partial}{\partial r}-\frac{1}{2r}\right)+\gamma_2\frac{1}{r}\frac{\partial}{\partial\phi}+\gamma_3\frac{\partial}{\partial z}\right]. \tag{312}$$

In the latter case, putting

$$q_1 = r = \sqrt{(x^2+y^2+z^2)}, \; q_2 = \theta \text{ (colatitude)}, \text{ and } q_3 = \phi,$$

we have $\qquad e_1 = 1, \qquad e_2 = r, \qquad e_3 = r\sin\theta,$

and consequently

$$\gamma\cdot\mathbf{P'} = \frac{h}{2\pi i}\bigg[\gamma_1\Big(\frac{\partial}{\partial r} - \frac{\partial}{\partial r}\log\{r\sqrt{(\sin\theta)}\}\Big) + \gamma_2\frac{1}{r}\Big(\frac{\partial}{\partial\theta} - \frac{\partial}{\partial\theta}\log\sqrt{(\sin\theta)}\Big) + \\ + \gamma_3\frac{1}{r\sin\theta}\Big(\frac{\partial}{\partial\phi} - \frac{\partial}{\partial\phi}\log\sqrt{r}\Big)\bigg],$$

that is,

$$\gamma\cdot\mathbf{P'} = \frac{h}{2\pi i}\bigg[\gamma_1\Big(\frac{\partial}{\partial r} - \frac{1}{r}\Big) + \gamma_2\frac{1}{r}\Big(\frac{\partial}{\partial\theta} - \tfrac{1}{2}\cot\theta\Big) + \gamma_3\frac{1}{r\sin\theta}\frac{\partial}{\partial\phi}\bigg]. \quad (312\,\text{a})$$

This expression can be used to reduce to its simplest form the problem of the hydrogen atom, which has been discussed already by a less straightforward method in § 33.

It should be mentioned that in calculating the product $\gamma\cdot\mathbf{A} = \sum \gamma_k A_k$ the quantities A_k must be understood to represent the components of the vector potential along the axes of the *local* cartesian systems, i.e. along the vectors $\mathbf{e}_1$, $\mathbf{e}_2$, $\mathbf{e}_3$ $(A_k = \mathbf{A}\cdot\mathbf{f}_k)$. The matrices γ_1, γ_2, γ_3, though identical with the original matrices γ_x, γ_y, γ_z, have now a different physical meaning, denoting the components of the vector γ along the axes of the *local* system and not of the original cartesian system of coordinates.

The preceding results can be further generalized for the case of a *non-orthogonal* system of curvilinear coordinates. We must distinguish in this case contravariant and covariant components of different vectors, the former transforming as dq_1, dq_2, dq_3 and the latter as $\partial/\partial q_1$, $\partial/\partial q_2$, $\partial/\partial q_3$. Putting $p_k' = \frac{h}{2\pi i}\frac{\partial}{\partial q_k}$ and denoting the contravariant components of the vector γ in the new system by γ'^k, we can write the operator $\gamma\cdot\mathbf{p}$ in the form $\sum_1^3 \gamma'^k p_k'$.

Introducing a *generalized* (non-unitary) transformation matrix L according to the condition

$$\gamma'^{(k)} = L^\dagger\gamma_k L$$

(where $\gamma_1 = \gamma_x$, $\gamma_2 = \gamma_y$, $\gamma_3 = \gamma_z$), we get

$$(\gamma\cdot\mathbf{p})\psi = L^\dagger\Big[\sum_{k=1}^3\gamma_k\{p_k' - (p_k'L - Lp_k')L^{-1}\}\Big]L\psi,$$

whence it follows that the transformed Dirac equation for the new wave functions $\psi' = L\psi$ will differ from the original one in the same way as in the case of orthogonal coordinates, the operators $p_k' = (h/2\pi i)\partial/\partial q_k$ being replaced by

$$P_k' = \frac{h}{2\pi i}\left(\frac{\partial}{\partial q_k} - \frac{\partial}{\partial q_k}\log L\right) = p_k'[1-(\log L)p_k'^{-1}].$$

We shall not determine here the matrix L for the general case of non-orthogonal coordinates, for it is not of practical interest.

The preceding results can be further generalized by introducing four-dimensional transformations, involving not only the space coordinates but also the *time*. Such transformations can be used to include the effects of the gravitational field on the motion of the electron in accordance with the relativity theory of gravitation. These considerations lie, however, beyond the scope of the present book.

In conclusion, the following transformation property of Dirac's equation should be mentioned.

The electromagnetic field is represented in Dirac's equation by the potentials $\mathbf{A}, \phi$. Now from the relations $\mathbf{E} = -\nabla\phi - \partial\mathbf{A}/c\partial t$, $\mathbf{H} = \mathrm{curl}\,\mathbf{A}$, it follows that the electromagnetic field strengths are not altered if $\mathbf{A}$ is replaced by $\mathbf{A}' = \mathbf{A} + \nabla\chi$ and ϕ by $\phi' = \phi - \partial\chi/c\partial t$, where χ is an arbitrary function of the coordinates and of the time. Since it is the *field strengths* and not the potentials which have a direct physical meaning, the above transformation of the potentials must be irrelevant for Dirac's equation; that is, the transformed equation

$$[(p_t + e\phi')/c + \boldsymbol{\gamma}\cdot(\mathbf{p} - e\mathbf{A}'/c) + \gamma_0 mc]\psi' = 0$$

must be equivalent to the equation

$$[(p_t + e\phi)/c + \boldsymbol{\gamma}\cdot(\mathbf{p} - e\mathbf{A}/c) + \gamma_0 mc]\psi = 0$$

with the original potentials. This is easily verified, the transformed wave function ψ' being connected with the original one by the equation $\psi' = e^{i2\pi e\chi/hc}\psi$. So long as χ is a real quantity (as of course it must be), the two functions, or rather function-quadruplets, ψ and ψ' correspond to identical values of the probabilities and thus determine the same motion.

This transformation can be considered as a special transformation of coordinates, the transformation matrix L being defined as the product of the matrix $\delta = 1$ by the function $e^{i2\pi e\chi/hc}$. It is clear that the coordinates are actually not affected by a transformation of this type.— We see at the same time that the introduction of our electromagnetic field can be described in a geometrical language as a generalization of ordinary coordinate transformations, the quantities $(h/2\pi i)\partial L/\partial q_k$ being replaced by eA_k/c.

VII

THE PROBLEM OF MANY PARTICLES

37. General Results, Virial Theorem, Linear and Angular Momentum

The problem of many particles has been considered already in the first part (Chapter IV) on the basis of the non-relativity mechanics of a single particle. Using the method of the configuration space, we arrived, in the case of two different particles, at the equation (101), which in the general case of a system of n different particles with the masses $m_1, m_2, ..., m_n$, and the potential energy $U(x_1, y_1, z_1; ...; x_n, y_n, z_n; t)$ can be written in the form

$$\left[\sum_{k=1}^{n} \frac{1}{m_k} \nabla_k^2 + \frac{8\pi^2}{h^2} \left(\frac{h}{2\pi i} \frac{\partial}{\partial t} - U \right) \right] \psi = 0, \tag{313}$$

where
$$\nabla_k^2 = \frac{\partial^2}{\partial x_k^2} + \frac{\partial^2}{\partial y_k^2} + \frac{\partial^2}{\partial z_k^2}.$$

Using the notation

$$p_k = \frac{h}{2\pi i} \nabla_k, \quad \text{i.e.} \quad p_{kx} = \frac{h}{2\pi i} \frac{\partial}{\partial x_k}, \quad p_{ky} = \frac{h}{2\pi i} \frac{\partial}{\partial y_k}, \quad p_{kz} = \frac{h}{2\pi i} \frac{\partial}{\partial z_k}, \tag{313a}$$

and
$$H = \sum_{k=1}^{n} \frac{1}{2m_k} \mathbf{p}_k^2 + U, \tag{313b}$$

we can rewrite (313) in the standard operator form

$$(H + p_t)\psi = 0, \tag{314}$$

p_t denoting as usual $-\dfrac{h}{2\pi i} \dfrac{\partial}{\partial t}$, while H represents the energy operator or Hamiltonian for the system under consideration. It agrees with the classical expression of the energy if the operators $\mathbf{p}_k$ are regarded as representing the momenta of the separate particles. The wave-mechanical equation (314) thus corresponds to the classical energy equation $H - W = 0$ if $-p_t$ is replaced by the value of the energy W.

This correspondence has exactly the same character as for a single particle, for which it has been discussed in detail in Chapters I and II. We need not repeat here all that has been stated there, as well as in the following three chapters, concerning the matrix representation, the transformation, and the perturbation theory. It may suffice to remark that a system of particles, defined by the Hamiltonian (313 b), can be dealt with from the mathematical point of view as a *single particle moving in a space of 3n dimensions*, with the coordinates

$$q_1 = \sqrt{\left(\frac{m_1}{m}\right)}x_1, \quad q_2 = \sqrt{\left(\frac{m_1}{m}\right)}y_1, \quad q_3 = \sqrt{\left(\frac{m_1}{m}\right)}z_1,$$

$$q_4 = \sqrt{\left(\frac{m_2}{m}\right)}x_2, \quad ..., \quad q_{3n} = \sqrt{\left(\frac{m_n}{m}\right)}z_n. \qquad (314\,\text{a})$$

Here m is an arbitrary coefficient of the dimension of a mass, which can be regarded as the mass of the 'equivalent' particle. We can put, for instance, $m = (m_1 m_2 ... m_n)^{1/n}$ which gives

$$dV = dx_1\,dy_1\,dz_1 ... dx_n\,dy_n\,dz_n = dq_1\,dq_2 ... dq_{3n}.$$

The corresponding momentum components are defined in the classical theory by the formulae

$$p_1 = m\frac{d}{dt}q_1 = \sqrt{(mm_1)}\frac{dx_1}{dt} = \sqrt{\left(\frac{m}{m_1}\right)}p_{1x}, \quad ..., \quad p_{3n} = \sqrt{\left(\frac{m}{m_n}\right)}p_{nz}.$$

They are represented in the wave-mechanical theory by the operators

$$p_1 = \sqrt{\left(\frac{m}{m_1}\right)}p_{1x} = \sqrt{\left(\frac{m}{m_1}\right)}\frac{h}{2\pi i}\frac{\partial}{\partial x_1}, \quad ..., \quad p_{3n} = \sqrt{\left(\frac{m}{m_1}\right)}\frac{h}{2\pi i}\frac{\partial}{\partial z_n},$$

that is, according to (314 a),

$$p_\alpha = \frac{h}{2\pi i}\frac{\partial}{\partial q_\alpha} \qquad (\alpha = 1, 2, ..., 3n), \qquad (314\,\text{b})$$

just as in the case of a single particle. Expressed in terms of these coordinates and momenta the Hamiltonian (313 b) assumes the standard form

$$H = \frac{1}{2m}\sum_{\alpha=1}^{3n} p_\alpha^2 + U(q_1, ..., q_{3n}). \qquad (314\,\text{c})$$

All the developments of the first five chapters of this part, referring to the motion of a particle in ordinary three-dimensional space, can be immediately generalized for the case of a symbolic particle representing a system of n ordinary particles in the $3n$-dimensional configuration space. The generalization is in fact so simple that it is hardly necessary to dwell upon it.

We shall therefore limit ourselves to the discussion of a few peculiarities connected with the physical meaning of the problem and to the possibility of completing and refining the theory in the same sense as has been done in the preceding chapter for the case of a single particle.

From equation (314 c) and its conjugate complex $(H - p_i)\psi^* = 0$

$(H^* = H)$ we can obtain in the usual way the 'conservation' or continuity equation

$$\frac{\partial \rho}{\partial t} + \sum_{\alpha=1}^{3n} \frac{\partial}{\partial q_\alpha} j_\alpha = 0, \tag{315}$$

where $\rho = \psi\psi^*$ is the probability density in the configuration space, and

$$j_\alpha = \frac{h}{2\pi m} \mathrm{R} \frac{1}{i} \psi^* \frac{\partial \psi}{\partial q_\alpha}$$

the components of the $3n$-dimensional probability current. If equation (315) is multiplied by the volume-element of the configuration space

$$dV = dV_1 dV_2 \dots dV_n = \left(\frac{m^n}{m_1 m_2 \dots m_n}\right)^{\frac{3}{2}} dq_1 dq_2 \dots dq_{3n}$$

and integrated over all this space, the result obtained is

$$\frac{d}{dt} \int \rho \, dV = 0,$$

expressing the law of conservation of probability.†

If, however, the integration is extended over the configuration space of the second, third,..., nth particle, while the coordinates of the first one, x, y, z, are kept constant, we obtain an equation of the usual three-dimensional form

$$\frac{\partial}{\partial t}\rho_1 + \frac{\partial}{\partial x_1}j_{1x} + \frac{\partial}{\partial y_1}j_{1y} + \frac{\partial}{\partial z_1}j_{1z} = 0, \tag{315a}$$

where the quantities

$$\left. \begin{array}{l} \rho_1 = \int \dots \int \rho \, dV_2 dV_3 \dots dV_n \\[2mm] j_{1x} = \sqrt{\frac{m}{m_1}} \int \dots \int j_1 \, dV_2 \dots dV_n = \frac{h}{2\pi m_1} \mathrm{R} \frac{1}{i} \int \dots \int \psi^* \frac{\partial \psi}{\partial x_1} \, dV_2 \dots dV_n, \text{ etc.} \end{array} \right\} \tag{315b}$$

can be interpreted as the probability density and current density for the first particle in the ordinary three-dimensional space. The same results hold, of course, for each of the other particles.

In the particular case of a system of particles which do not act on each other the equation $(H + p_t)\psi = 0$ has multiplicative solutions of the form $\psi = \psi_1 \psi_2 \dots \psi_n$, where ψ_k depends upon the coordinates of the kth particle alone; we get accordingly in this case

$$\rho_k = \psi_k \psi_k^*, \qquad j_k = \frac{h}{2\pi m_k} \mathrm{R} \frac{1}{i} \psi_k^* \nabla_k \psi_k$$

(provided the separate factors of ψ are normalized to unity) and con-

---

† We shall assume for the sake of simplicity that the integral $\int \rho \, dV$ is convergent, which means that the particles are bound to remain in a finite region of space.

sequently $\rho = \rho_1 \rho_2 \ldots \rho_n$. This result was the starting-point of our discussion of the problem of many particles in Part I. In the general case ρ is, of course, different from the product $\rho_1 \rho_2 \ldots \rho_n$; this circumstance corresponds to a mutual dependence of the particles, a dependence specified by the form of the potential-energy function U or also by statistical (i.e. symmetry) conditions, if the particles are all alike (see below).

The function U may be assumed to have the form

$$U = \sum_k U_k(\mathbf{r}_k, t) + \sum_{k<l} \sum U_{kl}(r_{kl}),$$

the first sum corresponding to the action of external forces, which can depend upon the time explicitly, while the second represents the mutual action of the particles ($U_{kl} = U_{lk}$, $r_{kl} = |\mathbf{r}_k - \mathbf{r}_l|$ = distance between the kth and lth particles).

If U does not depend upon t, then equation (314) admits solutions of the form $\psi = \psi^0_{H'}(x_1, \ldots, z_n) e^{-i2\pi H't/h}$, where $\psi^0_{H'}$ and H' are the characteristic functions and the characteristic values of the energy operator satisfying the usual equation

$$(H - H')\psi^0_{H'} = 0. \tag{316}$$

In the case of a discrete spectrum of H the functions $\psi^0_{H'}$ are easily proved to be orthogonal to each other (in the configuration space), this orthogonality being a consequence of the self-adjoint character of the operator H, since

$$f_1 H f_2 - f_2 H f_1 = \frac{1}{2m} \sum_k \frac{\partial}{\partial q_k}\left(f_1 \frac{\partial f_2}{\partial q_k} - f_2 \frac{\partial f_1}{\partial q_k}\right).$$

Another interesting consequence of this self-adjointness of H is the possibility of replacing the preceding equation by the variational equation,

$$\delta \int \psi^{0*} H \psi^0 \, dV = 0, \tag{316 a}$$

with the accessory condition,

$$\int \psi^{0*} \psi^0 \, dV = 1,$$

expressing the 'normalization' of the functions $\psi^0_{H'}$. Using

$$\int \psi^{0*} \frac{\partial^2 \psi^0}{\partial q_\alpha^2} \, dV = -\int \frac{\partial \psi^{0*}}{\partial q_\alpha} \frac{\partial \psi^0}{\partial q_\alpha} \, dV,$$

(316 a) can be rewritten in the form

$$\delta \int \left[\frac{h^2}{8\pi^2 m} \sum_{\alpha=1}^{3n} \frac{\partial \psi^{0*}}{\partial q_\alpha} \frac{\partial \psi^0}{\partial q_\alpha} + U \psi^{0*} \psi^0 \right] dV = 0, \tag{316 b}$$

which involves the first derivatives of ψ only ($dV = dq_1 \ldots dq_{3n}$).

An interesting application of the variational equation is afforded by the following very simple and general proof of the virial theorem (due to V. Fock). Let us replace the function $\psi^0(q_1,...,q_{3n})$, which is a solution of our problem, by the function $\psi' = c\psi^0(\lambda q_1,...,\lambda q_{3n})$, which is obtained from it by multiplying each coordinate by a certain parameter λ and introducing a normalizing factor c. Introducing further a new set of coordinates $q'_\alpha = \lambda q_\alpha$, we can write the normalizing condition $\int \psi'^*\psi' \, dV = 1$ in the form $\int \lambda^{-3n}\psi'^*\psi' \, dV' = 1$, where $dV' = dq'_1...dq'_{3n}$, which gives, on using the original normalizing condition,

$$\int \psi_0^*(q)\psi^0(q) \, dV = \int \psi^{0*}(q')\psi^0(q') \, dV' = 1,$$

$c = \lambda^{-\frac{3}{2}n}$. Using this value of c we can reduce the variational equation (316 a) or (316 b) to the form $\partial \overline{H}'/\partial\lambda = 0$, where $\overline{H}'$ is the value of the integral (316 a) or (316 b) which is obtained by replacing the function ψ^0 by the function ψ'. Its minimum value corresponds, of course, to $\lambda = 1$, which is the solution of the equation $\partial \overline{H}'/\partial\lambda = 0$.

Now using the coordinates q'_k, we have

$$\overline{H}' = \int \left[\lambda^2 \frac{h^2}{8\pi^2 m} \sum_{\alpha=1}^{3n} \frac{\partial \psi^{0*}(q')}{\partial q'_\alpha} \frac{\partial \psi^0(q')}{\partial q'_\alpha} + \right.$$
$$\left. + U(\lambda^{-1}q'_1,...,\lambda^{-1}q'_{3n})\psi^{0*}(q_1)\psi^0(q') \right] dV',$$

so that the preceding equation assumes the form

$$\int \left[2\lambda \frac{h^2}{8\pi^2 m} \sum_{\alpha=1}^{3n} \frac{\partial \psi^{0*}(q')}{\partial q'_\alpha} \frac{\partial \psi^0(q')}{\partial q'_\alpha} - \frac{1}{\lambda^2} \sum_{\alpha=1}^{3n} q'_\alpha \frac{\partial U}{\partial q_\alpha} \psi^{0*}(q')\psi^0(q'_\alpha) \right] dV' = 0.$$

Putting here $\lambda = 1$ and $q'_\alpha = q_\alpha$, we get

$$2\overline{T} = \sum_{\alpha=1}^{3n} \overline{q_\alpha \frac{\partial U}{\partial q_\alpha}}, \tag{317}$$

where $\overline{T}$ denotes the probable (average) value of the kinetic energy of the system, and $\sum_1^{3n} \overline{q_\alpha \frac{\partial U}{\partial q_\alpha}}$ its 'virial'. We have obviously

$$\sum_{\alpha=1}^{3n} q_\alpha \frac{\partial U}{\partial q_\alpha} = \sum_{k=1}^{n} \left(x_k \frac{\partial U}{\partial x_k} + y_k \frac{\partial U}{\partial y_k} + z_k \frac{\partial U}{\partial z_k} \right).$$

If the potential energy is a homogeneous function of the coordinates, this expression reduces to the product of U with the number specifying the corresponding power. In the special case of a system of electrified particles obeying the Coulomb law—which is approximately the case with any actual material system constituted by protons and electrons, we must have

$$2\overline{T} = -\overline{U} \qquad\qquad (317\,\mathrm{a})$$

or, since $\overline{T} + \overline{U} = W$ (= total energy of the system),

$$\overline{T} = -W. \qquad\qquad (317\,\mathrm{b})$$

It should be remembered that these relations hold only so long as the particles remain actually *bound* to each other, which is expressed mathematically by the convergence of the integral $\int |\psi|^2 \, dV$, a convergence that subsists so long as the energy W of the state under consideration belongs to the discrete spectrum. It should further be remarked that they remain valid if some of the particles are treated as *fixed* centres of force producing an 'external' Coulomb field of force.

We shall now establish a few other general laws which hold for a *closed* system of particles, i.e. a system unaffected by external forces, such as an isolated atom or molecule, etc.

These laws are the exact equivalents of the laws of classical mechanics concerning the conservation of the energy, momentum, and of the moment of momentum (or angular momentum) of the system. The first of them has been stated already. The other two can be established with the help of the relation

$$\frac{dF}{dt} = [H, F] = \frac{2\pi i}{h}(HF - FH).$$

We put

$$F \equiv \mathbf{p} = \sum_1^n \mathbf{p}_k,$$

or

$$F \equiv \mathbf{M} = \sum_1^n \mathbf{r}_k \times \mathbf{p}_k,$$

in accordance with the classical definition of the total momentum and angular momentum (the origin from which the vectors $\mathbf{r}_k$ are supposed to be drawn can be chosen arbitrarily).

Taking the x-component of $\mathbf{p}$, we have

$$[H, p_x] = [U, p_x] = \sum_k [U, p_{kx}] = -\sum_k \frac{\partial U}{\partial x_k}.$$

Now $-\partial U/\partial x_k$ represents the force acting on the kth particle in the direction of the x-axis; so long as there are no external forces, the sum of such forces for all the particles must obviously vanish. Hence we get

$$\frac{d}{dt}\mathbf{p} = 0.$$

In a similar way we have

$$[H, M_x] = \sum_k [H, y_k p_{kz} - z_k p_{ky}]$$

$$= \sum_k \{[H, y_k] p_{kz} + y_k [H, p_{kz}] - [H, z_k] p_{ky} + z_k [H, p_{ky}]\},$$

that is, since

$$[H, y_k] = \frac{\partial H}{\partial p_{ky}} = \frac{1}{m_k} p_{ky}; \quad [H, p_{kz}] = -\frac{\partial H}{\partial z_k} = -\frac{\partial U}{\partial z_k}, \text{ etc.,}$$

$$[H, M_x] = \sum_k \frac{1}{m_k}(p_{ky} p_{kz} - p_{kz} p_{ky}) - \sum_k \left(y_k \frac{\partial U}{\partial z_k} - z_k \frac{\partial U}{\partial y_k}\right).$$

The first sum vanishes since p_{ky} and p_{kz} commute with each other, while the second is equal to the x-component of the vector $\sum_k (\mathbf{r}_k \times \mathbf{F}_k)$, where $\mathbf{F}_k$ is the force acting on the kth particle. We thus get

$$\frac{d}{dt} \mathbf{M} = \sum_k \mathbf{r}_k \times \mathbf{F}_k,$$

just as in the classical theory. It is easy to see that in the case of central forces, which we are considering, the vector $\sum_k \mathbf{r}_k \times \mathbf{F}_k$ (representing the resulting torque of all the forces acting on all the particles) vanishes. We have in fact, putting $\mathbf{F}_k = \sum_{l \neq k} \mathbf{F}_{kl}$, and taking into account that $\mathbf{F}_{kl} = -\mathbf{F}_{lk} = f_{kl}(\mathbf{r}_k - \mathbf{r}_l)$,

$$\sum_k \mathbf{r}_k \times \mathbf{F}_k = \tfrac{1}{2} \sum_k \sum_{l \neq k} (\mathbf{r}_k - \mathbf{r}_l) \times \mathbf{F}_{kl} = 0.$$

Hence it follows that $\qquad \dfrac{d}{dt} \mathbf{M} = 0,$

i.e. the conservation law for the resulting angular momentum.

This result, as well as the preceding one, can be obtained by another method based on the invariance of the energy operator with regard to a transformation of the coordinates (and momentum components) involving a shift of the origin and a rotation of the axes about it. Let P be some fixed point in space (or in the configuration space) and P' another point which in the new system has the same coordinates as P has in the old one ($x'_k = x_k$, etc.). If $f(P)$ is some function of the old coordinates, then the transformed function will be defined by the condition $Tf(P) = f(P')$, T denoting the transformation under consideration. The coordinates of the point P' in the original system are defined by the linear transformation equations

$$\left. \begin{array}{l} x_k = x_0 + \alpha_{11} x'_k + \alpha_{12} y'_k + \alpha_{13} z'_k \\ y_k = y_0 + \alpha_{21} x'_k + \alpha_{22} y'_k + \alpha_{23} z'_k \\ z_k = z_0 + \alpha_{31} x'_k + \alpha_{32} y'_k + \alpha_{33} z'_k \end{array} \right\} \quad (k = 1, 2, ..., n).$$

In the special case of an *infinitesimal transformation* these equations reduce to

$$x_k - x'_k = \delta x_k = x_0 + \omega_y z'_k - \omega_z y'_k,$$
$$y_k - y'_k = \delta y_k = y_0 + \omega_z x'_k - \omega_x z'_k,$$
$$z_k - z'_k = \delta z_k = z_0 + \omega_x y'_k - \omega_y x'_k,$$

where ω_x, ω_y, ω_z are the components of an infinitesimal rotation $\boldsymbol{\omega}$, while x_0, y_0, z_0 are the components of an infinitesimal displacement $\mathbf{r}_0$. We obtain in this case

$$Tf(P) = f(P) + \sum_k \left(\frac{\partial f}{\partial x_k} \delta x_k + \frac{\partial f}{\partial y_k} \delta y_k + \frac{\partial f}{\partial z_k} \delta z_k \right)$$

$$= f(P) + x_0 \sum_k \frac{\partial f}{\partial x_k} + y_0 \sum_k \frac{\partial f}{\partial y_k} + z_0 \sum_k \frac{\partial f}{\partial z_k} +$$

$$+ \omega_x \sum_k \left(y'_k \frac{\partial f}{\partial z_k} - z'_k \frac{\partial f}{\partial y_k} \right) + \omega_y \sum_k \left(z'_k \frac{\partial f}{\partial x_k} - x'_k \frac{\partial f}{\partial z_k} \right) +$$

$$+ \omega_z \sum_k \left(x'_k \frac{\partial f}{\partial y_k} - y'_k \frac{\partial f}{\partial x_k} \right),$$

the derivatives of f being taken for the point P. Neglecting small quantities of the second order, we can replace in this equation the primed letters (referring to P') by the unprimed (referring to P), which gives

$$Tf(P) = f(P) + \frac{2\pi i}{h} [(\mathbf{r}_0 \cdot \mathbf{p} + \boldsymbol{\omega} \cdot \mathbf{M}) f]_p,$$

where $\mathbf{p} = \sum_k \mathbf{p}_k$, while $\mathbf{M}$ denotes, as before, the operator of the resulting angular momentum. We thus see that an infinitesimal transformation T can be represented by an ordinary linear differential operator

$$T = 1 + \frac{2\pi i}{h} (\mathbf{r}_0 \cdot \mathbf{p} + \boldsymbol{\omega} \cdot \mathbf{M}).$$

Now it is obvious from symmetry considerations that the energy H remains invariant under a transformation of the type T since the latter alters neither the value of the potential energy (depending on the *relative* position of the particles only) nor the expression of the kinetic energy operator (the operators ∇_k^2 being independent of the orientation of the coordinate system or of the position of its origin). This circumstance can be expressed by the condition $TH\psi = HT\psi$, that is, $HT = TH$, which, on the other hand, means that the operator T represents a constant of the motion. In view of the arbitrariness of the (infinitesimal) vectors $\mathbf{r}_0$ and $\boldsymbol{\omega}$, the equation $T = \text{const.}$ is split up into two independent equations: $\mathbf{p} = $ const. and $\mathbf{M} = $ const., expressing the conservation law of the resulting linear and angular momentum of the system.

These laws are, of course, no longer satisfied in the presence of external forces. If, however, the latter reduce to an attraction to a fixed point—as in the case of a system of electrons revolving about a fixed nucleus supposed to act like a point-charge—then we still have $\mathbf{M} = $ const. In the presence of a homogeneous field—magnetic or electric—parallel to a fixed direction in space, the energy operator remains invariant for rotations about this direction only, and we obtain accordingly the conservation law for the corresponding projection of the angular momentum, the components of the latter in the perpendicular directions being no longer constant.

The operator $\mathbf{M}_k = \mathbf{r}_k \times \mathbf{p}_k$ representing the angular momentum of a single particle satisfies, as we know, the relation

$$\mathbf{M}_k \times \mathbf{M}_k = -\frac{h}{2\pi i}\mathbf{M}_k.$$

Replacing $\mathbf{M}_k$ by the resultant angular momentum operator $\mathbf{M} = \sum_k \mathbf{M}_k$, we have

$$\mathbf{M} \times \mathbf{M} = \sum_k \mathbf{M}_k \times \mathbf{M}_k + \sum_{k<l}\sum (\mathbf{M}_k \times \mathbf{M}_l + \mathbf{M}_l \times \mathbf{M}_k) = \sum_k \mathbf{M}_k \times \mathbf{M}_k,$$

since the operators $\mathbf{M}_k$ and $\mathbf{M}_l$ referring to different particles obviously commute with each other. We thus get for the resulting angular momentum the same relation as for the component ones, viz.:

$$\mathbf{M} \times \mathbf{M} = -\frac{h}{2\pi i}\mathbf{M}. \tag{318}$$

It has been shown in Chap. III, § 13, that it is possible by means of the matrix method to derive from this relation the matrix elements of $\mathbf{M}$ in a representation specified by the condition that M^2 and M_z should be diagonal matrices (corresponding to a given value of the energy). The number of particles involved is obviously immaterial (so long as M commutes with H) and the results obtained before for the case of a single particle can be directly applied to the present case. We thus obtain, on denoting the angular quantum number by j (instead of l as before) and the axial one by m,

$$M_{j,j}^2 = \frac{h^2}{4\pi^2}j(j+1), \tag{318 a}$$

$$(M_z)_{m,m} = \frac{h}{2\pi}m \qquad (-j \leqslant m \leqslant j)$$

$$(M_x + iM_y)_{m+1,m} = \frac{h}{2\pi}\sqrt{\{(j+\tfrac{1}{2})^2 - (m+\tfrac{1}{2})^2\}}e^{i\alpha_m} \qquad (318\,\text{b})$$

$$(M_x - iM_y)_{m,m+1} = \frac{h}{2\pi}\sqrt{\{(j+\tfrac{1}{2})^2 - (m+\tfrac{1}{2})^2\}}e^{-i\alpha_m}$$

[cf. e.g. (96) and (96 a)]. As has been pointed out in § 13, the number j can assume, from the matrix-theory point of view, both integral and half-integral values (the values of m being of the same nature); half-integral values occur, however, only if the spin of the particles is included, and if M refers to total not orbital angular momentum.

38. Magnetic Forces and Spin Effects

A generalization and refinement of the preceding theory along the same lines as for a single particle—i.e. the establishment of a wave equation $(H+p_t)\psi = 0$ which would describe the behaviour of a system of particles in agreement with the relativity theory, taking account of magnetic forces and of the spin effect—is a problem which admits only of a partial and approximate solution. This circumstance is not characteristic of the wave mechanics, for we meet with a similar situation in the classical mechanics. The latter can be formulated in a relativistically invariant form for the case of a single particle moving in an external electromagnetic field—that is, in a *field which is supposed to be known a priori* and specified by the potentials ϕ and A. The more general problem of the motion of two or more particles, acting on each other according to the laws of the classical electromagnetic theory, cannot be solved with the help of a single equation involving the coordinates of all the particles for the same instant of time, for according to this theory the action emanating from each particle travels through space with a *finite velocity* (c). The force acting on a particle (1) at the instant t depends upon the position and motion of the other particles $(2, 3,...)$ at previous instants $t_{12} = t - R_{12}/c$, etc., R_{12} being the distance between the point where (1) is at the time t and the point where (2) was at the time t_{12}.

This fact, usually denoted as the law of retarded action, alone precludes the possibility of treating the problem of motion and interaction of a number of particles by means of a single equation of the Hamilton-Jacobi type. We must, instead, write the relativistic equation of motion for each individual particle assuming the electromagnetic potentials produced by the other particles to be known, and furthermore a set of equations defining the potentials produced by each particle, its motion being supposedly known.

This problem allows, however, only an exact formulation. It cannot be solved exactly even for the simplest case of two particles. And there is no doubt that such a solution, if it could be obtained, would be in contradiction to the experimental facts. Assuming that the latter can be described adequately, so far as the motion of a particle in a given external field is concerned, by means of the relativistic wave mechanics, we must find a method of describing adequately the electromagnetic field produced by a particle, whose motion is specified in terms of wave mechanics, i.e. in terms of the probability theory. This means that together with the classical mechanics *we must abandon the classical electrodynamics*, based upon the idea of exactly specified motion, and replace it by a new 'quantum electrodynamics', not involving this idea.

We shall consider this problem more closely later on (Chapter IX) and shall confine ourselves here to the more modest task of incorporating into the wave-mechanical theory the magnetic forces, and other effects connected with them, neglecting those which are due to the retarded character of the interaction between the electrified particles— electrons and protons—constituting matter.

So far as the action of an *external* magnetic—or electromagnetic— field on a system of such particles is concerned, the required generalization of the previous theory presents no difficulties. We have merely to replace in the expression of the energy operator the momentum operators of the single particles $\mathbf{p}_k$ by the differences

$$\mathbf{p}_k - \frac{e_k}{c}\mathbf{A}_k,$$

where $\mathbf{A}_k = \mathbf{A}(x_k, y_k, z_k, t)$ is the vector potential of the external field at the point where the particle in question is supposed to be situated at the instant t under consideration.

Putting further $U = \sum e_k \phi_k + U'$, where $\phi_k = \phi(x_k, y_k, z_k, t)$ is the scalar potential of the external field at the point (x_k, y_k, z_k), and $U' = \sum\sum_{i<k} \frac{e_i e_k}{r_{ik}}$ the mutual potential energy of the particles, we get

$$H = \sum_{k=1}^{n}\left[\frac{1}{2m_k}\left(\mathbf{p}_k - \frac{e_k}{c}\mathbf{A}_k\right)^2 + e_k\phi_k\right] + \sum\sum_{i<k}\frac{e_i e_k}{r_{ik}}. \qquad (319)$$

In the case (usually met with in practice) where the square of **A** can be neglected as well as div **A**, this expression reduces to the form

$$H = \sum_{k=1}^{n} \left[\frac{1}{2m_k} p_k^2 - \frac{e_k}{cm_k} \mathbf{A}_k \cdot \mathbf{p}_k + e_k \phi_k \right] + \sum_{i<k} \sum \frac{e_i e_k}{r_{ik}}. \qquad (319\,\text{a})$$

We meet a much more difficult problem when we try to incorporate in the energy operator terms representing the non-statical interaction of the particles with each other. This problem can be solved approximately if we neglect the retarded character of the electromagnetic actions and define accordingly the vector-potential produced by a particle with a charge e_i and velocity $\mathbf{v}_i$ at a distance r_{ik} by the expression $e_i \mathbf{v}_i/(cr_{ik})$.

The total value of the vector potential $\mathbf{A}_k$ at a given point (k) is then equal to the sum of the part $\mathbf{A}_k^0$ due to the external field and that $\mathbf{A}_k' = \sum_{i \neq k} \dfrac{e_i \mathbf{v}_i}{cr_{ik}}$ due to all the other particles. The total momentum of the kth particle, $\mathbf{p}_k = m_k \mathbf{v}_k + (e_k/c) \mathbf{A}_k$, is thus given by the expression

$$\mathbf{p}_k = \sum_i g_{ki} \mathbf{v}_i + (e_k/c) \mathbf{A}_k^0, \qquad (320)$$

where $g_{ki} = m_{ii}$ if $i = k$ and $e_i e_k/(c^2 r_{ik})$ if $i \neq k$.

The corresponding expression for the total kinetic energy T of the whole system [equal to the sum of the ordinary kinetic energy $\sum_k \frac{1}{2} m_k v_k^2$ and of the *mutual* kinetic energy $T' = \frac{1}{2} \sum_k (e_k/c) \mathbf{v}_k \cdot \mathbf{A}_k'$] is

$$T = \frac{1}{2} \sum_i \sum_k g_{ik} \mathbf{v}_i \cdot \mathbf{v}_k. \qquad (320\,\text{a})$$

Putting $\mathbf{p}_k - (e_k/c) \mathbf{A}_k = \mathbf{p}_k'$ and solving the equations $\mathbf{p}_k' = \sum_i g_{ki} \mathbf{v}_i$ with respect to the $\mathbf{v}_i$'s, we get $\mathbf{v}_i = \sum_k g^{ik} \mathbf{p}_k'$, where $g^{ik} = g^{-1}(\partial g/\partial g_{ik})$, g being the determinant $|g_{ik}|$, and

$$T = \frac{1}{2} \sum_i \sum_k g^{ik} \mathbf{p}_i' \mathbf{p}_k'. \qquad (320\,\text{b})$$

The classical Hamiltonian H is equal to the sum of this expression and the potential energy $U = \sum_k e_k \phi_k^0 + U'$. The simplest way to obtain the corresponding quantum Hamiltonian consists in replacing the p''s in (319 b) by the operators $(h/2\pi i)\nabla - (e/c)\mathbf{A}^0$. Since, however, these operators do not commute with the coefficients g^{ik} we might just as well write $\mathbf{p}_i' g^{ik} \mathbf{p}_k'$ instead of $g^{ik} \mathbf{p}_i' \mathbf{p}_k'$ or, more generally, $f^{-1} \mathbf{p}_i' g^{ik} f \mathbf{p}_k'$, where f is any function of the coordinates. If (following L. Landau) we put $f = \sqrt{g}$ we obtain for the quantum T an operator which can be considered as a generalization of the ordinary Laplacian in a curved space with the line-element $ds^2 = \sum_i \sum_k g_{ik} dq_i dq_k$.

We shall now discuss some further complications of the theory of a system of electrons, namely, those connected with the *spin effect*.

In the case of a single electron or proton this effect can be accounted for approximately by introducing, in addition to the three space coordinates of the particle x, y, z, a fourth 'spin coordinate' ζ, able to assume two values only. These values correspond, as we know, to two opposite orientations of the spin parallel to a fixed direction, that of the z-axis say, or, more exactly, to the two characteristic values of the z-component of the spin matrix σ_z. We thus get, instead of a single wave function $\psi(x, y, z)$ describing the motion of the particle in question, a function doublet $\psi(x, y, z, \zeta)$ which can be dealt with as a linear two-dimensional matrix with the elements $\psi_1(x, y, z) = \psi(x, y, z, 1)$ and $\psi_2(x, y, z) = \psi(x, y, z, 2)$, 1 and 2 being the two values of ζ. Instead of these two values it is often more convenient to use $-\frac{1}{2}$ and $+\frac{1}{2}$, which are equal to the respective values of the z-component of the spin angular momentum expressed in the standard $h/2\pi$ unit.

The energy operator, as well as all the other operators referring to the particle, must be defined accordingly as a square two-dimensional matrix involving either the spin matrix $\boldsymbol{\sigma}$ or the unit matrix which is equivalent to the square of any component of $\boldsymbol{\sigma}$.

These results can easily be generalized for a system of elementary particles (electrons or protons) so long as their mutual action is neglected. The wave function ψ describing the behaviour of the whole system can be defined as the product of the functions $\psi_k = \psi_k(x_k, y_k, z_k, \zeta_k)$ referring to the individual particles ($k = 1, 2, ..., n$). The expression $\psi\psi^*$ multiplied by the volume-element of the configuration space $dV = dV_1 ... dV_n = dx_1 dy_1 dz_1 ... dx_n dy_n dz_n$ is to be regarded as a measure of the probability of finding the system in the corresponding configuration with the specified values of the spin coordinates. The number of such specified values is obviously equal to 2^n, so that there are 2^n states corresponding to each configuration and differing from each other by the orientation of the separate particles inasmuch as this orientation is specified by the characteristic values of σ_z. The total probability of a given configuration, irrespective of the orientation of the particles, is measured by the sum

$$\sum_{\zeta_1} \sum_{\zeta_2} ... \sum_{\zeta_n} \psi^*\psi = \sum_{\zeta} \psi^*\psi$$

extended over the two possible values of each of the spin coordinates.

In the case of a motion belonging to a discrete spectrum this sum must be normalized according to the condition

$$\int \sum_\zeta \psi^*\psi \, dV = 1,$$

the integration being extended over the whole configuration space. With regard to the definition of ψ, we have

$$\int \sum_\zeta \psi^*\psi \, dV = \int \sum_{\zeta_1} \psi_1^*\psi_1 \, dV_1 \cdots \int \sum_{\zeta_n} \psi_n^* \psi_n \, dV_n,$$

$$\int \sum_{\zeta_k} \psi_k^* \psi_k \, dV_k = \int (\psi_{k1}^* \psi_{k1} + \psi_{k2}^* \psi_{k2}) \, dV_k = 1,$$

where

$$\psi_{k\zeta_k} \equiv \psi_{k\zeta_k}(x_k, y_k, z_k) = \psi_k(x_k, y_k, z_k, \zeta_k) \qquad (\zeta_k = 1, 2).$$

The product ψ considered as a function of the space coordinates alone can be dealt with as a linear matrix of 2^n dimensions

$$\psi_\zeta = \psi_{1\zeta_1} \psi_{2\zeta_2} \cdots \psi_{n\zeta_n}.$$

This involves the use of operators which should be defined as square matrices of the same rank. Such an operator, F say, can be defined by the equation

$$(F\psi)_{\zeta'} = \sum_{\zeta''} F_{\zeta'\zeta''} \psi_{\zeta''},$$

where $F_{\zeta'\zeta''}$ is an operator of the ordinary kind with respect to the space coordinates $x_1, \ldots, z_n$ and the corresponding momenta, specified by two sets of particular values of the spin coordinates, $\zeta' = (\zeta_1', \zeta_2', \ldots, \zeta_n')$ and $\zeta'' = (\zeta_1'', \zeta_2'', \ldots, \zeta_n'')$. Each of the individual wave functions ψ_k satisfies the matrix-operator equation

$$(H_k + \delta_k p_l)\psi_k = 0,$$

where δ_k is the two-dimensional unit matrix referring to the kth particle (with the elements $\delta_{\zeta_k' \zeta_k''}$). The factorized wave function ψ is easily seen to satisfy an equation of the same type,

$$(H + \delta p_l)\psi = 0, \tag{321}$$

where δ is the 2^n-dimensional unit matrix with the elements

$$\delta_{\zeta'\zeta''} = \delta_{\zeta_1' \zeta_1''} \delta_{\zeta_2' \zeta_2''} \cdots \delta_{\zeta_n' \zeta_n''}, \tag{321 a}$$

and H the energy operator defined by the formula

$$\left. \begin{aligned} H_{\zeta'\zeta''} = H_{1\zeta_1' \zeta_1''} \delta_{\zeta_2' \zeta_2''} \cdots \delta_{\zeta_n' \zeta_n''} + \delta_{\zeta_1' \zeta_1''} H_{2\zeta_2' \zeta_2''} \cdots \delta_{\zeta_n' \zeta_n''} + \\ + \cdots + \delta_{\zeta_1' \zeta_1''} \cdots \delta_{\zeta_{n-1}' \zeta_{n-1}''} H_{n\zeta_n' \zeta_n''} \end{aligned} \right\}, \tag{321 b}$$

$H_{k\zeta_k' \zeta_k''}$ being the elements of the ordinary two-dimensional matrix operator referring to the kth particle.

Equation (321) can naturally be extended to functions ψ of a more general type, equal, for instance, to a sum of particular solutions of the simple product type. It can be further generalized in order to account for the mutual action of the particles by adding to it terms representing the interaction energy multiplied by the unit matrix (321 a). (In problems of the atomic theory involving only a small number of electrons the mutual kinetic energy T' can be neglected.) There remains, however, still one step in this generalization, which consists in the addition to the interaction energy of terms characteristic of the spin effect. We can solve this problem in a tentative way with the help of the approximate theory of § 30. We found there that the additional 'spin' force acting on a particle (electron) in a given electromagnetic field $\mathbf{E}, \mathbf{H}$ can be derived from the energy operator

$$-\mu\left[\boldsymbol{\sigma}\cdot\mathbf{H}+\frac{1}{2m_0 c}\mathbf{E}\cdot(\mathbf{p}\times\boldsymbol{\sigma})\right]$$

[cf. equation (261 a), where $\mathbf{u}$ is replaced by $\mathbf{p}$]. It is natural to suppose that this result will still be valid for a system of particles, if $\mathbf{H}$ and $\mathbf{E}$ are defined as the total field acting on the given particle due both to external causes and to other particles constituting the system. The field $\mathbf{E}, \mathbf{H}$ produced by a certain particle at a distance $\mathbf{r}$ can be derived in the usual way from the potentials ϕ, $\mathbf{A}$ defined by the following formulae:

$$\phi = \frac{e}{r}, \qquad \mathbf{A} = \frac{e}{m_0 c r}\mathbf{p}+\frac{\mu}{r^3}\boldsymbol{\sigma}\times\mathbf{r}.$$

The first term in $\mathbf{A}$ represents the ordinary electromagnetic field of a moving point-charge, while the second is introduced as an equivalent for the field produced by an elementary magnet with a moment $\mu\boldsymbol{\sigma}$.

Neglecting the electric field due to the variation of $\mathbf{A}$ with the time, i.e. putting

$$\mathbf{E} = -\nabla\phi = \frac{e}{r^3}\mathbf{r}$$

and

$$\mathbf{H} = \operatorname{curl}\mathbf{A} = \frac{e}{m_0 c r^2}\mathbf{r}\times\mathbf{p}+\frac{\mu}{r^3}\left[\frac{3}{r^2}\mathbf{r}(\boldsymbol{\sigma}\cdot\mathbf{r})-\boldsymbol{\sigma}\right],$$

we get for the operator of the spin interaction energy the following expression:

$$U_s = U_s'+U_s'', \tag{322}$$

where

$$U_s' = -\sum_{k\neq i}\sum \frac{\mu_k e_i}{c r_{ki}^3}\boldsymbol{\sigma}_k\cdot\left[\mathbf{r}_{ki}\times\left(\frac{1}{m_i}\mathbf{p}_i+\frac{1}{2m_k}\mathbf{p}_k\right)\right], \tag{322 a}$$

and

$$U_s'' = \sum_{k<i}\sum \frac{\mu_k\mu_i}{r_{ki}^3}\left[\frac{3}{r_{ki}^2}(\boldsymbol{\sigma}_k\cdot\mathbf{r}_{ki})(\boldsymbol{\sigma}_i\cdot\mathbf{r}_{ki})-\boldsymbol{\sigma}_k\cdot\boldsymbol{\sigma}_i\right]. \tag{322 b}$$

In deriving the term U_s' which represents the linear or electromagnetic part of the spin interaction energy we have simply summed up the contributions of all the particles concerned ($\mathbf{r}_{ki}$ denoting the radius vector from the ith particle to the kth), whereas in deriving the quadratic or purely magnetic part of the energy U''_s, which is symmetrical with regard to each pair of particles, we have taken each pair only once (as indicated by the condition $k < i$).

It should be noticed further that in adding U_s to the Hamiltonian H in (321) we must multiply it by the unit matrix (321 a). This amounts to the multiplication of each term by those two-dimensional unit matrices only which refer to other particles than those represented by the matrices $\boldsymbol{\sigma}$. Dropping these unit matrices and neglecting the mutual kinetic energy we can write the total Hamiltonian in the form

$$H = \sum_k H_k + U' + U_s, \qquad (323)$$

where U_s is defined by (322), while

$$\left.\begin{aligned} H_k = \frac{1}{2m_k}p_k^2 - \frac{1}{8m_k^3 c^2}p_k^4 - \frac{e_k}{cm_k}\mathbf{A}_k\cdot\mathbf{p}_k + e_k\phi_k - \\ -\mu_k\left[\mathbf{H}_k\cdot\boldsymbol{\sigma}_k + \frac{1}{2m_k c}\mathbf{E}_k\cdot(\mathbf{p}_k\times\boldsymbol{\sigma}_k)\right] \end{aligned}\right\}; \quad (323\,a)$$

H_k is the energy operator for the kth particle, $\mathbf{A}_k, \phi_k, \mathbf{H}_k$, and $\mathbf{E}_k$ denoting the potentials and intensities of the *external* electromagnetic field at the point (x_k, y_k, z_k). If this field does not depend upon the time, the equation $(H + p_t)\psi = 0$ admits solutions of the type $\psi = \psi_{H'}^0 e^{-i2\pi H't/h}$ corresponding to a motion of the system with a fixed energy H', the function $\psi_{H'}^0$ being defined by $(H - H')\psi_{H'}^0 = 0$. To each state or energy-level defined by the approximate equation to which it reduces if the spin effect of all the particles is neglected, there correspond, in general, 2^n different states with slightly different energy-levels, which form what is called a 'spin multiplet'. The theory of such multiplets for the simplest case of a single particle has been discussed in the preceding chapter. The general results stated there (§ 29) about the orthogonality properties of the functions $\psi_{H'}^0$, the matrix and supermatrix representation of various physical quantities, the perturbation theory, and so on can easily be extended to the case $n > 1$. We shall not discuss these questions here, but shall leave some of them for a later section where they will be considered in connexion with Pauli's exclusion principle for identical elementary particles (electrons or protons).

The method which has been applied above for the description of the spin effect characteristic of such particles can be used in a somewhat generalized form for the description of the orientation or inner states

of complicated particles—such as atomic nuclei or whole atoms, etc.—
so long as they are treated as moving material points.

Let us consider, for example, a particle possessing an inner angular
momentum (which may be due both to orbital and spin motion of the
electrons and protons constituting it) of s units. Such a particle can
assume $2s+1$ quantized orientations, corresponding to the values

$$m = -s, -(s-1), -(s-2),..., +(s-1), +s \qquad (324)$$

of the z-component of s. These numbers can be defined as the charac-
teristic values of a matrix σ_z, which is the z-component of a matrix $\boldsymbol{\sigma}$
representing the inner angular momentum of the particle in question
(in units of $h/2\pi$). The matrix elements of σ_x, σ_y, and σ_z are defined
by the equations

$$\left.\begin{aligned}
(\sigma_x+i\sigma_y)_{m+1,m} &= \sqrt{\{(s+\tfrac{1}{2})^2-(m+\tfrac{1}{2})^2\}}e^{i\alpha m} \\
(\sigma_x-i\sigma_y)_{m,m+1} &= \sqrt{\{(s+\tfrac{1}{2})^2-(m+\tfrac{1}{2})^2\}}e^{-i\alpha m} \\
(\sigma_z)_{mm} &= m
\end{aligned}\right\} \qquad (324\,a)$$

which are obtained from the equations (94 b), (96), and (96 a) of § 13
(Chap. III), if $\mathbf{M}$ is replaced by $h\boldsymbol{\sigma}/2\pi$ and l by s. The motion of such
a particle in a given external field of force can be described in exactly
the same way as this has been done above for the particular case $s = \tfrac{1}{2}$,
namely, by introducing in addition to the 'external' coordinates x, y, z,
defining the position of the particle's centre of gravity of an 'inner'
angular momentum coordinate ζ, which should assume the values
$1, 2,..., 2s+1$, corresponding to the characteristic values (324) of σ_z. If,
moreover, the additional energy of the particle in a magnetic field $\mathfrak{H}$ is
represented by the operator $\mu\mathfrak{H}\cdot\boldsymbol{\sigma}$, we get a direct generalization of the
Pauli theory of the spin effect, discussed in § 29. A similar generaliza-
tion is obtained if we consider a system of particles—such as electrons
and atomic nuclei—which differ from each other not only with respect
to the charge and mass, but also in respect to the inner momentum
number s or the multiplicity $2s+1$. A problem of this sort is met with,
for instance, in connexion with the hyperfine structure of atomic
spectra, due to the fact that the nuclei of many atoms actually possess
an inner angular momentum and a very small magnetic moment associated with it. The magnetic field produced by the latter can be
specified by a vector potential of the same form,

$$\mathbf{A} = \frac{\mu}{r^3}\boldsymbol{\sigma}\times\mathbf{r},$$

as for an electron (or proton), giving rise to an interaction energy of the type (322 a, b), with σ_k denoting matrices of various ranks (2 for an electron; 1, 2, 3, etc., for a nucleus).

These considerations show, by the way, that an electron can be visualized not as a point but as a spinning sphere, according to the classical model, in spite of the fact that in the Pauli or Dirac theory it is treated as a point.

39. Complex Particles treated as Material Points with Inner Coordinates; Theory of Incomplete Systems

Complex particles can be treated as elementary, i.e., material points if inner coordinates and momenta are introduced to specify their orientation, the total value of the inner angular momentum, if it is variable, as well as other quantities, serving to describe their inner properties.

Let us denote by x (x, y, z) the coordinates of the centre of gravity of the particle, the coordinates specifying the relative motion of the elementary particles (electrons, protons) constituting it being denoted by q $(q_1, q_2, ...)$. Let us divide further the energy operator H into three parts, K, L, M, where K is a function of the x's $\left(\text{and of the associated momenta represented by the operators } \dfrac{h}{2\pi i}\dfrac{\partial}{\partial x}\right)$, L a function of the q's (and of the associated momenta $\dfrac{h}{2\pi i}\dfrac{\partial}{\partial q}$ as well as of the spin variables), while M is a function of both. We shall assume them all to be independent of the time and shall denote the characteristic values and functions of L by L' and $\chi_{L'}(q)$ respectively.

The solution of the equation $(H-H')\psi_{H'} = 0$ for a stationary state of the complex particle (supposed to move in a given external field of force) can be represented in the form

$$\psi_{H'} = \sum_{L'} \phi_{L'}(x)\chi_{L'}(q), \tag{325}$$

where $\phi_{L'}(x)$ are certain expansion coefficients with regard to the variables q, being themselves functions of the variables x. These functions can be determined by substituting (325) in the equation $(H-H')\psi_{H'} = 0$, which gives

$$\sum_{L'} (K\phi_{L'})\chi_{L'} + (L'-H')\phi_{L'}\chi_{L'} + M\chi_{L'}\phi_{L'} = 0.$$

Now the operator M applied to the function $\chi_{L'}$ and thereafter to the function $\phi_{L'}$ gives the same result as the operator

$$\sum_{L'} M_{L''L'}\chi_{L''}$$

acting directly on $\phi_{L'}$, where

$$M_{L'L'} = \int \chi_{L'}^* M \chi_{L'} \, dq$$

are the matrix elements of M with regard to the characteristic inner states of our complex particle (these matrix elements are functions of the x and, in general, of the associated operators $\dfrac{h}{2\pi i}\dfrac{\partial}{\partial x}$). We thus get

$$\sum_{L'} \chi_{L'}[K\phi_{L'} + (L' - H')\phi_{L'}] + \sum_{L'}\sum_{L'} \chi_{L'} M_{L'L'} \phi_{L'} = 0,$$

or, interchanging the summation indices in the double sum and equating to zero the coefficients of the functions $\chi_{L'}$,

$$K\phi_{L'} + \sum_{L'} M_{L'L'}\phi_{L'} = (H' - L')\phi_{L'}. \tag{325a}$$

The system of equations can be written in the form of a single 'operator-matrix' equation
$$J\phi = J'\phi \tag{325b}$$
if ϕ is defined as a one-column matrix with the elements $\phi_{L'}$ and J as a square matrix operator with the elements

$$J_{L'L'} = K\delta_{L'L'} + M_{L'L'}, \tag{325c}$$

$\delta_{L'L'}$ denoting the unit matrix and $J\phi$ the one-column matrix resulting from the matrix multiplication of J by ϕ; $J' = H' - L'$ are the characteristic values of J. We can also regard ϕ as a vector and J as a tensor in the state-space, corresponding to the inner motion (and orientation) of the particle under consideration, and specified by the quantum numbers L' (which must include besides the energy other constants of the inner motion). We can finally regard L' as a sort of 'inner' coordinate (or coordinates) of the particle so long as it is treated as a material point—in the same sense as this is done in Pauli's or Dirac's theory of the spinning electron, with the only difference that the number of possible values of L' is in general infinite, instead of being equal to 2 (as in Pauli's theory) or to 4 (as in that of Dirac). The 'inner' quantum numbers corresponding to these additional coordinates in the functions $\phi(x, L')$, compared with the functions $\phi_{K'}(x)$ which are the solutions of the 'unperturbed' equation $(K - K')\phi_{K'}(x) = 0$, can be represented by the values of the difference $J' - K'$ for the same value of K'.

The different solutions of the equation
$$J\phi_{J'} = J'\phi_{J'},$$
i.e. solutions referring to different values of J', if quadratically integrable, are orthogonal to each other and can be normalized according to the equation
$$\int \phi_{J'}^\dagger \phi_{J'} \, dx = \delta_{J'J'}, \tag{326}$$

where $\phi_{J'}^{\dagger}$ is the one-row matrix formed by the elements which are the conjugate complex of those constituting the one-column matrix $\phi_{J'}$. Introducing L' as an inner coordinate, we can rewrite the preceding equation in the form

$$\int \sum_{L'} \phi_{J'}^{*}(x, L')\phi_{J''}(x, L')\, dx = \delta_{J'J''}. \qquad (326\,\text{a})$$

This result easily follows from the self-adjoint character of the operator matrix J, which in its turn is a consequence of the self-adjoint character of the complete Hamiltonian H.

All quantities referring to the translational motion of the particle under consideration must be represented by operator-matrices of the type

$$F_{L'L''}\left(x, \frac{h}{2\pi i}\frac{\partial}{\partial x}\right) = F\left(x, L'; \frac{h}{2\pi i}\frac{\partial}{\partial x}, L''\right),$$

the inner coordinates appearing twice—in the role of ordinary co-ordinates, and in that of the momenta. The matrix element of such a quantity with regard to two states of motion, specified by the functions $\phi_{J'}$ and $\phi_{J''}$, is given by the expression

$$F_{J'J''} = \int \phi_{J'}^{\dagger}\, F\phi_{J''}\, dx = \int dx \sum_{L'}\sum_{L''} \phi_{J'}^{*}(x, L')F(L', L'')\phi_{J''}(x, L''). \quad (326\,\text{b})$$

This expression is a generalization of those appearing in the theory of Pauli and Dirac, with the inner ('spin') coordinate assuming two or four values only.

Let us suppose, for example, that the particle is an ion (charge e, mass m) moving in an electrostatic field, which within the particle can be dealt with as practically homogeneous and equal to $\mathbf{E} = -\nabla V(x, y, z)$ where $V(x, y, z)$ is the electric potential at the point (centre of gravity) representing the particle. We then have, by the ordinary Schrödinger theory,

$$K = -\frac{h^2}{8\pi m}\nabla_x^2 + eV(x, y, z),$$

as for an elementary particle with a charge e and a mass m, and further

$$M = -\mathbf{E}(x, y, z)\cdot\mathbf{P}(q),$$

where $\mathbf{P}$ is the resulting electric moment of the particle, the position of the electrons and protons being referred to the point (x, y, z). The operator L which specifies the inner motion of the particle—in the absence of the external electric field—need not be considered here. All we need to know are the matrix elements of $\mathbf{P}$ with regard to the stationary states representing this inner motion, the translational motion being determined by an equation of the type (325 a) with

$$M_{L'L''} = -\mathbf{E}(x){\cdot}\mathbf{P}_{L'L''}.$$

For a particle moving in an inhomogeneous magnetic field (a problem met with, for example, in the Stern-Gerlach experiments), we get in a similar manner

$$K = -\frac{h^2}{8\pi^2 m}\nabla_x^2, \qquad M_{L'L''} = -\mathfrak{H}(x){\cdot}\mathbf{\mu}_{L'L''},$$

$\mathbf{\mu}_{L'L''}$ being the matrix elements of the resulting magnetic moment of the particle.

The preceding theory can be easily extended to the general case of a *system* of complex particles, considered as material points, or to the still more general case of any 'incomplete' system A, which is a part of a complete system AB, specified by the Hamiltonian H. If the part of H corresponding to A taken alone is denoted by K, that corresponding to B with L and the rest, representing the mutual action or 'coupling' between A and B with M, we obtain for the motion of A the same results as before, the coordinates x specifying in the general case the configuration of A, and $\phi(x, L')$ being the probability amplitude of this configuration for a given stationary state L' of B.

In the case of two particles, for example, we have, denoting by x_1, x_2 the coordinates of the respective centres of gravity and by q_1, q_2 the inner coordinates,

$$\chi_{L'}(q) = \chi_{L_1'}(q_1)\chi_{L_2'}(q_2), \tag{327}$$

since the operator of the inner motion (without interaction) L obviously reduces to the sum of the corresponding operators L_1 and L_2 for each of the two particles taken separately. Putting further

$$\phi_{L'}(x) = \phi_{L_1'L_2'}(x_1, x_2), \tag{327 a}$$

we obtain for ϕ an equation of the same type as before. If the two particles are treated with regard to their mutual action as electrical dipoles, their mutual potential energy will be represented by the operator

$$M = \frac{1}{r^3}\left[\frac{3}{r^2}(\mathbf{r}{\cdot}\mathbf{P}_1)(\mathbf{r}{\cdot}\mathbf{P}_2) - \mathbf{P}_1{\cdot}\mathbf{P}_2\right],$$

where $\mathbf{r}$ is the radius vector drawn from one particle to the other (with the components $x_1 - x_2$, etc.), whence

$$M_{L'L''} = \frac{1}{r^3}\left[\frac{3}{r^2}(\mathbf{r}{\cdot}\mathbf{P}_{1L_1'L_1''})(\mathbf{r}{\cdot}\mathbf{P}_{2L_2'L_2''}) - \mathbf{P}_{1L_1'L_1''}{\cdot}\mathbf{P}_{2L_2'L_2''}\right]. \tag{327 b}$$

It should be noted that in spite of the incompleteness of the system A, specified by the energy operator $K+M$ which represents its own energy and the action on it produced by the 'ignored' part B, the motion of A is *exactly* determined if the operator M is defined as a matrix with regard to the stationary states of B. This method of describing the motion of an incomplete system A is especially convenient if its coupling with $\overset{\bullet}{B}$ is relatively weak and if for some reason we are not concerned with the details of the motion of B. As a further example of a (rather unconscious) application of this method we shall mention Fermi's theory of the hyperfine structure of spectra, due to the mutual action of an electron (A) with a nucleus (B) possessing a magnetic moment. The motion of the electron is determined in this theory with the help of Dirac's equation, the action of the nuclear magnetic moment on the electron being represented by the vector potential $\mathbf{A} = \dfrac{\mu}{r^3}\boldsymbol{\sigma}\times\mathbf{r}$, where $\boldsymbol{\sigma}$ is the well-known matrix of rank $2s+1$, specifying the angular momentum of the nucleus $hs/2\pi$. The wave function ψ must be treated accordingly as a rectangular matrix with four columns (corresponding to the four components of the Dirac wave function) and $2s+1$ rows.— We shall discuss later another interesting application of the same method (due to Heisenberg) to the problem of the interaction between matter (A) and radiation (B), the latter being described by ordinary electromagnetic oscillations, whose amplitudes are treated as matrices (Chap. IX).

If the interaction energy M is relatively small so that the second term on the left side of the equation,

$$K\phi(x, L') + \sum_{L''} M(L', L'')\phi(x, L'') = (H' - L')\phi(x, L'),$$

can be treated as a small perturbation, this equation can be solved approximately with the help of the ordinary perturbation method starting with the solution of the equation which is obtained by dropping the term M. More exactly, since our problem becomes degenerate, we must consider the whole set of solutions corresponding to the same *unperturbed* energy-level $H' - L' = K'$. Writing $(K', \bar{L}')$ for J', where $\bar{L}'$ denotes an inner quantum number independent of L' but identical with it in regard to the range of its possible values,† we can define an orthogonal and normal set of solutions of the unperturbed equation $K\phi = K'\phi$ by the formula,

$$\phi_{K'\bar{L}'}(x, L') = \omega_{K'}(x)\delta_{\bar{L}'L'}, \tag{328}$$

where $\omega_{K'}(x)$ denotes the solution of the above equation leaving out of

† In the same sense as the spin coordinate $\zeta = 1, 2$ and the spin quantum number $\lambda = 1, 2$ for a single electron of the Pauli theory (cf. § 29).

account the inner coordinates, while $\delta_{\bar{L}'L'}$ are the elements of the unit matrix. The function $\omega_{K'}(x)$ is supposed to be normalized according to the ordinary condition $\int |\omega_{K'}(x)|^2 \, dx = 1$; it is supposed, moreover, to be the only solution of the ordinary Schrödinger equation $K\omega = K'\omega$ corresponding to the energy-level K' (so that no further degeneracy outside of that which is specified by the quantum numbers $\bar{L}'$ need be considered).

The approximate solutions of the exact equation, 'stabilized' for the perturbation M, can be defined, according to the general theory, as linear combinations of the functions (328)

$$\phi_J(x, L') = \sum_{\bar{L}'} c_{\bar{L}'} \phi_{K'\bar{L}'}(x, L'). \tag{328 a}$$

The sum reduces in the present case to a single term, so that we get

$$\phi_{J'}(x, L') = c_{L'} \omega_{K'}(x). \tag{328 b}$$

If M were an ordinary operator not involving the inner coordinates, then the coefficients of the transformation (329) for each admissible value of the perturbation energy $H' - L' - K' = \Delta K'$ (together with the latter) would be determined by the system of equations

$$\sum M_{\bar{L}'\bar{L}'} \cdot c_{\bar{L}'} = \Delta K' c_{\bar{L}'},$$

where $M_{\bar{L}'\bar{L}'}$ are the matrix elements of M with respect to the unperturbed functions. These equations remain valid in the present case provided the matrix elements of M are defined according to the general formula (326 b) which gives, in virtue of (328 a),

$$M_{\bar{L}'\bar{L}'} = \int \omega_{K'}^*(x) M(\bar{L}', \bar{L}'') \omega_{K'}(x) \, dx.$$

Denoting this expression by $M_{K'\bar{L}',K'\bar{L}'}$ and dropping the bars over the L's, we get

$$\sum_{L'} M_{K'L',K'L'} c_{L'} = \Delta K' c_{L'}. \tag{329}$$

We shall not stop here to discuss these equations, since they are practically identical with those of the ordinary perturbation theory.

It should be added in conclusion that the preceding theory can easily be generalized for non-stationary phenomena corresponding to an explicit dependence of the energy operator H upon the time. So long as this dependence does not affect the operator L, it is sufficient to replace the characteristic value H' of H in (325 a) by the operator $-p_t = -\dfrac{h}{2\pi i} \dfrac{\partial}{\partial t}$, the functions $\phi_{L'}$ being determined by the equation

$$-\frac{h}{2\pi i} \frac{\partial}{\partial t} \phi_{L'} = (K + L')\phi_{L'} + \sum_{L'} M_{L'L'} \psi_{L'}. \tag{329 a}$$

40. Identical Particles (Electrons) and the Exclusion Principle

Returning to elementary particles, we shall now take into account the restrictive condition which follows from the identity of all the electrons or all the protons and which is expressed by Pauli's exclusion principle or by the Dirac antisymmetry principle for the wave functions ϕ describing the behaviour of a system of electrons or protons (see § 22, Part I). For the sake of simplicity we shall apply this principle to a system of electrons only, treating protons and atomic nuclei as fixed centres of force. Such a treatment can actually be applied with sufficient accuracy to many problems connected with the structure of atoms, molecules, and material bodies; for in view of the relatively large mass of the atomic nuclei—protons included—they can be dealt with to a certain approximation as fixed material points, producing the external electrostatic (and also magnetostatic) field in which the electrons are supposed to move.

We must, to begin with, check the validity of the Pauli principle in Dirac's form—in the sense of its permanence in time—from the point of view of the generalized equation of motion, involving the spin coordinates, which has been established in the preceding chapter.†

This equation can be written in the following form:

$$\sum_{\zeta_1''...\zeta''} H(x_1\,\zeta_1',...,x_n\,\zeta_n';p_1\,\zeta_1'',...,p_n\,\zeta_n'')\psi(x_1\,\zeta_1'',...,x_n\,\zeta_n'')$$

$$= -\frac{h}{2\pi i}\frac{\partial}{\partial t}\psi(x_1\,\zeta_1',...,x_n\,\zeta_n'), \quad (330)$$

i.e. as a system of 2^n equations for the set of 2^n wave functions ψ_ζ, where x_k and p_k stand short for coordinate triplets x_k, y_k, z_k and the momentum components p_{kx}, p_{ky}, p_{kz}. The space coordinates of each particle, together with its spin coordinate, form a coordinate quadruplet; the same is true of the momenta, the momentum corresponding to the spin coordinate being replaced by a duplication of the latter, which gives to H its operator-matrix character.

In view of the identity of all the electrons, H must be a symmetrical function with regard to the indices 1, 2,... distinguishing them. If, therefore, the wave function ψ is symmetrical or antisymmetrical with regard to these indices—i.e. with regard to all the coordinate quadruplets—at some instant t, its derivative $\partial\psi/\partial t$, and consequently its value for the next (or preceding) instant, will be so too. The symmetri-

---

† It should be remembered that the permanence of the antisymmetrical character of the wave function has been established in Part I on the basis of the ordinary Schrödinger equation for a system of identical particles without spin.

cal or antisymmetrical character of ψ can be regarded therefore as a permanent property. The fact that for a system of electrons (or protons) antisymmetrical wave functions only must be used to interpret the experimental data has been discussed at length in § 22 of Part I.

As the spin forces are very small compared with the electrostatic ones, a fairly good approximation (of 'zero order') can be obtained by totally neglecting them (as well as the magnetic forces of Biot and Savart, specified by the mutual kinetic energy T').

The energy operator-matrix $H_{\zeta'\zeta}$ reduces in this case to the product of the ordinary Hamiltonian operator for the system of particles under consideration:

$$K = K(x_1,...,x_n; p_1,...,p_n),$$

with the unit matrix (321 a). Limiting ourselves to solutions of the type $\psi = \psi^0(x_1 \zeta_1,...,x_n \zeta_n)e^{-i2\pi K't/h}$, which correspond to a motion with a fixed energy K', we thus get, instead of (330),

$$(K-K')\psi = 0. \tag{330 a}$$

This equation differs from that of the ordinary theory (not involving the spin) only by the fact that K is understood to contain as a factor the unit matrix and that ψ is to be regarded as a function both of the ordinary coordinates and of the spin coordinates $\zeta_1,...,\zeta_n$. Since K does not contain the latter—or more exactly the spin matrices $\sigma_1, \sigma_2,..., \sigma_n$— these matrices must commute with K and represent consequently constants of the motion. The characteristic values of their z-components $\sigma_{kz} = 2m_k = \pm 1$ can be considered accordingly as additional spin quantum numbers specifying 2^n solutions of (330 a), that is 2^n degenerate states which belong to the same value of the energy K'. We shall distinguish these 2^n states with the help of the indices $m_1,...,m_n$, writing m short for the whole set of them. It should be remembered that the product of m_k by $h/2\pi$ represents the projection of the spin of the kth electron on the z-axis.

If we write $\zeta_k = -\tfrac{1}{2}, +\tfrac{1}{2}$ instead of 1 and 2 respectively (as was done before), we can define a set of 2^n orthogonal and normal solutions of the equation $(K-K')\psi_{K'} = 0$ which belong to the same characteristic value of K by the formula

$$\psi_{K'm}(x, \zeta) = \phi_{K'}(x)\delta_{m\zeta}, \tag{331}$$

where $\delta_{m\zeta} = \delta_{m_1\zeta_1} \delta_{m_2\zeta_2} ... \delta_{m_n\zeta_n}$ is the 2^n-dimensional unit matrix equivalent to (321 a) and $\phi_{K'}(x)$ the normalized solution of the ordinary

Schrödinger equation $(K-K')\phi_{K'} = 0$ not involving any spin coordinates. We have in fact, by the definition (331),

$$\int \psi_{K'm'}^{\dagger} \psi_{K'm''} \, dV = \int \sum_{\zeta'} \sum_{\zeta''} \psi_{K'm'}^{*}(x\zeta')\psi_{K'm''}(x\zeta'') \, dV = \delta_{m'm''}. \quad (331\,a)$$

This form of the solution of the Schrödinger equation with the spin coordinates taken into account *cannot, however, be reconciled with the antisymmetry condition* for the functions ψ, except when all the n spin quantum numbers $m_1,...,m_n$ have the same value (either $\frac{1}{2}$ or $-\frac{1}{2}$). In this case $\delta_{m\zeta}$ is a symmetrical function of the spin coordinates, and in order to satisfy the antisymmetry condition we must define ϕ as an antisymmetrical function of all the n coordinate triplets $x_1,...,x_n$.

If some of the numbers m_k have the value $-\frac{1}{2}$ and others the value $+\frac{1}{2}$, the function ψ as defined by (331) will not be antisymmetrical, whatever the type of the space factor ϕ.

The spin factors $\delta_{m\zeta}$ can be used, however, in this case to obtain somewhat more complicated spin functions $\epsilon(\zeta)$ which are either symmetrical with regard to *all* the variables $\zeta_1,...,\zeta_n$ or with regard to *some* of them, being in the latter case antisymmetrical with regard to *definite pairs* of these variables.

A symmetrical spin function $\epsilon(\zeta)$ can be formed by permuting the variables ζ_i and ζ_k in those factors $\delta_{m_i\zeta_i}$ and $\delta_{m_k\zeta_k}$ for which $m_i \neq m_k$ and adding the results. If instead of adding we subtract them from each other, we shall get a function antisymmetrical with regard to the pair of variables (ζ_i, ζ_k). Putting for the sake of brevity

$$\begin{aligned} u(\zeta_i, \zeta_k) &= (\delta_{-\frac{1}{2},\zeta_i}\delta_{+\frac{1}{2},\zeta_k} - \delta_{-\frac{1}{2},\zeta_k}\delta_{+\frac{1}{2},\zeta_i}) = -u(\zeta_k, \zeta_i) \\ v(\zeta_i, \zeta_k) &= (\delta_{-\frac{1}{2},\zeta_i}\delta_{+\frac{1}{2},\zeta_k} + \delta_{-\frac{1}{2},\zeta_k}\delta_{+\frac{1}{2},\zeta_i}) = +v(\zeta_k, \zeta_i) \end{aligned} \Bigg\}, \quad (332)$$

we get for $\epsilon(\zeta)$ an expression of the form

$$\epsilon_{ij}(\zeta) = u(\zeta_1, \zeta_2)u(\zeta_3, \zeta_4) ... u(\zeta_{2i-1}, \zeta_{2i})v_j(\zeta_{2i+1},...,\zeta_n), \quad (332\,a)$$

where $v_j(\zeta_{2i+1},...,\zeta_n)$ is a symmetrical function of the $n-2i$ variables $\zeta_{2i+1},..., \zeta_n$ formed by taking the product of a certain number j of functions of the type $v(\zeta_k, \zeta_i)$ and of $n-2(i+j)$ simple functions $\delta_{m_k\zeta_k}$ with the same value m' of m_k, and summing such products for all non-trivial permutations of the variables $\zeta_{2i+1},..., \zeta_n$:

$$v_j(\zeta_{2i+1},...,\zeta_n) = \sum v(\zeta_{2i+1}, \zeta_{2i+2}) ... v(\zeta_{2i+2j-1}, \zeta_{2i+2j})\delta_{m'\zeta_{2(i+j)+1}} ... \delta_{m'\zeta_n}.$$

$$(332\,b)$$

The numbers i and j fully specify the spin functions $\epsilon_{ij}(\zeta)$ for a fixed arrangement of the variables $\zeta_1,...,\zeta_n$. By permuting the latter we can obtain other functions of the same symmetry type.

Before, however, proceeding to such permutations, let us multiply the function (332 a) by a space factor $\phi_i(x)$ which we shall assume to be symmetrical with regard to the pairs of coordinate triplets (x_1, x_2), $(x_3, x_4),..., (x_{2i-1}, x_{2i})$ and antisymmetrical with regard to the rest. The product

$$\phi_i(x)\epsilon_{ij}(\zeta) \tag{333}$$

will obviously be antisymmetrical with regard to the *pairs* of coordinate quadruplets $(x_1, \zeta_1, x_2, \zeta_2)$, $(x_3, \zeta_3, x_4, \zeta_4),..., (x_{2i-1}, \zeta_{2i-1}, x_{2i}, \zeta_{2i})$ and anti-symmetrical with regard to all the other coordinate quadruplets. It will have, however, no symmetry whatever with regard to permutations affecting the variables of different groups, corresponding, for example, to interchanges between the first and the third electron, or the first and the $(2i+1)$th one. If we now apply such permutations (P_i) to the function (333) and add the results, we can obtain a function

$$\phi_{ij}(x, \zeta) = \sum_{P_i} P_i[\phi_i(x)\epsilon_{ij}(\zeta)] \tag{333 a}$$

which will be antisymmetrical with regard to *all* the electrons, i.e. all the coordinate quadruplets. Permutations of this class can hardly be defined explicitly for the general case (arbitrary values of i and j). They can, however, be specified unambiguously by certain simple conditions which we shall not consider here.

The antisymmetrical wave functions (333 a) can also be obtained by starting from 'spinless' functions of the type $\phi_{ij}(x)$ symmetrical with regard to i pairs of electrons and antisymmetrical with regard to j other pairs, while antisymmetrical with respect to all the other $n-2(i+j)$ electrons. The complementary spin factors $\epsilon(\zeta)$ should reduce in this case to a product of i factors u, j factors v, and $n-2(i+j) = 2|m|$ factors $\delta_{m'\zeta}$. The permutations P_{ij} which must be applied to the products $\phi_{ij}(x)\epsilon_{ij}(\zeta)$ in order to obtain the functions

$$\phi_{ij}(x, \zeta) = \sum_{P_{ij}} P_{ij}[\phi_{ij}(x)\epsilon_{ij}(\zeta)],$$

identical with those defined by (333 a), will constitute a broader class than the permutations P_i. In fact, they can be defined as the products of the latter and of the permutations which must be applied to the spin functions

$$v(\zeta_{2i+1}, \zeta_{2i+2}) ... v(\zeta_{2(i+j)-1}, \zeta_{2(i+j)})\delta_{m'\zeta_{2(i+j)+1}} ... \delta_{m'\zeta_n}$$

in order to obtain upon addition the symmetrical function (332 b).

In constructing the functions (333 a) we have left out of account the condition that they must satisfy the 'spinless' Schrödinger condition. Now it is easily seen that this condition is fulfilled so long as it is fulfilled for the space factor $\phi_i(x)$ in the initially chosen function (333). Applying to the equation $K\phi_i(x) = K_i\phi_i(x)$ any permutation P_i, we have indeed, since K is symmetrical with regard to all the electrons and K_i is a pure number,

$$P_i[K\phi_i(x)] = K[P_i\phi_i(x)] = K_i[P_i\phi_i(x)].$$

This shows that if $\phi_i(x)$ is a characteristic function of the operator belonging to a certain characteristic value (energy-level) K_i, then all the functions resulting from it by permuting the electrons will also be characteristic functions, belonging to the same energy-level. This being so, any linear combination of such functions will have the same property, which therefore will be shared by the unique combination (333 a) satisfying the antisymmetry condition (the factors $P_i[\epsilon_{ij}(\zeta)]$, which are equal either to ± 1 or to 0, playing the role of ordinary coefficients with regard to the functions $P_i[\phi_i(x)]$).

It remains to be seen whether the equation $K\phi = K'\phi$ actually has solutions of the type ϕ_i, i.e. antisymmetrical with regard to all the n electrons ($i = 0$), or symmetrical with regard to one pair (1, 2), and antisymmetrical with regard to the rest ($i = 1$), or symmetrical with regard to two pairs [(1, 2), (3, 4)], and antisymmetrical with regard to the rest ($i = 2$), and so on. A rigorous proof of this existence theorem is not easy and we shall not stop to give it. The following remarks are worth mentioning, however, in this connexion:

1. The functions ϕ_i defined above (or their linear combinations) are not the only characteristic functions of a symmetrical operator K; the latter has besides, a number of characteristic functions with an entirely different symmetry character—for instance, symmetrical with regard to all the n coordinate triplets or antisymmetrical with regard to two or three of them, and symmetrical with regard to the rest, and so on. Such solutions, although they exist mathematically, are non-existent physically, i.e. they do not correspond to any real phenomenon, for they cannot provide a basis for constructing functions antisymmetrical with regard to all the coordinate quadruplets x_k, ζ_k. The fact that such a basis is provided only by functions of the type $\phi_i(x)$ is a consequence of the two-valuedness of the spin quantum numbers m_k of the individual electrons, this two-valuedness determining the symmetry type of the 'spin-factors' $\epsilon(\zeta)$ and thence indirectly the symmetry type of the associated space-factors $\phi(x)$.

2. The functions $\phi_i(x)$ (or their linear combinations) corresponding to different values of i belong in general to different characteristic

values K_i of the energy operator. They can be introduced as 'non-combining' solutions of the equation $\left(K+\dfrac{h}{2\pi i}\dfrac{\partial}{\partial t}\right)\phi = 0$ in that case also when K contains the time explicitly (i.e. when the electrons are supposed to move under the influence of a variable field of some external origin). In this case the symmetry character of ϕ remains a permanent property, if no difference is made between various linear combinations of the functions $P[\phi_i(x)]$ with the same value of i, the permanence of the antisymmetry character of ϕ_0 being a particular case of this theorem (the latter holds likewise for a number of solutions belonging to other symmetry classes, not realized in nature).

It will be convenient in the sequel to replace the numbers i and j, which specify the functions (333) or (333 a) by two other numbers,

$$s = \tfrac{1}{2}(n-2i) = \tfrac{1}{2}n-i, \tag{334}$$

and

$$m = \sum_{k=1}^{n} m_k = \pm(\tfrac{1}{2}n-i-j). \tag{334 a}$$

The latter can obviously be interpreted as the component of the resulting spin angular momentum of all the electrons along the z-axis (in $h/2\pi$ units); in fact it is equal to the algebraic sum of the characteristic values of the matrices $\tfrac{1}{2}\sigma_{zk}$ for the individual electrons. For a given value of s, m can assume $2s+1$ values differing from each other by 1 and lying between $+s$ and $-s$. This circumstance suggests the interpretation of s as the *magnitude of the vector specifying the resulting spin of all the electrons* (irrespective of its direction). The characteristic value of the square of this total spin is equal to the product of $(h/2\pi)^2$ with $s(s+1)$—just as in the case of the resulting 'orbital' momentum, defined by the number j (see § 37).

The above interpretation of the number s is also supported by the fact that its maximum value is equal to $\tfrac{1}{2}n$, which corresponds to the same direction of the spin vectors σ_k of the separate electrons. It thus appears that the resulting spin associated with a given solution ϕ_i of the 'spinless' Schrödinger equation is equal to one-half of the number of electrons with regard to which this function is antisymmetrical.

We shall now consider, for the sake of illustration, the special cases of systems consisting of two and three electrons, a helium and a lithium atom, say. In the first case we get functions $\phi_i(x)$ of two types only, namely, the antisymmetrical one $\phi_0(x) = \phi_0(\underline{x_1,x_2})$ and the symmetrical $\phi_1(x) = \phi_1(\overline{x_1,x_2})$ (following Heitler and London, we introduce lines under or over the neighbouring variables, to indicate the antisym-

metrical or symmetrical character of the wave function with regard
to these variables). Taking further the four combinations of the indi-
vidual spin quantum numbers m_1 and m_2, namely, $(-\frac{1}{2}, -\frac{1}{2})$, $(-\frac{1}{2}, +\frac{1}{2})$,
$(+\frac{1}{2}, -\frac{1}{2})$, $(+\frac{1}{2}, +\frac{1}{2})$, we can form three symmetrical spin functions,

$$v(\overline{\zeta_1, \zeta_2}) = \delta_{-\frac{1}{2}, \zeta_1} \delta_{-\frac{1}{2}, \zeta_2}, \qquad \delta_{-\frac{1}{2}, \zeta_1} \delta_{\frac{1}{2}, \zeta_2} + \delta_{-\frac{1}{2}, \zeta_2} \delta_{+\frac{1}{2}, \zeta_1}, \qquad \delta_{\frac{1}{2}, \zeta_1} \delta_{\frac{1}{2}, \zeta_2},$$

and one antisymmetrical

$$u(\zeta_1, \zeta_2) = \delta_{-\frac{1}{2}, \zeta_1} \delta_{\frac{1}{2}, \zeta_2} - \delta_{-\frac{1}{2}, \zeta_2} \delta_{\frac{1}{2}, \zeta_1}.$$

The products of the former with the antisymmetrical space function
$\phi_0(x_1, x_2)$ define three states, corresponding to the same resulting spin
$s = 1$ (parallel orientation of the two electrons) and to the values
$m = -1, 0, +1$ of its projection on the z-axis, whereas the product of
$u(\zeta_1, \zeta_2)$ with $\phi_1(\overline{x_1, x_2})$ defines a single state corresponding to $s = 0$ and
$m = 0$ ('anti-parallel' orientations of the spins).

In the case of three electrons we must distinguish likewise two types
of 'spinless' functions, namely, those antisymmetrical with regard to
all the three electrons $\phi_0(x) = \phi_0(x_1, x_2, x_3)$, and those symmetrical with
regard to two of them, $\phi_1(x) = \phi_1(\overline{x_1, x_2}, x_3)$, say (the third electron, being
alone, does not require any specific condition with respect to symmetry).

The functions of the first type must be combined with a symmetrical
spin factor $\epsilon(\overline{\zeta_1, \zeta_2, \zeta_3})$ which can be obtained either in the form

$$\epsilon = \delta_{m'\zeta_1} \delta_{m'\zeta_2} \delta_{m'\zeta_3},$$

if $m_1 = m_2 = m_3 = m' = \pm\frac{1}{2}$ $(\sum m_k = \pm\frac{3}{2})$, or in the form

$$\epsilon = v(\overline{\zeta_1, \zeta_2})\delta_{m''\zeta_3} + v(\overline{\zeta_3, \zeta_1})\delta_{m''\zeta_2} + v(\overline{\zeta_2, \zeta_3})\delta_{m''\zeta_1},$$

if one of the numbers m_k is different from the two others $(\sum m_k = \pm\frac{1}{2})$.
We thus get a 'quadruplet', i.e. four states with the same $s = \frac{3}{2}$ and consequently with the same value of the energy $K = K_0$, which are distinguished from each other by the values of the resulting 'axial' spin
numbers $m = -\frac{3}{2}, -\frac{1}{2}, \frac{1}{2}, \frac{3}{2}$.

The functions of the second type, $\phi_1(\overline{x_1, x_2}, x_3)$, must be combined
with spin factors of the form

$$\epsilon(\overline{\zeta_1, \zeta_2}, \zeta_3) = u(\overline{\zeta_1, \zeta_2})\delta_{m'\zeta_3},$$

and summed over the cyclic permutations of all the three electrons,
giving two antisymmetrical functions,

$$\psi(x, \zeta) = \phi_1(\overline{x_1, x_2}, x_3)u(\overline{\zeta_1, \zeta_2})\delta_{m'\zeta_3} + \phi_1(\overline{x_3, x_1}, x_2)u(\overline{\zeta_3, \zeta_1})\delta_{m'\zeta_2} +$$
$$+ \phi_1(\overline{x_2, x_3}, x_1)u(\overline{\zeta_2, \zeta_3})\delta_{m'\zeta_1},$$

for two different values of m'; the states defined by them belong to the same value $\frac{1}{2}$ of s and to the same energy $K = K_1$, forming what is called a 'spin doublet' of a similar type to that for a single electron. The antisymmetrical character of the functions $\psi(x, \zeta)$ is clearly seen from the fact that if two electrons, the first and the second, say, are interchanged, the first term changes its sign, whereas the second and third are transformed into each other with opposite signs. It should be mentioned that the normal state of a lithium atom, constituted by two equivalent inner electrons, forming its 'core', and one 'valence' electron, must be described by a wave function of the above type.

VIII

REDUCTION OF THE PROBLEM OF A SYSTEM OF
IDENTICAL PARTICLES TO THAT OF A SINGLE PARTICLE

41. Perturbation Theory of a System of Spinless Electrons and the Exchange Degeneracy

Further progress in the study of the problem of many electrons can be achieved only if we describe their motion in a way similar to that used in Bohr's theory of complex atoms, namely, by assigning to each electron an individual state of motion in a given field of force. The mutual action of the electrons can be partially accounted for by intro-ducing some constants like the screening constants, in the definition of the appropriate field of force for each electron, or by using the same suitably chosen field of force for all of them—a self-consistent field, for example (see below). The problem of the motion of the whole system is thus reduced to that of the motion of the separate particles constituting it and to the determination of the effective external field which can approximately represent their mutual action. Inasmuch as this mutual action is accounted for inexactly, we can obtain a better approximation by treating it, or that part of it which was not included to begin with in the effective field of force, as a small perturbation, and approach the exact solution by the methods of the perturbation theory, starting with the solution which corresponds to a distribution of the electrons between various individual states of motion (or 'orbits').

A characteristic distinction between Bohr's theory and the new quantum theory in connexion with this perturbation problem consists in the fact that *the electrons must be interchanged between all the individual orbits* in such a way as to be completely stripped of their individuality. This result which is expressed by the symmetry principle for the probability density $\psi\psi^*$ or the antisymmetry principle for the proba-bility amplitude ψ can be shown to be in harmony with the principles of the perturbation theory applied to the problem of a system of identical particles.

The wave function ϕ describing their motion can be represented to begin with as the product of the functions $\psi_1(x_1), \psi_2(x_2),..., \psi_n(x_n)$ describ-ing the behaviour of the individual electrons in the given external field of force. Putting
$$\phi(x) = \psi_1(x_1)\psi_2(x_2)...\psi_n(x_n) \tag{335}$$
and denoting by $P\phi$ the function into which ϕ is transformed when

the permutation $\dot{P}$ is applied to the electrons, we can represent the general solution of our undisturbed problem, belonging to the same energy as $\phi(x)$ by the expression

$$\chi(x) = \sum_P C_P P\phi, \tag{335a}$$

where C_P are arbitrary coefficients, the sum being extended over all the possible permutations, or at least over the 'effectively different' ones, i.e. such as lead to *different* functions $P\phi$.

If all the n individual wave functions $\psi_1, \psi_2, ..., \psi_n$ are different, every one of the $n!$ possible permutations P will be associated with a specific function $P\phi$. In the contrary case the permutations P can be subdivided into separate sets of equivalent permutations, which correspond to identical functions $P\phi$, and in writing down (335a) we shall have to consider only one representative of each set.

We shall assume for the sake of simplicity that apart from this 'exchange degeneracy', arising from the possibility of interchanging the electrons between different individual states without altering the total energy, no other type of degeneracy need be considered.

We shall disregard in this section the spin effects and treat the electrons as spinless particles, using for the determination of their motion the ordinary Schrödinger theory. We shall leave aside furthermore the question as to the symmetry of the functions $\chi(x)$ and shall try to determine the coefficients C_P by which they are defined in such a way as to ensure the approximate validity of the expression (335a) when the perturbing forces (i.e. the mutual action of the electrons or the neglected part of this mutual action) are taken into account. In this case the function (335a) is said to be 'stabilized' for the perturbation. It is meant by this that if the approximation is pushed further, the coefficients C_P will suffer but a slight variation. This question has been considered in its most general form in the perturbation theory of degenerate systems. As has been shown there, the degenerate set of states specified by the functions $P\phi$ gives rise to the same number of states belonging in general to different energy-levels H' and specified by the values of the coefficients C_P which satisfy the system of equations

$$\sum_Q H_{P,Q} C_Q = H' C_P, \tag{336}$$

where $H_{P,Q}$ are the matrix elements of the *total* energy with regard to the approximate functions $P\phi$ and $Q\phi$:

$$H_{P,Q} = \int P\phi^* H Q\phi \, dV, \tag{336a}$$

Q denoting, as well as P, a permutation of the electrons.

In writing down the equations (336) we are tacitly assuming that the different functions $P\phi$ are *mutually orthogonal*. This assumption is easily seen to be verified if the functions $\psi_i(x_n)$ describing the different individual states are orthogonal with regard to each other. Now the mutual orthogonality of the individual functions is automatically secured if they represent different stationary states of an electron in a given external field—*the same for all the n electrons*. In many actual problems it is more convenient, however, to assign to each electron a specific field of force (for instance, a Coulomb field, characterized by a specific value of the screening constant in the problem of the distribution of electrons in a heavy atom), in which case the individual wave functions can no longer be considered as mutually orthogonal.

The equations (336) must be replaced in this case according to (61), § 9, by the following ones:

$$\sum_Q (H_{P,Q} - H' J_{P,Q}) C_Q = 0, \tag{337}$$

where
$$J_{P,Q} = \int P\phi^* Q\phi \, dV. \tag{337a}$$

The value of this integral must obviously remain unaltered if the integration variables are replaced by any other ones (which amounts simply to a change of notation). We can, in particular, interchange them in a manner corresponding to an arbitrary permutation R of the electrons. The functions $P\phi^*$ and $Q\phi$ will be replaced accordingly by $RP\phi^*$ and $RQ\phi$, so that we shall get

$$J_{P,Q} = \int RP\phi^* RQ\phi \, dV = J_{RP,RQ}.$$

It should be noticed that the permutation R must not be applied to the functions ϕ^* and ϕ, the result

$$\int PR\phi^* QR\phi \, dV = J_{PR,QR}$$

being in general quite different from the preceding one.

If, in particular, R is identified with the reciprocal of Q ($R = Q^{-1}$), we get
$$J_{P,Q} = J_{Q^{-1}P}, \tag{338}$$

where J_S is an abbreviation for $J_{S,I}$, I denoting the identical permutation ($I\phi \equiv \phi$).

We get likewise, because of the symmetry of the energy operator H with regard to all the electrons,

$$H_{P,Q} = H_{RP,RQ}$$

and in particular
$$H_{P,Q} = H_{Q^{-1}P}, \tag{338a}$$

H_R being an abbreviation for $H_{R,I}$.

The relations $J_{Q,P} = J^*_{P,Q}$ and $H_{Q,P} = H^*_{P,Q}$ can be written accordingly in the following form:

$$J_{R^{-1}} = J^*_R; \qquad H_{R^{-1}} = H^*_R, \qquad (338\,b)$$

where $R = Q^{-1}P$ and $R^{-1} = P^{-1}Q$. We thus see that the number of different matrix elements $H_{P,Q}$ and $J_{P,Q}$ is actually reduced to the number, g say, of different states $P\phi$ instead of being equal to its square g^2.

The equations (337) can be rewritten as follows:

$$\sum_R (H_R - H'J_R)C_{PR^{-1}} = 0, \qquad (339)$$

the summation over all the permutations R being obviously equivalent to the original summation over the permutations Q, with a fixed permutation P, the latter specifying each of the g equations forming our system. The perturbed values of the energy H' are determined as the roots of the determinantal equation

$$|H_{Q^{-1}P} - H'J_{Q^{-1}P}| = 0, \qquad (339\,b)$$

which expresses the condition of their compatibility.

Two types of solution of our perturbation problem are immediately obtained from the equations (339)—namely, those which correspond to the symmetrical and to the antisymmetrical functions χ. In the former case all the coefficients C_Q are equal, so that they cancel out and the equations (339) reduce to the single equation

$$\sum_R (H_R - H'J_R) = 0,$$

which serves for the determination of the energy

$$H'_{\text{sym}} = \sum_R H_R \Big/ \sum_R J_R. \qquad (340)$$

In the latter case the coefficients C_Q are defined by the formula $C_Q = \epsilon_Q C$, where $\epsilon_Q = +1$ for even permutations (equivalent to an even number of transpositions) and $= -1$ for odd ones. Since in this case $C_{PR} = \epsilon_P \epsilon_R C$, the g equations (339) again reduce to the single equation

$$\sum_R \epsilon_R(H_R - H'J_R) = 0,$$

whence $\qquad H'_{\text{antisym}} = \sum_R \epsilon_R H_R \Big/ \sum_R \epsilon_R J_R. \qquad (340\,a)$

One might be tempted to look for more general solutions of (339) by assuming that $C_{PQ} = \text{const.}\, C_P C_Q$, or $C_P = \text{const.}\, e^{i\alpha_P}$. It can easily be shown, however, in the same way as in Part I, § 22, that this assumption leads to symmetrical and antisymmetrical functions only. The symmetry properties of all the other solutions can be determined by the following method due to Dirac.

According to Dirac, permutations can be dealt with in exactly the same way as ordinary linear operators which serve to represent various physical quantities. They can, in fact, be multiplied by each other, the product being in general non-commutative, i.e. depending upon the order of the factors, but satisfying the associative law (just as in the case of differential or matrix operators investigated hitherto). It is possible further to define the *sum* of two or more permutations as an operator, which without being itself a permutation is equivalent to them in the sense of the distributive law:

$$(P_1 + P_2)F = P_1 F + P_2 F,$$

where F denotes any other operator or function.

To each permutation

$$P = \begin{Bmatrix} 1, & 2, \ldots, & n \\ k_1, & k_2, \ldots, & k_n \end{Bmatrix},$$

there corresponds the reciprocal permutation

$$P^{-1} = \begin{Bmatrix} k_1, & k_2, \ldots, & k_n \\ 1, & 2, \ldots, & n \end{Bmatrix},$$

whose product with P, irrespective of the order of the two factors, is equal to 1, i.e. is equivalent to the 'identical' permutation

$$1 = \begin{Bmatrix} 1\,2 \ldots n \\ 1\,2 \ldots n \end{Bmatrix}.$$

Every permutation P can be represented as a product of 'cyclic' permutations, of the type

$$\begin{Bmatrix} 1 & 2 & 3 & 4 \\ 2 & 3 & 4 & 1 \end{Bmatrix} \equiv (1, 2, 3, 4),$$

where each element in the brackets ( ) is replaced by the next, the last one being replaced by the first. The different cycles into which P is thus factorized must have no common elements; they can be therefore commuted with each other without changing the result. We have for example,

$$\begin{Bmatrix} 1 & 2 & 3 & 4 & 5 & 6 & 7 & 8 & 9 \\ 7 & 5 & 4 & 2 & 3 & 9 & 1 & 8 & 6 \end{Bmatrix} = (1, 7)(2, 5, 3, 4)(6, 9)(8),$$

the two-element cycles $(1, 7)$ and $(6, 9)$ being simply transpositions (i.e. interchanges of two elements), while the one-element cycle (8) denotes that the corresponding element is not affected by the permutation considered.

Permutations which can be factorized into the same number of cycles with the same number of elements (which may be different for different permutations) are called 'similar' and form a 'class' specified by the 'partition' of the number n into summands giving the number of elements in each cycle. The partition for the above permutation is

$$n = 1+2+2+4.$$

Similar permutations P and Q can thus be obtained from each other by permuting the elements appearing in the cycles of one of them. Denoting by R the permutation which must be carried out in the cycles of P in order to obtain Q, we get

$$Q = RPR^{-1}.$$

The factor R^{-1} accounts for the fact that the permutation R should not affect the operator or function to which P or Q is supposed to be applied (RPF would be equivalent to applying the permutation R both to P and to F).

Since every permutation P commutes with the energy operator H (H being symmetrical with respect to all the electrons), it can be treated as a *constant of the motion*. The fact that the different permutations do not in general commute with each other shows that it is impossible to assign simultaneously definite values to all these constants. It is possible, however, to combine them linearly into a set of commutable operators, which can be constructed by adding together all the permutations belonging to the same *class*. With a fixed P and a variable R each permutation $Q = RPR^{-1}$ will be obtained several times—namely, $n!/n_k$, where n_k is the number of different permutations in the class under consideration. The sum of all such permutations, or their 'average'

$$\bar{P} = \frac{1}{n!} \sum_R RPR^{-1},$$

will obviously commute with all the permutations. We have in fact

$$T\bar{P}T^{-1} = \frac{1}{n!} \sum_R TRPR^{-1}T^{-1}$$

or putting $TR = S$ and $R^{-1}T^{-1} = S^{-1}$,

$$T\bar{P}T^{-1} = \frac{1}{n!} \sum_S SPS^{-1} = \bar{P}$$

(since for a fixed T and a variable R the product TR varies over the same range as R). Hence $T\bar{P} = \bar{P}T$. It follows in particular that the operators $\bar{P}_k$ referring to different classes ($k = 1, 2,...$) commute with each other. Since, moreover, they commute with the energy operator H, they can be considered as defining a set of independent constants of the motion whose characteristic values $\bar{P}'_k$ *can be determined simultaneously* and can serve, together with the characteristic values of the energy H', to specify the stationary states of the system.

The characteristic values of the operators $\bar{P}$ are obviously wholly independent of the form of the energy operator (so long as it is symmetrical between all the electrons). They must be connected therefore with the symmetry properties of the wave functions $\chi_{H'}$ which belong to them and can serve for the classification of the latter.

It should be noticed that the operators $\bar{P}$ preserve their role of constants of the motion in the general case of an energy operator containing the time explicitly. This means that if the wave function χ satisfying Schrödinger's equation $-\dfrac{h}{2\pi i}\cdot\dfrac{\partial}{\partial x}\chi = H\chi$ has at the initial moment $t = 0$ a definite symmetry type, specified by certain characteristic values of the operators $\bar{P}'$, it will maintain the same symmetry type at any other time. The same results can be expressed by saying that the stationary states of an unperturbed system belonging to different characteristic values of the permutation operators $\bar{P}$ do not combine with each other under any perturbation (symmetrical in all the electrons).

The simplest examples of this theorem are provided by the symmetrical and the antisymmetrical wave functions. The characteristic values of the $\bar{P}$ are equal to $+1$ for the former and to ± 1 for the latter ($+1$ for even permutations and -1 for odd ones).

So long as the spin effects are left out of account we have to consider symmetrical and antisymmetrical functions only; if, however, the spin effect is allowed for, spinless functions of a more complicated character have to be admitted; to each set of characteristic $\bar{P}$-values there corresponds in general not one but many wave functions of the same symmetry type (cf. Part I, § 22). If, moreover, the spin forces are taken into account (as a small perturbation), the states corresponding to different $\bar{P}$-values will combine with each other. We thus get rather complicated results which can, however, be reduced to the original simple form if the spin coordinates are introduced in the definition of the wave functions on the same footing as the geometrical ones.

If the electrons are associated with different individual states specified by mutually orthogonal wave functions, the set of functions $P\phi$ can be replaced by the set $P_\psi\phi$ obtained from $\phi = \psi_1(x_1)\psi_2(x_2)...\psi_n(x_n)$ by applying the different permutations P not to the *arguments* of the functions ψ but to their *indices, that is, by permuting not the electrons between the given states, but on the contrary the different states between the electrons.* Since by applying the *same* permutation P *both* to the arguments and to the indices, we obviously do not change the resulting factorized function, we can put

$$P_x P_\psi = P_\psi P_x = 1,$$

where the suffix x has been added to indicate explicitly that P is applied to the electrons. We thus see that P_ψ plays the same role as the reciprocal of P_x and vice versa.

Taking the matrix elements of the energy with respect to the new functions $H_{P,Q}^{(\psi)}$ and remembering that they are invariant with regard to any permutations R of the electrons (i.e. of the integration variables), we have

$$H_{P,Q}^{(\psi)} = \int P_\psi \phi^* H Q_\psi \phi \, dV = R_x \int P_\psi \phi^* H Q_\psi \phi \, dV$$
$$= \int P_\psi R_x \phi^* H Q_\psi R_x \phi \, dV,$$

(since we must first permute the integration variables in ϕ^* and ϕ and thereafter only carry out the permutations P_ψ, Q_ψ of the indices). The functions $R_x \phi^*$ and $R_x \phi$ can further be replaced by $R_\psi^{-1} \phi^*$ and $R_\psi^{-1} \phi$, the permutation R_x applied to the arguments of any factorized function ϕ being equivalent to the reciprocal permutation applied to the indices. We thus get

$$H_{P,Q}^{(\psi)} = \int P_\psi R_\psi^{-1} \phi^* H Q_\psi R_\psi^{-1} \phi \, dV = H_{PR^{-1},QR^{-1}}^{(\psi)}. \qquad (341)$$

With $R = Q$ this reduces to

$$H_{P,Q}^{(\psi)} = H_{PQ^{-1}}^{(\psi)}, \qquad (341\,\mathrm{a})$$

where $H_S^{(\psi)}$ is an abbreviation for $H_{S,I}^{(\psi)}$. The difference between this result and the expression (338a) for the matrix element of H with respect to the original functions $P_x \phi$ and $Q_x \phi$ consists only in the order in which the two permutations P and Q^{-1} must be multiplied by each other. We shall presently see that thanks to this difference it is possible to reduce our perturbation problem to a simpler form, corresponding to the replacement of the energy operator H by the equivalent 'permutation operator'

$$W = \sum_R H_R^{(\psi)} R_\psi. \qquad (342)$$

The fact that the two operators are equivalent so far as the first approximation equations (336) are concerned is proved by comparing the matrix elements of W and H with respect to the functions $P_\psi \phi$. We have, namely,

$$W_{P,Q}^{(\psi)} = \sum_R H_R^{(\psi)} \int P_\psi \phi^* R_\psi Q_\psi \phi \, dV,$$

which in view of the orthogonality and normalizing conditions for the functions $P_\psi \phi$ reduces to

$$W_{P,Q}^{(\psi)} = H_{PQ^{-1}}^{(\psi)}   (RQ = P),$$

that is, to $H_{P,Q}^{(\psi)}$ according to (341).

A similar result *cannot* be obtained with the wave functions $P_x \psi$ which have been used before, for with W defined by the formula $W = \sum A_R R_x$ we get $W_{P,Q} = A_{PQ^{-1}}$. There can, however, be no correspondence between this expression and the matrix element $H_{P,Q} = H_{Q^{-1}P}$ for the two permutations PQ^{-1} and $Q^{-1}P$ are in general quite different.

The form of the energy operator H has been left hitherto quite arbitrary (apart from its symmetry with respect to all the electrons). Now in all actual problems H can be written down in the form

$$H = \sum_i E(x_i, p_i) + \sum_i \sum_k F(x_i, x_k), \tag{343}$$

where the first term represents the sum of the energies of the separate electrons, supposed to move independently, while the second term is equal to their interaction energy, so that $F(x_i, x_k) = \dfrac{e^2}{r(x_i, x_k)}$ (r being the distance apart between the ith and the kth electrons).—It should be emphasized that in writing down the expression (343) we must not consider the energy $E(x_i, p_i)$ as corresponding to *the approximate* description of the motion by means of the individual wave function $\psi_i(x_i)$. The latter can correspond to a somewhat different energy operator $E_i(x_i, p_i)$ involving some additional terms which serve to account in a simplified way for the mutual action of the ith electron with the rest—by an adequately chosen value of the 'screening constant' in the case of a complex atom, or by some type of 'self-consistent' field. The difference

$$S = H - \sum_i E_i(x_i, p_i) \tag{343 a}$$

can be defined as the perturbation energy. In order to obtain by our perturbation method a good approximation to the truth we must adequately determine the 'effective' energy operators E_i for the individual electrons in such a way that the matrix elements of the perturbation energy S should be as small as possible. We shall come back to this question in § 43. We are interested here only in the specialization of our general theory for the actual case of an energy operator of the form (343).

We shall assume for the sake of simplicity the functions ψ_i and consequently $P\phi$ to be mutually orthogonal (and of course normalized to 1). The matrix element E_R of the energy $E(x_i, p_i)$ defined by the general formula

$$E_R = \int R\phi^* E(x_i, p_i)\phi \, dX \qquad (dX = dx_1 ... dx_n)$$

is then easily seen to vanish for all the permutations R except the identical one, in which case it reduces to

$$\overline{E}_i = \int \psi_i^* E(x_i, p_i)\psi_i \, dx_i, \qquad (344)$$

that is, to the average value of the energy of the ith electron with regard to the external field alone for the state of motion which was initially assigned to it. It should be kept in mind that this motion, inasmuch as it is described by the approximate energy operator $E_i(x_i, p_i)$ which contains some additional external field more or less equivalent to the mutual action of the ith electron with the rest, differs from the motion described by the operator $E(x_i, p_i)$, and that accordingly the energy $\overline{E}_i$ is in general different from the characteristic value E'_i of the energy corresponding to the wave function ψ_i.

Taking the matrix element F_R of the interaction energy $F(x_i, x_k)$,

$$F_R = \int R\phi^* F(x_i, x_k)\phi \, dV,$$

we easily see that it does not vanish in two cases only, namely, in the case of the identical permutation, when it reduces to

$$F_{ik} = \int\int \psi_i^*(x_i)\psi_k^*(x_k) F(x_i, x_k)\psi_i(x_i)\psi_k(x_k) \, dx_i \, dx_k, \qquad (344\,a)$$

and in that of a transposition $R = T_{ik}$ involving the interchange between the ith and kth electrons. We shall denote its value for this case by G_{ik}, where

$$G_{ik} = \int\int \psi_i^*(x_k)\psi_k^*(x_i) F(x_i, x_k)\psi_i(x_i)\psi_k(x_k) \, dx_i \, dx_k. \qquad (344\,b)$$

All the other matrix elements of E and F, and consequently all the coefficients H_R for such permutations R which are different from the identical permutation or from a transposition vanish.

It should be noted that we obtain the same expressions for the matrix elements of E and F with respect to the wave functions $R_\psi \phi$. The identification of the integration variables in (344 a) and (344 b) with the coordinates of the ith and the kth electrons is irrelevant for the value of F_{ik} and G_{ik}, this value being determined by the *states* to which the two electrons are referred, and not by the individuality of these electrons. We could therefore write

$$F_{ik} = F_{ik}^{\psi} = \iint \psi_i^*(x')\psi_k^*(x'')F(x',x'')\psi_i(x')\psi_k(x'')\,dx'dx''$$

and $$G_{ik} = G_{ik}^{\psi} = \iint \psi_i^*(x')\psi_k^*(x'')F(x',x'')\psi_i(x'')\psi_k(x')\,dx'dx'',$$

leaving the indices of the two electrons unspecified.

The permutation operator W is thus reduced in all actual problems to the relatively simple form

$$W = W^0 + \sum_{i<k} G_{ik}T_{ik}^{\psi}, \tag{345}$$

where $$W^0 = \sum_i \bar{E}_i + \sum_{i<k} F_{ik} \tag{345a}$$

can be defined as the approximate value of the energy of the system under consideration, the second term in (343) representing the operator of the 'exchange' energy.

42. Introduction of the Spin Coordinates and Solution of the Perturbation Problem with Antisymmetrical Wave Functions

The results of the preceding section cannot be directly applied to the general problem of the motion of a system of electrons, for this implies the introduction of the spin coordinates which have been ignored hitherto. Even if we neglect the spin forces—which we shall always do in the sequel—we must take into account the spin coordinates and the spin quantum numbers in order to set up the antisymmetrical wave functions which describe a system of electrons.

We shall consider here the problem of the *approximate* determination of the antisymmetrical wave functions with spin, which belong to a spinless energy operator H, with the help of the individual wave functions $\psi_i(x,\xi)$ describing the motion of the separate electrons in a given external field (ξ denotes the additional spin coordinate and the index i is supposed to contain the spin quantum number).

This problem admits at first sight a simple and unique solution expressed by the determinant

$$\Phi = \frac{1}{\sqrt{(n!)}} \begin{vmatrix} \psi_1(x_1,\xi_1) & \cdot & \cdot & \cdot & \psi_1(x_n,\xi_n) \\ \cdot & \cdot & \cdot & \cdot & \cdot & \cdot \\ \psi_n(x_1,\xi_1) & \cdot & \cdot & \cdot & \psi_n(x_n,\xi_n) \end{vmatrix} \tag{346}$$

since no other wave functions but the antisymmetrical one need be taken into account in connexion with the exchange phenomenon.

The simplification with regard to the exchange degeneracy introduced by the antisymmetry condition is, however, balanced by the *additional degeneracy, due to the possibility of assigning to each electron two different spin-states* connected with the same type of orbital motion and corresponding to the same value of the energy. We thus get for the whole system of n electrons, distributed between n 'orbits', i.e. spinless states, which can be specified by certain functions of the geometrical coordinates alone $\psi_1(x)$, $\psi_2(x)$,..., $\psi_n(x)$, a degenerate set of 2^n states differing from each other by the spin quantum numbers m_1, m_2,..., m_n, associated with each spinless state.

The individual states with spin can be described by the functions

$$\psi_i(x, \xi) = \psi_i(x)\delta_{m\,\xi}, \tag{346 a}$$

where m and ξ assume the values $\frac{1}{2}$ and $-\frac{1}{2}$, $\delta_{m\xi}$ being equal to 1 for $\xi = m$, and to 0 for $\xi \neq m$ (it should be remembered that m denotes the characteristic value of the component of the spin-matrix σ along some fixed axis).

The spinless functions $\psi_i(x)$ need not be all different; they can occur in pairs, under the condition that the associated spin quantum numbers m_i are different. Instead of four degenerate states we get for each such pair only two, so that the total number of degenerate states of the whole system is equal to $2^{n'+n''} = g$, where n' is the number of singly occupied spinless states and n'' the number of doubly occupied spinless states $(n = n' + 2n'')$.

In the absence of any other degeneracy except the spin one [and the exchange degeneracy which is taken care of by using as zero approximation the antisymmetrical function (346)], the problem of determining to the first approximation the wave functions with spin $\chi(x, \xi)$ corresponding to the spinless energy operator H can be solved by defining these functions as linear combinations of g functions of the type (346),

$$\chi(x, \xi) = \sum_{\alpha=1}^{g} C_\alpha \Phi_\alpha, \tag{347}$$

where the coefficients C_α satisfy the system of g equations,

$$\sum_\alpha (H_{\alpha\beta} - H' J_{\alpha\beta}) C_\beta = 0 \qquad (\alpha = 1, 2, ..., g), \tag{347 a}$$

under the compatibility condition

$$|H_{\alpha\beta} - H' J_{\alpha\beta}'| = 0 \tag{347 b}$$

which serves for the determination of the energy-levels H'.

The matrix elements $H_{\alpha\beta}$ and $J_{\alpha\beta}$ must be defined here by the expressions

$$\left. \begin{aligned} H_{\alpha\beta} &= \sum_\xi \int \Phi_\alpha^* H \Phi_\beta \, dX \\ J_{\alpha\beta} &= \sum_\xi \int \Phi_\alpha^* \Phi_\beta \, dX \end{aligned} \right\}, \tag{348}$$

where $\sum\limits_{\xi}$ denotes a summation over the spin coordinates of all the n electrons involved in the functions Φ.

Taking into account the relation

$$\sum_{\xi'} \delta_{m_i'\xi'}\,\delta_{m_k'\xi'} = \delta_{m_i'm_k'} \qquad (348\,\mathrm{a})$$

which follows from the definition of the symbols δ (where ξ' refers to one particular electron), we can easily find that the matrix elements (348) can be different from zero only if the functions Φ_α and Φ_β are associated *with the same value of the resulting spin component*

$$m = \sum_{i=1}^{n} m_i. \qquad (348\,\mathrm{b})$$

In fact, $H_{\alpha\beta}$ and $J_{\alpha\beta}$ can be expressed as a sum of terms each involving a product of n factors of the type (348 a). Now unless the two states α and β are associated with an *equal number* of spins pointing in the same direction, i.e. specified by spin quantum numbers m_i having the same value ($\frac{1}{2}$ or $-\frac{1}{2}$), one at least of these n factors will vanish in each such term.

We thus see that the functions Φ_i can be divided into a number of non-combining groups belonging to different characteristic values of the total spin component m of all the electrons along a certain axis, z say. This result is a direct corollary of the fact that the spinless energy operator H commutes with each of the spin matrices σ_{zi} and consequently with their sum

$$\sigma_z = \sum_{i=1}^{n} \sigma_{zi}.$$

Now this means that the matrix of H is diagonal with respect to m. We have in fact (leaving other variables out of account)

$$(H\sigma_z - \sigma_z H)_{m'm''} = \sum_{m} (H_{m'm}\sigma_{zmm''} - \sigma_{zm'm}H_{mm''}) = H_{m'm''}(m'' - m') = 0,$$

whence it follows that $H_{m'm''} = 0$ unless $m' = m''$.

The subdivision of the function Φ into groups belonging to the same value of m greatly simplifies the perturbation problem under consideration, for the g equations (347 a) are split up hereby into a number of separate systems, containing coefficients which refer to functions Φ of the same group only. The function $\chi(x,\xi)$ stabilized for the perturbation will belong accordingly to a definite characteristic value m of σ_z specifying the corresponding group. The equations (347), (347 a), and (347 b) will be understood in the sequel to refer to one particular group of g states with the same value of m.

If all the spinless states $\psi_1, ..., \psi_n$ are different, the number g is given by the formula [C_n^r is the usual binomial coefficient $n!/\{r!(n-r)!\}$]

$$g(m) = C_n^{n \pm 2m}. \qquad (349)$$

In fact the number of ways in which n_+ positive and n_- negative spins can be associated with the n different orbits is obviously equal to $C_n^{n_+} = C_n^{n_-}$, which reduces to (349) since

$$m = \tfrac{1}{2}(n_+ - n_-), \qquad (349\,\text{a})$$

that is,

$$n_\pm = n \pm 2m. \qquad (349\,\text{b})$$

The sum $\sum g(m)$ taken for all values of m from $-\tfrac{1}{2}n$ to $\tfrac{1}{2}n$ is equal to $\sum\limits_{n_+=0}^{n} C_n^{n_+} = 2^n$, as of course it should be.

The $g(m)$ functions Φ_α forming a certain group can be obtained from one of them Φ by permuting the spin quantum numbers $m_1, m_2, ..., m_n$ associated with the separate orbits between the latter, with the condition that identical orbits—if present—should always be associated with opposite spins. Such permutations P must be distinguished from those which we have considered before and which referred either to the distribution of the electrons between the (spinless) states or of the states between the electrons.

Just as before, however, it can be concluded from this circumstance that the number of different matrix elements $H_{\alpha\beta}$ and $J_{\alpha\beta}$ is reduced from g_m^2 to g_m. We shall not stop to investigate this question, for, as has been shown by Slater, all we need to know are *the diagonal* elements of the energy, from which the perturbed energy-levels can easily be computed without directly solving the perturbation equations (347 a).

The diagonal elements of H are easily seen to have the same value, $\bar{H}(m)$ say, for all the $g(m)$ functions Φ. If the individual wave functions (with spin) $\psi_1, ..., \psi_n$ are orthogonal and normalized to 1, i.e. if $J_{\alpha\beta} = \delta_{\alpha\beta}$ (which we shall assume to be the case), then according to (347 b) the sum of the diagonal elements of H, that is, the product $\bar{H}(m)g(m)$, must be equal to the sum of the $g(m)$ characteristic values of H belonging to m which are the roots of equation (347 b). Now whereas m, being the characteristic values of the projection σ_z of the resulting spin $\boldsymbol{\sigma}$ on the direction of the arbitrarily chosen z-axis, depends upon the choice of its direction in space, the characteristic values of the energy must obviously be independent of the choice of this direction, being in fact invariant with respect to the rotations of the coordinate axes. They must be determined therefore by the characteristic values s of the resulting spin itself, which are also invariant both with respect to rotations of the coordinate axes and to the permutations of the electrons.

So long as the forces due to the spin of the electrons (including the effects of their orientation in an external magnetic field) are neglected, all those states which belong to the same value of the resulting spin form a degenerate set, so that their energy is wholly determined by s. The number of such states $f(s)$ and their energy $H(s)$ can easily be calculated from $g(m)$ and $\overline{H}(m)$ if we take into account the fact that, for a given m, s can assume the following values:

$$s = |m|, |m|+1,..., \tfrac{1}{2}n.$$

Subdividing all the states belonging to a definite m into groups specified by different values of s, we thus get

$$g(m) = \sum_{s=|m|}^{\frac{1}{2}n} f(s) \tag{350}$$

and

$$g(m)\overline{H}(m) = \sum_{s=|m|}^{\frac{1}{2}n} f(s)H(s). \tag{350a}$$

The latter equation can be rewritten in the form

$$\overline{H}(m) = \frac{\sum_{s=|m|}^{\frac{1}{2}n} f(s)H(s)}{\sum_{s=|m|}^{\frac{1}{2}n} f(s)}, \tag{350b}$$

which expresses the fact that the diagonal elements of the energy H are equal to the average value of the energy for all the states associated with the corresponding value of m.

From (350) and (350a) we obtain

$$-f(s) = g(s+1)-g(s) = \Delta g(s) \tag{351}$$

and

$$-f(s)H(s) = g(s+1)\overline{H}(s+1)-g(s)\overline{H}(s) = \Delta[g(s)\overline{H}(s)] \tag{351a}$$

whence

$$H(s) = \frac{\Delta[g(s)\overline{H}(s)]}{\Delta g(s)}. \tag{351b}$$

Since $g(s)$ is known, being determined by the equation (349) in the case of n different orbits, our problem reduces to the calculation of a diagonal element of H for a given value of m $(= s)$.

We shall take for the operator H the expression (343), i.e.

$$H = \sum_i E(x_i, p_i) + \sum_{i<k}\sum F(x_i, x_k),$$

which is the only one occurring in practice.

We shall further write one of the functions Φ defined by the determinant (346) in the form

$$\Phi = \frac{1}{\sqrt{(n!)}} \sum_P \epsilon_P P_x \phi(x) P_\xi \delta(\xi), \qquad (352)$$

where $\phi(x) = \psi_1(x_1)\psi_2(x_2)...\psi_n(x_n)$ is the product of the spinless functions and $\delta_m(\xi) = \delta_{m_1\xi_1}\delta_{m_2\xi_2}...\delta_{m_n\xi_n}$ the product of the corresponding spin factors, ϵ_P being equal to $+1$ or -1 for permutations of the even and odd type respectively (the permutations P_x refer to the geometrical coordinates and P_ξ to the spin coordinates of the electrons).

Let us consider the case when all the n orbits $\psi_1, \psi_2, ..., \psi_n$ are different (and orthogonal to each other). The expression

$$\bar{H} = \sum_\xi \int \Phi^* H \Phi \, dX = \frac{1}{n!} \sum_P \sum_Q \epsilon_P \epsilon_Q \int P_x \phi H Q_x \phi \, dX \sum_\xi P_\xi \delta(\xi) Q_\xi \delta(\xi), \qquad (352\,a)$$

which defines the diagonal matrix element of H with respect to the state Φ (or the corresponding average value) is then easily simplified. The integral $H_{P,Q} = \int P_x \phi H Q_x \phi \, dX$ does not vanish, as we know, either when the permutations P and Q are identical ($P = Q$) or when they differ by a transposition T_{ik} of any two electrons ($Q = PT_{ik}$). It reduces in the first case to $H_I = W^0 = \sum_i \bar{E}_i + \sum_{i<k} \sum F_{ik}$ and in the second to G_{ik} [cf. equations (344), (344 a), (344 b), and (345 a) of the preceding section].

We have further, when $P = Q$,

$$\frac{1}{n!} \sum_P \sum_\xi P_\xi \delta . P_\xi \delta = \sum_\xi P_\xi \delta . P_\xi \delta = 1,$$

since the total number of different permutations is just equal to $n!$.

A little more care is required for the calculation of the preceding expressions when $Q = PT_{ik}$. It is clear that the function

$$\delta = \delta_{m_1\xi_1}\delta_{m_2\xi_2}...\delta_{m_n\xi_n}$$

remains unaltered if the same permutation R is applied both to the spin coordinates ξ_i and to the spin quantum numbers m_i (or more exactly, to the *indices* of these variables). Any permutation P_ξ of the former can therefore be replaced by the reciprocal permutation P_m^{-1} of the latter. We thus have

$$\sum_\xi P_\xi \delta . P_\xi T_{ik}^\xi \delta = \sum_\xi P_m^{-1} \delta . P_m^{-1} T_{ik}^\xi \delta,$$

where T_{ik}^ξ denotes, as before, the interchange of the coordinates ξ_i and ξ_k, which in the original distribution were assigned to the ith and kth electrons.

Now in the function $P_m^{-1}\delta$ these coordinates will be associated with the spin quantum numbers $P_{m_i}^{-1} = m_{i'}$ and $P_{m_k}^{-1} = m_{k'}$, where i' and k' are the numbers derived from i and k by the permutation P^{-1}. In the function $P_m^{-1}T_{ik}\delta$ the same coordinates will be associated with the spin quantum numbers m_k, and m_i, respectively. The sum $\sum\limits_{\xi} P_m^{-1}\delta \,.\, P_m^{-1}T_{ik}^{\xi}\delta$ will obviously be equal to 1 if these two numbers are equal $(+\tfrac{1}{2}$ or $-\tfrac{1}{2})$ and to 0 if they are different.

Let us suppose that the numbers $m_1, m_2, ..., m_n$, are labelled in such a way that the first n_+ of them are equal to $\tfrac{1}{2}$ and the last n_- to $-\tfrac{1}{2}$ $(n_+ + n_- = n)$. If now all the permutations P_m^{-1} are applied to their indices, then each index will have an equal chance of being found at any place of the line, under the condition that two originally different indices will always have different places.

The number of positions which any two indices corresponding originally to i and k can assume in the row of the n_+ positive spins is obviously equal to $n_+(n_+-1)$, and in that of the n_- negative spins to $n_-(n_--1)$. The sum of these two numbers multiplied by $(n-2)!$ will give the total number of distributions (i.e. permutations P). We thus see that in the case $Q = PT_{ik}$ the expression

$$\frac{1}{n!}\sum_{P}\sum_{\xi} P_{\xi}\delta : Q_{\xi}\delta = \frac{1}{n!}\sum_{P}\delta_{m_{i'}m_{k'}}$$

is equal, irrespective of the choice of i and k, to

$$\frac{n_+(n_+-1) + n_-(n_--1)}{n(n-1)}.$$

The expression (352a) for the average value of the energy assumes accordingly the following form

$$\bar{H} = \sum_i \bar{E}_i + \sum_{i<k}\sum F_{ik} - \frac{n_+(n_+-1) + n_-(n_--1)}{n(n-1)}\sum_{i<k}\sum G_{ik}, \quad (353)$$

where the negative sign corresponds to the fact that $\epsilon_P \epsilon_Q = -1$ for two permutations differing from each other by a transposition (one of them being of the even and the other of the odd type). Writing W^0 for the sum of the first two terms and putting $m = \tfrac{1}{2}(n_+ - n_-)$, i.e. $n_+ = \tfrac{1}{2}n + m$, $n_- = \tfrac{1}{2}n - m$, we can represent $\bar{H}$ as a function of m explicitly by the formula

$$\bar{H}(m) = W^0 - \frac{\tfrac{1}{2}n^2 + 2m^2 - n}{n(n-1)}\sum_{i<k}\sum G_{ik}. \quad (353\,\text{a})$$

As would be expected, this expression is a function of m alone, and is independent of the choice of Φ out of the group belonging to a given m, i.e. is the same for all diagonal elements of the energy matrix. We can now pass on to the calculation of the characteristic values of the energy as functions of the resulting spin s.

In the first place we have, according to (351) in conjunction with (349),

$$f(s) = C_n^{\frac{1}{2}n+s} - C_n^{\frac{1}{2}n+s+1} = C_n^{\frac{1}{2}n+s} \frac{2s+1}{\frac{1}{2}n+s+1}. \tag{354}$$

Further, according to (351 a) and (353 a),

$$f(s)H(s)$$
$$= f(s)W^0 - \left[C_n^{\frac{1}{2}n+s} \frac{\frac{1}{2}n^2+2s-n}{n(n-1)} \ C_n^{\frac{1}{2}n+s+1} \frac{\frac{1}{2}n^2+2(s+1)^2-n}{n(n-1)} \right] \sum_{i<k} \sum G_{ik},$$

whence

$$H(s) = W^0 - \frac{\frac{1}{2}n(n-4)+2s(s+1)}{n(n-1)} \sum_{i<k} \sum G_{ik}. \tag{354 a}$$

This formula was originally derived by Heitler in connexion with the spin theory of chemical forces. The derivation given above is a modification of that given by Slater (in his theory of energy-levels in a complex atom) and by Pauli (in connexion with Heisenberg's theory of ferromagnetism).

Pauli's method of dealing with the perturbation problem under consideration differs from that of Slater in the choice of the original wave functions with spin. Instead of taking the antisymmetrical functions defined by the determinant (346) we can use as the zero approximation, just as in the spinless case, the factorized functions obtained by multiplying by each other the individual functions $\psi_i(x_i)\delta_{m_i\xi_i}$.

We shall slightly modify our previous notation by introducing the letters $J_1, J_2, ..., J_n$ to specify the different spinless orbits with which the separate electrons are associated and by writing $(J_i|x_k)$ instead of $\psi_{J_i}(x_k)$, and $(m_i|\xi_k)$ instead of $\delta_{m_i\xi_k}$. The factorized function with which we must start can be obtained from one of them

$$\phi(x)\delta(\xi) = (J_1|x_1)...(J_n|x_n)(m_1|\xi_1)...(m_n|\xi_n) = (J|x)(m|\xi) \tag{355}$$

by permuting the different electrons, i.e. by applying the same permutations P to the arguments x and ξ, and also taking the two possible values for each of the spin quantum numbers m_i. Now, as has been shown before, only those functions (355) must be combined with each other which correspond to the same value of the sum $\sum m_i = m$ and which accordingly can be obtained from each other by applying various permutations R (independent of P) to the indices m_i. The set of degenerate states which must be taken into account for the construction of the wave function $\chi(x, \xi)$ stabilized for the perturbation can thus be specified by the expression

$$(J|Px)(Rm|P\xi), \tag{355a}$$

where P and R are arbitrary permutations. Since a permutation of the arguments (x, ξ) is equivalent to the reciprocal permutation of the indices (J, m), we can replace the preceding expression by

$$(P^{-1}J|x)(P^{-1}Rm|\xi)$$

or by

$$\phi_{P,Q} = (PJ|x)(Qm|\xi), \tag{355b}$$

P and Q being independent of each other.

The $n!$ different permutations Q actually lead to

$$g(m) = C_n^{n+} = C_n^{n-} = C_n^{n-2m}$$

different spin factors $(Qm|\xi) = (m|Q^{-1}\xi)$ which are distinguished from each other by the coordinates $\xi_1, ..., \xi_n$ associated with the values $m_i = \frac{1}{2}$ and $m_i = -\frac{1}{2}$ respectively. In what follows we shall assume the permutations Q to be subdivided into $g(m)$ classes, corresponding to the different functions $(Qm|\xi)$, and shall take for Q only one representative of each class, treating all the permutations of each class as identical.

The function $\chi(x, \xi)$ can now be defined by the formula

$$\chi(x, \xi) = \sum_P \sum_Q C_{P,Q} \phi_{P,Q}, \tag{356}$$

where the coefficients $C_{P,Q}$ are determined by the equations

$$\sum_{P'} \sum_{Q'} (H_{P,Q;\, P',Q'} - H' J_{P,Q;\, P',Q'}) C_{P',Q'} = 0 \tag{356a}$$

with

$$H_{P,Q;\, P',Q'} = \sum_\xi \int \phi_{P,Q}^* H \phi_{P',Q'}\, dV$$

$$= \sum_\xi (Qm|\xi)(Q'm|\xi) \int (x|PJ) H (P'J|x)\, dV$$

and

$$J_{P,Q;\, P',Q'} = \sum_\xi \int \phi_{P,Q} \phi_{P',Q'}\, dV = \sum_\xi (Qm|\xi)(Q'm|\xi) \int (x|PJ)(P'J|x)\, dV.$$

So long as we are considering effectively different permutations Q and Q' only we can assume the sums $\sum_\xi (Qm|\xi)(Q'm|\xi)$ to vanish except for the case $Q = Q'$ when they are equal to 1. The non-vanishing matrix elements of H and J thus reduce to

$$H_{P,Q;\, P',Q'} = H_{P,P'}^\psi = H_{PP'^{-1}}, \qquad J_{P,Q;\, P',Q'} = J_{P,P'}^\psi = J_{PP'^{-1}},$$

where $H_{P,P'}^\psi$ and $J_{P,P'}^\psi$ are the usual matrix elements of H and $J = \delta$

with regard to the spinless functions $(PJ|x)$ and $(P'J|x)$. The equations (356 a) can therefore be rewritten in the form

$$\sum_{P'} (H_{PP'^{-1}} - H' J_{PP'^{-1}}) C_{P',Q} = 0,$$

or, if we put $PP'^{-1} = R$,

$$\sum_{R} (H_R - H' J_R) C_{R^{-1}P,Q} = 0. \tag{356 b}$$

We can now make use of the fact that the only functions (356) we need are the antisymmetrical ones. This means that $\chi(Sx, S\xi) = \epsilon_S$, where $\epsilon_S = 1$ for a permutation S of even type and -1 for one of odd type. Since the application of a permutation S or S^{-1} to the arguments x, ξ of the functions (355 b) is equivalent to the application of the reciprocal permutation to the indices J, we get

$$\sum_{P} \sum_{Q} C_{P,Q} \phi_{S^{-1}P, S^{-1}Q} = \epsilon_S \sum_{P} \sum_{Q} C_{P,Q} \phi_{P,Q},$$

or, replacing $S^{-1}P$ and $S^{-1}Q$ in the first sum by P' and Q',

$$\sum_{P'} \sum_{Q'} C_{SP', SQ'} \phi_{P',Q'} = \epsilon_S \sum_{P} \sum_{Q} C_{P,Q} \phi_{P,Q} = \epsilon_S \sum_{P'} \sum_{Q'} C_{P',Q'} \phi_{P',Q'},$$

whence it follows that $\qquad C_{SP,SQ} = \epsilon_S C_{P,Q}.$ \hfill (357)

This gives, if SQ is replaced by Q (i.e. Q by $S^{-1}Q$) and S by R^{-1},

$$C_{R^{-1}P,Q} = \epsilon_R C_{P,RQ},$$

so that the equations (356 b) can be rewritten in the form

$$\sum_{R} \epsilon_R (H_R - H' J_R) C_{P,RQ} = 0. \tag{357 a}$$

The index P is irrelevant, as it is the same for the whole system of equations and can therefore be left out of account. So far as the coefficients $C_{P,RQ} = C_{RQ}$ are concerned the summation over R can lead to $g(m)$ different values only, which will be multiplied in equations (357 a) by the sum of the expressions $\epsilon_R(H_R - H' J_R)$ for all the R's which correspond to equivalent permutations RQ.

Putting as before $H = \sum_i E(x_i, p_i) + \sum_i \sum_k F(x_i, x_k)$ and assuming the functions $(PJ|x)$ to be mutually orthogonal, we get

$$(H_I - H') C_Q - \sum_i \sum_k G_{ik} C_{T_{ik}Q} = 0, \tag{357 b}$$

where I denotes the identical permutation, so that

$$H_I = W^0 = \sum_i \bar{E}_i + \sum_i \sum_k F_{ik},$$

while T_{ik} corresponds to an interchange between the spin quantum numbers m_i and m_k.

The $g(m)$ different coefficients C_R can be specified unambiguously by the indices of the n_+ electrons with a positive component of their spin along the z-axis. We can thus write (following Pauli)

$$C_Q = C(r_1, r_2, ..., r_{n_+}),$$

where r_1, r_2,..., r_{n_+} are the indices in question, C being independent of the order in which they appear. We can put in particular $r_1 = 1$, $r_2 = 2$,..., $r_{n_+} = n_+$ without affecting the generality of our theory, since the choice of the permutation Q in the equations (357 b) is irrelevant for their solution. Putting accordingly

$$C_{T_{ik}Q} = T_{ik}C_Q = T_{ik}C(r_1, r_2, ..., r_{n_+}) = C(r_1', r_2', ..., r_{n_+}')$$

we can rewrite the equation (357 b) in the form

$$(H_I - H')C(r_1, r_2, ..., r_{n_+}) - \sum_{i<k}\sum G_{ik}T_{ik}C(r_1, r_2, ..., r_{n_+}) = 0. \quad (357\,\text{c})$$

If we consider the determinant of these equations, whose roots give the allowed values of the energy H', we see at once that the sum of these values for all the $g(m)$ perturbed states is equal to the sum of the coefficients of $C(r_1, r_2, ..., r_{n_+})$ (without of course the term H'), that is, to the expression

$$\sum_r \left(H_I - \sum_{i<k}{}' G_{ik} \right).$$

The summation $\sum'$ is extended over those pairs of states (or electrons) which interchange either two of the indices r_1, r_2,..., r_{n_+} or two of the remaining indices, s_1, s_2,..., s_{n_-} say (corresponding to negative spins), without interchanging any r with any s,[†] whereas the summation $\sum_r$ is extended over the $g(m)$ different combinations of the r's. As a result we obtain each G_{ik} multiplied by the number of combinations for which the spins associated with the states i and k (or the ith and the kth electrons) are both positive or both negative, i.e.

$$C_{n-2}^{n_+} + C_{n-2}^{n_-} = C_n^{n_+} \frac{n_+(n_+-1) + n_-(n_--1)}{n(n-1)},$$

H_I being multiplied by $g(m)C_n^{n_+}$. We thus get for the average value of the energy H' of the $g(m)$ perturbed states the expression

$$\overline{H}(m) = H_I - \frac{n_+(n_+-1) + n_-(n_--1)}{n(n-1)} \sum_{i<k}\sum G_{ik},$$

which has been obtained before.

As has been shown by Dirac, the transpositions T_{ik} occurring in (357 c) can be replaced by operators, involving Pauli's spin matrices $\boldsymbol{\sigma}_i$ and $\boldsymbol{\sigma}_k$. Let us consider the scalar product of these spin vectors,

† i.e. over those indices i, k which *both* occur either among the n_+ indices r or among the n_- indices s.

that is, the operator $\boldsymbol{\sigma}_i \cdot \boldsymbol{\sigma}_k$, applied to some function of $\boldsymbol{\sigma}_i$ and $\boldsymbol{\sigma}_k$, and in the first place to $\boldsymbol{\sigma}_i$ and $\boldsymbol{\sigma}_k$ themselves or their components along some axis, z say. We have, putting $i = 1$ and $k = 2$,

$$(\boldsymbol{\sigma}_1 \cdot \boldsymbol{\sigma}_2)\sigma_{1z} = (\sigma_{1x}\sigma_{2x} + \sigma_{1y}\sigma_{2y} + \sigma_{1z}\sigma_{2z})\sigma_{1z}$$
$$= (\sigma_{1x}\sigma_{1z})\sigma_{2x} + (\sigma_{1y}\sigma_{1z})\sigma_{2y} + (\sigma_{1z}\sigma_{1z})\sigma_{2z},$$

since the vectors $\boldsymbol{\sigma}_1$ and $\boldsymbol{\sigma}_2$ commute with each other, and further, in virtue of the relations (253), § 29,

$$(\boldsymbol{\sigma}_1 \cdot \boldsymbol{\sigma}_2)\sigma_{1z} = -i\sigma_{1y}\sigma_{2x} + i\sigma_{1x}\sigma_{2y} + \sigma_{2z}$$

or

$$(1 + \boldsymbol{\sigma}_1 \cdot \boldsymbol{\sigma}_2)\sigma_{1z} = i(\sigma_{1x}\sigma_{2y} - \sigma_{1y}\sigma_{2x}) + \sigma_{1z} + \sigma_{2z} = [i(\boldsymbol{\sigma}_1 \times \boldsymbol{\sigma}_2) + \boldsymbol{\sigma}_1 + \boldsymbol{\sigma}_2]_z.$$

Similar expressions are obtained if σ_{1z} is replaced by σ_{1x} or σ_{1y}, so that

$$(1 + \boldsymbol{\sigma}_1 \cdot \boldsymbol{\sigma}_2)\boldsymbol{\sigma}_1 = i\boldsymbol{\sigma}_1 \times \boldsymbol{\sigma}_2 + \boldsymbol{\sigma}_1 + \boldsymbol{\sigma}_2.$$

We get likewise

$$(1 + \boldsymbol{\sigma}_1 \cdot \boldsymbol{\sigma}_2)\boldsymbol{\sigma}_2 = i\boldsymbol{\sigma}_2 \times \boldsymbol{\sigma}_1 + \boldsymbol{\sigma}_1 + \boldsymbol{\sigma}_2,$$

and

$$\boldsymbol{\sigma}_2(1 + \boldsymbol{\sigma}_1 \cdot \boldsymbol{\sigma}_2) = i\boldsymbol{\sigma}_1 \times \boldsymbol{\sigma}_2 + \boldsymbol{\sigma}_1 + \boldsymbol{\sigma}_2,$$

whence

$$(1 + \boldsymbol{\sigma}_1 \cdot \boldsymbol{\sigma}_2)\boldsymbol{\sigma}_1 = \boldsymbol{\sigma}_2(1 + \boldsymbol{\sigma}_1 \cdot \boldsymbol{\sigma}_2). \tag{358}$$

We have on the other hand

$$(\boldsymbol{\sigma}_1 \cdot \boldsymbol{\sigma}_2)^2 = (\sigma_{1x}\sigma_{2x} + \sigma_{1y}\sigma_{2y} + \sigma_{1z}\sigma_{2z})^2$$
$$= \sigma_{1x}^2\sigma_{2x}^2 + \sigma_{1y}^2\sigma_{2y}^2 + \sigma_{1z}^2\sigma_{2z}^2 + \sigma_{1x}\sigma_{2x}\sigma_{1y}\sigma_{2y} + \sigma_{1y}\sigma_{2y}\sigma_{1x}\sigma_{2x} + \cdots$$
$$= 3 + 2i\sigma_{1z}\,i\sigma_{2z} + \cdots$$
$$= 3 - 2\boldsymbol{\sigma}_1 \cdot \boldsymbol{\sigma}_2,$$

and consequently

$$(1 + \boldsymbol{\sigma}_1 \cdot \boldsymbol{\sigma}_2)^2 = 4. \tag{358 a}$$

It follows from these equations that the spin operator

$$O_{12} = \tfrac{1}{2}(1 + \boldsymbol{\sigma}_1 \cdot \boldsymbol{\sigma}_2) \tag{358 b}$$

has the same properties with respect to any function of the spin variables $\boldsymbol{\sigma}_1$, $\boldsymbol{\sigma}_2$ as the permutation operator T_{12}. This becomes quite clear if we rewrite the equation (358) in the form

$$O_{12}\boldsymbol{\sigma}_1 O_{12}^{-1} = \boldsymbol{\sigma}_2,$$

or in the equivalent form

$$O_{12}^{-1}\boldsymbol{\sigma}_2 O_{12} = \boldsymbol{\sigma}_1,$$

which reduces to

$$O_{12}\boldsymbol{\sigma}_2 O_{12}^{-1} = \boldsymbol{\sigma}_1$$

in view of the equation $O_{12}^2 = 1$ which corresponds to the relation $T_{12}^2 = 1$ (= identical permutation).

The equivalence between O_{12} and T_{12} is preserved with regard to the functions of the other spin variables $\boldsymbol{\sigma}_3$, $\boldsymbol{\sigma}_4$, etc., since they commute with $\boldsymbol{\sigma}_1$ and $\boldsymbol{\sigma}_2$, and further with regard to any function of the type

$f(r_1, r_2,..., r_n)$ since we can replace the indices r_k of the electrons by the corresponding spin variables σ_k (or their squares). We can accordingly replace the permutation operators T_{ik} in the system of equations (357 c) by the spin operators O_{ik} (the fact that the sign need not be changed can easily be ascertained by considering a particular case). This system of equations can thus be written in the standard form of a wave equation

$$(W - H')C = 0, \tag{359}$$

where

$$W = H_I - \tfrac{1}{2} \sum_{i<k} \sum G_{ik}(1 + \sigma_i \cdot \sigma_k) \\ = \sum_i \bar{E}_i + \sum_{i<k} \sum (F_{ik} - \tfrac{1}{2}G_{ik}) - \tfrac{1}{2} \sum_{i<k} \sum G_{ik} \, \sigma_i \cdot \sigma_k \left.\right\} \tag{359 a}$$

is the approximate energy operator, which is equivalent to H as far as the first approximation of the perturbation theory is concerned.

This result, due to Dirac, is very important both from the practical point of view—for in many cases it enables one to calculate very easily the perturbed energy-levels—and from the theoretical point of view, for it shows that the 'exchange energy' in connexion with the anti-symmetry principle can be interpreted—in a purely formal way—as due to a fictitious kind of *magnetism* associated with the spin. In fact the expression

$$W_{ik}^{(m)} = -\tfrac{1}{2}G_{ik} \, \sigma_i \, \sigma_k \tag{359 b}$$

can be considered as representing the energy of a fictitious magnetic interaction between the ith and kth electrons, their actual magnetic moments being replaced by quantities of an electrostatic nature. It should be noted that only a part of the exchange energy can be interpreted in this way; another part $-\tfrac{1}{2} \sum_{i<k} \sum G_{ik}$ goes over into the ordinary electrostatic energy $\sum_{i<k} \sum F_{ik}$.

We shall consider in Part III some important applications of the quasi-magnetic effects determined by (359 b) to the theory of the magnetic properties of atoms and of ferromagnetic bodies. Another illustration of equations (359 a) will be found in the theory of the chemical forces between two atoms, inasmuch as no other type of degeneracy than that due to the exchange and spin effect has to be taken into account.

The above theory can easily be extended to the more general case when an additional degeneracy (such as that due to the different orientations of the electron orbits in a complex atom) must be included in the perturbation problem. We shall not stop here, however, to examine this general case.

43. The Method of the Self-consistent Field with Factorized Wave Functions

The reduction of the problem of many electrons to that of a single electron in that form in which it has been considered in the two preceding sections is based on the description of the unperturbed motion of each electron in a *given external field*, that is, by means of an individual wave function of a given form. Now in actual problems, connected with the structure of atoms and molecules, such a field cannot be defined beforehand in a way which would ensure the degree of accuracy of the zero-order approximation which is necessary for the successful application of the perturbation theory. We must now turn to the consideration of this problem, namely, the problem of the determination of the 'equivalent external field' for the separate electrons forming a more or less complicated system (such, for example, as a complex atom).

A relatively simple method which is quite similar to that used in the earlier (Bohr's) quantum theory of complex atoms, consists in the identification of the external field acting on a given electron with that of a bare nucleus (or nuclei, if there is more than one) with an electric charge differing from the actual one by a certain constant, which, divided by the elementary charge, is denoted as the 'screening constant' and is to be chosen in such a way as to represent with the highest possible degree of accuracy the effect of the repulsive forces acting on each electron due to all the rest.

To get a more exact description of this action it is sometimes preferable to distribute the electric charge of all the electrons except that under consideration in a continuous way over some surface, or in a certain volume, with a uniform density or a density varying according to some more or less arbitrarily chosen law.

In all these cases we get a problem containing a *finite number of constant parameters* which must be adjusted in a way leading to the least possible error.

This problem is solved very easily—at least in principle—with the help of the variational form of the equations of motion, namely,

$$\delta \frac{\int \phi^* H \phi \, dV}{\int \phi^* \phi \, dV} = 0,$$

where $\phi(x_1, x_2, ..., x_n)$ is determined as the product of n individual functions $\psi_1(x_1; a_1, b_1, ...)$, $\psi_2(x_2; a_2, b_2, ...)$, ..., $\psi_n(x_n; a_n, b_n, ...)$ of *known* form, containing a number of undetermined parameters† a_1, a_2,..., etc. [cf. § 9, Chap. II].

Under these conditions the expression $W = \int \phi^* H \phi \, dV / \int \phi^* \phi \, dV$, which is equal to the energy of the system, is defined as a certain function of the parameters a, whose values must be determined from the equations

$$\frac{\partial W}{\partial a_1} = 0, \quad \frac{\partial W}{\partial b_1} = 0, \quad ..., \quad \frac{\partial W}{\partial a_2} = 0, \quad ..., \quad \frac{\partial W}{\partial a_n} = 0, \text{ etc.}$$

The equation $\delta W = 0$ can be used, however, not only to adjust the values of a finite number of parameters introduced in the more or less arbitrarily specified functions $\psi_1,..., \psi_n$, but also *to determine these functions themselves* without the explicit introduction of any parameters (implicitly they are contained in the definition of the functions ψ if the latter are supposed to be expanded in some sort of series). Now the factorized form of the wave function ϕ describing the behaviour of the whole system of electrons corresponds to the possibility of assigning to each of them a separate 'orbit', i.e. a motion independent—explicitly —of that of the rest (in the sense of the wave-mechanical probability interpretation). Inasmuch as the variational principle $\delta W = 0$ ensures the highest accuracy of the results consistent with any given assumption about the character of the motion, we can thus state that the most accurate description of the motion of a system of electrons in terms of the quasi-independent motions of the separate electrons is obtained by defining the functions $\psi_1(x_1), \psi_2(x_2),..., \psi_n(x_n)$, describing these individual motions, with the help of the variational equation, with

$$\phi(x_1,..., x_n) = \psi_1(x_1)...\psi_n(x_n).$$

The above method has the advantage of avoiding the introduction of an arbitrary effective external field for each electron. Such a field is, however, introduced implicitly and can easily be determined in an explicit form. This is the so-called 'self-consistent field' which we have already alluded to many times, and which was applied for the first time to the problem of complex atoms by Hartree.

In his original theory of the self-consistent field Hartree did not make any use of the variational principle (which was introduced for this purpose later on by V. Fock and J. C. Slater) but was guided by the idea that the action experienced by one electron due to the rest can be calculated approximately by distributing in space the electric

---

† We shall leave aside for the time being the complications arising from the spin effect.

charge of the latter with a density proportional to the probability of
their respective positions. The contribution of each electron to the
probable density of charge ρ at a given point is obviously given by
$\rho_k = e|\psi_k(x)|^2$ under the condition that all the individual functions ψ
are normalized to 1:

$$\int |\psi_k(x)|^2 \, dx = 1$$

(where dx is an abbreviation for the element of volume $dx\,dy\,dz$). The
potential energy U_i of the ith electron with respect to all the others
can be determined accordingly by the expression

$$U_i = \sum_{k \neq i} U_{ik},$$

where
$$U_{ik} = e^2 \int \frac{|\psi_k(x_k)|^2}{r_{ik}} \, dx_k,$$

or, with a slightly different notation,

$$U_i'(\mathbf{r}) = e^2 \int \frac{1}{|\mathbf{r}-\mathbf{r}'|} \sum_{k \neq i} |\psi_k(r')|^2 \, dV'. \tag{360}$$

Adding to this expression the potential energy $U_0(\mathbf{r})$ of the external
forces (which must obviously have the same form for all the electrons)
and substituting the resulting 'effective' energy

$$U_i(\mathbf{r}) = U_{0i}(\mathbf{r}) + U_i'(\mathbf{r}) \tag{360a}$$

in the Schrödinger equation

$$\left[-\frac{h^2}{8\pi^2 m} \nabla^2 + U_i(\mathbf{r}) - W_i \right]\psi_i = 0, \tag{360b}$$

we can determine the wave function ψ_i describing the motion of the
electron in question if the functions ψ_k ($k \neq i$) describing that of the
other electrons are supposed to be known. Now as a matter of fact they
are not known beforehand, each of them being determined through the
rest by an equation of the form (360 b). We obtain in this way a system
of n integro-differential equations which can serve for the simultaneous
determination of all the n individual wave functions $\psi_1, ..., \psi_n$.

It may seem at first sight that the total energy W of the whole
system is equal to the sum of the individual energies W_i. This is, however, easily seen *not* to be the case. In fact multiplying equation (360 b)
on the left by ψ_i^* and integrating, we have, in view of the supposed
normalization of ψ_i,

$$W_i = \int \psi_i^* \left[-\frac{h^2}{8\pi^2 m} \nabla_i^2 + U_i \right]\psi_i \, dx,$$

or, according to the definition of U_i,

$$W_i = \int \phi^* \left[-\frac{h^2}{8\pi^2 m} \nabla_i^2 + U_{0i} + \sum_{k \neq i} \frac{e^2}{r_{ik}} \right] \phi \, dV,$$

whence it follows that

$$\sum W_i = \int \phi^* \left[\sum_{i=1}^{n} \left(-\frac{h^2}{8\pi^2 m} \nabla_i^2 + U_{0i} \right) + \sum_{i=1}^{n} \sum_{k \neq i} \frac{e^2}{r_{ik}} \right] \phi \, dV,$$

whereas the actual value of the total energy, corresponding to our approximation, is

$$W = \int \phi^* H \phi \, dV = \int \phi^* \left[\sum_{i=1}^{n} \left(-\frac{h^2}{8\pi^2 m} \nabla_i^2 + U_{0i} \right) + \frac{1}{2} \sum_{i=1}^{n} \sum_{k \neq i} \frac{e^2}{r_{ik}} \right] \phi \, dV,$$

the mutual potential energy of all the electrons thus being doubled in the expression $\sum W_i$.

In order to calculate the total energy W with the help of the 'partial energies' W_i we must introduce in addition the 'proper energies' of the separate electrons

$$E_i = \int \psi_i^* \left(-\frac{h^2}{8\pi^2 m} \nabla_i^2 + U_{0i} \right) \psi_i \, dx = \int \phi^* \left(-\frac{h^2}{8\pi^2 m} \nabla_i^2 + U_{0i} \right) \phi \, dV.$$

Denoting their sum $\sum E_i$ by E, we get

$$W - \tfrac{1}{2} \sum W_i = \tfrac{1}{2} E,$$

whence

$$W = \tfrac{1}{2} \left(E + \sum_{i=1}^{n} W_i \right) = \tfrac{1}{2} \sum_{i=1}^{n} (E_i + W_i). \tag{360 c}$$

It should be mentioned that Hartree's self-consistent field can be defined either by the resulting probable density of the electric charge $\rho = e \sum_{i=1}^{n} |\psi_i|^2$, from which the electric potential with due allowance for the contribution of the external field can be derived by means of Poisson's equation, or by the electric density $\rho_i' = \rho - \rho_i = \rho - e|\psi_i|^2$ and the potential energy (360) which corresponds to an electric field of specific form for each of the electrons.

We shall now come back to the variational equation in the form

$$\delta \int \phi^* H \phi \, dV = 0, \tag{361}$$

with ϕ defined as the product $\psi_1(x_1) \ldots \psi_n(x_n)$, and the n additional normalizing conditions $\int \psi_i^* \psi_i \, dx = 1$ or

$$\delta \int \psi_i^* \psi_i \, dx = 0. \tag{361 a}$$

We have $\delta \int \phi^* H \phi \, dV = \int \delta \phi^* H \phi \, dV + \int \phi^* H \delta \phi \, dV.$

Now in virtue of the self-adjoint character of the operator H (which we shall suppose to involve real quantities only) we have further

$$\int \phi^* H \delta\phi \, dV = \int \delta\phi H \phi^* \, dV,$$

so that (361) can be written in the form

$$\int \delta\phi^* H\phi \, dV + \int \delta\phi H\phi^* \, dV = 0.$$

Substituting here the product $\psi_1(x_1) \ldots \psi_n(x_n)$ for ϕ we get

$$\sum_{i=1} \int \delta\psi_i^* \prod_{k\neq i} \psi_k^* H\phi \, dV + \sum_{i=1} \int \delta\psi_i \prod_{k\neq i} \psi_k H\phi^* \, dV = 0.$$

If we subtract from this equation the n equations equivalent to (361 a)

$$\int \delta\psi_i^* \prod_{k\neq i} \psi_k^* \phi \, dV + \int \delta\psi_i \prod_{k\neq i} \psi_k \phi^* \, dV = 0$$

multiplied by suitably chosen parameters, λ_i say, we can equate to zero the coefficients of all the variations $\delta\psi_i^*$ and $\delta\psi_i$ (Lagrange's method of undetermined multipliers). This gives

$$(H_i - \lambda_i)\psi_i = 0, \tag{362}$$

where

$$H_i = \int \prod_{k\neq i} \psi_k^* H \prod_{k\neq i} \psi_k \prod_{k\neq i} dx_k \tag{362 a}$$

is an operator which can be defined as the average value of the actual energy operator H for a given position of the ith electron and for all the configurations of the other ones. Similar equations are obtained by equating to zero the coefficients of the variations $\delta\psi_i$ with H_i replaced by $H_i^* = \int \prod_{k\neq i} \psi_k H \prod_{k\neq i} \psi_k^* \prod_{k\neq i} dx_k$. They need not be considered separately for they are actually equivalent to the equations (362). The latter provide the mathematical justification for the physical principle which was used by Hartree† and are practically equivalent to Hartree's equation (360 b) if H is determined, as usual, by the formula

$$H = \sum_{i=1}^n E(x_i, p_i) + \tfrac{1}{2} \sum_{i=1}^n \sum_{k\neq i} F(x_i, x_k)\ldots \tag{362 b}$$

with

$$F(x_i, x_k) = \frac{e^2}{r_{ik}}.$$

The only difference between them consists, as is easily seen, in the fact that H_i involves in addition to the proper energy of the ith electron $-\dfrac{h^2}{8\pi^2 m} \nabla_i^2 + U_{0i}$ and its average potential energy with respect to the rest, the average of the energies of all the other electrons. Hence the

† It may be remembered that essentially the same principle had been used before by Schrödinger in connexion with his attempt to re-establish the wave theory of light emission on the basis of wave mechanics. (See Part I, § 17.)

constants λ_i appearing in (362) are easily seen to have the same value, namely, W, the total energy of the system. It should be mentioned that the normal state of the latter corresponds to the condition that W should have the least possible value of all the 'stationary' values which are allowed by the variational equation (361), in conjunction with (361a).

The preceding theory applies not only to a system of electrons but just as well to a system consisting of different particles or indeed of systems of any sort if x_i denotes the totality of the coordinates specifying the state of the corresponding elementary system and if the total energy (362b) is written in the somewhat more general form

$$H = \sum E_i(x_i, p_i) + \sum_{i<k} \sum F_{ik}(x_i, x_k). \tag{362c}$$

44. The Method of the Self-consistent Field with Antisymmetrical Functions and Dirac's Density Matrix

In the particular case of a system of electrons the accuracy of Hartree's method is limited not only intrinsically but also by the fact that a specific distribution of electrons among the n orbits $\psi_1, ..., \psi_n$ such as that defined by the function ϕ violates the identity principle. The function ϕ defined by the product $\psi_1(x_1) ... \psi_n(x_n)$ must serve merely as a starting-point for the perturbation theory which has been considered in § 37 in connexion with the exchange degeneracy.

Instead of accounting for the latter *a posteriori* we can take it into account from the beginning if we replace the factorized function ϕ in the variational equation by a linear combination of such functions, corresponding to the different permutations P of the electrons between the individual states $\psi_1, ..., \psi_n$:

$$\chi = \sum_P C_P P\phi.$$

The functions $\psi_1, ..., \psi_n$ obtained in this way will of course be somewhat different from those which are defined by the equations (361c) and which do not involve the exchange effect. As to the coefficients C_P, they can be shown to be the same as in the case of the perturbation problem corresponding to functions $\psi_1, ..., \psi_n$ known *a priori*.

We shall determine the latter for the antisymmetrical functions with spin which have been dealt with in the preceding section. We put accordingly

$$\chi(x, \xi) = C \begin{vmatrix} \psi_1(x_1, \xi_1) & \cdot & \cdot & \cdot & \psi_1(x_n, \xi_n) \\ \cdot & \cdot & \cdot & \cdot & \cdot & \cdot \\ \psi_n(x_1, \xi_1) & \cdot & \cdot & \cdot & \psi_n(x_n, \xi_n) \end{vmatrix} = C \sum_P \epsilon_P P\phi(x, \xi), \tag{363}$$

where
$$\psi_i(x,\xi) = \psi_i(x)\delta_{mi}(\xi)$$

and
$$\phi(x,\xi) = \psi_i(x_1,\xi_1)\psi_2(x_2,\xi_2)\ldots\psi_n(x_n,\xi_n).$$

We shall further assume for the sake of simplicity all the individual wave functions with spin not only to be normalized but also to be *mutually orthogonal* in the sense of the equations

$$\sum_\xi \int \psi_i^*(x,\xi)\psi_k(x,\xi)\,dx = \delta_{ik}. \tag{363a}$$

It should be mentioned that if this orthogonality condition were not fulfilled for the original wave functions ψ we could replace them by certain linear combinations satisfying these conditions. The *a priori* introduction of the latter does not therefore impair the generality of the theory. It serves, however, materially to simplify its external form. The normalizing condition for the function (363) under the assumption (363a) gives $C = 1/\sqrt{(n!)}$.

It will be convenient in what follows to write x_i for x_i, ξ_i and $\int$ for $\sum \int$, thus keeping externally the notation corresponding to spinless functions. We can formally proceed in the same way as if we were dealing with an antisymmetrical function (363) without spin.† Substituting it instead of ϕ in the variational equation (361) (which in our case should be written in the form $\delta \sum_\xi \int \chi^*H\chi\,dV$) and taking account of the self-adjointness of the operator H, we get as before

$$\int \delta\chi^*H\chi\,dV + \int \delta\chi H\chi^*\,dV = 0 \tag{364}$$

(the summation over the ξ's being understood).

Now we have according to (363)

$$\delta\chi^* = \frac{1}{\sqrt{(n!)}} \sum_P \epsilon_P P\delta\phi^*,$$

and further, since the integral $\int P\delta\phi^*H\chi\,dV$ (or more exactly $\sum_\xi \int P\delta\phi^*H\chi\,dV$) does not change if any permutation, P^{-1} in particular, is applied to all the integration variables,

$$\int \delta\chi^*H\chi\,dV = \frac{1}{\sqrt{(n!)}} \sum_P \epsilon_P \int \delta\phi^*HP^{-1}\chi\,dV;$$

or finally, since $P^{-1}\chi = \epsilon_P\chi$,

$$\int \delta\chi^*H\chi\,dV = \frac{1}{\sqrt{(n!)}} \sum_P \int \delta\phi^*H\chi\,dV = \sqrt{(n!)} \int \delta\phi^*H\chi\,dV, \tag{364a}$$

† The variations $\delta\psi$ must of course refer to the factor $\psi_i(x)$ only, leaving the spin factor $\delta_{mi}(\xi)$ unaltered.

and in the same way

$$\int \delta\chi H\chi^* \, dV = \sqrt{(n!)} \int \delta\phi H\chi^* \, dV.$$

If we now substitute for H the operator (362 b) (by definition not involving the spin) and replace $\sqrt{(n!)}\chi$ by the expression $\sum_P \epsilon_P P\phi$, we get

$$\int \delta\chi^* H\chi \, dV = \sum_P \epsilon_P \int \delta\phi^* H P\phi \, dV$$

$$= \sum_P \epsilon_P \left\{ \sum_{i=1}^n \int \delta\phi^* E(x_i, p_i) P\phi \, dV + \sum_{i<k} \int \delta\phi^* F(x_i, x_k) P\phi \, dV \right\}.$$

The integral $\int \delta\phi^* E(x_i, p_i) P\phi \, dV$, where $\delta\phi = \sum_{j=1}^n \delta\psi_j^* \prod_{k\neq j} \psi_k^*$, is easily seen to be different from zero only if P denotes the identical permutation (because of the orthogonality conditions $\int \psi_k^* \psi_l \, dx = \delta_{kl}$) when it reduces to $\int \delta\psi_i^* E(x_i, p_i)\psi_i \, dx_i$. We have further, if P is the identical permutation,

$$\int \delta\phi^* F(x_i, x_k) P\phi \, dV$$
$$= \iint [\psi_i^*(x_i)\delta\psi_k^*(x_k) + \psi_k^*(x_k)\delta\psi_i^*(x_i)] F(x_i, x_k)\psi_i(x_i)\psi_k(x_k) \, dx_i \, dx_k,$$
and

$$\int \delta\phi^* F(x_i, x_k) P\phi \, dV$$
$$= \iint [\psi_i^*(x_i)\delta\psi_k^*(x_k) + \psi_k^*(x_k)\delta\psi_i^*(x_i)] F(x_i, x_k)\psi_i(x_k)\psi_k(x_i) \, dx_i \, dx_k$$

if P is equal to the transposition T_{ik}, i.e. the interchange between the ith and kth electrons, and zero in all other cases. We thus get, on account of the symmetry relation $F(x_i, x_k) = F(x_k, x_i)$,

$$\int \delta\chi^* H\chi \, dV = \sum_{i=1}^n \int dx_i \delta\psi_i^* \left\{ \left[E(x_i, p_i) + \sum_{k\neq i} \int dx_k F(x_i, x_k)|\psi_k(x_k)|^2 \right] \psi_i(x_i) - \right.$$
$$\left. - \sum_{k\neq i} \left[\int dx_k F(x_i, x_k)\psi_k^*(x_k)\psi_i(x_k) \right] \psi_k(x_i) \right\}.$$

Putting for the sake of brevity

$$A_{ki}(x) = \int F(x, x')\psi_k^*(x')\psi_i(x') \, dx' \qquad (365)$$

and
$$B(x) = \sum_{k=1}^n A_{kk}(x), \qquad (365\,a)$$

we can rewrite the preceding expression as follows:

$$\int \delta\chi^* H\chi \, dV$$
$$= \sum_{i=1}^n \int dx \delta\psi_i^*(x) \left\{ [E(x, p_x) + B(x)]\psi_i(x) - \sum_{k=1}^n A_{ki}\psi_k(x) \right\} = 0. \qquad (365\,b)$$

Subtracting from this equation and the conjugate complex equation $\int \delta\chi H\chi^* = 0$ the expressions

$$\lambda_{ki} \int \delta\psi_i^*(x)\psi_k(x)\,dx + \lambda_{ki} \int \psi_i^*(x)\delta\psi_k(x)\,dx = 0,$$

which are derived from the orthogonality and normalizing conditions $\int \psi_i^*\psi_k\,dx = \delta_{ik}$, and equating to zero the coefficients of the variations $\delta\psi_i^*$, we obtain the following system of equations for the functions $\psi_i(x)$:

$$(E+B)\psi_i(x) - \sum_{k=1}^{n} (A_{ki}+\lambda_{ki})\psi_k(x) = 0, \tag{366}$$

and a similar system for the conjugate complex functions. If we multiply these equations on the left by $\psi_j^*(x)$ and integrate over x (including summation over ξ) we get, in virtue of the orthogonality and normalizing relations,

$$\lambda_{ji} = \int \psi_j^*(x)(E+B)\psi_i(x)\,dx - \sum_{k=1}^{n} \int A_{ki}\psi_j^*(x)\psi_k(x)\,dx$$

or, according to (365) and (365 a),

$$\left.\begin{aligned}\lambda_{ji} = E_{ji}+ &\iint F(x,x')\psi_j^*(x)\psi_i(x) \sum_{k=1}^{n} \psi_k^*(x')\psi_k(x')\,dx dx' - \\ &- \iint F(x,x')\psi_j^*(x)\psi_i(x') \sum_{k=1}^{n} \psi_k^*(x')\psi_k(x)\,dx dx'\end{aligned}\right\}, \tag{366 a}$$

where

$$E_{ji} = \int \psi_j^*(x)E(x,p_x)\psi_i(x)\,dx \tag{366 b}$$

are the matrix elements of the proper energy of an electron [including its external potential energy $U_0(x)$] with respect to the states i and j.

Although the coefficients λ_{ki} are completely determined by these equations, they can actually be considered as arbitrary constants forming an Hermitian matrix, i.e. satisfying the relations $\lambda_{ik}^* = \lambda_{ki}$, and further subject to the condition that the diagonal sum $\sum_i \lambda_{ii}$ should have a given constant value.

This conclusion follows from the fact that the set of normalized and orthogonal wave functions ψ_i can be replaced by any set of linear combinations of these functions, provided the transformed functions

$$\psi_{i'}' = \sum_i C_{i'i}\psi_i$$

also satisfy the normalizing and orthogonality conditions. In fact the functions A_{ik} are transformed by (365) according to the equations

$$A_{i'k'}' = \sum_i \sum_k C_{i'i} C_{k'k} A_{ik},$$

i.e. like the components of a *tensor* in the n-dimensional space, whose coordinates are defined by the values of the n functions $\psi_i(x)$. The latter can also be considered as the components of a vector ψ referred to a certain set of orthogonal coordinate axes, ψ'_i being its components with respect to another system of such axes (with the same origin). In other words, the equations (366) can be considered as invariant with regard to all the orthogonal transformations or 'rotations' of the co-ordinate axes, if the coefficients λ_{ik} are likewise defined as the components of an arbitrary tensor λ, the operators E and B being obviously scalars.

As has been pointed out by Dirac, the arbitrariness involved in the determination of the components $\psi_i(x)$ of a vector $\psi(x)$ can be removed if instead of such a vector we consider its scalar product with the conjugate complex $\psi^*(x')$ of a vector $\psi(x')$ associated with some other point x'. This product, which will be denoted as

$$\rho(x, x') = \sum_{i=1}^{n} \psi_i(x)\psi_i^*(x'), \tag{367}$$

is invariant under the above transformation and is therefore the only quantity that can be determined unambiguously in connexion with our problem. It can, moreover, easily be shown to be the only quantity we actually need know, the energy

$$W = \int \chi^* H \chi \, dV$$

of the system of electrons being expressible as a function of ρ.

In fact the preceding formula is reduced (in the same way as the expression $\int \delta \chi^* H \chi \, dV$) to the form

$$W = \int \phi^* H \chi \, dV = \sum_P \epsilon_P \int \phi^* H P \phi \, dV,$$

or, if the energy operator is defined by (362 b),

$$W = \int \phi^* H \phi \, dV - \sum \int \phi^* H T_{ik} \phi \, dV.$$

Hence we get in the same way as in the derivation of (365 b)

$$W = \sum_{i=1}^{n} E_{ii} + \tfrac{1}{2} \iint F(x, x')[\rho(x, x)\rho(x', x') - |\rho(x, x')|^2] \, dV, \tag{367 a}$$

where
$$|\rho(x, x')|^2 = \rho(x, x')\rho(x', x).$$

It should be mentioned that the sum $\sum_i \lambda_{ii}$ differs from this expression by the absence of the factor $\tfrac{1}{2}$ in the second term which corresponds to the mutual energy of the different electrons, so that we can put

$$W = \tfrac{1}{2} \sum_{i=1}^{n} (E_{ii} + \lambda_{ii}).$$

The quantities λ_{ii} are thus easily seen to correspond to the partial energies of our previous theory.

The integral $\frac{1}{2} \iint F(x,x')\rho(x,x)\rho(x',x)\,dxdx'$ with $F(x,x') = \dfrac{e^2}{r(x,x')}$ represents the mutual potential energy which is obtained if the charges of the electrons are distributed in space with a volume density $e|\psi_i(x)|^2$, $e\rho(x,x) = e\sum_{i=1}^{n} |\psi_i(x)|^2$ being the resulting density of the 'electron cloud'. This includes the action of an electron spread out into a cloud upon itself, which is devoid of physical meaning. Such self-action is, however, cancelled out by the second integral on the right side of (367 a),

$$-\tfrac{1}{2} \iint F(x,x')|\rho(x,x')|^2 \, dxdx',$$

which also represents the exchange effect or, as it is usually denoted, the 'exchange energy' of the electrons.†

The first term in (367 a) does not seem at first sight to be consistent with the representation of the energy as a function of the 'density matrix' ρ. If, however, we introduce the elements of the electron's own energy matrix E from the point of view of the coordinates x

$$E(x,x') = \int \delta(x-x'')E(x'',p_{x''})\delta(x''-x') \, dx''$$

(cf. § 17), we can put, since $E_{ii} = \int \psi_i^*(x)E\psi_i(x) \, dx$,

$$\sum_{i=1}^{n} E_{ii} = \iint E(x,x')\rho(x',x) \, dxdx'. \tag{367 b}$$

The fact that the energy $W = \int \chi^* H \chi \, dV$ is expressed as a function (or rather a 'functional') of the density matrix ρ alone, shows that the latter can be determined directly without the functions $\psi_1(x),...,\psi_n(x)$ which have initially served for its definition. Multiplying the equations (366) by $\psi^*(x')$, subtracting therefrom the product by $\psi_i(x)$ of the corresponding equations for the conjugate complex of $\psi_i(x')$, and summing over i, taking into account the relations $A_{ik}^* = A_{ki}$ and $\lambda_{ik}^* = \lambda_{ki}$, we can eliminate the coefficients λ_{ik} with the result

$$[E(x,p_x)+B(x)-E(x',p_{x'})-B(x')]\sum \psi_i(x)\psi_i^*(x') - $$
$$- \sum\sum [A_{ki}(x)-A_{ki}(x')]\psi_k(x)\psi^*(x') = 0. \tag{368}$$

† As has been stated at the beginning, the integration sign in the preceding equations actually means both integration with regard to the geometrical coordinates and a summation over the spin coordinates. The latter can easily be introduced explicitly in the final results. They are, however, wholly irrelevant so long as we are dealing with a spinless energy. Their only effect is to allow the introduction of doubly occupied spinless states $\psi_i(x)$ (with opposite spin) without the violation of Pauli's exclusion principle. As a result we get a number of relations of the form $A_{ik}(x) = A_{ii}(x) = A_{kk}(x)$ and $A_{ij}(x) = A_{kj}(x)$ for indices i and k which correspond to identical spinless states.

If we substitute here the expression (365) for $A_{ki}(x)$ with x' replaced by x'' and similarly put $A_{ki}(x') = \int F(x', x'')\psi_k^*(x'')\psi_i(x'')\,dx''$, we obtain the following equation, containing the density matrix alone,

$$(E_x + B_x - E_{x'} - B_{x'})\rho(x, x') -$$
$$- \int [F(x, x'') - F(x', x'')]\rho(x, x'')\rho(x'', x')\,dx'' = 0, \quad (368\,\mathrm{a})$$

where E_x, etc., is an abbreviation for $E(x, p_x)$, etc.

Introducing a matrix K defined from the point of view of x by the formula

$$K(x, x') = E(x, x') + \delta(x - x')B(x') - A(x, x'), \quad (369)$$

where

$$A(x, x') = F(x, x')\rho(x, x') = e^2 \frac{\rho(x, x')}{r(x, x')} \quad (369\,\mathrm{a})$$

and, according to (365 a),

$$B(x) = \int F(x, x')\rho(x', x')\,dx' = e^2 \int \frac{\rho(x', x')}{r(x, x')}\,dx', \quad (369\,\mathrm{b})$$

we can consider the left-hand side of the equation (368 a) as the (x, x') element of the matrix $K\rho - \rho K$ and accordingly rewrite it in the following matrix form:

$$K\rho - \rho K = 0. \quad (370)$$

It should be mentioned that the matrix $A(x, x')$ subtracts from the matrix $B(x, x') = \delta(x - x')B(x')$ physically irrelevant terms corresponding to the action of an electron upon itself and at the same time accounts for the exchange effect.

With the new matrix notation we can rewrite the expression of the energy as a function of ρ derived above

$$W = \iint dx\,dx' \{E(x, x')\rho(x', x) + \tfrac{1}{2}F(x, x')[\rho(x, x)\rho(x', x') - |\rho(x, x')|^2]\}$$
$$(371)$$

in the form

$$W = D[\rho(E + \tfrac{1}{2}B - \tfrac{1}{2}A)] = D[(E + \tfrac{1}{2}B - \tfrac{1}{2}A)\rho], \quad (371\,\mathrm{a})$$

where $D(M)$ is an abbreviation for the so-called *diagonal sum* (German, *Spur*), i.e. sum (or integral) of the diagonal elements of the matrix M; in the present case we have

$$D(M) = \int M(x, x)\,dx.$$

The equation (370) which is satisfied by ρ can be obtained directly, i.e. without the use of the functions $\psi_1(x), ..., \psi_n(x)$, from the variational equation $\delta W = 0$. With the expression (371) for W we get, since $F(x, x') = F(x', x)$,

$$\delta W = \iint dx\,dx' \{E(x, x')\delta\rho(x', x) +$$
$$+ F(x, x')[\rho(x, x)\delta\rho(x', x') - \rho(x, x')\delta\rho(x', x)]\}$$

$$= \iint dx dx' \, [E(x,x') + \delta(x-x')B(x') - A(x,x')] \delta\rho(x',x)$$

$$= \iint dx' dx \, \delta\rho(x,x')[E(x',x) + \delta(x'-x)B(x) - A(x',x)],$$

that is, according to (369),

$$\delta W = D(\delta\rho \, K) = D(K \, \delta\rho) = 0. \tag{371 b}$$

It must not be concluded from this equation that $K = 0$, for the matrix ρ satisfies a certain accessory condition which is obtained by comparing it with its square.

We have in fact, from the definition of matrix multiplication,

$$\rho^2(x,x') = \int \rho(x,x'')\rho(x'',x') \, dx'' = \sum_i \sum_k \int \psi_i(x)\psi_i^*(x'')\psi_k^*(x')\psi_k(x'') \, dx''$$

$$= \sum_i \sum_k \psi_i(x)\psi_k^*(x')\delta_{ik} = \sum_i \psi_i(x)\psi_i^*(x') = \rho(x,x')$$

(because of the orthogonality and normalization of the functions ψ_i), i.e.

$$\rho^2 = \rho. \tag{372}$$

It follows that $\delta\rho = \rho \, \delta\rho + \delta\rho \, \rho$, that is,

$$\delta\rho(x',x'') = \int \rho(x',x''') \, \delta\rho(x''',x'') \, dx''' + \int \delta\rho(x',x''')\rho(x''',x'') \, dx'''$$

which in conjunction with (371 b) leads to (370).

The relation (372) shows that the characteristic values ρ' of the matrix ρ are equal either to 0 or to 1 (since they satisfy the same equation $\rho'^2 = \rho'$). We thus obtain, according to Dirac, a new formulation of Pauli's exclusion principle, for although the matrix ρ can be introduced irrespective of the statistical properties of the particles under consideration, yet it can be shown to possess a dynamical meaning—in the sense of describing the motion of a system of particles—for the Pauli-Fermi statistics only (see below, p. 463), so that Pauli's principle is expressed *implicitly* by the property (372) of ρ.

If in the equation (367) we sum over all values of i specifying a complete set of individual wave functions ψ_i—which corresponds to $n = \infty$, so long as all these wave functions are normalized and orthogonal to each other, we obtain

$$\rho(x,x') = \delta(x-x') \tag{372 a}$$

This expression can be used as an approximation to ρ for large values of n. It is easily seen to satisfy the relation (372).

The preceding results can be generalized for a non-stationary motion of the electrons, determined, in the method of the configuration space, by the equation

$$\left(H + \frac{h}{2\pi i}\frac{\partial}{\partial t}\right)\chi = 0. \tag{373}$$

In order to obtain the corresponding generalized form of the equations (366) or of the equation (370) for the density matrix, we need only remember that the equation (373) is equivalent to the variational equation

$$\int \delta\chi^* \left(H + \frac{h}{2\pi i} \frac{\partial}{\partial t} \right) \chi \, dV = 0. \tag{373a}$$

[cf. § 26, eq. (207a)]. Now

$$\int \delta\chi^* \frac{\partial \chi}{\partial t} \, dV = \sum_P \epsilon_P \int \delta\phi^* \frac{\partial}{\partial t} P\phi \, dV = \int \delta\phi^* \frac{\partial\phi}{\partial t} \, dV$$

$$= \sum_{i=1}^n \int \delta\psi_i^* \left[\frac{\partial\psi_i}{\partial t} + \left(\sum_{i' \neq i} \int \psi_{i'}^* \frac{\partial\psi_{i'}}{\partial t} \, dx_{i'} \right) \psi_i \right] dx.$$

Putting for the sake of brevity

$$-\frac{h}{2\pi i} \int \psi_i^* \frac{\partial\psi_i}{\partial t} \, dx = a_i, \qquad \sum_{i=1}^n a_i = b, \qquad b - a_i = b_i,$$

we thus get

$$-\frac{h}{2\pi i} \int \delta\phi^* \frac{\partial\phi}{\partial t} \, dV = \sum_{i=1}^n \int \delta\psi_i^* \left(-\frac{h}{2\pi i} \frac{\partial}{\partial t} + b_i \right) \psi_i \, dx.$$

Equating this expression to the expression (365b) for $\int \delta\chi^* H\chi \, dV$, and taking account of the orthogonality and normalizing conditions in the form

$$\int \delta\psi_i^*(x)\psi_k(x) \, dx = 0,$$

we get instead of (366) the equations

$$\left(E + B + \frac{h}{2\pi i} \frac{\partial}{\partial t} \right) \psi_i(x) - \sum_{k=1}^n (A_{ki} + b_{ki})\psi_k(x) = 0, \tag{374}$$

where b_{ki} are numerical coefficients, or more generally functions of the time.

These can be determined in the same way as the coefficients λ_{ij}, i.e. by expressions similar to (366a) and differing from the latter by additional terms $\frac{h}{2\pi i} \int \psi_j^* \frac{\partial\psi_i}{\partial t} \, dx$:

$$b_{ki} = \lambda_{ki} + \frac{h}{2\pi i} \int \psi_k^* \frac{\partial\psi_i}{\partial t} \, dx. \tag{374a}$$

Hence we see that they must satisfy the conditions

$$b_{ki} = b_{ik}^*$$

and are otherwise quite arbitrary. Taking the sum

$$\sum_{i=1}^n b_{ii} = \sum_{i=1}^n \lambda_{ii} + \sum_i \frac{h}{2\pi i} \int \psi_i^* \frac{\partial\psi_i}{\partial t} \, dx,$$

we have, according to (374),

$$\sum_i b_{ii} = \sum_i \lambda_{ii} - \sum_i \int \psi_i^*(E+B)\psi_i \, dx + \sum_i \sum_k \int (A_{ki}+b_{ki})\psi_i^*\psi_k \, dx.$$

Now in view of the orthogonality and normalizing relations

$$\sum_i \sum_k \int b_{ki} \psi_i^* \psi_k \, dx = \sum_i b_{ii}.$$

The sum $\sum_i b_{ii}$ thus drops out of the preceding equation which reduces to the equation (367 a) for $\sum_i \lambda_{ii}$.

The arbitrary coefficients b_{ki} can be eliminated from the equations (374) in the same way as from the equations (366), namely, by multiplying (374) by $\psi_i^*(x')$, subtracting the product with $\psi_i(x)$ of the corresponding (conjugate complex) equation for $\psi_i^*(x')$, and summing over i. We thus get, instead of (368),

$$-\frac{h}{2\pi i}\frac{\partial \rho(x,x')}{\partial t} = (E_x+B_x-E_{x'}-B_{x'})\rho(x,x')- $$
$$- \int [F(x,x'')-F(x',x'')]\rho(x,x'')\rho(x'',x') \, dx'', \quad (375)$$

or in the matrix form corresponding to (370)

$$-\frac{h}{2\pi i}\frac{\partial \rho}{\partial t} = K\rho-\rho K. \qquad (375\,a)$$

This relation should be distinguished from the expression

$$+\frac{h}{2\pi i}\frac{dM}{dt} = (HM-MH)$$

for the time derivative of any matrix or operator which is specified in terms of the same variables as the Hamiltonian H of the system and which does not contain the time explicitly. If K is considered as the energy matrix of our system of electrons reduced by the method of the self-consistent field to a single particle, then the expression

$$\frac{2\pi i}{h}(K\rho-\rho K) = [K,\rho]$$

gives that part of the time derivative of ρ which corresponds to the rate of change of the dynamical variables (x and p_x for example) through which it can be expressed. The total derivative of ρ with respect to the time will thus be

$$\frac{d\rho}{dt} = \frac{\partial \rho}{\partial t}+\frac{2\pi i}{h}(K\rho-\rho K) = 0 \qquad (375\,b)$$

in virtue of (375 a), which means that ρ is a constant of the motion determined by K.

The total energy of the system of electrons W as given by (371) or (371 a) is not a matrix but an ordinary number. If the external field involved in the proper energy of an electron E does not depend upon the time, W can be shown to be a constant of the motion. We have in fact, in exactly the same way as in the derivation of (371 b)

$$\frac{dW}{dt} = D\left[\frac{\partial \rho}{\partial t} K\right],$$

or, according to (375 a),

$$-\frac{h}{2\pi i}\frac{dW}{dt} = D[(K\rho - \rho K)K] = D[K\rho K] - D(\rho K^2),$$

which is easily seen to vanish.

The matrix
$$\rho(E + \tfrac{1}{2}B - \tfrac{1}{2}A) = \tfrac{1}{2}\rho(E + K)$$

could be formally defined as the energy matrix of the system of electrons, without, however, attaching any dynamical meaning to this definition, for it is the matrix K only which is entitled to play the role of the energy matrix for a single particle. The matrix K differs from an ordinary energy matrix such as E, by the fact that it is itself determined by the character of the motion, and that accordingly it cannot be represented by an operator of the usual form $(p^2/2m) + U(x)$ even with an unknown potential-energy function $U(x)$.

One might be tempted to replace the equation (375 a) by an equation of the usual Schrödinger type

$$-\frac{h}{2\pi i}\frac{\partial}{\partial t}\psi = K\psi(x).$$

The latter can in fact be shown to be equivalent to (375 a) or to (375) in the special case of a *single* electron (but not otherwise). Replacing K by an energy operator of the ordinary type, E say, multiplying the equation

$$-\frac{h}{2\pi i}\frac{\partial}{\partial t}\psi(x) = E_x\psi(x)$$

by $\psi^*(x')$ and subtracting from it the equation

$$+\frac{h}{2\pi i}\frac{\partial}{\partial t}\psi^*(x') = E_{x'}\psi^*(x'),$$

multiplied by $\psi(x)$, we get

$$-\frac{h}{2\pi i}\frac{\partial}{\partial t}\{\psi^*(x)\psi(x')\} = (E_x - E_{x'})\psi(x)\psi^*(x'),$$

which is a special case of (375 b). The equation (375) or (375 a) can thus be considered as the generalization of the wave mechanics of a single electron, which makes it possible, through the introduction of the density matrix $\rho(x, x')$ instead of ordinary wave functions, to describe the motion of a system of n electrons in exactly the same way (with a modified definition of the energy matrix K) as the motion of a single electron.

The complete disappearance of the number of electrons from the equations of the general theory seems at first sight very puzzling. This number must obviously be introduced *a posteriori* as an integration constant, or more exactly as a sort of quantum number, specifying the system under consideration.

We thus see that the theory of the density matrix naturally leads to a further development of quantum theory in the sense of second quantization discussed already in Part I (see next chapter).

45. Approximate Solutions (Thomas-Fermi-Dirac Equation)

Using Dirac's notation for the matrix elements and for the wave functions we can transform the matrix ρ from the point of view of x to that of K with the help of the following equations:

$$(K'|\rho|K'') = \iint (K'|x')\, dx'\, (x'|\rho|x'')\, dx''\, (x''|K''), \qquad (376)$$

the matrix elements $(K'|\rho|K'')$ and $(x'|\rho|x'')$ being both of the 'pure' type, corresponding to a definite point of view. We can, however, define in a similar way the mixed elements of ρ corresponding to a 'double' point of view (K, E) which serves to connect the two matrices K and E with each other. These elements are given by the formula

$$(E'|\rho|K') = \iint (E'|x')\, dx'\, (x'|\rho|x'')\, dx''\, (x''|K''), \qquad (376\,\text{a})$$

which is similar to the equation

$$(E'|K') = \int (E'|x)\, dx\, (x|K') \qquad (376\,\text{b})$$

for the transformation coefficients $(E'|K')$ (cf. § 18), and reduces to it in the limiting case $n = \infty$ according to (372 a). The wave function $(x|K')$ appearing in the transformation equations (376 a) and (376 b) replaces in a certain sense the whole set of individual wave functions $\psi_1(x), ..., \psi_n(x)$ associated with the given value of K', in agreement with the fact that each of the n electrons on account of the exchange phenomenon must be distributed over all of them.

The introduction of the wave functions $(x|K')$—although it is by no means necessary nor even convenient—raises the question as to the possibility of representing the energy K as a function (of a perhaps unusual type) of the dynamical variables x and p $(= p_x)$ used in the wave mechanics of a single electron. Now, since K is defined as a function of the density matrix, this question amounts to the transformation of the latter from the original viewpoint of x to the 'mixed' viewpoint (x, p). In other words, we must find the transformation from the 'pure' matrix elements $(x|\rho|x')$ to the 'mixed' matrix elements $(p'|\rho|x')$. This transformation is given by the equation

$$(x|\rho|x') = \int (x|\rho|p)\, dp\, (p|x) \tag{377}$$

or the reciprocal equation

$$(x|\rho|p) = \int (x|\rho|x')\, dx'\, (x'|p), \tag{377 a}$$

where $(x|p) = (p|x)^*$ is the well-known function

$$(x|p) = e^{i2\pi \mathbf{x}\cdot\mathbf{p}/h}, \tag{377 b}$$

$\mathbf{x}\cdot\mathbf{p}$ being an abbreviation for $xp_x + yp_y + zp_z$. The function (377 b) is understood to be normalized according to the condition

$$\int (x|p)(p'|x)\, dx = \delta\!\left(\frac{p-p'}{h}\right).$$

We shall give here, following Dirac, an approximate solution of this problem by treating x and p as ordinary, i.e. mutually commuting, quantities in the sense of classical mechanics. The density ρ (as well as the energy K) will thus appear as a function $\rho(x, p)$ of the coordinates and momenta of an electron, its product with the volume element of the phase space $dx\,dp$ being proportional to the probability of finding the electron in this volume element, or, in other words, to the relative number of electrons to be expected in the latter. This physical meaning of ρ will become apparent from the following argument.

Let us consider $\rho(x, p) = \rho_x(p)$ as a function of p for a fixed value of x and expand it in a Fourier integral†

$$\rho_x(p) = \int \rho_{x\xi}\, e^{i2\pi \mathbf{p}\cdot\boldsymbol{\xi}/h}\, d\xi. \tag{378}$$

This expansion is quite similar to the expansion of a function of the time t, the coordinate of an electron for example, for a motion with a fixed energy W

$$f_W(t) = \int f_{W,w}\, e^{i2\pi t w/h}\, dw,$$

w/h being the frequency. Now in the latter case the Fourier coefficient $f_{W,w}$ is well known (by the correspondence principle, Chap. III, § 12) to represent approximately the matrix element of f $(W|f|W+w)$ for two neighbouring states with the energies W and $W+w$ (provided $w \ll W$).

† It should be remembered that x and p are meant to denote the triplets of coordinates and momenta, and that dx actually means $dx\,dy\,dz$.

Since a coordinate x and the corresponding momentum p_x are related to each other in exactly the same way as the energy and the time (being canonically conjugate quantities), the Fourier coefficients of $\rho_x(p)$ in (378) must likewise represent approximately the matrix elements $(x|\rho|x+\xi)$ of ρ. The function $\rho(x,p)$ corresponding to the classical definition of p (as a quantity commuting with x) can thus be calculated with the help of the matrix $(x|\rho|x')$ by the formula

$$\rho(x,p) = \int (x|\rho|x+\xi)e^{i2\pi p\cdot\xi/h}\,d\xi. \tag{378a}$$

Comparing this with (377 a) and (377 b) we obtain the relation

$$(x|\rho|p) = \rho(x,p)e^{i2\pi p\cdot x/h}. \tag{379}$$

The Fourier coefficients in (378) can be calculated by the formula

$$\rho_{x\xi} = (x|\rho|x+\xi) = \int \rho(x,p)e^{-i2\pi p\cdot\xi/h}\,dp/h^3, \tag{380}$$

h^3 appearing instead of h because dp actually denotes here the product $dp_x\,dp_y\,dp_z$.

Putting here $\xi = 0$, we get

$$(x|\rho|x) = \frac{1}{h^3}\int \rho(x,p)\,dp, \tag{380a}$$

whence it is clear that $\rho(x,p)$ can be defined as the probable number of electrons per volume h^3 of the phase-space.

The preceding equations are obviously valid not only for the matrix p but also for any other matrix of the same type, and in particular for the energy matrix K. Expressing it as a function of the variables x, p we thus get

$$K(x,p) = E(x,p)+B(x,p)-A(x,p), \tag{381}$$

where $E(x,p)$ is the usual (classical) expression for the electron's own energy $p^2/2m + U(x)$,

$$B(x,p) = B(x)\int \delta(\xi)e^{i2\pi p\cdot\xi/h}\,d\xi;$$

that is,

$$B(x,p) = B(x) = e^2\int \frac{\rho(x',x')}{r(x,x')}\,dx', \tag{381a}$$

the usual expression for the Coulomb energy of an electron in a cloud of electric charge with the volume density $e\rho(x',x')$, and

$$A(x,p) = \int (x|A|x+\xi)e^{i2\pi p\cdot\xi/h}\,d\xi. \tag{381b}$$

Taking for the matrix $(x|A|x+\xi) = A(x,x+\xi)$ its expression (369 a) and substituting for $(x|\rho|x+\xi)$ the expression (380), we get

$$A(x,p) = \iint F(x,x+\xi)\rho(x,p')e^{i2\pi(p-p')\cdot\xi/h}\,d\xi dp'/h^3.$$

Now $(\mathbf{p}-\mathbf{p}')\cdot\boldsymbol{\xi}$ is the scalar product $(p_x-p_{x'})\xi_x+(p_y-p_{y'})\xi_y+(p_z-p_{z'})\xi_z$ of the vectors $\mathbf{p}-\mathbf{p}'$ and $\boldsymbol{\xi}$. Keeping the vector $\mathbf{p}-\mathbf{p}' = \mathbf{g}$ fixed and denoting by θ the angle made with it by the variable vector $\boldsymbol{\xi}$, we can replace the volume-element $d\xi$ $(= d\xi_x\,d\xi_y\,d\xi_z)$ by the expression $2\pi\xi^2 d|\boldsymbol{\xi}|\sin\theta\,d\theta$; since $F(x, x+\xi)$ depends on the magnitude $|\boldsymbol{\xi}| = r$ of the vector $\boldsymbol{\xi}$ only, we can carry out the integration over θ, keeping r constant. This gives

$$\int e^{i2\pi\mathbf{g}\cdot\boldsymbol{\xi}/h}\,d\xi = 2\pi r^2\,dr\int\limits_{-1}^{+1} e^{i2\pi gr\cos\theta/h}\,d(\cos\theta)$$

$$= 2\pi r^2\,dr\,\frac{\sin(2\pi gr/h)}{\pi gr/h} = 2r\,dr\,\frac{\sin(2\pi gr/h)}{g/h},$$

and consequently

$$\int (x|A|x+\xi)e^{i2\pi\mathbf{p}\cdot\boldsymbol{\xi}/h}\,d\xi = 2e^2\int\frac{dp'\rho(x,p')}{g}\int\limits_0^\infty dr\,\sin(2\pi gr/h).$$

Now

$$\int\limits_0^\infty \sin\alpha r\,dr = -\frac{1}{\alpha}[\cos\alpha r]_0^\infty,$$

which is equal to $1/\alpha+$ an indeterminate constant which can actually be dropped. In fact, if instead of integrating over r to ∞ we first extend the integration to some large finite value, R say, and pass to the limit $R = \infty$, after carrying out the subsequent integration over p', the term containing R vanishes. We thus get finally

$$A(x,p) = \frac{e^2}{\pi h}\int\frac{\rho(x,p')}{|\mathbf{p}-\mathbf{p}'|^2}\,dp'. \tag{382}$$

If the function $\rho(x,p')$ is replaced here by the function $f(x,p') = \rho/h^3$, giving the probable number of electrons per *unit volume* of the phase-space, the preceding expression assumes the form

$$A(x,p) = \frac{e^2 h^2}{\pi}\int\frac{f(x,p')\,dp'}{|\mathbf{p}-\mathbf{p}'|^2}, \tag{382a}$$

which shows that the exchange energy, being purely a quantum effect, vanishes with h, as of course it should provided the function f *remains finite* (which simply means that the number of electrons is finite).

If the function $f(x,p')$ vanishes for large values of p', then for sufficiently large values of p we can put approximately

$$\int\frac{f(x,p')\,dp'}{|\mathbf{p}-\mathbf{p}'|^2} = \frac{1}{p^2}\int f(x,p')\,dp' = \frac{1}{p^2}\,\rho(x,x),$$

and consequently

$$A(x,p) \cong \frac{e^2 h^2}{\pi p^2}\,\rho(x,x). \tag{383}$$

It was shown by Fock that this expression can be applied *for all* *values* of p in the case of an electron moving in the electric field of a number of other electrons, if its reaction upon the latter can be neglected. Thus, for example, if we consider an alkali atom containing n electrons of which $n-1$ form its inner core, while one can be treated as an outsider (although it actually 'dives' into the core), then the effect of the interchange of roles between this outsider and the core electrons is the same as if the energy of the external electron were decreased by the amount (383). Fock's formula can be obtained by applying the variation principle to that part of the total energy $W = \int \chi^* H \chi \, dV$ which, besides the proper energy E of the 'external' electron, contains terms representing its interaction with the other electrons (whose motion is supposed to be given, i.e. to remain unaffected by this interaction).

Taking for W the expression (371) and putting $\rho = \rho_0 + \rho_1$, we easily get for the part in question the expression

$$W_1 = \int \psi_1^* E \psi_1 \, dx +$$

$$+ \iint F(x, x')[\rho_0(x', x')\rho_1(x, x) - \rho_0(x, x')\rho_1(x, x')] \, dx dx' \qquad (384)$$

where
$$\rho_1(x, x') = \psi_1(x)\psi_1^*(x')$$

is the contribution to the total density matrix $\rho(x, x')$ of the electron under consideration and $\psi_1(x)$ its wave function. The latter is to be determined from the condition $\delta W_1 = 0$ (the normalization condition being now irrelevant). This leads to the equation

$$[E(x, p) + B_0(x) - A_0]\psi_1 = W_1 \psi_1, \qquad (385)$$

where $B_0(x) = e^2 \int \dfrac{\rho_0(x', x')}{r(x, x')} \, dx'$ is the Coulomb energy of the electron in question with respect to the rest, while A_0 is the operator of the exchange energy [including the physically irrelevant action of the electron upon itself which must be subtracted from $B_0(x)$]. It has an unusual form, being defined by

$$A_0 \psi(x) = e^2 \int \dfrac{\rho_0(x, x')}{r(x, x')} \psi(x') \, dx'. \qquad (385\,\text{a})$$

Now, as has been pointed out by Fock, the quantity $1/r(x, x')$, i.e. the reciprocal of the distance between the points x and x', can be considered (if we leave aside for a while the spin coordinates) as the matrix element with respect to x and x' of the operator $-4\pi/\nabla^2$, where ∇^2 is Laplace's operator. This follows from the fact that

$$\phi(x) = \int \frac{f(x')}{r(x, x')} \, dx'$$

is the solution of the equation

$$\nabla^2 \phi = -4\pi f,$$

which can be rewritten symbolically in the form

$$\phi = -\frac{4\pi}{\nabla^2} f.$$

In applying this result to (385 a) we must take care of the fact that $1/\nabla^2$ operates on a function of x' leaving x constant. We must accordingly come back to the original expression $\rho_0(x, x') = \sum_{i=1}^{n-1} \psi_i(x)\psi_i^*(x')$ for the density (where $n-1$ denotes the number of electrons in the core) and insert the operator $1/\nabla^2$ between the $\psi_i(x)$ and $\psi_i^*(x')$ of the separate terms.

Since $-\dfrac{h^2}{4\pi^2} \nabla^2 = p^2$, we obtain the following expression for $A_0 \psi_1(x)$:

$$A_0 \psi_1(x) = \frac{h^2}{\pi} \sum_{i=1}^{n-1} \psi_i(x) p^{-2} \psi_i^*(x)\psi_1(x),$$

where x' in $\psi_i^*(x')$ and $\psi_1(x')$ has been replaced by x in view of the fact that p^{-2}, by definition, converts a function $f(x')$ of x' into a function $\phi(x)$ of x.

If we now wish to consider the approximation corresponding to the classical mechanics we must treat p as an ordinary number, which enables us to rewrite the preceding formula as follows:

$$A_0 \psi_1(x) = \frac{h^2}{\pi p^2} \rho_0(x, x)\psi_1(x)$$

and leads us back to the expression (383) for the operator A_0.

We have hitherto made no explicit use of the spin variables which were understood to be included in x and p whenever they were necessary. It is easy to rewrite the preceding equations with an explicit notation for the spin variables. So long, however, as the dynamical effects of the spin are neglected, its only influence will be to double the maximum value of $\rho(x, p)$ which is allowed by the exclusion principle. As has been stated above, $\rho(x, p)$ can be considered as the number of electrons per volume h^3 of the classical phase-space (which, as we know, corresponds to one single spinless state in the sense of classical mechanics). Inasmuch as the inclusion of the spin allows each spinless state to be doubly occupied (by electrons with their spin axes in opposite directions), the effect of the spin will be simply to increase the maximum value of $\rho(x, p)$ from 1 to 2.

If we consider a system of electrons, such as a complex atom, for example, in the normal state, i.e. in the state of lowest energy W, we can assume all the individual states of lowest energy to be doubly occupied, or, in other words, all that part of the phase-space x, p which corresponds to the least possible value of the energy to be filled with the maximum density $\rho = 2$ and the rest to remain quite empty. The shape of the boundary surface can be determined from the condition that ρ is a constant of the motion as determined by the energy K. This means, since $\partial\rho/\partial t = 0$, that ρ must be a function of K, and that consequently the boundary surface we are looking for must be a surface of constant K.

Now we have

$$K = E(\mathbf{r}, \mathbf{p}) + B(\mathbf{r}) - \frac{e^2}{\pi h} \int \frac{\rho(\mathbf{r}, \mathbf{p}')}{|\mathbf{p} - \mathbf{p}'|^2}\, dp', \qquad (386)$$

where $\mathbf{r}$ is written instead of x in order to indicate the fact that we no longer include the spin coordinate. Since within the part of the phase-space which comes into play

$$\rho(\mathbf{r}, \mathbf{p}') = \text{const.} = 2,$$

the preceding equation is reduced to

$$K = E(\mathbf{r}, \mathbf{p}) + B(\mathbf{r}) - \frac{2e^2}{\pi h}\left\{ \int \frac{dp'}{|\mathbf{p} - \mathbf{p}'|^2} \right\}_r, \qquad (386\,\text{a})$$

where the integral

$$\left\{ \int \frac{dp'}{|\mathbf{p} - \mathbf{p}'|^2} \right\}_r = \iiint \frac{dp'_x\, dp'_y\, dp'_z}{(p_x - p'_x)^2 + (p_y - p'_y)^2 + (p_z - p'_z)^2}$$

must be extended over all the saturated part of the momentum space $\mathbf{p}'$ which is associated with a given point of the ordinary space $\mathbf{r}$.

In order to evaluate this integral we must make some assumption as to the shape of this saturated momentum space. We shall assume it to be spherical, its radius P_r being a certain (for the present undetermined) function of $\mathbf{r}$. We then get

$$A(\mathbf{r}, \mathbf{p}) = \frac{2e^2}{h}\left[\frac{P_r^2 - |p|^2}{p} \log\left| \frac{P_r + p}{P_r - p} \right| + 2P_r \right]. \qquad (387)$$

We have further

$$\rho(\mathbf{r}, \mathbf{r}) = \frac{1}{h^3} \int \rho(\mathbf{x}, \mathbf{p})\, dp = \frac{8\pi}{3h^3} P_r^3, \qquad (388)$$

and consequently $$B(\mathbf{r}) = \frac{8\pi}{3h^3} e^2 \int \frac{P_{r'}^3}{|\mathbf{r} - \mathbf{r}'|}\, dr', \qquad (388\,\text{a})$$

At the boundary surface we must have $p = P$, and consequently

$$A(\mathbf{r}, \mathbf{p_r}) = \frac{4e^2}{h} P_\mathbf{r}.$$

The equation of this boundary reduces accordingly to

$$K(\mathbf{r}, \mathbf{p}) = E(\mathbf{r}, P_\mathbf{r}) + B(\mathbf{r}) - \frac{4e^2}{h} P_\mathbf{r} = \text{const.} \qquad (389)$$

This equation serves to determine P as a function of $\mathbf{r}$. It can be replaced by a differential equation of the Poisson type if we take into account the fact that $B(\mathbf{r})$ is the product of the charge e of an electron and the potential ϕ due to a distribution of charge with a density (388) multiplied by e. We thus get, applying the Laplace operator ∇^2 to the equation (389) and assuming $E(\mathbf{r}, \mathbf{p})$ to be of the usual form $p^2/(2m) + U(\mathbf{r})$ with $\nabla^2 U = 0$,

$$\nabla^2 \left(\frac{P^2}{2m} + B(\mathbf{r}) - \frac{4e^2}{h} P \right) = 0$$

or $\qquad \nabla^2 \left(\dfrac{P^2}{2m} - \dfrac{4e^2}{h} P \right) = 4\pi e^2 \rho(\mathbf{r}, \mathbf{r}) = \dfrac{32\pi^2 e^2}{3h^3} P^3. \qquad (390)$

This equation (due to Dirac) is a generalization of the equation of the Thomas-Fermi theory which has been considered in Part I, § 32. It differs from the latter by the additional term $-4e^2 P/h$ which represents the exchange effect (and also eliminates the self-action of the electrons), the electric potential or the density function being replaced by the function P.

IX

SECOND (INTENSITY) QUANTIZATION AND QUANTUM ELECTRODYNAMICS

46. Second Quantization with respect to Electrons

The reduction of the problem of the motion of a number of identical particles to that of a single one, carried out in the preceding chapter, involves a more or less rough approximation. A similar reduction can, however, be achieved in a different way, which corresponds to the method of copies which was sketched in Part I, § 20, and is connected with a quantization of the amplitudes of the waves representing the motion of a single particle. This procedure may be denoted as 'second' or 'intensity' quantization.

This method was inaugurated by Dirac in connexion with the theory of light quanta for a system of particles which are describable by a symmetrical wave function. We shall, however, develop it in the first place for a system of electrons which will lead us to a generalization and improvement of the results obtained in the preceding chapter.

In describing a system of N electrons we have used hitherto only N individual wave functions $\psi_1(x)$, $\psi_2(x)$,..., $\psi_N(x)$ which enable us in the case of stationary states to account for the exchange degeneracy only. We shall now introduce an *infinite* set of mutually orthogonal and normalized wave functions of this sort (with spin), leaving their form undetermined for a while (they may, for example, represent the motion of an electron in the external field alone with neglect of its mutual action with all the other electrons). We shall further combine them into sets of N functions and for each set form an antisymmetrical function χ in the same way as before. Instead of, however, identifying χ with the exact wave function $\Omega(x_1, x_2,..., x_N, t)$ describing the motion of the electrons, we shall define the latter as a linear combination of all such functions,

$$\Omega = \sum C_n \chi_n, \tag{391}$$

and shall determine the coefficients C_n as functions of the time in such a way as to make Ω an actual solution of the exact wave equation

$$\left(H + \frac{h}{2\pi i} \frac{\partial}{\partial t}\right)\Omega = 0 \tag{392}$$

(which can involve the spin variables). The coefficients C_n satisfying this condition are determined by the well-known equations of the perturbation theory

$$-\frac{h}{2\pi i}\frac{dC_n}{dt} = \sum_{n'} H_{nn'} C_{n'},$$ (392 a)

where

$$H_{nn'} = \int \chi_n^* H \chi_{n'} \, dX$$ (392 b)

(the 'integration' over the coordinates X of all the electrons being understood to include a summation over the spin coordinates).

The indices n specifying the functions χ can be considered as representing the totality of the numbers $n_1, n_2,..., n_r,...$ corresponding to the individual wave functions $\psi_1, \psi_2,..., \psi_r,...$ and equal to 1 if these functions are included in the set forming χ_n and to 0 in the converse case. Thus $n_r = 1$ if the function ψ_r is contained in χ_n and 0 if it is not contained in it. We could also write more fully $\chi_n = \chi(n_1, n_2,..., n_r; X, t)$ and $C_n = C(n_1, n_2,..., n_r,...; t)$. The numbers n_r may be denoted as the partition numbers, indicating whether the corresponding rth individual state is occupied by an electron or not. In calculating the matrix elements (392 a) we can use the formula [cf. (364 a), § 44]

$$H_{nn'} = \int \chi_n^* H \chi_{n'} \, dX = \sqrt{(N!)} \int \phi_n^* H \chi_{n'} \, dX = \sum_P \epsilon_P \int \phi_n^* H P \phi_{n'} \, dX,$$ (393)

where ϕ_n and $\phi_{n'}$ are the factorized wave functions corresponding to a definite distribution of the electrons between the N occupied states, for instance,

$$\phi_n(X) = \psi_{r_1}(x_1)\psi_{r_2}(x_2) \ldots \psi_{r_N}(x_N)$$ (394)

and

$$\phi_{n'}(X) = \psi_{r_1'}(x_1)\psi_{r_2'}(x_2) \ldots \psi_{r_N'}(x_N).$$ (394 a)

It will be convenient to assume for a while that the indices $r_1, r_2,..., r_N$ of the occupied states are arranged in the same order as the indices $1, 2,..., N$ of the electrons, i.e. that

$$r_1 < r_2 < r_3 \ldots.$$ (394 b)

This means merely a certain (arbitrary) denomination of the N wave functions ψ forming the set under consideration. We could put, for example, so long as we are concerned with this particular set, $r_1 = 1$, $r_2 = 2,..., r_N = N$. The order of the indices in the other sets n' must of course be left arbitrary. So long as H has the usual form

$$H = \sum_{i=1}^{N} E(x_i, p_i) + \sum_{i<k}\sum F(x_i, x_k)$$

the matrix elements (393) will vanish identically if the set n' differs by more than two individual states from the set n (in view of the orthogonal property of the wave functions ψ). We must therefore distinguish three cases:

(1) $n = n'$, i.e. $n_r = n'_r$, for all values of r, or simply $\chi_n = \chi_{n'}$. In this case the matrix element (393) reduces to the value of the energy W already calculated in § 40. Putting

$$\int \psi_r^* E \psi_{r'}\, dx = E_{rr'} \tag{395}$$

and

$$\iint \psi_r^*(x)\psi_s^*(x')F(x,x')\psi_{r'}(x)\psi_{s'}(x')\, dx dx' = F_{rs;r's'} \tag{395a}$$

we can rewrite it in the following form:

$$H_{nn} = \sum_r E_{rr} + \sum_{r<s}\sum (F_{rs;rs} - F_{rs;sr}), \tag{396}$$

which is easily seen to coincide with (368a).

(2) The set n differs from n' by the fact that *one* function, $\phi_{r_i}(x)$ say, is replaced by another, $\psi_{r'_i}(x)$, all the other factors in (394) and (394a) being the same. We then get in a similar way, putting $r_i = p$ and $r'_i = p'$,

$$H_{nn'} = E_{pp'} + \sum (F_{pr;p'r} - F_{pr;rp'}), \tag{396a}$$

where the sub-subscript i has been dropped.

(3) The set n differs from n' by the fact that two functions $\psi_{r_i}(x_i)$ and $\psi_{r_k}(x_k)$ are replaced by different functions (not belonging to the original set) $\psi_{r'_i}(x_i)$ and $\psi_{r'_k}(x_k)$. We get in this case, writing p for r_i and q for r_k,

$$H_{nn'} = F_{pq;p'q'} - F_{pq;q'p'} \quad (p<q;\ p' \neq p, q' \neq q). \tag{396b}$$

Let α_r denote an operator which when applied to $C_n = C(n_1, n_2, ..., n_r, ...)$ increases n_r by unity if $n_r = 0$, that is, transforms

$$C(n_1, n_2, ..., n_{r-1}, n_r, n_{r+1}, ...)$$

into $C(n_1, n_2, ..., n_{r-1}, n_r + 1, n_{r+1}, ...)$; if, on the other hand, $n_r = 1$, the operator α_r reduces C to zero. Let, further, $\alpha_r^\dagger$ denote an operator which *decreases* n_r by 1 if $n_r = 1$ and reduces C to zero if $n_r = 0$. The coefficient $C_{n'}$, corresponding to case (2), can be written accordingly as $\alpha_r^\dagger \alpha_{r'} C_n$, and the coefficient $C_{n'}$ corresponding to case (3) as $\alpha_r^\dagger \alpha_s^\dagger \alpha_{r'} \alpha_{s'} C_n$. It is now possible to write the equations (392a) as follows:

$$-\frac{h}{2\pi i}\frac{dC_n}{dt} = K_n C_n, \tag{397}$$

where

$$K_n = \sum_r E_{rr} + \sum_p \sum_{p'} E_{pp'}\, \alpha_p^\dagger \alpha_{p'} +$$
$$+ \sum_{r<s}\sum (F_{rs;rs} - F_{rs;sr}) + \sum_{p\neq p'}\sum \sum_{r<p}(F_{pr;p'r} - F_{pr;rp'})\alpha_p^\dagger \alpha_{p'} +$$
$$+ \sum_{p<q}\sum_{p'\neq p}\sum_{q'\neq q}\sum (F_{pq;p'q'} - F_{pq;q'p'})\alpha_p^\dagger \alpha_q^\dagger \alpha_{q'} \alpha_{p'}. \tag{397a}$$

The summation over r and s includes all those individual states which are contained in the set n, i.e. represented by partition numbers n_r and n_s equal to 1. The summation over p and q is extended only over such of these states as are replaced by one or two other states in the set n'. Thus the indices p, q on the one hand, and p', q' on the other, are not independent of each other. The expression (397 a) can be further simplified with the help of the relations $\alpha_r C_n = 0$ if $n_r = 1$, $\alpha_r^\dagger C_n = 0$ if $n_r = 0$. Applying the operator α_r to C_n and omitting all the arguments except n_r, we thus get

$$\alpha_r\, C(n_r) = \begin{cases} C(n_r + 1) & \text{if } n_r = 0, \\ 0 & \text{if } n_r = 1, \end{cases}$$

and

$$\alpha_r^\dagger\, C(n_r) = \begin{cases} C(n_r - 1) & \text{if } n_r = 1, \\ 0 & \text{if } n_r = 0. \end{cases}$$

Under these conditions it is possible to represent the operators α_r and $\alpha_r^\dagger$ as matrices from the point of view of n_r, considered itself as a diagonal matrix

$$n_r = \begin{pmatrix} 0 & 0 \\ 0 & 1 \end{pmatrix} \tag{398}$$

with the characteristic values 0 and 1 or, what amounts to the same thing, as a one-column matrix $n_r = \begin{Bmatrix} 0 \\ 1 \end{Bmatrix}$. It should be mentioned that the difference $1 - n_r$ must be defined accordingly as the matrix $\begin{pmatrix} 1 & 0 \\ 0 & 0 \end{pmatrix}$ or $\begin{Bmatrix} 1 \\ 0 \end{Bmatrix}$ respectively.

Regarded from this point of view the operators α_r and $\alpha_r^\dagger$ are represented by the matrices

$$\alpha_r = \begin{pmatrix} 0 & 1 \\ 0 & 0 \end{pmatrix}, \qquad \alpha_r^\dagger = \begin{pmatrix} 0 & 0 \\ 1 & 0 \end{pmatrix} \tag{398a}$$

satisfying the relations

$$\alpha_r^\dagger \alpha_r = n_r, \qquad \alpha_r \alpha_r^\dagger = 1 - n_r. \tag{398b}$$

Any function $C(n_1, n_2, ..., n_r, ...)$ of the matrix arguments n_r, or more exactly of their characteristic values, must likewise be dealt with as a matrix. Leaving all the arguments but n_r aside, we can define it as a one-column matrix

$$C(n_r) = \begin{Bmatrix} C(0) \\ C(1) \end{Bmatrix} \tag{399}$$

whose elements correspond to the two characteristic values of n_r. This gives, according to the definition (398 a) of the operators α_r and $\alpha_r^\dagger$

$$\alpha_r\, C(n_r) = \begin{Bmatrix} C(1) \\ 0 \end{Bmatrix}, \qquad \alpha_r^\dagger C(n_r) = \begin{Bmatrix} 0 \\ C(0) \end{Bmatrix}, \qquad (399\,\text{a})$$

which is in agreement with the original definition of α_r and $\alpha_r^\dagger$. If therefore we agree to consider the partition numbers as the characteristic values of the corresponding operators (which will be denoted by the same letters), we can rewrite the sum of the first two terms in (397 a), corresponding to the proper energy of the electrons E, as follows:

$$\sum_r E_{rr} + \sum_p \sum_{p'} E_{pp'}\,\alpha_p^\dagger \alpha_{p'} = \sum_{r=1}^{\infty} \sum_{r'=1}^{\infty} E_{rr'}\,\alpha_r^\dagger \alpha_{r'}, \qquad (400)$$

since for all values of r and r' which are not actually represented in the sum on the left-hand side of this equation, the operator $\alpha_r^\dagger \alpha_{r'}$ is equivalent to 0.

Turning to the other terms of (397 a) which correspond to the mutual energy of the electrons, we shall show in the first place that they can be collected together in a form similar to the last term with no other restriction imposed on the summation indices p, q, p', q' than the condition $p < q$.

In fact the second term is easily seen to be obtained from the last if we put $q' = q = r$ and interpret the product $\alpha_r^\dagger \alpha_r$ as the operator n_r. Since this operator commutes with $\alpha_p^\dagger$ (so long as $p \neq q$) we can write it on the left of $\alpha_p^\dagger$ and extend the summation over all values of r which are larger than p, those terms which correspond to values of r not represented in n being automatically cancelled.

It should be emphasized in this connexion that the order of the four factors $\alpha_p^\dagger \alpha_q^\dagger \alpha_{q'} \alpha_{p'}$ in the last term of (397 a) is not taken at random, but precisely with a view to ensuring the inclusion of the preceding term under the condition $q' = q = r$. It is easily seen in the same way that the first term containing F in (397 a) is obtained from the following one if we put $p' = p$, or consequently from the last term if we put simultaneously $p = p' = r$ and $q = q' = s$ with the one restriction $r < s$, i.e. $p < q$. We thus get

$$\sum_{r<s} (F_{rs;rs} - F_{rs;sr}) + \sum_{p \neq p'} \sum_{r<p} (F_{pr;p'r} - F_{pr;rp'})\alpha_p^\dagger \alpha_{p'} +$$
$$+ \sum_{p<q,\,p'\neq p,\,q'\neq q} \sum \sum (F_{pq;p'q'} - F_{pq;q'p'})\alpha_p^\dagger \alpha_q^\dagger \alpha_{q'} \alpha_{p'} \qquad (400\,\text{a})$$
$$= \sum_{p<q} \sum_{p'} \sum_{q'} (F_{pq;p'q'} - F_{pq;q'p'})\alpha_p^\dagger \alpha_q^\dagger \alpha_{q'} \alpha_{p'},$$

and consequently

$$K_n = K = \sum_r \sum_{r'} E_{rr'}\,\alpha_r^\dagger \alpha_{r'} + \sum_{r<s} \sum_{r'} \sum_{s'} (F_{rs,r's'} - F_{rs,s'r'})\alpha_r^\dagger \alpha_s^\dagger \alpha_{s'} \alpha_{r'}, \quad (400\,\text{b})$$

where the indices p and q have been replaced by r and s in order to indicate the fact that the summation can be extended over *all* values of these indices, the terms represented by non-vanishing partition numbers n_r, n_s corresponding to the state n being actually the only ones left. This is why we are now entitled to drop the index n for K. If instead of writing $\alpha_r^\dagger \alpha_s^\dagger \alpha_{s'} \alpha_{r'}$ in the second term of (400 b) we had written $\alpha_r^\dagger \alpha_s^\dagger \alpha_{r'} \alpha_{s'}$, it would have been impossible to include all the three terms of (397 a) containing F in one.

The *second* step in the simplification of the operator consists in the removal of the restrictive condition $r < s$ and in the simultaneous unification of the positive and negative summands in the second term of (400 b), representing the mutual action of the electrons. In order to carry out this simplification we must introduce instead of the α's new operators

$$a_r = \pm \alpha_r, \quad a_r^\dagger = \pm \alpha_r^\dagger$$

with an appropriate rule for chosing the upper or lower sign, so that we could write

$$\alpha_r^\dagger \alpha_r = a_r^\dagger a_r \tag{401}$$

and

$$\alpha_r^\dagger \alpha_s^\dagger \alpha_{s'} \alpha_{r'} = a_s^\dagger a_r^\dagger a_s a_{r'} = a_s^\dagger a_r^\dagger a_{r'} a_{s'} \tag{401 a}$$

$$\alpha_r^\dagger \alpha_s^\dagger \alpha_{s'} \alpha_{r'} = -a_r^\dagger a_s^\dagger a_{r'} a_{s'} = -a_s^\dagger a_r^\dagger a_{s'} a_{r'}. \tag{401 b}$$

This enables us to put

$$\sum_r \sum_{r'} E_{rr'} \alpha_r^\dagger \alpha_{r'} = \sum \sum E_{rr'} a_r^\dagger a_{r'}$$

and

$$\sum_{r<s} \sum_{r'} \sum_{s'} (F_{rs,r's'} - F_{rs,s'r'}) \alpha_r^\dagger \alpha_s^\dagger \alpha_{s'} \alpha_{r'}$$

$$= \sum_{r<s} \sum_{r'} \sum_{s'} F_{rs,r's'} a_r^\dagger a_s^\dagger a_{s'} a_{r'} + \sum_{r<s} \sum_{r'} \sum_{s'} F_{rs,s'r'} a_r^\dagger a_s^\dagger a_{r'} a_{s'}$$

$$= \sum_{r<s} \sum_{r'} \sum_{s'} F_{sr,s'r'} a_s^\dagger a_r^\dagger a_{r'} a_{s'} + \sum \sum \sum \sum F_{sr,r's'} a_s^\dagger a_r^\dagger a_{s'} a_{r'}$$

in view of the obvious relation

$$F_{rs,r's'} = F_{sr,s'r'}$$

and the relations (401 a), or finally

$$K = \sum_r \sum_{r'} E_{rr'} a_s^\dagger a_r^\dagger + \tfrac{1}{2} \sum_r \sum_s \sum_{r'} \sum_{s'} F_{rs,r's'} a_r^\dagger a_s^\dagger a_{s'} a_{r'}, \tag{402}$$

the summation being extended over *all* the values of the indices r, r', s, s' without any restrictive conditions whatsoever, all the restrictions being carried out automatically.

In order to define the operators a explicitly we must take into account the condition which has been stated at the beginning of this section as to the arrangement of the indices r_1, r_2,... specifying the individual states in the set n:

$$r_1 < r_2 < \dots.$$

This condition has been used in all our preceding expressions for K up to the expression (400 b), and has been dropped only in the last expression (402).

Now the operators a must be defined in such a way as actually to enable us to get rid of this condition. This can be done, following Jordan and Wigner, by putting

$$a_r = \alpha_r \nu_r, \qquad a_r^\dagger = \nu_r \alpha_r^\dagger, \tag{402 a}$$

where ν_r is an operator with the characteristic values 1 and -1 (i.e. equivalent to taking α with the $+$ or $-$ sign) which is defined as the product‡

$$\nu_r = \prod_{s-1}^{r-1} (1 - 2n_s). \tag{402 b}$$

The separate factors in this product are themselves operators of the same kind as ν_r (the characteristic values of n_s being 0 and 1, those of the difference $1 - 2n_s$ must be $+1$ and -1). The operators a defined in this way are easily seen to satisfy the conditions (401), (401 a), and (401 b), or the more simple conditions not involving the original α's:

$$a_r^\dagger a_r = n_r \tag{403}$$

$$a_r a_s + a_s a_r = a_r^\dagger a_s^\dagger + a_s^\dagger a_r^\dagger = 0 \tag{403 a}$$

and finally

$$a_r^\dagger a_{r'} + a_{r'} a_r^\dagger = \delta_{rr'}. \tag{403 b}$$

We have in fact

$$a_r^\dagger a_r = \nu_r \alpha_r^\dagger \alpha_r \nu_r = \nu_r n_r \nu_r = n_r \nu_r^2 = n_r,$$

since n_r is represented by a diagonal matrix, just as ν_r is and therefore commutes with ν_r, whose square is equal to 1, i.e. to the unit matrix

$$\begin{pmatrix} 1 & 0 \\ 0 & 1 \end{pmatrix}.$$

Further, if $r < s$, we obviously have

$$\alpha_r \alpha_s = \alpha_s \alpha_r$$

(the case $r = s$ is devoid of interest since the operator $\alpha_r \alpha_r$ applied to any function C_n gives identically zero). On the other hand,

$$a_r a_s = \alpha_r \nu_r \alpha_s \nu_s = \nu_r \alpha_r \alpha_s \nu_s = \nu_r \alpha_s \alpha_r \nu_s,$$

since, according to the definition (402 b), α_r commutes with all the factors in ν_r. It does not commute, however, so long as $r < s$, with one

‡ We slightly diverge here from Jordan and Wigner by extending the product over s to $s = r - 1$ instead of $s = r$.

factor in ν_s, namely, $(1-2n_r)$. Applying it to the latter we have

$$\alpha_r(1-2n_r) = \alpha_r - 2\alpha_r n_r.$$

Now $\alpha_r n_r = (n_r+1)\alpha_r$ if $n_r = 0$, and 0 if $n_r = 1$. In both cases we get

$$\alpha_r(1-2n_r) = -(1-2n_r)\alpha_r,$$

and consequently $\alpha_r \nu_s = -\nu_s \alpha_r \quad (r < s).$

The preceding relation can be derived in a somewhat different way if we replace n_r in $1-2n_r$ by the product $\alpha_r^\dagger \alpha_r$. We then get

$$\alpha_r(1-2\alpha_r^\dagger \alpha_r) = \alpha_r - 2\alpha_r(\alpha_r^\dagger \alpha_r) = \alpha_r - 2(\alpha_r \alpha_r^\dagger)\alpha_r$$
$$= (1-2\alpha_r \alpha_r^\dagger)\alpha_r = [1-2(1-n_r)]\alpha_r$$

according to (398 b), which coincides with our previous result.

Coming back to our original expression for $a_r a_s$, we have

$$a_r a_s = \nu_r \alpha_s \alpha_r \nu_s = -\nu_r \alpha_s \nu_s \alpha_r,$$

or, since the three operators ν_r, α_s, ν_s commute with each other while ν_r commutes also with α_r,

$$a_r a_s = -\alpha_s \nu_s \nu_r \alpha_r = -\alpha_s \nu_s \alpha_r \nu_r = -a_s a_r.$$

The second relation (403 a) is proved in exactly the same way.

In the case $r = r'$ relation (403 b) immediately follows from the relations $\alpha_r^\dagger \alpha_r = n_r$ and $\alpha_r \alpha_r^\dagger = 1-n_r$ (see 398 b). In order to prove it for the case $r < r'$ (or in general $r \neq r'$) we must use the fact that the operators $\alpha_r^\dagger$ and $\alpha_{r'}$ commute with each other just as the operators α_r and $\alpha_{r'}$ do. We have further, if $1-2n_r$ is written in the form

$$(1-2n_r) = -[1-2(1-n_r)] = -(1-2\alpha_{r'}\alpha_r^\dagger);$$
$$\alpha_r^\dagger(1-2n_r) = -\alpha_r^\dagger(1-2\alpha_r \alpha_r^\dagger) = -[\alpha_r^\dagger - 2\alpha_r^\dagger(\alpha_r \alpha_r^\dagger)]$$
$$= -[\alpha_r^\dagger - 2(\alpha_r^\dagger \alpha_r)\alpha_r^\dagger] = -(1-2n_r)a_r^\dagger,$$

so that $\alpha_r^\dagger \nu_{r'} = -\nu_{r'}\alpha_r^\dagger \quad (r < r')$

as before, and consequently, since

$$\alpha_{r'}\nu_r = \nu_r \alpha_{r'},$$
$$a_r^\dagger a_{r'} = \nu_r \alpha_r^\dagger \alpha_{r'}\nu_{r'} = \alpha_{r'}\nu_r \alpha_r^\dagger \nu_{r'} = -\alpha_{r'}\nu_r \nu_{r'}\alpha_r^\dagger = -a_{r'}a_r^\dagger.$$

Now that the relations (403), (403 a), and (403 b) are all proved, we no longer need to think of the auxiliary operators α_r and ν which have been used in their derivation and which depend on the physically irrelevant order in which the different individual states are numbered in the set n. The above relations are self-supporting, for they specify in a perfectly unambiguous way the operators a which serve to express the energy operator of our problem K. These operators can be represented by certain matrices, from the point of view of the matrix formed by the totality of the partition numbers n_1, n_2,..., in a way implying a certain ordered arrangement of the different individual states. So long as we are interested in one particular state only we can define the corresponding partition number n_r as a two-dimensional matrix (398) and represent the operators a_r and $a_r^\dagger$ by the same matrices

$$a_r = \begin{pmatrix} 0 & 1 \\ 0 & 0 \end{pmatrix}, \qquad a_r^\dagger = \begin{pmatrix} 0 & 0 \\ 1 & 0 \end{pmatrix}$$

as those representing the operators α_r and $\alpha_r^\dagger$. The difference between them and the operators a_r, $a_r^\dagger$ becomes apparent when we take into account all the other states s ($= 1, 2, 3,...$). The general representation of the operators α_r, $\alpha_r^\dagger$ can be derived from (398 a) by multiplication by unit matrices $\delta_s = \begin{pmatrix} 1 & 0 \\ 0 & 1 \end{pmatrix}$, referring to all the other states ($s \neq r$):

$$\alpha_r = ...\delta_{r+2} \times \delta_{r+1} \times \begin{pmatrix} 0 & 1 \\ 0 & 0 \end{pmatrix} \times \delta_{r-1} \times \delta_{r-2} \times ... \times \delta_1$$

$$\alpha_r^\dagger = \delta_1 \times \delta_2 \times ... \times \delta_{r-1} \times \begin{pmatrix} 0 & 0 \\ 1 & 0 \end{pmatrix} \times \delta_{r+1} \times ...,$$

the product $M_1 \times M_2$ of the matrices M_1 and M_2 denoting a matrix M whose elements are obtained by combining multiplicatively the elements of M_1 and M_2. In order to obtain the general representation of a_r and $a_r^\dagger$ we must replace the $r-1$ matrices δ_1, δ_2,..., δ_{r-1} by the matrices $1-2n_1$, $1-2n_2$,..., $1-2n_{r-1}$. The matrices so defined

$$a_r = ...\delta_{r+1}\begin{pmatrix} 0 & 1 \\ 0 & 0 \end{pmatrix}(1-2n_{r-1})(1-2n_{r-2})...(1-2n_1)$$

$$a_r^\dagger = (1-2n_1)(1-2n_2)...(1-2n_{r-1})\begin{pmatrix} 0 & 0 \\ 1 & 0 \end{pmatrix}\delta_{r+1}... .$$

can easily be verified to satisfy all the relations (403 a, b). The totality of the numbers n_1, n_2,... must be represented accordingly by the product of the diagonal matrices representing each of them:

$$n = n_1 \times n_2 \times ....$$

This operator product has, of course, nothing to do with an ordinary product of the numbers which give the characteristic values of the operators n_r and which, as will be remembered, must satisfy the relations

$$\sum_{r=1}^{\infty} n_r = N.$$

The operators a_r are not Hermitian, although the symbol $a_r^\dagger$ preserves its meaning as the operator adjoint to a_r, i.e. as the conjugate complex of the transposed matrix $\tilde{a}_r = \begin{pmatrix} 0 & 0 \\ 1 & 0 \end{pmatrix}$. They can, however, be expressed with the help of the Hermitian operators

$$\sigma_x = \begin{pmatrix} 0 & 1 \\ 1 & 0 \end{pmatrix}, \qquad \sigma_y = \begin{pmatrix} 0 & i \\ -i & 0 \end{pmatrix}, \qquad \sigma_r = \begin{pmatrix} -1 & 0 \\ 0 & 1 \end{pmatrix},$$

whose products with $h/4\pi$ represent the components of the electron's spin [cf. § 29]. We have, namely, limiting ourselves to one particular state,

$$\sigma_x = (a_r + a_r^\dagger), \qquad \sigma_y = i(a_r - a_r^\dagger),$$

whence $\qquad a_r = \tfrac{1}{2}(\sigma_x - i\sigma_y), \qquad a_r^\dagger = \tfrac{1}{2}(\sigma_x + i\sigma_y). \qquad (404)$

Hence it follows that

$$n_r = a_r^\dagger a_r = \tfrac{1}{4}[\sigma_x^2 + \sigma_y^2 + i(\sigma_x\sigma_y - \sigma_y\sigma_x)],$$

or, according to (253), § 29,

$$n_r = \tfrac{1}{4}(\sigma_x^2 + \sigma_y^2 + 2\sigma_z),$$

or, since $\sigma_x^2 = \sigma_y^2 = \delta$, $\qquad n_r = \tfrac{1}{2}(\delta + \sigma_z), \qquad\qquad (404\,a)$

which agrees with the definition $n_r = \begin{pmatrix} 0 & 0 \\ 0 & 1 \end{pmatrix}$. It should be noticed further that

$$1 - 2n_r = \tfrac{1}{2}(\delta - \sigma_z),$$

and that accordingly

$$\nu_r = \prod_{s=1}^{r-1} \tfrac{1}{2}(\delta - \sigma_{zs}),$$

the subscript s in σ_{zs} serving to show that it refers to the sth state.

We thus see that the energy operator K (402) can be expressed with the help of the familiar spin operators associated with the different states. This is natural if we remember that it is possible to represent the interaction energy of the electrons in connexion with the exchange effect with the help of the operators $\tfrac{1}{2}(1 + \boldsymbol{\sigma}_r \cdot \boldsymbol{\sigma}_s)$, as has been shown in § 42 of the preceding chapter. The problem is complicated in the present case by the necessity of introducing the operators ν_r in order to ensure the anticommutation of the operators a_r and a_s (or $a_r^\dagger$ and $a_s^\dagger$) referring to different states (whereas the operators $\boldsymbol{\sigma}_r$ and $\boldsymbol{\sigma}_s$ must commute with each other).

The fact that the operators n_r can have only two different characteristic values 0 and 1, which has been used as the basis of the above definition of the operators a_r, can be considered as *a consequence* of the properties of these operators expressed by the relations (403 a) and (403 b) in connexion with the equation (403) which from this point of view serves simply for the definition of the operator n_r. We have, namely, multiplying the relation $a_r a_r^\dagger = 1 - n_r$ on the left by $a_r^\dagger$,

$$a_r^\dagger a_r a_r^\dagger = a_r^\dagger - a_r^\dagger n_r,$$

or, since $a_r^\dagger a_r = n_r$, $n_r a_r^\dagger = a_r^\dagger - a_r^\dagger n_r,$

whence, by right-hand multiplication by a_r, we get

$$n_r^2 = n_r - a_r^\dagger n_r a_r.$$

Now $a_r^\dagger n_r a_r = a_r^\dagger a_r^\dagger a_r a_r$, and according to the relations (403 a) we must have $a_r a_r = a_r^\dagger a_r^\dagger = 0$. We thus get

$$n_r^2 - n_r = 0,$$

whence it follows that the only characteristic values of n_r are 0 and 1.

The preceding theory can be put in a still more significant form by introducing the expression

$$\Psi(x) = \sum_{r=1}^{\infty} a_r \psi_r(x). \tag{405}$$

Being an ordinary function of the coordinates of an electron (and eventually of the time), it is to be considered at the same time as an operator with respect to the amplitude coefficients $C(n_1, n_2, \ldots)$, which play the role of the wave function in the equation

$$-\frac{h}{2\pi i} \frac{d}{dt} C = KC$$

with the energy operator K defined by (400 b).

Multiplying $\Psi(x)$ on the left by the adjoint operator

$$\Psi^\dagger(x) = \sum a_r^\dagger \psi_r^*(x), \tag{405 a}$$

and integrating over x (which includes as usual the summation over the spin coordinates), we get in virtue of the orthogonality and normalization of the function $\psi_r(x)$:

$$\int \Psi^\dagger \Psi \, dx = \sum_{r=1}^{\infty} a_r^\dagger a_r = \sum_{r=1}^{\infty} n_r. \tag{405 b}$$

This equation is quite similar to that corresponding to the ordinary case of functions of the type (405) with amplitude coefficients a_r defined as ordinary numbers. Replacing such numbers by operators satisfying the conditions (403 a) and (403 b)—or even the less restrictive conditions $a_r a_r = 0$, $a_r^\dagger a_r^\dagger = 0$, $a_r^\dagger a_r + a_r a_r^\dagger = 1$—we obtain for the number of electrons associated with any individual state one of the two characteristic values 0, 1 of the operator $a_r^\dagger a_r = n_r$ in agreement with the exclusion principle. The total number of electrons N can be defined accordingly as a characteristic value of the sum $\sum_{i=1}^{\infty} n_r$, so that it appears in the role of an additional 'intensity' or 'quantitative' quantum number (cf. Part I, § 20). The operator

$$N = \sum_{r=1}^{\infty} n_r$$

is easily seen to commute with the energy operator K in virtue of the relations (403 a, b) and to represent accordingly a constant of the motion—which means that the number of electrons forming any particular system is constant—as of course it should be. The operator K can itself be expressed in terms of the operator-functions $\Psi(x)$ and its adjoint operator $\Psi^\dagger(x)$ not containing explicitly the operator-coefficients a_r. We have, namely,

$$\sum_r \sum_{r'} E_{rr'} a_r^\dagger a_{r'} = \int \Psi^\dagger(x) E \Psi(x) \, dx$$

and

$$\sum_r \sum_s \sum_{r'} \sum_{s'} F_{rs;r's'} a_r^\dagger a_s^\dagger a_{s'} a_{r'} = \iint \Psi^\dagger(x) \Psi^\dagger(x') F(x,x') \Psi(x') \Psi(x) \, dx dx',$$

so that K can be written in the following form:

$$K = \int \Psi^\dagger(x) E \Psi(x) \, dx + \tfrac{1}{2} \iint \Psi^\dagger(x) \Psi^\dagger(x') F(x,x') \Psi(x') \Psi(x) \, dx dx',$$

$$(406)$$

which is somewhat similar to the expression for the value of the energy W given by the equation (371), § 44, if the density matrix $\rho(x, x')$ is replaced by the product $\Psi^\dagger(x)\Psi(x')$. The main difference between the two expressions lies in the fact that the exchange effect which is represented by the negative term under the double integral sign in (371) is not present in (406) where this exchange effect is automatically accounted for by the properties of the operators $\Psi(x)$.

Putting $F(x, x') = e^2/r(x, x')$, which corresponds to an ordinary Coulomb interaction between the electrons, and introducing further the operator

$$\varphi(x) = e \int \Psi^\dagger(x') \Psi(x') \frac{dx'}{r(x, x')},$$

$$(406 a)$$

which represents the electric potential due to a distribution of electricity with a density

$$e\rho(x', x') = e\Psi^\dagger(x')\Psi(x'),$$

we can replace (406) by an expression of still more familiar type,

$$K = \int \Psi^\dagger(x)(E + \tfrac{1}{2}e\varphi)\Psi(x) \, dx,$$

$$(406 b)$$

corresponding to the average value of the energy W for an electron moving in an electric field which consists of an external part (included in E) and a quasi-external part, due, as it were, to its own field and represented by the electric potential φ with the extra factor $\tfrac{1}{2}$. It must clearly be understood that no actual self-action of a single electron is implied by our theory, the commutation properties of the operator-functions Ψ being precisely such as to exclude any self-action.

These commutation properties are easily derived from those of the operators a, and from the orthogonality and normalizing conditions for the functions $\psi_r(x)$. We have, namely, multiplying $\Psi(x)$ by $\Psi(x')$,

$$\Psi(x)\Psi(x') = \sum_r a_r \psi_r(x) \sum_s a_s \psi_s(x')$$

$$= \sum \sum a_r a_s \psi_r(x)\psi_s(x') = - \sum_r \sum_s a_s a_r \psi_r(x)\psi_s(x'),$$

that is, $$\Psi(x)\Psi(x')+\Psi(x')\Psi(x) = 0, \qquad (407)$$

and likewise, $$\Psi^\dagger(x)\Psi^\dagger(x')+\Psi^\dagger(x')\Psi^\dagger(x) = 0.$$

We have further

$$\Psi^\dagger(x)\Psi(x') = \sum_r \sum_s a_r^\dagger a_s \psi_r^*(x)\psi_s(x')$$

$$= - \sum_r \sum_s a_s a_r^\dagger \psi_r^*(x)\psi_s(x') + \sum_r \sum_s \delta_{rs} \psi_r^*(x)\psi_s(x'),$$

whence $$\Psi^\dagger(x)\Psi(x')+\Psi(x')\Psi^\dagger(x) = \delta(x-x'), \qquad (407\,\text{a})$$

where $\delta(x-x')$ denotes the product of the Dirac δ-functions for the geometrical coordinates by $\delta_{\xi\xi'}$ if ξ and ξ' are the values of the spin coordinates associated with the points x and x'. It should be remarked that the formula $a_r^\dagger a_r = n_r$ is replaced in the present case by the formula (405 b) or

$$\int \Psi^\dagger(x)\Psi(x)\, dx = N. \qquad (407\,\text{b})$$

The functions $\psi_r(x)$ which serve to define the operator $\Psi(x)$ have been left hitherto entirely arbitrary apart from the condition of being mutually orthogonal and normalized. The actual problem, which was put at the beginning of this section, was to find the coefficients C_k, which determine the wave function $\Omega = \sum_n C_n \chi_n$ describing the behaviour of the system of electrons under consideration in the configuration space. From this point of view the functions $\psi_r(x)$ play only an auxiliary role.

But on the other hand, it is clear that the preceding theory can give results of real practical value only in the case when the separate anti-symmetrical functions χ_n form a good approximation to the functions Ω_W, which describe the stationary states of the system when the external field does not depend upon the time, or specific types of motion in a given variable external field. Assuming the latter to be constant, we are thus led to the problem of determining the individual wave functions $\psi_r(x)$ in such a way as to make the functions χ_n the best possible approximations to the exact antisymmetrical wave functions describing the stationary states of the system.

Let us consider a stationary state of the system as determined by the exact equation

$$KC = WC \qquad (408)$$

to which the general equation $-\dfrac{h}{2\pi i}\dfrac{dC}{dt} = KC$ is reduced if the operator $-\dfrac{h}{2\pi i}\dfrac{d}{dt}$ is replaced by the characteristic value of the energy W, i.e. if all the values of the function $C(n_1, n_2, \ldots)$ for which $\sum n_r = N$ are assumed to be proportional to $e^{-i2\pi W t/h}$ just as in the case of an ordinary Schrödinger equation. We then get, denoting the amplitude of C_n by C^0_{nW}, the following exact representation of a stationary state (in the configuration space):

$$\Omega_W = \sum_n C^0_{nW}\, \chi_n(X), \qquad (408\,a)$$

where X denotes the totality of the coordinates of all the electrons. Now the equation (408) must obviously be equivalent to the variational equation $\delta W = \delta \int \Omega^*_W\, H\Omega\, dX = 0$ with Ω_W written in the form (408 a), in conjunction with the condition $\sum_n C^*_n C_n = 1$. This variational equation can serve for the determination of the coefficients C^0_n if the functions χ_n, i.e. the individual functions ψ_r, are known. Or it can be used for the determination of the latter if the coefficients C^0_n are known. Assuming them for the moment to vanish for all the subscripts n except one, we get back to the self-consistent field considered in the preceding section.

The question we were discussing above is thus reduced to the following one: Is it possible to determine both the functions ψ_r *and* the coefficients C_n from the same variational equation $\delta W = 0$, where $W = \int \Omega^*_W\, H\Omega_W\, dX$? Such a determination is certainly possible for a function (408 a) containing a *finite* number of terms; if only one of them is different from zero we get back to the problem of the self-consistent field already solved.

However, the solution thus obtained will contain, as in the simple case just mentioned, a certain amount of arbitrariness in the form of the functions $\psi_r(x)$ (the latter being replaceable by any other set derived from them by a linear orthogonal transformation). This arbitrariness will increase with the number of non-vanishing terms and will become infinite in the limiting case of an infinite series (408 a). So long however as we are looking not for a *formal* but for a *practical* solution of our problem, we can deal with it as if the number of terms in (408 a) were finite; this procedure will ensure the most rapid convergence of the series obtained in the limiting case. Dropping the affixes W and 0 in (408 a), we have

$$W = \int \Omega^* H \Omega \, dX = \sum_n \sum_{n'} C_n^* C_{n'} \int \chi_n^* H \chi_{n'} \, dX,$$

that is,

$$W = \sum_n \sum_{n'} C_n^* H_{nn'} C_{n'},$$

which according to our previous results can be rewritten in the form

$$W = \sum_n C_n^* K C_n. \tag{409}$$

The problem we have considered hitherto was equivalent to the variation of the coefficients C_n, the operator K being fixed. It could thus be expressed by the equation

$$\sum_n \delta C_n^* K C_n + \sum_n C_n^* K \delta C_n = 0$$

along with

$$\sum_n \delta C_n^* C_n + \sum_n C_n^* \delta C_n = 0,$$

which brings us back to the equation (408). The next step which we must undertake in order to secure the best possible approximation consists in the variation of the functions $\psi_r(x)$, i.e. of the operator K which they define. We thus get the additional equation

$$\sum_n C_n^* \delta K C_n = 0. \tag{409 a}$$

With the help of the expressions (406) and (406 b) this is easily reduced to the following form:

$$\sum_n C_n^* \Big\{ \delta \int \Psi^\dagger(x)[E + e\varphi(x)]\Psi(x) \, dx \Big\} C_n = 0,$$

provided we consider the variations of the operators $\Psi(x)$ and $\Psi^\dagger(x)$ as independent of each other, apart from being subject to the condition $\int \delta\Psi^\dagger(x)\cdot\Psi(x) \, dx = 0$ [and $\int \Psi^\dagger(x)\cdot\delta\Psi(x) \, dx = 0$]. Let us consider C and $C^\dagger$ as a one-column or a one-row matrix and introduce the functions

$$\omega = \Psi C, \qquad \omega^\dagger = C^\dagger \Psi^\dagger. \tag{409 b}$$

The preceding equations can then be rewritten as follows:

$$\int \delta\omega^\dagger(x)[E + e\varphi(x)]\omega(x) \, dx = 0$$

and

$$\int \delta\omega^\dagger(x)\cdot\omega(x) \, dx = 0,$$

where

$$\delta\omega^\dagger = C^\dagger \delta\Psi^\dagger.$$

Applying Lagrange's method of undetermined multipliers we thus obtain the equation

$$[E + e\varphi(x) - W]\omega(x) = 0$$

or

$$[E + e\varphi(x) - W]\Psi(x)C = 0, \tag{410}$$

where $\varphi(x)$ is defined by (406 a) and W denotes a constant—the characteristic value of the energy we are looking for. This equation can serve for the determination of the functions ψ_r so long as the coefficients C_n are supposed to be known for any choice of these functions. The equation (410) is a good illustration of the method of double quantization, as it is operational in the double sense of $\Psi(x)$ operating on the matrix C and $E + e\varphi(x) - W$ operating on $\Psi(x)$.

Assuming the first of these operations to be understood, we can rewrite the preceding equation in the form

$$[E + e\varphi(x) - W]\Psi(x) = 0 \qquad (410\,a)$$

as for an ordinary wave function, with the only difference that the additional potential energy $e\varphi(x)$ is itself dependent upon the function Ψ. It should be mentioned that this dependence can be expressed by the differential equation

$$\nabla^2 \varphi = -4\pi e \Psi^\dagger(x) \Psi(x), \qquad (410\,b)$$

which is equivalent to the integral expression (406 a) for the operator φ. This circumstance can be used, as will be shown later on, for a very important generalization of the theory in the sense of taking into account the exact electrodynamical laws which govern the interaction of the electrons.

47. Intensity Quantization of Particles described in the Configuration Space by a Symmetrical Wave Function (Einstein-Bose Statistics)

The reduction of the problem of a system of identical particles to that of a single particle—corresponding to the method of copies (Part I, § 20) —has been considered hitherto for the case of electrons—or more generally such particles as in the method of the configuration space are described by antisymmetrical wave functions. We are now going to consider the same question for the case of particles which belong to the symmetrical type, and conform accordingly to the statistics of Einstein-Bose (for instance, α-particles, hydrogen atoms considered as elementary particles, etc.).

Let us start as before with a set of N *different* individual states specified by the mutually orthogonal and normalized functions $\psi_1(x)$, $\psi_2(x),..., \psi_n(x)$. Introducing the factorized wave function

$$\phi(X) = \psi_1(x_1)\psi_2(x_2)...\psi_N(x_N)$$

we can define the symmetrical wave function describing the whole system by the formula

$$\chi(X) = \frac{1}{\sqrt{(N!)}} \sum_P P\phi, \qquad (411)$$

which differs from the corresponding antisymmetrical wave function by the absence of the sign-factors ϵ_P. This is of course a slight simplification so long as we are considering a set of N *different* individual states. We get in this case from the variational equation

$$\delta \int \chi^* H\chi \, dX = 0$$

in conjunction with the conditions

$$\int \psi_r^*(x)\psi_s(\dot{x}) \, dx = \delta_{rs}$$

the following system of equations for the functions ψ_r [corresponding to the method of the self-consistent field, cf. (366)],

$$(E+B-A_{ii})\psi_i(x) + \sum_{k\neq i}(A_{ki}+\lambda_{ki})\psi_k(x) = 0, \qquad (411\,\text{a})$$

the functions $B(x)$ and $A_{ki}(x)$ being defined by the same formulae, (365), (365 a), as before. The energy (or its probable value) is expressed accordingly by the formula

$$\sqrt{(N!)} \int \phi^* H\chi \, dX = \sum_P \int \phi^* HP\phi \, dX,$$

which gives

$$W = \sum_i \int \psi_i^*(x)\Big[(E+\tfrac{1}{2}B-\tfrac{1}{2}A_{ii})\psi_i(x) + \tfrac{1}{2}\sum_{k\neq i}A_{ki}\,\psi_k(x)\Big],$$

that is,

$$W = \sum_i \Big(E_{ii} - \int A_{ii}\psi_i(x)\psi_i^*(x)\, dx\Big) +$$
$$+ \tfrac{1}{2}\iint F(x,x')[\rho(x,x)\rho(x',x') + |\rho(x,x')|^2]\, dxdx'$$

or

$$W = \sum_i \Big[E_{ii} - \iint F(x,x')|\psi_i(x)|^2|\psi_i(x')|^2\, dxdx'\Big] +$$
$$+ \tfrac{1}{2}\iint F(x,x')[\rho(x,x)\rho(x',x') + |\rho(x,x')|^2]\, dxdx'. \qquad (411\,\text{b})$$

We thus see that in the case of symmetrical wave functions the density matrix $\rho(x,x')$ cannot replace the separate wave functions. Using the notation (395 a) for the matrix elements of F and affixing the index n to χ, we can rewrite the preceding expression in the form

$$H_{nn} = \int \chi_n^* H\chi_n \, dX = \sum_r (E_{rr} - F_{rr;rr}) + \sum_{r<s}\sum (F_{rs;rs} + F_{rs;sr}) \qquad (412)$$

similar to the expression (396) which corresponds to the antisymmetrical case with a similar condition as to the arrangement of the indices $r_1, r_2, \ldots$ in $\phi = \psi_{r_1}(x_1)\psi_{r_2}(x_2)\ldots\psi_{r_N}(x_N)$.

If χ_n is replaced by a function $\chi_{n'}$ differing from χ_n in that a single individual function ψ_n is replaced by $\psi_{p'}$, we get likewise

$$H_{nn'} = E_{pp'} + \sum_{r<p} (F_{pr;p'r} + F_{pr;rp'}). \tag{412a}$$

If finally two of the functions serving to construct χ_n, ψ_p and ψ_q say, are replaced by *two* new ones different from each other and from all the other functions in the original set, we get

$$H_{nn'} = F_{pq;p'q'} + F_{pq;q'p'} \quad (p < q). \tag{412b}$$

Let us now pass to the general case, which has no parallel in the theory of antisymmetrical functions χ, where certain individual states are *multiply occupied*, so that, for instance, each function $\psi_r(x)$ occurs n_r times ($n_r \geqslant 0$) in the set specified by the index n, where the sum $\sum n_r$ must of course be equal to the number of particles.

The formula (411) will still be valid in this case, except for the normalization factor which must be replaced by $\sqrt{\left(\dfrac{n_1! n_2! \dots}{N!}\right)}$ if only effectively different permutations P are included in the sum (411), i.e. such permutations as interchange particles associated with different individual states. Thus, leaving aside trivial permutations, we can define the normalized symmetrical wave functions by the formula

$$\chi_n = \frac{1}{\sqrt{(g_n)}} \sum_P P\phi_n, \tag{413}$$

where

$$g_n = \frac{N!}{n_1! n_2! n_3! \dots} = \frac{N!}{\prod_r n_r!}. \tag{413a}$$

We then get, instead of (412),

$$H_{nn} = \sum_r n_r (E_{rr} - F_{rr;rr}) + \sum_{r<s} \sum n_r n_s (F_{rs;rs} + F_{rs;sr}). \tag{414}$$

The calculation of the matrix elements corresponding to (412a) requires a little more care.

We must in the first place determine the number of times a given variable, x_r say, will be met in the sum $\sum_P P\phi_n$ associated with a certain function ψ_p. The number is obviously equal to

$$\frac{(N-1)!}{(n_p-1)! \prod_{s \neq p} n_s!} = \frac{n_p}{N} g_n.$$

The function ϕ_n' will differ from ϕ_n by the fact that it will contain $n_p' = n_p - 1$ factors ψ_p and $n_{p'}' = n_{p'} + 1$ factors $\psi_{p'}$. Now the matrix element of E_r with respect to the functions $P\phi_n$ and $P'\phi_{n'}$ will be different from zero only if the variable x_r is shifted from ψ_p to $\psi_{p'}$, all the rest remaining in their places. There will thus be $n_p g_n/N$ terms equal to $(E_r)_{pp'}$. Now since H contains the sum of N terms E_r, corresponding to the proper energy of all the N particles, the matrix element $E_{pp'}$ will appear in the expression $\sum_p \sum_{p'} P\phi_n H P'\phi_{n'}$ just $n_p g_n$ times. The coefficient of $E_{pp'}$ in H_{nn} will thus be

$$\frac{n_p g_n}{\sqrt{(g_n g_{n'})}} = n_p \sqrt{\left(\frac{g_n}{g_{n'}}\right)} = \sqrt{n_p}\sqrt{(n_{p'}+1)}.$$

The same argument apples to the second term in (412 a) which corresponds to the mutual energy of the particles and must besides be multiplied by n_r. We get accordingly, instead of (412 a),

$$H_{nn'} = \sqrt{(n_p)}\sqrt{(n_{p'}+1)}\Big[E_{pp'}+\sum_{r>p}n_r(F_{pr;p'r}+F_{pr;rp'})\Big]. \qquad (414\,\mathrm{a})$$

By a similar argument we obtain, instead of (412 b),

$$H_{nn'} = \sqrt{n_p}\,\sqrt{n_q}\sqrt{(n_{p'}+1)}\sqrt{(n_{q'}+1)}(F_{pq;p'q'}+F_{pq;q'p'}). \qquad (414\,\mathrm{b})$$

If we substitute these expressions in the equations

$$-\frac{h}{2\pi i}\frac{dC_n}{dt} = \sum_{n'} H_{nn'}C_{n'}$$

which determine the coefficients of the expansion $\Omega = \sum_n C_n \chi_n$ and introduce the operators α_r already used, we can bring them to the standard form

$$-\frac{h}{2\pi i}\frac{dC_n}{dt} = KC_n$$

with the following expression for the operator K:

$$
\begin{aligned}
K = &\sum_r n_r E_{rr} + \sum_p \sum_{p'} \sqrt{n_p}(\sqrt{n_{p'}}+1)E_{pp'}\,\alpha_p^\dagger \alpha_{p'} - \\
&- \sum_r n_r F_{rr;rr} + \sum_{r<s} n_r n_s (F_{rs;rs}+F_{rs;sr}) + \\
&+ \sum_{p\neq p'}\sqrt{n_p}\sqrt{(n_{p'}+1)}\sum_{r>p}n_r(F_{pr;p'r}+F_{pr;rp'})\alpha_p^\dagger \alpha_{p'} + \\
&+ \sum_{\substack{p\neq p';\,q\neq q'\\ p<q}}\sqrt{n_p}\,\sqrt{n_q}\sqrt{(n_{p'}+1)}\sqrt{(n_{q'}+1)}(F_{pq;p'q'}+F_{pq;q'p'})\alpha_p^\dagger \alpha_q^\dagger \alpha_{q'}\alpha_{p'},
\end{aligned}
$$

or

$$
\begin{aligned}
K = &\sum_r E_{rr} n_r + \sum_{p\neq p'} E_{pp'}\sqrt{n_p}\,\alpha_p^\dagger \alpha_{p'}\sqrt{n_{p'}} + \sum_{r\leq s} n_r(n_s - \delta_{rs})(F_{rs;rs}+F_{rs;sr}) + \\
&+ \sum_{r>p}\sum_{p\neq p'} n_r(F_{pr;p'r}+F_{pr;rp'})\sqrt{n_p}\,\alpha_p^\dagger \alpha_{p'}\,\sqrt{n_{q'}} + \\
&+ \sum_{\substack{p<q;\,p'\neq p;\,q'\neq q}}(F_{pq;p'q'}+F_{pq;q'p'})\sqrt{n_p}\,\alpha_p^\dagger\sqrt{n_q}\,\alpha_q^\dagger \alpha_{q'}\,\sqrt{n_{q'}}\,\alpha_{p'}\,\sqrt{n_{p'}}.
\end{aligned}
$$

This result can further be simplified if we replace the numbers n_r by operators, represented by the diagonal matrices

$$n_r = \left\{ \begin{matrix} 0 & 0 & 0 & 0 & . & . & . \\ 0 & 1 & 0 & 0 & . & . & . \\ 0 & 0 & 2 & 0 & . & . & . \\ 0 & 0 & 0 & 3 & . & . & . \\ . & . & . & . & . & . & . \end{matrix} \right\} \qquad (415)$$

and represent accordingly the operators α_r and $\alpha_r^\dagger$ (from the point of view of n_r) by the matrices

$$\alpha_r = \left\{ \begin{matrix} 0 & 1 & 0 & 0 & . & . & . \\ 0 & 0 & 1 & 0 & . & . & . \\ 0 & 0 & 0 & 1 & . & . & . \\ 0 & 0 & 0 & 0 & . & . & . \\ . & . & . & . & . & . & . \end{matrix} \right\}, \quad \alpha_r^\dagger = \left\{ \begin{matrix} 0 & 0 & 0 & 0 & . & . & . \\ 1 & 0 & 0 & 0 & . & . & . \\ 0 & 1 & 0 & 0 & . & . & . \\ 0 & 0 & 1 & 0 & . & . & . \\ . & . & . & . & . & . & . \end{matrix} \right\}, \quad (415\,\text{a})$$

which are a generalization of the matrices used to represent the operators n_r, α_r, and $\alpha_r^\dagger$ in the antisymmetrical case. We can then put, since

$$\alpha_r^\dagger \alpha_r = \left\{ \begin{matrix} 0 & 0 & 0 & . & . & . \\ 0 & 1 & 0 & . & . & . \\ 0 & 0 & 1 & . & . & . \\ . & . & . & . & . & . \end{matrix} \right\},$$

$$n_r = \sqrt{n_r}\, \alpha_r^\dagger \alpha_r \sqrt{n_r},$$

where

$$\sqrt{n_r} = \left\{ \begin{matrix} 0 & 0 & 0 & 0 & . & . & . \\ 0 & \sqrt{1} & 0 & 0 & . & . & . \\ 0 & 0 & \sqrt{2} & 0 & . & . & . \\ 0 & 0 & 0 & \sqrt{3} & . & . & . \\ . & . & . & . & . & . & . \end{matrix} \right\}, \qquad (415\,\text{b})$$

and combine the first two terms of K into a single one,

$$\sum_r \sum_{r'} E_{rr'} \sqrt{n_r}\, \alpha_r^\dagger \alpha_{r'} \sqrt{n_{r'}},$$

the summation over r and r' being unrestricted (i.e. vanishing terms being cancelled out automatically).

The other three terms corresponding to the mutual energy F can likewise be combined into a single one,

$$\sum_{p \leqslant q} \sum (F_{pq;p'q'} + F_{pq;q'p'}) \sqrt{n_p}\, \alpha_p^\dagger \sqrt{n_q}\, \alpha_q^\dagger \alpha_{q'} \sqrt{n_{q'}}\, \alpha_{p'} \sqrt{n_{p'}},$$

the second term corresponding to the case $q' = q$ and the first to the case $q' = q$; $p' = p$. It should be noticed that the term $n_r F_{rr;rr}$ is subtracted automatically in virtue of the relation $n_r \alpha_r = \alpha_r(n_r - 1)$, which reduces the product

$$\sqrt{n_r}\,\alpha_r^\dagger\,\sqrt{n_r}\,\alpha_r^\dagger\,\alpha_r\,\sqrt{n_r}\,\alpha_r\,\sqrt{n_r} = \sqrt{n_r}\,\alpha_r^\dagger\,n_r\,\alpha_r\,\sqrt{n_r}$$

to $$\sqrt{n_r}\,\alpha_r^\dagger\,\alpha_r(n_r-1)\sqrt{n_r} = n_r(n_r-1).$$

It now remains to introduce, instead of the operators n_r, α_r, and $\alpha_r^\dagger$, combined operators which can be defined by the formulae

$$b_r = \alpha_r\,\sqrt{n_r}, \qquad b_r^\dagger = \sqrt{n_r}\,\alpha_r^\dagger \qquad (416)$$

or by the relations

$$b_r^\dagger b_r = n_r, \qquad b_r b_r^\dagger = n_r+1 \qquad (416\,a)$$

following therefrom, and which will be subject to the commutation conditions

$$\left.\begin{array}{l} b_r b_s - b_s b_r = 0 \\ b_r^\dagger b_s^\dagger - b_s^\dagger b_r^\dagger = 0 \end{array}\right\} \qquad (417)$$

$$b_r b_s^\dagger - b_s^\dagger b_r = \delta_{rs} \qquad (417\,a)$$

(the latter being in agreement with (416 a) in the case $r = s$). With the help of these operators, which are quite similar to the operators a_r, $a_r^\dagger$ [differing from the latter by the sign only in the commutation relations (417 a, b)], the operator K can be written in the form

$$K = \sum_r \sum_{r'} E_{rr'}\,b_r^\dagger b_{r'} + \tfrac{1}{2}\sum_r \sum_s \sum_{r'} \sum_{s'} F_{rs;r's'}\,b_r^\dagger b_s^\dagger b_{s'} b_{r'} \qquad (417\,b)$$

which can be obtained from (402) by replacing the a's by the b's. It should be noticed that the order of the two last factors in (417 b) is irrelevant [while it is very important in (402)] since they commute with each other.

The commutation relations (417 a), just like their analogues (403 a) and (413 b), are actually self-supporting and can be used to define the operators n_r by one of the expressions (416). The fact that the characteristic values of these operators are equal to 0, 1, 2,... can be considered as a consequence of the relations (417) and (417 a). We need not repeat in detail all that has been said in the preceding section about the operator

$$N = \sum_r n_r$$

representing the total number of particles, and the functional operators

$$\psi(x) = \sum_r b_r^\dagger \psi_r(x), \qquad \psi^\dagger(x) = \sum_r b_r^\dagger \psi_r(x). \qquad (418)$$

It need only be stated that they satisfy the relations

$$\left.\begin{array}{l} \psi(x)\psi(x') - \psi(x')\psi(x) = 0 \\ \psi^\dagger(x)\psi^\dagger(x') - \psi^\dagger(x')\psi^\dagger(x) = 0 \end{array}\right\} \qquad (418\,a)$$

$$\psi(x)\psi^\dagger(x') - \psi^\dagger(x')\psi(x) = \delta(x-x') \qquad (418\,b)$$

and can serve to express the energy operator in the form

$$K = \int \psi^\dagger(x) E \psi(x) \, dx + \tfrac{1}{2} \iint \psi^\dagger(x)\psi^\dagger(x') F(x, x')\psi(x')\psi(x) \, dx dx',$$

the order of the first two or of the last two factors in the double integral being irrelevant. In the case of a stationary state of the system of particles the equation of motion reduces to the form

$$KC = W.C$$

which can be derived from the variation principle $\delta \sum C_n^* K C_n = 0$ in conjunction with the condition $\sum C_n^* C_n = 1$. The same principle when applied once more to the operator K itself, i.e. in the form

$$\sum_n C_n^* \delta K C_n = 0,$$

leads to a double operator equation

$$C^\dagger \Big[E + \int F(x, x')\psi^\dagger(x')\psi(x') \, dx' \Big] \psi(x) C = 0$$

for the determination of the functions $\psi_r(x)$.

In the special case when there is no interaction between the particles ($F = 0$) the transition from the equations

$$-\frac{h}{2\pi i} \frac{dc_r}{dt} = \sum_{r'} E_{rr'} c_{r'} \qquad (419)$$

describing the motion of a single particle, specified by the energy operator E and the wave function $\psi(x) = \sum_r c_r \psi_r(x)$, to the equations

$$-\frac{h}{2\pi i} \frac{dC_n}{dt} = \sum_n H_{nn'} C_{n'} \qquad (419\,\text{a})$$

for any number N of such particles $\Big(H = \sum_{r=1}^{N} E_r \Big)$ can be carried out, according to Dirac, in the following way:

The right-hand side of the equation (419) can be defined as the differential coefficient with respect to c_r^* of the expression

$$\bar{E} = \sum_r \sum_{r'} c_r^* E_{rr'} c_{r'} \qquad (420)$$

which represents the probable value of the energy in the state specified by the wave function $\psi(x) = \sum_r c_r \psi_r(x)$ We thus get

$$-\frac{h}{2\pi i} \frac{dc_r}{dt} = \frac{\partial \bar{E}}{\partial c_r^*},$$

and in a similar way $\qquad \dfrac{h}{2\pi i} \dfrac{dc_r}{dt} = \dfrac{\partial \bar{E}}{\partial c_r}.$

If we now put $\qquad c_r = -Q_r, \qquad \dfrac{h}{2\pi i} c_r^* = P_r,$ $\qquad\qquad$ (420 a)

or $\qquad\qquad c_r^* = Q_r, \qquad \dfrac{h}{2\pi i} c_r = P_r,$ $\qquad\qquad$ (420 b)

these equations can be rewritten in the form

$$dP_r/dt = -\partial \bar{E}/\partial Q_r, \qquad dQ_r/dt = \partial \bar{E}/\partial P_r \qquad\qquad (420\,\text{c})$$

i.e. in the standard canonical form of the classical equations of motion. The variables Q_r and P_r can be identified with the generalized coordinates and momenta, the Hamiltonian $\bar{E}$ being a bilinear function of them both and the number of degrees of freedom being infinite. Let us now pass over from the equations (420 c) to the corresponding wave-mechanical equation

$$\bar{E}\omega = -\frac{h}{2\pi i}\frac{\partial}{\partial t}\omega, \qquad\qquad (421)$$

where ω is the wave function, or probability amplitude for given values of the coordinates Q, the classical momenta P_r being replaced by the differential operators $\dfrac{h}{2\pi i}\dfrac{\partial}{\partial Q_r}$. Or let us take the equations (420) directly over into the quantum theory considering the variables Q and P as operators (matrices) which satisfy the commutation relations

$$Q_r Q_{r'} - Q_{r'} Q_r = P_r P_{r'} - P_{r'} P_r = 0$$

$$P_r Q_{r'} - Q_{r'} P_r = \delta_{rr'} \frac{h}{2\pi i}.$$

Replacing here P_r and Q_r by their expressions in terms of c_r and c_r^*, we get

$$\left. \begin{aligned} c_r^* c_{r'}^* - c_{r'}^* c_r^* = c_{r'} c_r - c_r c_{r'} = 0 \\ c_r^* c_{r'} - c_{r'} c_r^* = -\delta_{rr'} \end{aligned} \right\}. \qquad\qquad (421\,\text{a})$$

These relations are equivalent to the wave-mechanical relation

$$c_r^* = -\frac{\partial}{\partial c_r}, \quad \text{or} \quad c_r = \frac{\partial}{\partial c_r^*}, \qquad\qquad (421\,\text{b})$$

which follows from $P_r = \dfrac{h}{2\pi i}\dfrac{\partial}{\partial Q_r}$. We thus see that the coefficients c and c^* satisfy exactly those conditions which have been established above for the operators b and $b^\dagger$, and can accordingly be identified with the latter.

The application of the quantization process just shown ('second quantization') to the coefficients c, c^*, i.e. their replacement by the operators b and $b^\dagger$, thus leads us directly from the equations (419) (which with their conjugate complex can be considered as a system of canonical equations in the classical sense) to the 'wave-mechanical' equation (421), that is,

$$\left[\sum_r \sum_{r'} E_{rr'} b_r^\dagger \frac{\partial}{\partial b_{r'}^\dagger}\right]\omega = -\frac{h}{2\pi i}\frac{\partial}{\partial t}\omega$$

or the equivalent (operator) equation

$$[\sum_r \sum_{r'} E_{rr'} b_r^\dagger b_{r'}]\omega = W.\omega.$$

This is no other than our previous equation

$$KC = W.C$$

with ω replacing C and with an operator K of the form

$$K = \sum_r \sum_{r'} E_{rr'} b_r^\dagger b_{r'},$$

which corresponds to a system of identical particles describable by symmetrical wave functions in the configuration space *without any interaction*.

In other words, the quantization of the equations (419), describing the motion of a single particle, leads us to an equation describing the motion of any number of such particles—provided they conform to the statistics of Einstein and Bose. The actual number of these particles is equal to one of the characteristic values of the operator

$$N = \sum b_r^\dagger b_r$$

and remains a constant of the motion since N commutes with K. The motion of the whole assembly of particles is described by the operator-function

$$\psi(x) = \sum_r b_r \psi_r(x)$$

with the help of which the energy operator can be written in the form

$$K = \int \psi^\dagger(x) E \psi(x)\, dx.$$

An exactly similar scheme can be applied, according to Jordan and Klein, in the general case of a system of identical particles of the 'symmetrical type' interacting with each other, if this interaction is represented by a 'quasi-external' potential energy of the form

$$\tfrac{1}{2}V(x) = \tfrac{1}{2}\int \psi^*(x')F(x, x')\psi(x')\, dx',$$

the operator of the proper energy being replaced accordingly by $E + \tfrac{1}{2}V$. We then get, putting $\psi(x) = \sum c_r \psi_r(x)$,

$$V(x) = \sum_s \sum_{s'} V_{ss'} c_s^* c_{s'},$$

and consequently

$$\overline{K} = \int \psi^*(x)(E + \tfrac{1}{2}V)\psi(x)\,dx$$

$$= \int \psi^*(x)E\psi(x)\,dx + \tfrac{1}{2}\iint \psi^*(x)\psi^*(x')F(x,x')\psi(x)\psi(x')\,dxdx',$$

or
$$\overline{K} = \sum_r \sum_{r'} E_{rr'}\,c_r^*\,c_{r'} + \tfrac{1}{2}\sum_r \sum_s \sum_r \sum_{s'} F_{rs;r's'}\,c_r^*\,c_s^*\,c_{s'}\,c_{r'}$$

with
$$F_{rs;r's'} = (V_{ss'})_{rr'} = \iint \psi_r^*(x)\psi_s^*(x')F(x,x')\psi_{r'}(x)\psi_{s'}(x')\,dxdx'.$$

It now remains to replace the numerical coefficients c and c^* by the operators b and $b^\dagger$ in order to obtain the energy operator K corresponding to the problem of many particles.

It should be mentioned that the 'quasi-classical equations' for the coefficients c can be written in the general case in the same canonical form (420 b) as in the special case of no interaction, and that the transition to the quantum (or doubly quantum) equations can be effected as before by treating the coefficients c_r^* as the operators $-\partial/\partial c_r$ (or c_r as $\partial/\partial c_r^*$).

The preceding scheme for carrying out the process of second (intensity) quantization could be applied in principle to the case of particles of the antisymmetrical type just as well as to particles of a symmetrical type— namely, by substituting the operators a instead of the b's for the coefficients c. It would, however, be impossible in this case to consider the conjugate complex coefficients c^* as differential operators $-\partial/\partial c$ and to repeat with regard to the quasi-classical equations for the c's and c^*'s the same process which leads from the classical equations of the motion of a particle to the wave-mechanical equation.

The operators b_r and $b_r^\dagger$ are written by Dirac in the form

$$b_r = e^{i2\pi\theta_r/h}\sqrt{n_r}, \qquad b_r^\dagger = \sqrt{n_r}\,e^{-i2\pi\theta_r/h}, \tag{422}$$

corresponding to the usual expressions for the coefficients c_r, $\sqrt{n_r}$ playing the role of the modulus and $2\pi\theta_r/h$ that of the argument or phase angle. It follows from a comparison of (422) with (416) that the operators $e^{i2\pi\theta_r/h}$ and $e^{-i2\pi\theta_r/h}$ are no other than the operators α_r and $\alpha_r^\dagger$ considered before. Hence it follows that the operators θ_r can be represented from the point of view of the operators n_r by the formula

$$\theta_r = \frac{h}{2\pi i}\frac{\partial}{\partial n_r}. \tag{422a}$$

We have in fact, applying the operator

$$\alpha_r = e^{i2\pi\theta_r/h} = e^{\partial/\partial n_r} = \sum_{k=0}^{\infty}\frac{1}{k!}\left(\frac{\partial}{\partial n_r}\right)^k$$

to any function of n_r,

$$e^{\partial/\partial n_r}f(n_r) = \sum \frac{1}{k!}\frac{\partial^k f(n_r)}{\partial n_r^k} = f(n_r+1)$$

by Taylor's theorem, and in a similar way

$$e^{-i2\pi\theta_r/h}f(n_r) = e^{-\partial/\partial n_r}f(n_r) = \sum \frac{(-1)^k}{k!}\frac{\partial^k f(n_r)}{\partial n_r^k} = f(n_r-1).$$

If instead of considering b_r and $b_r^\dagger$ from the point of view of n_r we consider b_r and n_r from the point of view of $b_r^\dagger$, we get, as has been shown before,

$$b_r = \frac{\partial}{\partial b_r^\dagger}, \tag{422 b}$$

and consequently $n_r = b_r^\dagger \dfrac{\partial}{\partial b_r^\dagger}$. Replacing $b_r^\dagger$ by b_r as the basic quantity, we get likewise

$$b_r^\dagger = -\frac{\partial}{\partial b_r} \tag{422 c}$$

and

$$n_r = -\frac{\partial}{\partial b_r}b_r.$$

Representations of a similar type are not possible in the case of the operators a and $a^\dagger$.

Just as in the latter case, the operators b and $b^\dagger$, which are not Hermitian, can, however, be reduced to Hermitian operators p and q by means of the relations

$$b = \tfrac{1}{2}(q+ip), \qquad b^\dagger = \tfrac{1}{2}(q-ip), \tag{423}$$

which correspond to the relations (404).

The operators p and q are represented by the matrices

$$q = \begin{Bmatrix} 0 & \sqrt{1} & 0 & 0 & \cdots \\ \sqrt{1} & 0 & \sqrt{2} & 0 & \cdots \\ 0 & \sqrt{2} & 0 & \sqrt{3} & \cdots \\ 0 & 0 & \sqrt{3} & 0 & \cdots \\ \cdots \end{Bmatrix}, \qquad p = \begin{Bmatrix} 0 & -i\sqrt{1} & 0 & 0 & \cdots \\ i\sqrt{1} & 0 & -i\sqrt{2} & 0 & \cdots \\ 0 & i\sqrt{2} & 0 & -i\sqrt{3} & \cdots \\ 0 & 0 & i\sqrt{3} & 0 & \cdots \\ \cdots \end{Bmatrix},$$

which follow at once from (415a), (415b), and (416), and are easily seen to coincide with the matrices representing the coordinate and the momentum of a linear harmonic oscillator (cf. Chap. III, § 13). Their non-vanishing matrix elements can indeed be written in the form

$$\left.\begin{aligned} q_{n,n-1} &= q_{n-1,n} = \sqrt{n} \\ p_{n,n-1} &= -p_{n-1,n} = -i\sqrt{n} \end{aligned}\right\} \tag{423 a}$$

(where the index r has been dropped), and differ by certain proportionality coefficients only from the expressions (88 a) derived in § 13.

From (423) we get

$$b^\dagger b = n = \tfrac{1}{4}[p^2+q^2-i(pq-qp)]$$
$$bb^\dagger = n+1 = \tfrac{1}{4}[p^2+q^2+i(pq-qp)],$$

whence
$$pq-qp = \frac{2}{i}. \tag{423 b}$$

This reduces to the usual relation $PQ-QP = h/2\pi i$ between the momentum P and the coordinate Q if they are defined as $\sqrt{(h\omega/4\pi)}p$ and $\sqrt{(h/4\pi\omega)}q$ respectively. With the help of the preceding relations we find the following expression for n:

$$n = \tfrac{1}{4}(p^2+q^2-2), \tag{423 c}$$

which can be rewritten in the form

$$\tfrac{1}{2}(P^2+Q^2\omega^2) = h(n+\tfrac{1}{2})\frac{\omega}{2\pi}$$

corresponding to the quantized values of the energy of a harmonic oscillator with the frequency $\nu = \omega/2\pi$, n playing the role of the quantum number.

These results bring us back to the elementary theory of the quantized waves which has been sketched in Part I, § 20, with the trivial difference that we do not have to worry about the half-integral energy values of the harmonic oscillators representing the different states, since it is not their energy, but the quantum number n which gives the number of particles associated with the corresponding state. It is of more importance that we have now obtained an exact and general expression for the energy K of the system of particles in terms of the auxiliary variables b_r, $b_r^\dagger$, whereas it was assumed before without sufficient justification that this energy is simply equal to the sum $\sum_{r=1}^{\infty} E_r n_r$. In reality it reduces to this expression in the special case only of no interaction and for a special (though of course most natural) choice of the wave functions ψ_r, as corresponding to the stationary states, specified by the energy operator E ($E_r = E_{rr}$). In this case the energy K can be expressed as a simple function of the Hermitian variables p and q, namely,

$$K = \tfrac{1}{4} \sum E_{rr}(p^2+q^2-2).$$

Their introduction in the general case instead of the variables b_r and $b_r^\dagger$ would, however, lead only to a useless complication of the theory.

It is interesting to find the harmonic oscillator variables replaced in the case of electrons (or any other particles described by antisymmetrical functions) by the spin variables σ_x, σ_y—a fact which could hardly be anticipated in the early development of the theory of quantized waves, given in Part I.

48. Interaction between a 'Doubly Quantized' System and an Ordinary System: Application to Photons

We have considered hitherto a system of identical particles, with or without interaction, in a given external field of force (specified by the potential energy $U_0(x)$ or the operator E). We shall consider now the more general case of such a system in interaction with some system of a different kind which will be described to begin with in the usual way, i.e. by giving the coordinates of all the particles constituting it. The energy H of the combined system $A + B$ will consist of three parts: the energy of A taken alone (H_A), that of B taken alone (H_B), and their mutual energy $M = H_{AB}$, which can be considered as a perturbation.

The method of the 'intensity quantization' discussed in the two preceding sections can easily be extended to the present case if the wave function Ω describing the whole system in the method of configuration space is written in the form

$$\Omega(X, Y) = \sum_n \omega_n(Y, t)\chi_n(X), \tag{424}$$

where X and Y denote the totality of coordinates specifying the corresponding system, while ω_n denotes a symmetrical or antisymmetrical function of the coordinates $x_1, x_2, \ldots$ of the particles constituting X, according to the nature of these particles. Substituting (424) in the wave equation

$$-\frac{h}{2\pi i}\frac{d\Omega}{dt} = H\Omega,$$

we obtain a system of equations

$$-\frac{h}{2\pi i}\frac{d\omega_n}{dt} = \sum_{n'} H_{nn'}\omega_{n'}$$

of the same kind as before, with the only difference that $H_{nn'}$ must now be treated as an operator with regard to coordinates Y, and the 'coefficients' ω_n as functions of these coordinates and of the time.

Introducing the individual states ψ_r ($r = 1, 2, \ldots$) serving to define the functions χ_n we shall thus obtain an equation of exactly the same sort as before for the coefficients ω_n, considered as functions of the partition numbers $n_1, n_2, \ldots, n_r, \ldots$, of the coordinates Y, and of the time, with the energy operator $\sum_i E_i$ increased by H_B and by the interaction energy M of A and B. Putting

$$M = \sum_i V(x_i, Y),$$

where, in view of the identity of all the particles of A, V is the same function for all of them, we must simply add to the energy operator E_x of an individual particle the function $V(x, Y)$. We thus get the following equation:

$$\left\{ H_B + \sum_r \sum_{r'} [E_{rr'} + V_{rr'}(Y)]C_r^\dagger C_s + \tfrac{1}{2} \sum_r \sum_s \sum_{r'} \sum_{s'} F_{rs;r's'} \, C_r^\dagger C_s^\dagger C_{s'} C_{r'} \right\} \omega_n$$

$$= -\frac{h}{2\pi i} \frac{\partial}{\partial t} \omega_n, \qquad (425)$$

where the operators C stand for a or for b as the case may be.

It has been shown in Chap. VII, § 39, that it is possible to treat one part, B say, of a complex system $A+B$ as a complete system by treating all the quantities referring to this part as matrices with elements defined with respect to the different stationary states of A taken alone. This result has been proved by using for the function Ω describing the whole system just the expansion (424) with the important restriction that the functions χ should be *exact* solutions of the equation

$$H_A \chi = H_A' \chi.$$

This treatment can be conveniently applied to the present problem only when there is no interaction between the particles of A and when the individual functions $\psi_r(x)$ are exact solutions of the equation $E\psi_r(x) = E_r' \psi_r(x)$. In this case the symmetrical or antisymmetrical functions $\chi_n(X)$ will also be exact solutions of the equation

$$H_A \chi_n = H_A' \chi_n,$$

where $H_A = \sum_{i=1}^N E_{xi}$, and the theory of § 39 will be wholly applicable to our problem.

This application is derived directly from the equation (425) if we put $F = 0$ and $E_{rr'} = \delta_{rr'} E_r'$. Denoting further the sum $\sum_r E_r' C_r^\dagger C_r = \sum E_r' n_r$ by W_{An} and putting

$$\omega_n = \omega_n' e^{-i2\pi W_{An} t/h}, \qquad (425\,a)$$

we get

$$\left\{ H_B + \sum_r \sum_{r'} V_{rr'}(Y) C_r^\dagger C_s \right\} \omega_n' = -\frac{h}{2\pi i} \frac{\partial}{\partial t} \omega_n'. \qquad (425$$

This equation coincides with the equation (329 a) of § 39 if the operator of the interaction energy M is defined as $\sum_r \sum_{r'} V_{rr'}(Y) C_r^\dagger C_s$. As a matter of fact, the result of its application to the function ω_n' can be written in the form $\sum M_{nn'} \omega'_{n'}$, where n and n' denote two sequences of the partition numbers $n_1, n_2, ..., n_r, ...$ and $n'_1, n'_2, ..., n'_r, ...$, differing from each other (as in the previously considered case) by one of the numbers in the second sequence being greater and another less by 1 than the corresponding numbers of the first sequence. In other words, the matrix components of the interaction energy M appearing in (425 b) are taken with respect to collective states of the 'ignored' part A of the system $A+B$ which differ by just *one* particle jumping from one individual state to another, or, in other words, by a one-quantum jump in opposite directions of two of the quantized partition numbers $n_1, n_2,...$ which specify the states of A.

The system B can in its turn consist of a number of identical particles of a different kind from those constituting the system A (for instance, A may be a system of photons or protons and B a system of electrons). In this case it is possible to apply the method of intensity quantization to the two systems simultaneously, by defining the functions $\omega_n(Y,t)$ in (424) as symmetrical or antisymmetrical combinations of certain orthogonal and normalized functions $\phi_1(y), \phi_2(y),..., \phi_r(y),...$ describing a sequence of stationary states of the separate particles of B. We can then take the equations (425 b) as our starting-point and transform them by putting

$$\omega_n(Y,t) = \sum_m C_{nm}(t)\omega_{nm}(Y),$$

where $\omega_n(Y)$ depends (symmetrically or antisymmetrically) on the coordinates Y only. We can also—and this is perhaps a more natural procedure—carry out the two quantization processes simultaneously, starting from the original equation $-\dfrac{h}{2\pi i}\dfrac{\partial}{\partial t}\Omega = H\Omega$ and putting

$$\Omega(X,Y,t) = \sum_m \sum_n C_{mn}(t)\omega_m(Y)\chi_n(X). \tag{426}$$

We thus obtain an equation of the following form:

$$(L+K+M)C = -\frac{h}{2\pi i}\frac{\partial C}{\partial t}, \tag{426 a}$$

where L and K are the quantized energy operators referring to the two systems A and B taken separately, while M is the operator of their interaction energy. If A is antisymmetrical and B symmetrical, we can use for L and K the expressions (402) and (417 b) respectively (affixing the indices x and y to the operators E and F in order to distinguish the particles of the two sorts), whereas the operator M is expressed in this case by the formula

$$M = \sum_r \sum_{r'} \sum_s \sum_{s'} v_{rr',ss'} a_r^\dagger a_{r'} b_s^\dagger b_{s'}, \qquad (426\,\text{b})$$

where $v(x, y)$ is the interaction energy between one particle of the sort A and one particle of the sort B, and

$$v_{rr',ss'} = \iint \psi_r^*(x)\phi_s^*(y)v(x, y)\psi_{r'}(x)\psi_{s'}(y) \, dx dy.$$

In the equations (426 a) $C = C_{mn}(t)$ is to be considered as a wave function whose arguments are the partition numbers m_r and n_s, or rather the corresponding operators, defined as $b_r^\dagger b_r$ and $a_s^\dagger a_s$ respectively. These results can be generalized further for the case of three or more systems of identical particles, for instance electrons, protons, and photons, interacting with each other.

We are now going to consider more closely the particular case of the photons, i.e. light waves, in interaction with an ordinary material system, which for the sake of simplicity we shall suppose to consist of a single electron, forming with the fixed source of the external field in which it moves a hydrogen-like atom. The peculiarity of this problem lies in the fact that photons cannot actually be treated as ordinary particles. As has been emphasized in Part I (§ 24) the analogy between light and matter has a very limited scope, and the notion of photons must be considered as a useful fiction of the same sort as that of 'phonons' (sound-quanta). In applying this fiction to the interaction between light and matter we must remember in the first place the fact that the *number* of photons does not remain constant, photons being created in the act of emission and destroyed in the act of absorption. This fact excludes the possibility of describing a system of photons by the method of configuration space. Under such conditions a *strict* application of the intensity quantization scheme devised for ordinary particles to the case of photons is impossible. It is nevertheless possible to apply the final results to this rather fictitious case, thanks to the fact that we do not have to introduce any interaction between the photons. We must, however, suitably define the expression for the mutual energy between the photons on the one hand, and the material system (electron, atom) on the other, in terms of the partition numbers which describe the distribution of the photons over the different states, and, moreover, provide in a physically irrelevant way for a formal conservation of the total number of photons.

This latter circumstance can easily be achieved by introducing an additional state of zero energy corresponding by definition to an actual absence of the photons. Emission or absorption of a photon will be interpreted under this condition as the transition of a photon from or into the zero state.

The total energy of the photons taken alone (if this part of the system is referred to as B) can thus be represented by the operator

$$H_B = \sum_{r=0}^{\infty} E_{rr}\, n_r = \sum_{r=0}^{\infty} h\nu_r\, b_r^\dagger b_r, \qquad (427)$$

where $\nu_0 = 0$. The operators b, $b^\dagger$ are introduced here not on the ground that a system of photons is describable in the configuration space by a symmetrical wave function, but because we know that the photons conform to the statistics of Einstein and Bose, i.e. behave like material particles of the 'symmetrical' type. It should further be remarked that the quantities $E_{rr} = h\nu_r$ are introduced here not by the general formula $E_{rr} = \int \psi_r^* E\psi_r\, dy$ (since neither the operator E_y nor the wave functions $\psi(y)$ have a meaning for photons) but by way of definition.

The part of the energy corresponding to the atom alone can be defined in the usual way. It thus remains to define suitably the interaction energy $M = \sum_{i=0}^{\infty} V(X, y_i)$, or rather the matrix elements $V_{rr'}(X)$, the function $V(X, y_i)$ being itself just as meaningless as the operator E_y.

In looking for such a definition we can be guided by the classical expression for the energy of an atom or electron in the electromagnetic field of the light waves. This field, according to classical electrodynamics, is fully determined by its vector potential $\mathbf{A}$ as a function of the coordinates and the time, while the scalar potential ϕ can without any loss of generality be set equal to zero. The electric and magnetic intensity can be calculated with the help of $\mathbf{A}$ by means of the formulae

$$\mathbf{E} = -\frac{1}{c}\frac{\partial \mathbf{A}}{\partial t}, \qquad \mathbf{H} = \operatorname{curl} \mathbf{A}.$$

Now the energy of an electron in an additional field specified by the vector potential $\mathbf{A}$ is equal, if terms quadratic in $\mathbf{A}$ are neglected, to

$$\frac{e}{c}\mathbf{A}\cdot\mathbf{v} = \frac{e}{cm}\mathbf{A}\cdot\mathbf{p}_x,$$

where $\mathbf{p}_x$ is the electron's momentum. This formula can be taken over into the wave mechanics if $\mathbf{p}$ is defined as the operator $\dfrac{h}{2\pi i}\nabla$. In order to be able to treat this expression as the *mutual* energy of the electron and of the photons, it remains to split up $\mathbf{A}$ into separate parts, $\mathbf{A}_i$ say, which may be assumed to correspond to the separate photons, and to find the matrix elements of A_i with respect to the different 'states' r and s of the photons. Putting, for the sake of brevity,

$$\frac{e}{cm}(A_i)_{rs} = P_{rs},$$

where P_{rs} is obviously independent of the individuality of the photon (specified by the index i), we thus get for the energy of the electron with respect to the light waves the expression

$$M = \mathbf{p} \cdot \sum_r \sum_{r'} P_{rr'} b_r^\dagger b_{r'}, \tag{427 a}$$

which can be interpreted as the *mutual* energy of the electron and the photons. The problem is thus reduced to the determination of the matrix elements.

The simplest way to determine them is based on the assumption that the perturbation energy (427 a) must be responsible for such acts as the emission or absorption of light only. This means that the non-vanishing elements $P_{rr'}$ must correspond either to $r = 0$ or $r' = 0$. Since the number of photons in the zero state can be assumed to be infinite (i.e. actually indeterminate) the operators $b_0 = \alpha_0 \sqrt{n_0}$ and $b_0^\dagger = \sqrt{n_0}\,\alpha_0^\dagger$ must also have infinite characteristic values, so that the matrix elements P_{0r} and P_{r0} must be infinitely small. All we need, however, is their products with $b_0^\dagger$ and b_0. Denoting these products by $\mathbf{v}_r^\dagger$ and $\mathbf{v}_r$ respectively, we can reduce (427 a) to the form

$$M = \mathbf{p} \cdot \sum_r (\mathbf{v}_r^\dagger b_r + \mathbf{v}_r b_r^\dagger). \tag{427 b}$$

The operator $\mathbf{p} \cdot \mathbf{v}_r^\dagger b_r$ determines the probability of emission and the operator $\mathbf{p} \cdot \mathbf{v}_r b_r^\dagger$ the probability of absorption of a photon $h\nu_r$. Our problem would be completely solved if we knew the dependence of $\mathbf{v}_r$ and $\mathbf{v}_r^\dagger$ on $h\nu_r$. This dependence can be found by comparing the quantum interaction operator (427 b) with the classical one

$$\frac{e}{cm}\mathbf{p} \cdot \mathbf{A} = \mathbf{p} \cdot \frac{e}{cm}\sum_r \mathbf{A}_r,$$

where $\mathbf{A}_r$ is the harmonic component in the Fourier analysis of $\mathbf{A}$ with the frequency ν_r. The energy per unit volume corresponding to this component is equal to $(E_r^0)^2/8\pi$, where E_r^0 is the amplitude of the electric intensity (since in the case of light waves the amplitudes of the electric and magnetic vectors are numerically equal). Now according to the relation

$$\mathbf{E} = -\frac{1}{c}\frac{\partial \mathbf{A}}{\partial t}$$

we have
$$E_r^0 = \frac{2\pi \nu_r}{c} A_r^0.$$

The energy corresponding to a given harmonic vibration in the whole volume V of the enclosure where they take place is thus equal to $\frac{1}{2}\pi \frac{\nu_r^2}{c^2}(A_r^0)^2 V$. On the other hand, this energy must be equal to the product of $h\nu_r$ with the number of photons associated with the vibrations under consideration. We have therefore

$$\frac{\pi}{2c^2}\nu_r^2(A_r^0)^2 V = h\nu_r\, n_r,$$

whence .
$$\frac{e}{c}A_r^0 = e\,\sqrt{\left(\frac{2h}{\pi V \nu_r}\right)}\sqrt{n_r}. \qquad (428)$$

This expression, multiplied by the phase factor $\cos(2\pi\nu_r t + \gamma_r) = \cos\phi_r$, must obviously correspond to the quantum expression

$$\mathbf{v}_r^\dagger b_r + \mathbf{v}_r\, b_r^\dagger$$

which can be written in a similar way if we assume that $v_r = v_r^\dagger$ and if further the operators $\alpha_r = e^{i2\pi\theta_r/h}$ and $\alpha_r = e^{-i2\pi\theta_r/h}$ *are identified with the complex phase factors $e^{i\phi_r}$ and $e^{-i\phi_r}$.* In the limiting case of very high characteristic values of n_r we can treat $\sqrt{n_r}$ and α_r as commuting (neglecting 1 compared with n_r) and write accordingly

$$\mathbf{v}_r^\dagger b_r + \mathbf{v}_r\, b_r^\dagger = \mathbf{v}_r(b_r + b_r^\dagger)$$
$$= \mathbf{v}_r\sqrt{n_r}(e^{i2\pi\theta_r/h} + e^{-i2\pi\theta_r/h}) \cong 2\mathbf{v}_r\sqrt{n_r}\cos\phi_r. \quad (428\,\mathrm{a})$$

Hence it follows that
$$\frac{e}{cm}A_r^0 = 2v_r\sqrt{n_r},$$

which is identical with (428) if we put

$$v_r = v_r^\dagger = \frac{e\sqrt{h}}{m\sqrt{(2\pi V \nu_r)}}. \qquad (428\,\mathrm{b})$$

The direction of the vector $\mathbf{v}_r$ coincides with that of $\mathbf{A}_r$, i.e. with the direction of the electrical vibrations. The wave equation which determines the motion and interaction of the atom (electron) with the photons can be written accordingly in the form

$$-\frac{h}{2\pi i}\frac{\partial\omega}{\partial t} = \sum_{r=1}^{\infty}[H_A + h\nu_r\, b_r^\dagger b_r + \mathbf{p}\cdot\mathbf{v}_r(b_r + b_r^\dagger)]\omega, \qquad (429)$$

which can be obtained from the general equation (425) if we put $F = 0$, interchange x with y, and determine, as shown above, the interaction energy matrix $V_{rr'}$. Substituting in (429) $\omega = \omega' e^{-i2\pi W_n t/h}$, where $W_n = \sum_r h\nu_r n_r$, we can reduce the preceding equation to the form

$$-\frac{h}{2\pi i}\frac{\partial\omega'}{\partial t} = \sum_{r=1}^{\infty}[H_A + \mathbf{p}\cdot\mathbf{v}_r(b_r + b_r^\dagger)]\omega', \qquad (429\,\text{a})$$

which is a special case of (425 b).

Regarding $M = \sum_r \mathbf{p}\cdot\mathbf{v}_r(b_r + b_r^\dagger)$ as the operator of the perturbation energy causing transitions between the stationary states of the atom (electron) with emission or absorption of radiation, we can determine the probability of such transitions by calculating the corresponding matrix elements of M. Now these matrix elements can be written in the form
$$(J, n|M|J', n') = \sum_r (\mathbf{p}\cdot\mathbf{v}_r)_{J,J'}(b_r + b_r^\dagger)_{n,n'}.$$

By the definition of the operators b we have
$$b_r \omega_n = \alpha_r \sqrt{n_r}\,\omega(n_r) = \sqrt{(n_r+1)}\omega(n_r+1)\alpha_r,$$

whence it follows, in view of the orthogonality and normalization of the functions ω, that the matrix element $(b_r)_{nn'}$ is different from zero only if $n_r' = n_r + 1$, all the other numbers of the two sequences n_r and n_r' (apart from n_0) being the same. The value of this matrix element is equal in this case to $\sqrt{(n_r+1)}$. For the matrix element $(b_r^\dagger)_{nn'}$ we find likewise a non-vanishing value, namely, $\sqrt{n_r}$ if $n_r' = n_r - 1$, all the other numbers of the two sequences being the same cf. [eq. (423 a), § 47].

We thus see that the probability of the emission of a quantum of frequency ν_r is proportional to
$$|(\mathbf{p}\cdot\mathbf{v}_r)_{J,J'}|^2(n_r+1), \qquad (429\,\text{b})$$
while that of its absorption is proportional to
$$|(\mathbf{p}\cdot\mathbf{v}_r)_{J,J'}|^2 n_r, \qquad (429\,\text{c})$$

the proportionality coefficient being, of course, the same in both cases. The energies of the two states of the atom J and J' must differ from each other by an amount approximately equal to $\pm h\nu_r$. The fact that the absorption probability is proportional to the number of photons in the initial state, i.e. to the energy of the latter, is quite natural. It is, however, very remarkable to find that the emission probability is proportional to the number of photons not in the initial, but in the *final* state, being thus different from zero even if $n_r = 0$, i.e. if no photons of the given sort were present at the beginning (except in the zero state). This result gives an interpretation of the *spontaneous* emission of light as stimulated by a photon which was initially in the zero state. The sum $n_r + 1$ in (429 b) can be interpreted accordingly as the expression of the fact that the emission of light takes place in two ways, namely, as a result of the stimulative action of the light already present, the probability of this induced emission being exactly equal to the probability of the absorption, and also spontaneously. The ratio $n_r : 1$ must therefore be equal to the ratio $B\rho/A$ of the probability of absorption or induced emission to the probability of spontaneous emission, A and B being the well-known Einstein coefficients (see Part I, §§ 17 and 18) and ρ the density of the energy per unit volume and per unit frequency range.

This result can easily be verified. We have, in fact,

$$\rho \, d\nu = \frac{1}{V} \sum_{d\nu} n_r h\nu_r,$$

where the summation is extended over all the frequencies within the given range. Now, as has been shown in Part I, §§ 11 and 37, the number dz of free oscillations of any kind in an enclosure with a volume V, whose wave number lies in the range dk, is equal to $4\pi V k^2 \, dk$. Applying this to light oscillations (with a given state of polarization) we get, since $k = \nu/c$,

$$dz = \frac{4\pi V}{c^3} \nu^2 \, d\nu.$$

If n_r is considered as a practically continuous function of the frequency, it can be assumed to have the same value for all oscillations within the small range $d\nu$. We then get

$$\rho \, d\nu = \frac{1}{V} n_r h\nu_r \, dz = \frac{4\pi}{c^3} n_r h\nu^3 \, d\nu,$$

whence

$$\frac{\rho}{n_r} = \frac{4\pi}{c^3} h\nu^3,$$

which actually coincides with the ratio A/B found in Part I, eq. (103 a). We thus see that the theory of the emission and absorption of radiation developed in this section (and due to Dirac) has the advantage of interpreting the spontaneous transitions with emission of radiation, actually combining such spontaneous emissions with the induced ones.

It is easy to obtain from the above theory the *absolute* values of the emission and absorption probabilities. To do this we must multiply the expressions (429 b) and (429 c) by (π^2/h^2) and further by $\dfrac{dz}{d\nu} = \dfrac{4\pi V}{c^3} \nu^2$, so long as we are interested in the emission or absorption not of a particular photon with the frequency ν_r and a given direction of motion, but of any photon with a frequency lying within a narrow range $\Delta\nu$

irrespective of the direction of motion. In view of the unsharp character
of the resonance, summation of all the transition probabilities within
the range $\Delta\nu$ leads to a result which is independent of the actual
magnitude of $\Delta\nu$.

The resulting probability of a 'spontaneous' emission, for example,
per unit time and unit frequency range thus turns out to be

$$A = |(\mathbf{p}\cdot\mathbf{v}_r)_{J,J'}|^2 \frac{\pi^2}{h^2} \frac{4\pi V\nu^2}{c^3}.$$

Substituting here the expression (428 b) for $\mathbf{v}_r$ and denoting the component of $\mathbf{p}$ in the direction of the vector $\mathbf{v}_r$ (i.e. the direction of the
electrical oscillations) by p_r, we get

$$A = |(p_r)_{J,J'}|^2 \frac{e^2}{hm^2} \frac{2\pi^2}{c^3}\nu,$$

or, if p_r is replaced by $m\dfrac{dx_r}{dt} = m2\pi\nu_r\, ix_r$,

$$A = \frac{8\pi^4 e^2\nu^3}{h} |(x_r)_{J,J'}|^2,$$

which coincides with the formula (93) of Part I -if we take account
of a definitely polarized radiation only.

In order to account not only for the emission and absorption but
also for the *scattering* of radiation, we must consider the hitherto
neglected term of the perturbation energy, which is proportional to
the square of the vector potential $\mathbf{A}$.

Subtracting from the operator $\dfrac{1}{2m}\Big(\mathbf{p}-\dfrac{e}{c}\mathbf{A}\Big)^2$ the operator $p^2/2m$ which
corresponds to $A = 0$, we find for M—the operator of the mutual
energy between the electron and the light—the expression

$$M = -\frac{e}{cm}\mathbf{A}\cdot\mathbf{p} + \frac{e^2}{2mc^2}A^2, \tag{430}$$

differing from the previous one by the extra term $e^2A^2/2mc^2$.

In order to find its quantum interpretation let us put $\mathbf{A} = \sum_r \mathbf{A}_r$,
where $\mathbf{A}_r = \mathbf{A}_r^0\cos\phi_r$ denotes a harmonic component of $\mathbf{A}$. This gives

$$A = \sum_r\sum_s \mathbf{A}_r\cdot\mathbf{A}_s = \sum_r\sum_s \mathbf{A}_r^0\cdot\mathbf{A}_s^0\cos\phi_r\cos\phi_s,$$

and consequently, according to (428 a),

$$M_s = \frac{e^2}{2mc^2}A^2 = 2m\sum_r\sum_s \mathbf{v}_r\cdot\mathbf{v}_s\sqrt{n_r}\sqrt{n_s}\cos\phi_r\cos\phi_s$$
$$= \tfrac{1}{2}m\sum_r\sum_s \mathbf{v}_r\cdot\mathbf{v}_s\sqrt{n_r}\sqrt{n_s}(e^{i\phi_r}+e^{-i\phi_r})(e^{i\phi_s}+e^{-i\phi_s}),$$

which in view of the correspondence between the complex phase factors $e^{i\phi}$, $e^{-i\phi}$ and the operators $\alpha = e^{i2\pi\theta/h}$, $\alpha^{\dagger} = e^{-i2\pi\theta/h}$ can be considered as the approximate form of the operator

$$M_s = \tfrac{1}{2}m \sum_r \sum_s \mathbf{v}_r \cdot \mathbf{v}_s (b_r^{\dagger} b_s + b_s^{\dagger} b_r) = m \sum_r \sum_s \mathbf{v}_r \cdot \mathbf{v}_s\, b_r^{\dagger} b_s$$

if we leave aside extra terms of the type $\tfrac{1}{2} \sum_r \sum_s \mathbf{v}_r \cdot \mathbf{v}_s (b_r b_s + b_r^{\dagger} b_s^{\dagger})$ which correspond to a double emission or a double absorption and which do not seem to have any real physical significance. Substituting here the expression (428 b) for v and denoting by θ_{rs} the angle between the directions of the electrical vibrations of the types r and s, we get

$$M_s = \frac{e^2}{m} \frac{h}{2\pi V} \sum_r \sum_s \frac{\cos \theta_{rs}}{\sqrt{\nu_r} \sqrt{\nu_s}} b_r^{\dagger} b_s. \tag{430 a}$$

This operator, considered as a perturbation energy, determines the probability of those transitions, in which one photon $(h\nu_r)$ is absorbed and another $(h\nu_s)$ is emitted. Since the state of the atom must not change [this follows from the fact that its coordinates do not explicitly appear in (430 a)], i.e. its energy must remain the same, the two frequencies ν_r and ν_s of the absorbed and emitted light must likewise be the same; we thus have to do with a change of its direction only. This is the normal *coherent scattering*. As has been pointed out in § 23, the scattered light can in reality be different from the incident one (as in the Raman or Compton effect). The above theory cannot be extended to such cases of combined scattering.†

49. Electromagnetic Waves with Quantized Amplitudes; Theory of Spontaneous Transitions and of Radiation Damping

The preceding theory (due to Dirac) can be greatly simplified if, following Jordan, Pauli, and especially Heisenberg, we do not explicitly introduce the notion of photons but treat the phenomena of light from the point of view of the *wave theory*, replacing, however, the classical electromagnetic waves by *waves (oscillations) with quantized amplitudes*. Let $\phi(x, y, z, t)$ denote a plane harmonic wave of some quantity ϕ characteristic of the electromagnetic field—electric or magnetic field-strength, scalar or vector potential, etc. It may be a wave travelling in a definite direction or a standing wave formed by the superposition of two waves

---

† As a matter of fact, it is not strictly applicable even to simple scattering: if instead of the Schrödinger equation containing terms quadratic in the potential A, we used Dirac's equation which is linear in A, we should obtain to the first approximation (corresponding to simple transitions) no scattering at all.

of the same frequency and amplitude, travelling in opposite directions. In the former case we can put

$$\phi(x, y, z, t) = C_{\mathbf{k}} e^{i 2\pi (\mathbf{k} \cdot \mathbf{r} - vt)} + C_{\mathbf{k}}^{*} e^{-i 2\pi (\mathbf{k} \cdot \mathbf{r} - vt)}, \tag{431}$$

where $\mathbf{r}$ is the vector with the components x, y, z and $\mathbf{k}$ the wave vector; the magnitude of the latter is connected with the frequency by the relation $k = cv$, c being the velocity of light. The two amplitudes $C_{\mathbf{k}}$ and $C_{\mathbf{k}}^{*}$ must be conjugate complex quantities so that ϕ may be real. The expression (431) can be rewritten accordingly in the form

$$\phi(x, y, z, t) = A_{\mathbf{k}} \cos 2\pi (\mathbf{k} \cdot \mathbf{r} - vt) + B_{\mathbf{k}} \sin 2\pi (\mathbf{k} \cdot \mathbf{r} - vt), \tag{431 a}$$

where $A_{\mathbf{k}}$ and $B_{\mathbf{k}}$ are two real coefficients. Taking the sum of the expressions (431) or (431 a) for various magnitudes and directions of the vector $\mathbf{k}$ (forming a discrete or a continuous sequence) with suitably chosen complex amplitude coefficients $C_{\mathbf{k}}$ (or $A_{\mathbf{k}}$, $B_{\mathbf{k}}$), we can represent the value of the quantity ϕ as a function of the space coordinates and of the time for any electromagnetic field in 'empty space', i.e. satisfying d'Alembert's equation

$$\nabla^2 \phi - \frac{1}{c^2} \frac{\partial^2 \phi}{\partial t^2} = 0. \tag{432}$$

It should be kept in mind, however, that this representation does not hold for an electromagnetic field produced by electric charges situated within the region under consideration, since such a field is determined by a non-homogeneous equation of the form

$$\nabla^2 \phi - \frac{1}{c^2} \frac{\partial^2 \phi}{\partial t^2} = -4\pi \rho, \tag{432 a}$$

ρ being the volume density of the charges if ϕ is the scalar potential, or the electric current density if ϕ is the vector potential.

So long, however, as we are dealing with *radiation*, we may safely assume equation (432) to hold, and accordingly represent its general solution in the form of a sum (or integral) of the expressions (431).

The transition from the classical electromagnetic theory of light to the quantum theory can be achieved in the simplest way (without introducing the notion of light quanta) by regarding the amplitude coefficients $C_{\mathbf{k}}$, $C_{\mathbf{k}}^{*}$ not as ordinary complex numbers but as non-commuting *quantum operators* proportional to the operators b, $b^{\dagger}$ which have been used before with conjugate complex proportionality coefficients $\gamma_{\mathbf{k}}$, $\gamma_{\mathbf{k}}^{*}$ which are determined by the normalization condition for the function $\phi_{\mathbf{k}}$. Adding to $\mathbf{k}$ the further suffix ξ to indicate the polarization ($\xi = 1, 2$), we obtain the following quantum expression for a plane polarized harmonic wave of light,

$$\phi_{\mathbf{k}, \xi}(x, y, z, t) = \gamma_{\mathbf{k}, \xi} b_{\mathbf{k}, \xi} e^{i 2\pi (\mathbf{k} \cdot \mathbf{r} - vt)} + \gamma_{\mathbf{k}, \xi}^{*} b_{\mathbf{k}, \xi}^{\dagger} e^{-i 2\pi (\mathbf{k} \cdot \mathbf{r} - vt)}. \tag{433}$$

The substitution of the operators b, $b^\dagger$ for the coefficients C, C^* secures the 'quantization' of all those quantities which are expressed as volume integrals of the *square* of ϕ (extended over the whole region in which ϕ is different from zero).

Thus, for instance, taking the square of (433) and integrating over a volume V outside which ϕ can be assumed to vanish, we get

$$\int_V \phi_{\mathbf{k},\xi}^2 \, dV = \gamma_{\mathbf{k},\xi}\gamma_{\mathbf{k},\xi}^* V(b_{\mathbf{k},\xi}^\dagger b_{\mathbf{k},\xi} + b_{\mathbf{k},\xi} b_{\mathbf{k},\xi}^\dagger), \qquad (433\,\text{a})$$

the squares of the two terms of (433) giving no contribution to the integral on account of the periodic factors $e^{\pm i 4\pi \mathbf{k}\cdot\mathbf{r}}$.

Now by the definition of the operators b, $b^\dagger$ we have

$$b^\dagger b = N, \qquad bb^\dagger = N+1,$$

where N is an integer or, more exactly, an operator capable of assuming integral positive values only. Affixing to it the suffixes $\mathbf{k}$, ξ which specify the oscillations under consideration, we thus get

$$\int_V \phi_{\mathbf{k},\xi}^2 \, dV = 2|\gamma_{\mathbf{k},\xi}|^2 V(N_{\mathbf{k},\xi} + \tfrac{1}{2}). \qquad (433\,\text{b})$$

If $\phi_{\mathbf{k},\xi}$ is identified with the electric intensity E, the expression (433 b) divided by 4π can be interpreted as the electromagnetic energy $W_{\mathbf{k},\xi}$ enclosed in the volume V (since the magnetic part of the energy is equal to the electric one). Putting

$$\gamma_{\mathbf{k},\xi} = \sqrt{\frac{2\pi h\nu}{V}} = \gamma_{\mathbf{k},\xi}^* \quad (\nu = ck), \qquad (433\,\text{c})$$

we obtain for this energy the expression

$$W = (N_{\mathbf{k},\xi} + \tfrac{1}{2})h\nu,$$

which differs from that of the photon theory by the presence of the term $\tfrac{1}{2}$ in the brackets (N being the number of photons).

In order to get rid of this term one usually replaces the sum $b^\dagger b + bb^\dagger$ in (433 a) by $2b^\dagger b$, thus putting

$$\int \phi_{\mathbf{k},\xi}^2 \, dV = 2|\gamma_{\mathbf{k},\xi}|^2 b_{\mathbf{k},\xi}^\dagger b_{\mathbf{k},\xi} = 2|\gamma_{\mathbf{k},\xi}|^2 N_{\mathbf{k},\xi},$$

which, however, is a wholly unwarranted procedure. It can be shown, however, that in the accurate expression of the electromagnetic energy which involves the sum of four terms (corresponding to the scalar potential and to the three components of the vector potential) or of six terms (corresponding to the three components of the electric intensity and the three components of the magnetic intensity) the $\tfrac{1}{2}$ cancels out so that the energy reduces to an integral multiple of $h\nu$.

In the general case of an electromagnetic field represented by a sum of terms of the form (433) satisfying given boundary conditions (corresponding, for example, to radiation enclosed in a vessel with perfectly reflecting walls), the integral $\int \phi^2 \, dV$, on account of the mutual orthogonality of the different normal oscillations $\phi_{\mathbf{k},\xi}$, reduces to the sum of the expressions (433 b) for all the values of $\mathbf{k}, \xi$ concerned.

We shall now apply the method of quantized electromagnetic waves to the interaction between light and matter. The light will be considered as a perturbation and the matter described in the usual way by a superposition of the stationary states that would persist in the absence of the perturbation, i.e.

$$\psi = \sum_r a_r \psi_r = \sum a_r \psi_r(x) e^{-i2\pi \nu_r t}.$$

The amplitude coefficients a_r will be treated to begin with as ordinary numbers; for the sake of simplicity the material system will be imagined to consist of a single electron bound to a fixed centre of force (hydrogen-like atom).

The perturbation due to the light will result in the variation of the coefficients a with the time; this is determined by the well-known equations

$$-\frac{h}{2\pi i} \frac{da_r}{dt} = \sum_s S_{rs} a_s. \tag{434}$$

The perturbation energy can be written in the form

$$S = T\phi = \sum_{\mathbf{k},\xi} T\phi_{\mathbf{k},\xi}, \tag{434 a}$$

where T is some quantity characteristic of the atom, for instance, its electric moment if ϕ represents the electric force.

Substituting in (434 a) the expression (433) for $\phi_{\mathbf{k},\xi}$, we get

$$S = \sum_\alpha \gamma_\alpha (T_\alpha^+ b_\alpha e^{-i2\pi \nu_\alpha t} + T_\alpha^- b_\alpha^\dagger e^{i2\pi \nu_\alpha t}), \tag{434 b}$$

where the index α is an abbreviation for $\mathbf{k}, \xi$; $T_\alpha^\pm = \frac{e}{cm} p_\alpha e^{\pm i2\pi \mathbf{k} \cdot \mathbf{r}}$ if ϕ denotes the vector potential, and $\nu_\alpha = ck$. Hence we get

$$S_{rs} = \sum_\alpha \gamma_\alpha \{ (T_\alpha^+)_{rs} b_\alpha e^{i2\pi(\nu_{rs} - \nu_\alpha)t} + (T_\alpha^-)_{rs} b_\alpha^\dagger e^{i2\pi(\nu_{rs} + \nu_\alpha)t} \}.$$

So far the present theory is formally identical with the previously considered theory of the perturbation produced by classical (i.e. non-quantized) electromagnetic waves. We can therefore use for the amplitudes a_r the same approximate expressions as have been derived before [(175), § 22]. It must be remembered, however, that the corresponding probabilities $|a_r|^2$—just as the probability amplitudes a_r $(r \neq s)$—are to be dealt with not as ordinary numbers but as *operators*.

In order to obtain results comparable with the experimental data we must consider the *characteristic values* of these operators, or their *probable values* for a number of states corresponding to different characteristic values. We need not discuss here the method of calculating these probable values since in the applications they are usually known *a priori*. The important thing to be noticed is that the use of quantized electromagnetic waves involves the introduction of 'second-order probabilities', i.e. of the probability that the ordinary ('first-order') probability of some state (r) should have a given value, out of a number of possible characteristic values. Instead of directly giving the value of the transition probabilities, the operators $|a_r|^2$ considered as functions of the time (with the condition that at $t = 0$ one of them only has a characteristic value different from zero), will serve to determine the *probable* (or average) *values* of these transition probabilities.

Another important point is the fact that in calculating the probability operators $|a_r|^2$ we must take into account the *non-commutative* character of the operators b_α, $b_\alpha^\dagger$ whose squares or products occur in the expression of the product of a_r with a_r^*. It thus becomes necessary to define in an unambiguous way the order in which the operators a_r and a_r^* must be multiplied by each other. This order being adequately fixed, the commutation relations which are satisfied by the operators b_α, $b_\alpha^\dagger$ enable one to incorporate in the perturbation theory of the radiative transitions those transitions which are classically distinguished as spontaneous on exactly the same footing as the ordinary 'induced' ones.

We shall consider, just as in § 22 (or § 18, Part I), a radiation with a practically continuous spectrum (such as the thermal radiation in statistical equilibrium at a given temperature). Assuming the material system (atom) to be initially in a given state s, we get to a first approximation $(r \neq s)$

$$a_r = \Delta a_r = -\frac{1}{h} a_s^0 \sum_\alpha \gamma_\alpha \left\{ b_\alpha \frac{e^{i2\pi(\nu_{rs}-\nu_\alpha)t}-1}{\nu_{rs}-\nu_\alpha}(T_\alpha^+)_{rs} + b_\alpha^\dagger \frac{e^{i2\pi(\nu_{rs}+\nu_\alpha)t}-1}{\nu_{rs}+\nu_\alpha}(T_\alpha^-)_{rs} \right\},$$

where $a_s^0 = a_s^{0*} = 1$.   (435)

Let us consider in the first place a transition $s \to r$ to a state of *higher* energy $W_r > W_s$ under the condition of unsharp resonance with the electromagnetic waves in a small frequency range near $\nu_\alpha = \nu_{rs} = (W_r - W_s)h$. We can then drop the second term in (435) compared with the first one. It now remains to multiply a_r by its conjugate complex, dropping all terms containing the b_α's with different values of α and to sum over the frequency range considered.

Before we do this we must, however, make the following important remark about the order of the factors in the product of a_r with a_r^*. According to (435) a_r $(r \neq s)$ must be considered not as an ordinary number but as an operator of the same type as b; its conjugate complex must be replaced accordingly by the adjoint operator

$$a_r^\dagger \cong (\Delta_1 a_r)^\dagger = -\frac{1}{h} a_s^{0*} \sum_\alpha \gamma_\alpha (T_\alpha^+)_{rs}^* b_\alpha^\dagger \frac{e^{-i2\pi(\nu_{rs}-\nu_\alpha)t}-1}{\nu_{rs}-\nu_\alpha}$$

[which corresponds to the first term of (435)].

Correct results are then obtained if the operator which determines the probability of the state is defined by the product $a_r^\dagger a_r$ and not by $a_r a_r^\dagger$.

In carrying out the summation over the different oscillations we can drop all those products $b_\alpha^\dagger b_\beta$ for which $\alpha \neq \beta$ (in view of the supposed incoherent character of the radiation). This gives

$$a_r^\dagger a_r \cong a_s^{0*} a_s^0 \frac{\gamma_{\nu_0}^2}{h^2} \overline{|(T_\alpha^+)_{rs}|^2} \frac{\sum_\alpha^{(\Delta\nu)} b_r^\dagger b_r}{\Delta\nu} \int_{-\infty}^{+\infty} \left| \frac{e^{i2\pi(\nu-\nu_{rs})t}-1}{\nu-\nu_{rs}} \right|^2 d(\nu-\nu_{rs}),$$

where $\nu_0 = \nu_{rs}$ is the resonance frequency, $\overline{|(T_\alpha^+)_{rs}|^2}$ the average value of $|(T_\alpha^+)_{rs}|^2$ for all the directions of the vector $\mathbf{k}$ with the fixed magnitude c/ν_0, and $\Delta\nu$ a small frequency range containing the resonance frequency and yet large enough to make the integrand very small compared with 1 for $\nu-\nu_{rs} = \pm\Delta\nu$. The integral being equal to $4\pi^2 t$, we thus get

$$a_r^\dagger a_r \cong \frac{4\pi^2}{h^2} a_s^{0*} a_s^0 \gamma_{\nu_0}^2 \overline{|(T_\alpha^+)_{rs}|^2} \frac{\sum^{\Delta\nu} b_\alpha^\dagger b_\alpha}{\Delta\nu} t.$$

Let $Z_\nu \Delta\nu$ be the number of different oscillations in the frequency range under consideration, i.e. the number of summands in $\sum^{\Delta\nu} b_\alpha^\dagger b_\alpha$. For isotropic thermal radiation $Z_\nu \Delta\nu = \frac{8\pi V}{c^3} \nu^2 \Delta\nu$ [cf. Part I, § 29, (141)]; we can then put

$$\frac{\sum^{\Delta\nu} b_\alpha^\dagger b_\alpha}{\Delta\nu} = Z_\nu \overline{b_\alpha^\dagger b_\alpha},$$

and consequently

$$a_r^\dagger a_r = a_s^{0*} a_s^0 B_{rs}^+ \frac{Z_\nu}{V} h\nu \, \overline{b_\alpha^\dagger b_\alpha} \cdot t, \tag{435a}$$

where

$$B_{rs}^+ = \frac{4\pi^2 V}{h^3 \nu} \gamma_{\nu_0}^2 \overline{|(T_\alpha^+)_{rs}|^2} \quad (\nu = \nu_{rs}). \tag{435b}$$

Let us now consider the opposite transition $r \to s$ due to the (unsharp) resonance with electromagnetic oscillations of the same frequency as in the preceding case. Reversing the indices s and r, we obtain for the probability amplitude of the transition $r \to s$ the expression

$$a_s = \Delta_1 a_s = -\frac{1}{h} a_r^0 \sum_\alpha \gamma_\alpha \Big\{ (T_\alpha^+)_{sr}\, b_\alpha \frac{e^{i2\pi(\nu_{sr}-\nu_\alpha)t}-1}{\nu_{sr}-\nu_\alpha} +$$

$$+ (T_\alpha^-)_{sr}\, b_\alpha^\dagger \frac{e^{i2\pi(\nu_{sr}+\nu_\alpha)t}-1}{\nu_{sr}+\nu_\alpha} \Big\}. \quad (436)$$

Since $\nu_{sr} = -\nu_{rs}$, and consequently $\nu_{sr}+\nu_\alpha \cong 0$, we can now drop the *first* term of this expression and not the second one, which gives

$$a_s^\dagger a_s = a_r^{0*} a_r^0\, B_{rs}^-\, Z_\nu\, h\nu\, \overline{b_\alpha b_\alpha^\dagger} \cdot t. \quad (436\,\text{a})$$

This differs from (435 a) by the inverse order of the factors b_α and $b_\alpha^\dagger$, and also in a minor way through the substitution of B_{rs}^- for B_{rs}^+.

Now we have $\qquad b_\alpha^\dagger b_\alpha = N_\alpha, \qquad b_\alpha b_\alpha^\dagger = N_\alpha + 1,$

where N_α is the operator representing the (integral) number of light quanta associated with the oscillations of the type α. Passing from operators to probable values, we get

$$\frac{Z_\nu}{V} h\nu\, \overline{b_\alpha^\dagger b_\alpha} = Z_\nu \frac{\overline{N_\alpha}}{V} h\nu = \rho_\nu,$$

where ρ_ν is the spectral density of radiation per unit volume and

$$\overline{b_\alpha b_\alpha^\dagger} \frac{Z_\nu h\nu}{V} = (\overline{N_\alpha}+1)h\nu = \rho_\nu\Big(1 + \frac{8\pi\nu^2}{c^3} h\nu\Big).$$

Hence the probable values of the probabilities for the transitions $s \to r$ and $r \to s$ referred to unit time are

$$\Gamma_{s\to r} = B_{rs}^+ \rho_{\nu_{rs}} \quad \text{if} \quad W_r > W_s,$$

and $\qquad \Gamma_{r\to s} = B_{rs}^-\Big(\rho_{\nu_{rs}} + \frac{8\pi\nu^2}{c^3} h\nu\Big) = A_{rs} + B_{rs}^- \rho_{\nu_{rs}}. \quad (436\,\text{b})$

We thus see that on the present theory 'spontaneous' transitions from a state of higher energy to that of lower energy become completely fused with the induced transitions of the same type. The relation

$$A_{rs} = \frac{8\pi\nu^2}{c^3} h\nu B_{rs}^-$$

between the probability coefficients A and B referring to spontaneous and induced transitions is just that which has been obtained in Part I, §§ 17 and 18, by the method of 'classical' electromagnetic waves. The only difference consists in the multiplication of the quantity T characterizing the atom by the factors $e^{\pm i2\pi \mathbf{k} \cdot \mathbf{r}}$ characterizing the radiation, which corresponds to the introduction of two somewhat different coefficients B_{rs}^+ (for absorption) and B_{rs}^- (for emission) instead of the single one considered before. It should be remarked, however, that for an isotropic radiation characterized by all the directions of the vector **k** being equally probable, the two coefficients are identical. If, moreover, the wave-length $\lambda = 1/k$ is large compared with the effective linear extension of the atom the factors $e^{\pm i 2\pi \mathbf{k \cdot r}}$ can be dropped altogether. The expression (435 b) reduces in this case to that obtained before (Part I, § 17), if T is defined as the electric moment of the atom in the direction of the electric intensity ϕ. Substituting the corresponding expression (433 c) for γ_α in (435 b), we get, since

$$|\overline{T_{rs}}|^2 = \tfrac{1}{3} e^2 (|x_{rs}|^2 + |y_{rs}|^2 + |z_{rs}|^2),$$
$$B_{rs} = \frac{8\pi^3}{3h^2} e^2 (|x_{rs}|^2 + |y_{rs}|^2 + |z_{rs}|^2),$$

in agreement with (103), § 18 of Part I.

As a second illustration of the method of quantized electromagnetic waves we shall apply it, following Rosenfeld, Weisskopf and Wigner to the problem of the *radiation damping*.

Let us return to the perturbation equations (434) and let us assume for the sake of simplicity that S_{rs} is different from zero for two states only, $r = 1$ and $s = 0$ say (the diagonal elements S_{11} and S_{00} likewise vanishing).

The equations (434) reduce under these conditions to the following two:

$$-\frac{h}{2\pi i} \dot{a}_1 = f a_0, \qquad -\frac{h}{2\pi i} \dot{a}_0 = g a_1, \qquad (437)$$

where
$$f = \sum_\alpha \gamma_\alpha [(T_\alpha^+)_{10} b_\alpha e^{i 2\pi (\nu_{10} - \nu_\alpha) t} + (T_\alpha^-)_{10} b_\alpha^\dagger e^{i 2\pi (\nu_{10} + \nu_\alpha) t}]$$
$$g = \sum_\alpha \gamma_\alpha [(T_\alpha^+)_{01} b_\alpha e^{i 2\pi (-\nu_{10} - \nu_\alpha) t} + (T_\alpha^-)_{01} b_\alpha^\dagger e^{i 2\pi (-\nu_{10} + \nu_\alpha) t}]. \qquad (437\,\text{a})$$

We shall assume that at the initial moment $(t = 0)$ $a_1 = 1$ and $a_0 = 0$, which means that the atom was initially in the excited state, and shall try to solve our problem more exactly than was done before (when a_1 was considered as constant) by putting

$$a_1 = e^{-2\pi \Gamma t}. \qquad (438)$$

This corresponds to a radioactive-like decay of the number of atoms in the excited state (1) owing to their spontaneous transition to the normal one (0). Substituting this expression in the second equation (437) and integrating, we get

$$a_0 = -\frac{1}{h} \sum_\alpha \gamma_\alpha \Big\{ (T_\alpha^+)_{01} b_\alpha \frac{e^{-i 2\pi (\nu_{10} + \nu_\alpha - i\Gamma) t} - 1}{-(\nu_{10} + \nu_\alpha - i\Gamma)} + \\ + (T_\alpha^-)_{01} b_\alpha^\dagger \frac{e^{i 2\pi (\nu_\alpha - \nu_{10} + i\Gamma) t} - 1}{\nu_\alpha - \nu_{10} + i\Gamma} \Big\}. \qquad (438\,\text{a})$$

The first term in this sum can be dropped so long as ν_α lies in the vicinity of ν_{10} just as in the derivation of (436 a).

In order to find the decay or damping constant Γ we must substitute this expression in the first equation (437) with due account of the order of the factors b, $b^\dagger$ and sum over all the α's in the resonance range $\delta\nu$. In doing this we can drop the second term in f, for in view of the incoherent character of the oscillations the probable (average) value of $b^\dagger_\alpha b^\dagger_\beta$ vanishes both when $\alpha \neq \beta$ and $\alpha = \beta$, the only non-vanishing terms being those containing the products $b_\alpha b^\dagger_\alpha = N_\alpha + 1$. We thus find

$$\frac{h}{i}\Gamma e^{-2\pi\Gamma t} = -\frac{1}{h}\sum_\alpha \gamma^2_\alpha (T^+_\alpha)_{10}(T^-_\alpha)_{01}(N_\alpha+1)\frac{e^{-i2\pi\Gamma t}-e^{i2\pi(\nu_{10}-\nu_\alpha)t}}{\nu_\alpha-\nu_{10}+i\Gamma},$$

that is, $\Gamma = -\dfrac{1}{h^2}\displaystyle\sum_\alpha \gamma^2_\alpha (T^+_\alpha)_{10}(T^-_\alpha)_{01}(N_\alpha+1)\dfrac{1-e^{i2\pi(\nu_{10}-\nu_\alpha-i\Gamma)t}}{i(\nu_{10}-\nu_\alpha-i\Gamma)}.$ (438 b)

Replacing here the operator N_α as before by its probable (average) value $(c^3/8\pi h\nu^3)\rho_\nu$, and further replacing the summation over α by an integration over ν with the expression $Z_\nu\,d\nu = 8\pi V\nu^2\,d\nu/c^3$ for the number of α-values in the range $d\nu$, we get

$$\Gamma = \frac{\gamma^2_{\nu_0}}{h^2}\overline{(T^+_\alpha)_{10}(T^-_\alpha)_{01}}\,Z_\nu\left(\frac{c^3}{8\pi h\nu^3_0}\rho_{\nu_0}+1\right)\int\limits_{-\infty}^{+\infty}\frac{1-e^{i2\pi(\nu_{10}-\nu-i\Gamma)t}}{i(\nu-\nu_{10}+i\Gamma)}\,d(\nu-\nu_{10}),$$

where ν_0 denotes the resonance frequency $\nu_{10},\ldots$ and $\overline{(T^+_\alpha)_{10}(T^-_\alpha)_{01}}$ the average value of the product $(T^+_\alpha)_{10}(T^-_\alpha)_{01}$ for all the directions of the vector $\mathbf{k}$ with the fixed magnitude $k = \nu/c$. The integral J appearing in this formula is easily seen to be independent of the value of the parameter Γ and to be equal to π. We have in fact, putting $\Gamma = 0$ and $\nu-\nu_{10} = \xi$,

$$J = \int\limits_{-\infty}^{+\infty}\frac{1-e^{-i2\pi\xi t}}{i\xi}\,d\xi = -i\int\limits_{-\infty}^{+\infty}\frac{1-\cos 2\pi\xi t}{\xi}\,d\xi + \int\limits_{-\infty}^{+\infty}\frac{\sin 2\pi t\xi}{\xi}\,d\xi.$$

The first term obviously vanishes since the integrand is an odd function of ξ, while the second reduces to the well-known integral of Laplace, which is equal to π.

Thus, if we neglect the difference between the factors T^+_α and T^-_α replacing them simply by T (which is always permissible if the resonance wave-length, $\lambda = c/\nu_{10}$, is large compared with the effective dimensions of the atom), and take into account the relation (435 b), we obtain for the constant Γ the following expression:

$$\Gamma = \frac{1}{4\pi} \frac{Z_\nu}{V}\left(1 + \frac{c^3}{8\pi h \nu_0^3}\rho_{\nu_0}\right)B_{10},$$

whence $4\pi\Gamma = A_{10} + B_{10}\rho_\nu. \qquad (439)$

This quantity is usually denoted as the *damping exponent* since the number of atoms in the excited state $a_1^\dagger a_1$ decreases with the time as $e^{-4\pi\Gamma t}$. Under ordinary circumstances the second term in (439) is small compared with the first one, so that the damping constant is numerically equal to the probability of a spontaneous transition between the corresponding states.

In the general case when the atom is initially in an excited state r from which spontaneous transitions are possible to several states of lower energy s, the damping constant is equal to the sum of the corresponding transition probabilities

$$4\pi\Gamma_r = \sum_{s<r} A_{rs} \quad (W_s < W_r). \qquad (439\,\mathrm{a})$$

The probability amplitude of the rth state a_r decreases with the time like $e^{-2\pi\Gamma_r t}$. Multiplying this expression by $\psi_r = \psi_r^0(x)e^{-i2\pi\nu_r t}$ we can treat the resulting function

$$a_r\psi_r = \psi_r^0(x)e^{-i2\pi(\nu_r - i\Gamma_r)t}$$

as representing *damped vibrations*, corresponding to a complex value of the frequency $\nu_r - i\Gamma_r$. Such damped vibrations starting at a certain instant $t = 0$ can be analysed into a series of undamped harmonic vibrations, according to the equation

$$f(t) = e^{-i2\pi(\nu_r - i\Gamma_r)t} = \int_{-\infty}^{+\infty} A_\nu e^{-i2\pi\nu t}\,d\nu \quad (t \geqslant 0),$$

where $A_\nu = \int_0^\infty f(t)e^{i2\pi\nu t}\,dt = \int_0^\infty e^{i2\pi(\nu - \nu_r + i\Gamma_r)t}\,dt$

$$= \int_0^\infty e^{-2\pi[\Gamma_r - i(\nu - \nu_r)]t}\,dt = \frac{1}{2\pi[\Gamma_r - i(\nu - \nu_r)]},$$

or $|A_\nu|^2 = \dfrac{1}{4\pi^2[(\nu - \nu_r)^2 + \Gamma_r^2]}. \qquad (439\,\mathrm{b})$

This corresponds to an effective spectral width Γ_r of the state in question —in agreement with the interpretation of complex energy values given in Part I, § 15, in connexion with the problem of radioactive decay.

50. Application of Quantized Electron Waves to the Emission and Scattering of Radiation

If in the function

$$\psi(x,t) = \sum_r a_r \psi_r(x,t) = \sum_r a_r \psi_r^0(x) e^{-i2\pi\nu_r t}, \qquad (440)$$

representing the undisturbed motion of the electron, the coefficients a_r are treated not as ordinary complex numbers, but as operators satisfying the relations

$$a_r^\dagger a_s + a_s a_r^\dagger = \delta_{rs}, \qquad a_r a_s + a_s a_r = 0, \qquad a_r^\dagger a_s^\dagger + a_s^\dagger a_r^\dagger = 0, \qquad (440\,a)$$

ψ will represent the motion of any given number of electrons, distributed over the individual states ψ_r, the number of electrons associated with a particular state r being defined as the characteristic value of the operator

$$a_r^\dagger a_r = n_r \qquad (440\,b)$$

(i.e. 1 or 0); it should be remembered that the product $a_r a_r^\dagger$ is equal to $1-n_r$.

It has been shown by Heisenberg that with this definition of ψ corresponding to *quantized electron waves*, it is possible to give an adequate description of the emission (and scattering) of radiation in terms of the classical electromagnetic theory, if, following Schrödinger, we replace the classical mechanical quantities (coordinates, velocities, etc.) by their average or probable values.

This wave-mechanical theory of light emission has been discussed already in Part I, § 17, with the help of 'classical' (i.e. unquantized) electron waves as giving rise to classical electromagnetic waves. It has been shown there that light vibrations defined as 'beats' ('difference tones') between two electron waves have correct frequencies, but that their amplitude is proportional not only to the probability of the initial state but also to that of the final one—which contradicts the photon theory of radiation. Now this contradiction can be removed if the 'classical' electron waves are replaced by quantized ones; the resulting electromagnetic waves appear likewise as quantized although in a way somewhat different from that considered in the preceding section.

The mechanical quantity which determines the radiation emitted by an atom can be defined according to Schrödinger's theory as the probable value of the electric moment of the atom

$$\overline{\mathbf{P}} = \int \psi^* \mathbf{P} \psi \, dV.$$

If we are concerned with several electrons $\mathbf{P}$ must denote the sum

$\sum_i e\mathbf{r}_i$, where $\mathbf{r}_i$ is the radius vector of the ith electron (with respect to the nucleus), and ψ an antisymmetrical function of the coordinates of all the electrons, the integration being extended over the whole configuration space. Introducing quantized electron waves, we can represent the totality of the electrons by the three-dimensional operator-function (440), and replace the preceding expression for the probable value of the resulting electric moment by the operator

$$\overline{\mathbf{P}} = \int \psi^{\dagger}\mathbf{P}\psi \, dV, \tag{441}$$

whose characteristic values must be considered as the probable values of $\mathbf{P}$. Just as for the quantized electromagnetic waves discussed in the preceding section, we are thus concerned with probabilities of the 'second order', i.e. the probabilities of certain probable values of $\mathbf{P}$, the corresponding second-order probability amplitudes C being defined by an equation of the form $\overline{\mathbf{P}}C = \overline{\mathbf{P}}'C$. As a matter of fact, we need not bother about these probabilities, for the quantity we are actually interested in, and which can be directly compared with the experimental facts, is the *probable* value $\overline{\overline{\mathbf{P}}}$ of the operator $\overline{\mathbf{P}}$, which, as we shall presently see, can usually be determined directly.

It should be emphasized that the order in which the two factors $\psi^{\dagger}$ and ψ appear in the expression (441) is an *essential feature* of this expression, since these factors do not commute with each other. We should obtain wrong results if the operator $\overline{\mathbf{P}}$ were defined as $\int \psi\mathbf{P}\psi^{\dagger} \, dV$.

Substituting in (441) the expression (440) for ψ, we get

$$\overline{\mathbf{P}}(t) = \sum_r \sum_s a_r^{\dagger} a_s \, \mathbf{P}_{rs}^0 e^{i2\pi\nu_{rs}t}, \tag{441 a}$$

and consequently

$$\frac{d^2\overline{\mathbf{P}}(t)}{dt^2} = -\sum_{r \neq s} a_r^{\dagger} a_s \, \mathbf{P}_{rs}^0 (2\pi\nu_{rs})^2 e^{i2\pi\nu_{rs}t}. \tag{441 b}$$

This expression can be considered as defining in the same way as in the classical electromagnetic theory the electric and magnetic field generated by the atom at sufficiently remote points.

The electrical intensity in a given direction τ, say, at a distance R from this atom (the unit vector τ being perpendicular to $\mathbf{R}$) is thus represented by the operator

$$E_\tau(R,t) = -\frac{1}{c^2 R} \ddot{\overline{\mathbf{P}}}_\tau(t - R/c),$$

c being the velocity of light, that is,

$$E_\tau \equiv E_\tau^- + E_\tau^+ = \frac{1}{c^2 R} \sum_r \sum_{r \neq s} a_r^{\dagger} a_s (P_\tau^0)_{rs} (2\pi\nu_{rs})^2 e^{i2\pi\nu_{rs}(t - R/c)}, \tag{442}$$

where E_τ^- corresponds to terms with negative frequencies and E_τ^+ to those with positive frequencies.

The electric field defined by (442) is an operator, of a type somewhat similar to that defined in the preceding section with the help of the operators b, $b^\dagger$, the operators $a_r^\dagger a_s$ corresponding to b if $\nu_{rs} < 0$ $(W_r < W_s)$ and to $b^\dagger$ if $\nu_{rs} > 0$ $(W_r > W_s)$. The connexion between the two types of operators will be examined later on. We are concerned here only with the fact that in order to obtain the observed electric field we must take the characteristic or probable values of (442). In the absence of definite phase relations between the operators a_r and a_s referring to different states, i.e. when the different harmonic terms in (440) are incoherent with regard to each other, the probable values of $a_r^\dagger a_s$ are equal to zero so long as $r \neq s$, so that the probable value of (442) vanishes. This is practically equivalent to the fact that the average value of E_r *with respect to the time* is equal to zero. The quantity we are interested in is, however, not the electric field-strength but the corresponding *energy*. According to the classical theory, the latter (or more exactly the energy-density) is proportional to the square of E_r. In order to obtain the *operator* which serves to define the energy in agreement with the photon theory of radiation we must, instead of squaring E_r, multiply E_τ^+ by E_τ^- in the order stated (just as in the preceding section where E^+ was replaced by $\phi^\dagger$ and E^- by ϕ). This gives

$$E^+E^- = \frac{1}{c^4 R^2} \sum_{r>s} \sum \sum_{r'>s'} \sum a_r^\dagger a_s a_{s'}^\dagger a_{r'} (16\pi^4 \nu_{rs}^2 \nu_{r's'}^2) P_{rs}^0 P_{s'r'}^0 e^{i2\pi(\nu_{rs}+\nu_{s'r'})(t-R/c)},$$

$$(442\,a)$$

it being understood that $\nu_{rs} > 0$ if $r > s$ (the index τ is dropped for convenience).

We shall take in the first place the *time average* of this expression, which can be done by keeping those terms only for which $\nu_{rs} + \nu_{s'r'} = 0$, that is, $r' = r$ and $s' = s$. We thus get

$$\overline{E^+E^-}^{(t)} = \frac{1}{c^4 R^2} \sum_{r>s} \sum a_r^\dagger a_s a_s^\dagger a_r |P_{rs}^0|^2 (2\pi\nu_{rs})^4.$$

It should be mentioned that the same result is obtained by averaging over the phases of the operators a_r, etc., if they are assumed to correspond to incoherent vibrations.

Now $a_r^\dagger a_s a_s^\dagger a_r = -a_r^\dagger a_s a_r a_s^\dagger = a_r^\dagger a_r a_s a_s^\dagger = n_r(1-n_s),$

so that $$\overline{E^+E^-}^{(t)} = \frac{1}{c^4 R^2} \sum_{r>s} \sum n_r(1-n_s)|P_{rs}^0|^2 (2\pi\nu_{rs})^4. \qquad (442\,b)$$

This formula shows that the intensity of the emitted light is equal to the sum of terms corresponding to a combination of two states (r, s), *provided the upper state is occupied* $(n_r = 1)$ *and the lower vacant* $(n_s = 0)$. This result is in complete harmony with what should be expected on the photon theory of light emission in connexion with Pauli's exclusion principle. The formula (442 b) can thus be regarded as the improved version of the 'classical' wave-mechanical equation (92) of Part I, § 17, where the upper and lower states appeared in a quite symmetrical manner. Indeed, we come back to this result if we consider the amplitudes a_r, a_s as ordinary numbers and not as operators.

If in the expression (441 a) a_r and a_s are multiplied by the damping factors $e^{-i2\pi\Gamma_r t}$ and $e^{-i2\pi\Gamma_s t}$, the light vibrations with the frequency $\nu_{rs} = (W_r - W_s)/h$ due to the combination of the corresponding states appear as damped with the damping constant

$$\Gamma_{rs} = \Gamma_r + \Gamma_s = \sum_{p<r} A_{rp} + \sum_{q<s} A_{sq}.$$

The effective width of the spectral line emitted in a transition from one state to another is thus equal to the sum of the widths of both the initial and final states.

We shall now investigate, with the help of the formula (442), the light emitted by an atom under the perturbing influence of 'primary' electromagnetic waves, or, in other words, the phenomenon of the *scattering* of radiation. As has been shown in Chap. V, § 23, the interpretation of this phenomenon from the purely mechanical point of view necessitates the consideration of *double* transitions, which correspond to the second approximation in the solution of the perturbation problem. If, however, we consider the *radiation* emitted (scattered) by the perturbed atom, we can confine ourselves to the first approximation, which in conjunction with equation (442) gives equivalent results.

Let us for a moment treat the coefficients a_r as ordinary numbers, and define the electric field of the primary light waves by the expression

$$E^0 = \tfrac{1}{2}(be^{-i2\pi\nu t} + b^\dagger e^{i2\pi\nu t}),$$

where b is the (complex) amplitude of E^0. Let us assume further that at the initial moment, $t = 0$, the coefficients a_q, $a_{q'}$, $a_{q''}$ are different from 0, while all the other coefficients a_r, a_s,... vanish. We then get from (435), with $T_\alpha^\pm$ replaced by P_σ, the component of $\mathbf{P}$ in the direction σ of the vector E^0, and the summation over α by a summation over q:

$$a_r = \Delta_1 a_r = -\frac{1}{2h} \sum_q a_q^0 (P_\sigma^0)_{rq} \left[b \frac{e^{-i2\pi(\nu - \nu_{rq})t} - 1}{\nu_{rq} - \nu} + b^\dagger \frac{e^{i2\pi(\nu + \nu_{rq})t} - 1}{\nu_{rq} + \nu} \right].$$

Substituting this expression and the similar expression for the conjugate complex

$$a_r^\dagger = \Delta_1 a_r^\dagger = -\frac{1}{2h} \sum_q a_q^{0\dagger}(P_\sigma^0)_{qr}\left[b^\dagger \frac{e^{i2\pi(\nu-\nu_{rq})t}-1}{\nu_{rq}-\nu} + b\frac{e^{-i2\pi(\nu+\nu_{rq})t}-1}{\nu_{rq}+\nu}\right]$$

in the formula (441 a) for the electric moment or its projection in a given direction τ and dropping small terms of the second order, we have

$$P_\tau(t) = \sum_r \sum_{q'} [\Delta_1 a_r^\dagger a_{q'}^0 (P_\tau^0)_{rq'} e^{i2\pi\nu_{rq'}t} + a_{q'}^{0\dagger} \Delta_1 a_r (P_\tau^0)_{q'r} e^{i2\pi\nu_{q'r}t}].$$

If furthermore we drop irrelevant terms which do not contain the primary frequency (they can actually be considered as fading away owing to the damping), we get, with the help of the relations

$$\nu_{rq} + \nu_{q'r} = \nu_{q'q} = -\nu_{qq'},$$

$$\bar{P}(t) = -\frac{1}{2h}\sum_q \sum_{q'} \sum_r \left\{a_q^{0\dagger} a_{q'}^0 (P_\sigma^0)_{qr}(P_\tau^0)_{rq'}\left[b^\dagger \frac{e^{i2\pi(\nu-\nu_{q'q})t}}{\nu_{rq}-\nu} + b\frac{e^{-i2\pi(\nu+\nu_{q'q})t}}{\nu_{rq}+\nu}\right] + \right.$$

$$\left. + a_{q'}^{0\dagger} a_q^0 (P_\tau^0)_{q'r}(P_\sigma^0)_{rq}\left[b\frac{e^{-i2\pi(\nu-\nu_{q'q})t}}{\nu_{rq}-\nu} + b^\dagger\frac{e^{i2\pi(\nu+\nu_{q'q})t}}{\nu_{rq}+\nu}\right]\right\},$$

or, rearranging the different terms,

$$\bar{P}_\tau(t) = \sum_q \sum_{q'} [a_q^{0\dagger} a_{q'}^0 u_{q'q}^- b e^{-i2\pi(\nu-\nu_{q'q})t} + a_q^{0\dagger} a_{q'}^0 u_{qq'}^- b^\dagger e^{i2\pi(\nu-\nu_{q'q})t}] +$$

$$+ \sum_q \sum_{q'} [a_q^{0\dagger} a_{q'}^0 u_{qq'}^+ b e^{-i2\pi(\nu+\nu_{q'q})t} + a_q^{0\dagger} a_{q'}^0 u_{q'q}^+ b^\dagger e^{i2\pi(\nu+\nu_{q'q})t}]. \quad (443)$$

In this formula

$$\left. \begin{array}{ll} u_{q'q}^- = -\dfrac{1}{2h}\sum_r \dfrac{(P_\tau^0)_{q'r}(P_\sigma^0)_{rq}}{\nu_{rq}-\nu}, & u_{qq'}^- = -\dfrac{1}{2h}\sum_r \dfrac{(P_\sigma^0)_{qr}(P_\tau^0)_{rq'}}{\nu_{rq}-\nu} \\[3mm] u_{qq'}^+ = -\dfrac{1}{2h}\sum_r \dfrac{(P_\sigma^0)_{qr}(P_\tau^0)_{rq'}}{\nu_{rq}+\nu}, & u_{q'q}^+ = -\dfrac{1}{2h}\sum_r \dfrac{(P_\tau^0)_{q'r}(P_\sigma^0)_{rq}}{\nu_{rq}+\nu} \end{array} \right\}. \quad (443\,a)$$

The electric field strength of the scattered radiation at a distance R,

$$E_\tau(t) = -\frac{1}{c^2 R}\ddot{\bar{P}}_\tau\left(t - \frac{R}{c}\right),$$ is thus given by the formula

$$E_\tau(t) = -\frac{1}{c^2 R}\{[2\pi(\nu-\nu_{q'q})]^2[a_q^{0\dagger} a_{q'}^0 u_{q'q}^- b e^{-i2\pi(\nu-\nu_{q'q})(t-R/c)} +$$

$$+ a_q^{0\dagger} a_{q'}^0 u_{qq'}^- b^\dagger e^{i2\pi(\nu-\nu_{q'q})(t-R/c)}]\} -$$

$$- \frac{1}{c^2 R}\{[2\pi(\nu+\nu_{q'q})]^2[a_q^{0\dagger} a_{q'}^0 u_{qq'}^+ b e^{-i2\pi(\nu+\nu_{q'q})(t-R/c)} +$$

$$+ a_q^{0\dagger} a_{q'}^0 u_{q'q}^+ b^\dagger e^{i2\pi(\nu+\nu_{q'q})(t-R/c)}]\}. \quad (443\,b)$$

Although in the preceding calculation the coefficients a_r, etc., were dealt with as ordinary numbers, the results obtained remain valid if we regard them as operators, since in writing down the products $a_r^\dagger a_s$, etc., we have always preserved the correct order of the factors. The smallness of the first-order coefficients $\Delta_1 a_r$ must be understood to mean in this case the smallness of the average (or probable) values of the corresponding probabilities $|a_r|^2$ (i.e. the predominance of the characteristic values $|a_r|^2 = 0$).

Let us consider separately the special case when the atom is supposed to be initially in a definite state q. The double sum (443) reduces in this case to the single term

$$\bar{P}_\tau(t) = a_q^{0\dagger} a_q^0 w_{qq} (b e^{-i2\pi\nu t} + b^\dagger e^{i2\pi\nu t}), \tag{444}$$

where

$$w_{qq} = -\frac{1}{\hbar} \sum_r \frac{\nu_{qr}(P_\sigma^0)_{qr}(P_\tau^0)_{rq}}{\nu_{rq}^2 - \nu^2}, \tag{444a}$$

and the electric field strength (443 b) to

$$E_\tau(t) = -\frac{(2\pi\nu)^2}{c^2 R} \bar{P}_\tau \left(t - \frac{R}{c} \right). \tag{444b}$$

The scattered radiation has in this case the same frequency as the primary one. This is the so-called simple or Rayleigh scattering. In the general case of equation (443 a) we obtain in addition to this simple scattering a 'combination' or Raman scattering with a number of modified frequencies $\nu \mp \nu_{q'q}$.

In order to obtain the average energy of the scattered rays we must take the square of E_τ or, more exactly, the product of E_τ^+ with E_τ^-. For Rayleigh scattering this gives

$$E_\tau^+ E_\tau^- \sim w_{qq}^2 (a_q^{0\dagger} a_q^0)^2 b^\dagger b,$$

that is,

$$E_\tau^+ E_\tau^- \sim w_{qq}^2 n_q^2 b^\dagger b = w_{qq}^2 n_q b^\dagger b, \tag{445}$$

since the characteristic values of n_q^2 and n_q are the same (1 or 0).

For the Raman scattering the situation is somewhat more complicated. We shall consider separately the scattered rays with the frequency $\nu - \nu_{q'q}$ and those with the frequency $\nu + \nu_{qq'}$.

Taking the time average of $E_\tau^+ E_\tau^-$, according to (443 b) we get

$$J_{\nu-\nu_{q'q}} \sim (\nu - \nu_{q'q})^4 u_{qq'}^- u_{q'q}^- a_q^{0\dagger} a_{q'}^0 a_{q'}^{0\dagger} a_q^0 b^\dagger b,$$

that is,

$$J_{\nu-\nu_{q'q}} \sim (\nu - \nu_{q'q})^4 u_{qq'}^- u_{q'q}^- n_q^0 (1 - n_{q'}^0); \tag{445a}$$

and in a similar way

$$J_{\nu+\nu_{q'q}} \sim (\nu + \nu_{q'q})^4 u_{q'q}^+ u_{qq'}^+ a_q^{0\dagger} a_{q'}^0 a_q^{0\dagger} a_{q'}^0 b^\dagger b$$

or

$$J_{\nu+\nu_{q'q}} \sim (\nu + \nu_{q'q})^4 u_{q'q}^+ u_{qq'}^+ n_q^0 (1 - n_{q'}^0) b^\dagger b. \tag{445b}$$

These results are in harmony with the experimental data and with the elementary theory (due to Smekal) of the Raman effect, based on the idea of photons. In order to secure complete agreement we must make, however, the additional assumption that $\nu_{q'q}$ is positive, i.e. that $W_{q'} > W_q$.

The scattered photon with the decreased frequency $\nu - \nu_{q'q}$ is obtained on this view if the atom was initially in the lower state $(n_q^0 = 1)$, the higher state q' being vacant $(n_{q'}^0 = 0)$. In the contrary case $(n_{q'}^0 = 1, n_q^0 = 0)$ the atom jumps from the higher state to the lower one, adding the energy $h\nu_{q'q}$ to that of the incident photon, which results in the emission of the scattered photon with the increased frequency $\nu + \nu_{q'q}$.

It should be mentioned that the intermediate states r, which determine the intensity of the scattered radiation through the factors $u^{\pm}$, in contradistinction to the final state q or q', need not be vacant, since the corresponding numbers (operators) n_r do not appear in the equations (444 a) and (444 b).—This can be explained by the fact that if some intermediate state r is occupied, the electron starting from the state q, say, is interchanged with the electron in the state r, which passes to the final state q'.

The probability amplitude of such double transitions $q \to r \to q'$ with interchange must be the same as for double transitions without interchange, since the electrons are indistinguishable.

The expressions

$$(\nu - \nu_{q'q})^4 u_{qq'}^- u_{q'q}^-$$

and

$$(\nu + \nu_{q'q})^4 u_{q'q}^+ u_{qq'}^+,$$

which are a measure of the intensity of the scattered radiation with the frequency $\nu \mp \nu_{q'q}$, are in agreement with the expressions (184) derived in § 23 for the probability of the double transitions which are responsible for the scattering.

The preceding theory of the scattering process can be improved by taking account of the damping which is described by adding to the frequency ν_r of each state the imaginary term Γ_r considered above. This correction becomes especially important in the neighbourhood of resonance. We thus get, for example, instead of (444 a),

$$w_{qq} = -\frac{1}{h} \sum_r \frac{\nu_{qr}(P_\sigma^0)_{qr}(P_\tau^0)_{rq}}{\nu_{qr}^2 - \nu^2 + i\nu\Gamma_{qr}},$$

where $\Gamma_{qr} = \Gamma_q + \Gamma_r$ is the damping factor for the line emitted in the transition between the states q and r. This expression remains finite when $\nu = \nu_{qr}$, determining the polarization and intensity of the so-called 'resonance radiation'.

The radiation theory sketched above is inexact in the sense that it does not take into account adequately the retarded character of the electromagnetic actions. This has been done approximately by substituting the difference $t - R/c$ for t, where R is the distance of some point (centre, say) of the atom from the point in question. This approximation does not hold, however, if the wave-length of the emitted or scattered light $\lambda = c/\nu$ is of the same order of magnitude as or smaller than the linear extension of the atom. The electromagnetic field generated by the latter can be determined in this case by the classical expressions for the scalar and the vector potential

$$\left.\begin{array}{l} \phi(\mathbf{r}, t) = \epsilon \int \dfrac{\rho(\mathbf{r}', t - R/c)}{R} \, dV' \\[2ex] \mathbf{A}(\mathbf{r}, t) = \epsilon \int \dfrac{\mathbf{j}(\mathbf{r}', t - R/c)}{R} \, dV' \end{array}\right\}, \qquad (446)$$

where $R = |\mathbf{r} - \mathbf{r}'|$ is the distance of the point considered from some point r' in the volume-element dV' of the electron-cloud. Here ϵ denotes the charge of the electron, while

$$\rho = \psi^\dagger \psi \qquad (446\,\mathrm{a})$$

is the density of the cloud and $\mathbf{j}$ the corresponding current density.‡ According to Schrödinger's theory, the latter is given by

$$\mathbf{j} = \frac{1}{m} \psi^\dagger \mathbf{u} \psi, \qquad (446\,\mathrm{b})$$

where $\mathbf{u} = \dfrac{h}{2\pi i} . \nabla - \dfrac{\epsilon}{c} \mathbf{A}$ is the operator of proper momentum, whereas according to Dirac's theory $\quad \mathbf{j} = \psi^\dagger \boldsymbol{\gamma} \psi, \qquad (446\,\mathrm{c})$

$c\boldsymbol{\gamma}$ being the velocity matrix and ψ the operator corresponding to Dirac's wave function. Substituting for the latter the expression (440), where x is an abbreviation for the geometrical coordinates and the spin-coordinate, we get

$$\rho = \sum_r \sum_s a_r^\dagger a_s \psi_r^{0\dagger}(x) \psi_s^0(x) e^{i2\pi\nu_{rs}t}$$
$$\mathbf{j} = \sum_r \sum_s a_r^\dagger a_s \psi_r^{0\dagger}(x) \boldsymbol{\gamma} \psi_s^0(x) e^{i2\pi\nu_{rs}t}.$$

Before substituting these expressions in (446) we must replace x by x' (coordinates of the point $\mathbf{r}'$) and t by $t' = t - R/c$. Now so long as R is very large compared with the atomic dimensions we can put

$$R = R_0 - \mathbf{n} \cdot \mathbf{r}',$$

where R_0 is the distance of the point $\mathbf{r}$ from the centre (nucleus) of the

‡ More exactly, the operators whose characteristic values are the probable values of the respective densities.

atom and $\mathbf{n} = \mathbf{R}_0/R_0$ the unit vector pointing in the corresponding direction. We thus have

$$\rho(\mathbf{r}', t') = \sum_r \sum_s a_r^\dagger a_s \psi_r^{0\dagger}(x') \psi_s^0(x'') e^{i2\pi\nu_{rs}(t-R_0/c+\mathbf{n}\cdot\mathbf{r}'/c)}$$

and a similar expression for $\mathbf{j}(r', t')$.

Replacing R in the denominator of the integrands in (446) by R_0—which is permissible so long as R_0 is supposed to be sufficiently large—we obtain the following expressions for the electromagnetic potentials,

$$\left.\begin{aligned}\phi(\mathbf{r}, t) &= \frac{\epsilon}{R_0} \sum_r \sum_s a_r^\dagger a_s e^{i2\pi\nu_{rs}(t-R_0/c)} f_{rs}\\\mathbf{A}(\mathbf{r}, t) &= \frac{\epsilon}{R_0} \sum_r \sum_s a_r^\dagger a_s e^{i2\pi\nu_{rs}(t-R_0/c)} \mathbf{g}_{rs}\end{aligned}\right\}, \qquad (447)$$

where

$$\left.\begin{aligned}f_{rs} &= \int \psi_r^{0\dagger} \psi_s^0 e^{i2\pi\nu_{rs}\,\mathbf{n}\cdot\mathbf{r}'/c} \, dV'\\\mathbf{g}_{rs} &= \int \psi_r^{0\dagger} \boldsymbol{\gamma} \psi_s^0 e^{i2\pi\nu_{rs}\,\mathbf{n}\cdot\mathbf{r}'/c} \, dV'\end{aligned}\right\} \qquad (447\,a)$$

The electric and magnetic field strengths can be calculated from (447) with the help of the classical equations

$$\mathbf{E} = -\nabla\phi - \frac{1}{c}\frac{\partial\mathbf{A}}{\partial t}, \qquad \mathbf{H} = \operatorname{curl}\mathbf{A}, \qquad (448)$$

which give (if R_0 in the denominator of (447) is treated as a constant)

$$\mathbf{E} = \frac{i\epsilon}{cR_0} \sum_r \sum_s a_r^\dagger a_s e^{i2\pi\nu_{rs}(t-R_0/c)} 2\pi\nu_{rs}(\mathbf{n}f_{rs} - \mathbf{g}_{rs}),$$

$$\mathbf{H} = -\frac{i\epsilon}{cR_0} \sum_r \sum_s a_r^\dagger a_s e^{i2\pi\nu_{rs}(t-R_0/c)} 2\pi\nu_{rs}(\mathbf{n}\times\mathbf{g}_{rs}). \qquad (448\,a)$$

These expressions are easily seen to satisfy the relations

$$\mathbf{H} = \mathbf{n}\times\mathbf{E}, \qquad \mathbf{E} = -\mathbf{n}\times\mathbf{H}$$

characteristic of the classical radiation field. Indeed the only non-classical feature of the preceding equations besides the quantum frequencies ν_{rs} (which appear just as well in the old Schrödinger theory) is the non-commutative character of the coefficients a_r. This feature becomes manifest, however, only when we pass to the calculation of the electromagnetic energy.

51. Connexion between Quantized Mechanical (Electron) Waves and Electromagnetic Waves

As we have already pointed out, in order to obtain a correct expression for the energy (as well as for the other quadratic quantities) we must split up the linear parameters of the electromagnetic field ϕ, $\mathbf{A}$,

E, H into two parts: ϕ^-, $\mathbf{A}^-$, $\mathbf{E}^-$, $\mathbf{H}^-$ and ϕ^+, $\mathbf{A}^+$, $\mathbf{E}^+$, $\mathbf{H}^+$, corresponding to terms with negative and positive frequencies respectively. The energy density is then represented by the operator

$$\eta = \frac{1}{8\pi}(\mathbf{E}^+\mathbf{E}^- + \mathbf{H}^+\mathbf{H}^-). \tag{449}$$

In a similar way the energy stream (Poynting's vector) is represented by the operator

$$\mathbf{K} = \frac{c}{8\pi}(\mathbf{E}^+\times\mathbf{H}^- - \mathbf{H}^+\times\mathbf{E}^-). \tag{449a}$$

The negative and positive frequency terms of ϕ, etc., should not be identified with the operators ϕ and $\phi^\dagger$ which have been introduced in § 49 with the help of the operators b, $b^\dagger$ of the Einstein-Bose statistics. In fact the electromagnetic waves we are now considering are not plane waves but spreading spherical waves, with amplitudes which vary as the reciprocal distance from the emitting atom and decrease exponentially with the time, the vibration (r, s) being in fact damped according to the law $e^{-2\pi(\Gamma_r+\Gamma_s)t}$. These damped spherical waves are, moreover, quantized in a way different from the plane waves considered before, namely, through the operators $a_r^\dagger a_s$ and $a_s^\dagger a_r$, instead of the operators $b^\dagger$ and b of the previous theory.

It is interesting, however, to note that the operators of these two types are to some extent very similar. If $r > s$ (i.e. $W_r > W_s$), then $a_r^\dagger a_s$ obviously corresponds to $b_{rs}^\dagger$ and $a_s^\dagger a_r$ to b_{rs} (in the sense that the former relate to harmonic terms with positive frequencies and the latter to terms with negative frequencies). Putting accordingly

$$a_r^\dagger a_s = b_{rs}^+ \quad \text{and} \quad a_s^\dagger a_r = b_{rs}^-,$$

we get

$$b_{rs}^- b_{rs}^+ = a_s^\dagger a_r a_r^\dagger a_s = a_s^\dagger a_s a_r a_r^\dagger = n_s(1-n_r)$$

$$b_{rs}^+ b_{rs}^- = a_r^\dagger a_s a_s^\dagger a_r = a_r^\dagger a_r a_s a_s^\dagger = n_r(1-n_s)$$

and consequently

$$b_{rs}^- b_{rs}^+ - b_{rs}^+ b_{rs}^- = n_s - n_r.$$

In the case of an emission due to the transition $r \to s$ the characteristic values of n_r and n_s *after the transition* are $n_r = 0$ and $n_s = 1$, so that the preceding expression reduces to 1, just like $b_\alpha b_\alpha^\dagger - b_\alpha^\dagger b_\alpha$. In a similar way it can be shown that the operators $a_r^\dagger a_s = b_{rs}^+$ and $a_{s'}^\dagger a_{r'} = b_{r's'}^-$ commute with each other unless $r' \neq r$ or $s' \neq s$ (if $r' = r$, then $b_{rs'}^- b_{rs}^+ - b_{rs}^+ b_{rs'}^- = a_s^\dagger a_{s'}$), while b_{rs}^+ always commutes with $b_{r's'}^+$ and b_{rs}^- with $b_{r's'}^-$.

These results seem to indicate that it is neither necessary nor possible to build up a theory of quantized electromagnetic waves in empty space on the basis of the very restricted analogy between these waves and the quantized waves representing the motion of ordinary particles which conform to the statistics of Einstein-Bose. The true relationship between the electromagnetic waves and the quantized electron waves in three-dimensional space is probably much more adequately represented by the fact that the amplitudes of the former are quadratic in the amplitudes of the latter, the 'symmetrical' operators b being thus replaced by quadratic combinations of the 'antisymmetrical' operators a.

The theory of quantized electromagnetic waves developed in § 49 must therefore be regarded as a convenient though artificial method for dealing with radiation problems involving 'spontaneous' transitions, rather than the true picture of a physical reality. As a matter of fact, this method implies that the radiation emitted by an atom which is situated in a rectangular enclosure with reflecting walls *is converted into plane standing waves*, which represent the normal modes of electromagnetic vibrations consistent with the corresponding boundary conditions. Under such circumstances it is not necessary to consider the damped spherical electromagnetic waves which are emitted during the transition of the atom from one state to another, this transition along with the resulting change in the radiation field being described as a transition of the complete system: atom $+$ radiation (in the form of normal vibrations) from one stationary state to another. It should be noted that this is exactly the same type of description as that used in the perturbation theory of ordinary transitions not involving any radiation effects: the transition is not investigated as a process with a definite course in time, it being simply assumed that this process brings the system from one unperturbed state to another.

If we wished to consider the 'spontaneous' transition of the atom from a higher to a lower state as the result of its own radiation field, described by spherical waves, we should use a more complicated perturbation method, involving damped vibrations, the transition appearing not as an instantaneous jump with a certain probability per unit time, but as a continuous process starting at $t = 0$ and ending at $t = \infty$, with an effective duration of the order of $1/A$.

It should be mentioned further that from this point of view (which seems to be the really correct one) the electromagnetic radiation ought to be considered always in conjunction with the matter by which it is emitted, absorbed, or scattered. In fact the radiation enclosed in an empty vessel with perfectly reflecting walls and considered as an independent dynamical system is merely a fiction, since its reflection by the walls is actually due to the absorption and re-emission, or to the scattering, by the atoms constituting these walls. The absorption of radiation which, according to the method of quantized electromagnetic waves in an enclosure, is simply a transition of the absorbing atom from a state of lower energy to that of a higher energy with the accompanying decrease of the energy of the corresponding electromagnetic wave system by just one quantum, must be considered as the result of the superposition on the primary radiation, causing the transition, of the secondary radiation emitted by the atom. This is the picture of the absorption process which is given by classical electrodynamics, and it must remain fundamentally unchanged in a consistent quantum theory, where actual processes must only be replaced by probable ones.

The current idea that the emission of radiation can be due only to a transition of the atom from a higher to a lower state is fundamentally wrong; the converse transition is just as well accompanied by emission of radiation, which, however, cuts down the primary radiation causing the transition, and is therefore manifested as the decrease—i.e. absorption—of the latter.

In the preceding discussion of the connexion between the quantized mechanical (electron) waves and the electromagnetic waves, the former were dealt with as the cause of the latter. This relation can, however, be reversed in the sense that the motion of the electrons is influenced by electromagnetic waves of external origin. This influence has been actually examined already by the method of the perturbation theory in the preceding section (in connexion with the scattering) and especially in § 49. It remains to be seen whether the two types of quantization, assumed for the two kinds of waves, are consistent with each other in this respect.

The expressions obtained in § 50 by the perturbation theory for the amplitudes a_r which were supposed to have initially a characteristic value zero, must obviously satisfy the general commutation relations $a_r^\dagger a_s + a_s a_r^\dagger = \delta_{rs}$, etc. Assuming for the sake of simplicity that all the coefficients a_q^0 but one vanish, we get, preserving the order of all the non-trivial factors involved,

$$a_r^\dagger a_r = \frac{1}{4h^2} \left\{ \frac{|P_{rq}|^2}{(\nu_{rq}-\nu)^2} a_q^{0\dagger} b^\dagger b a_q^0 + \frac{|P_{rq}|^2}{(\nu_{rq}+\nu)^2} a_q^{0\dagger} b b^\dagger a_q^0 \right\}$$

+ a number of harmonically oscillating terms which we shall leave aside, since their average value vanishes.

Now the products $b^\dagger b$ and $bb^\dagger$, whether b and $b^\dagger$ are defined as the amplitude-operators of the Bose-Einstein statistics or as the products of the type $a_p^\dagger a_s$ and $a_s^\dagger a_p$ (with suitably chosen values of p and s) commute with a_q^0 and $a_q^{0\dagger}$. We thus get

$$a_r^\dagger a_r = a_q^{0\dagger} a_q^0 \frac{1}{4h^2} |P_{qr}|^2 \left[\frac{b^\dagger b}{(\nu_{rq}-\nu)^2} + \frac{bb^\dagger}{(\nu_{rq}+\nu)^2} \right],$$

and in a similar way

$$a_r a_r^\dagger = a_q^0 a_q^{0\dagger} \frac{1}{4h^2} |P_{qr}|^2 \left[\frac{bb^\dagger}{(\nu_{rq}-\nu)^2} + \frac{b^\dagger b}{(\nu_{rq}+\nu)^2} \right].$$

We see from these equations that the relation $a_r^\dagger a_r + a_r a_r^\dagger = 1$ will follow from the relation $a_q^{0\dagger} a_q^0 + a_q^0 a_q^{0\dagger} = 1$ only if it is assumed that $bb^\dagger = b^\dagger b$, that is, if b and $b^\dagger$ are treated as *ordinary* (commutable) *numbers*. As to the relations $a_r^\dagger a_s + a_s a_r^\dagger = 0$, etc., they are easily seen to hold (if $r \neq s$); in fact, so long as oscillating terms are dropped, we get separately $a_r^\dagger a_s = a_s a_r^\dagger = 0$.

52. The Quantum Electrodynamics of Heisenberg, Pauli, and Dirac.

The absence of complete harmony between the mechanical and the electromagnetic waves from the point of view of their quantization is a very unsatisfactory feature of the preceding theory. It can be shown, however, to be due, at least to some extent, to the approximate form in which this theory has been developed hitherto. We shall now briefly consider its more exact formulation due to Heisenberg and Pauli. This formulation is at the same time a generalization, which treats the radiation field as but a special case of the electromagnetic field, produced by matter and acting upon it, and includes ordinary electric and magnetic forces, treating them in the same way as radiation effects.

The theory of Heisenberg and Pauli can be condensed into the following equations:

1. The equation of motion

$$[p_t + e\phi + c\boldsymbol{\gamma}\cdot\mathbf{A} + \gamma_0 m_0 c^2]\psi = 0, \tag{450}$$

where ψ is Dirac's one-column matrix with the four components $\psi_1, \psi_2, \psi_3, \psi_4$.

2. The equations of the electromagnetic field

$$\left. \begin{aligned} \left(\nabla^2 - \frac{1}{c^2}\frac{\partial^2}{\partial t^2}\right)\phi &= -4\pi e\psi^\dagger\psi \\ \left(\nabla^2 - \frac{1}{c^2}\frac{\partial^2}{\partial t^2}\right)\mathbf{A} &= -4\pi e\psi^\dagger\boldsymbol{\gamma}\psi \end{aligned} \right\}, \tag{451}$$

with the usual relations

$$\mathbf{E} = -\nabla\phi - \frac{1}{c}\frac{\partial}{\partial t}\mathbf{A}, \quad \mathbf{H} = \operatorname{curl}\mathbf{A} \qquad (451\,\mathrm{a})$$

between the potentials ϕ, $\mathbf{A}$ and the field strengths $\mathbf{E}$, $\mathbf{H}$.

3. The commutability equations expressing the quantization of the mechanical field according to the Pauli-Fermi statistics:

$$\left.\begin{array}{l} \psi(x)\psi^{\dagger}(x') + \psi^{\dagger}(x')\psi(x) = \delta(x-x') \\ \psi(x)\psi(x') + \psi(x')\psi(x) = 0 \\ \psi^{\dagger}(x)\psi^{\dagger}(x') + \psi^{\dagger}(x')\psi^{\dagger}(x) = 0 \end{array}\right\}. \qquad (452)$$

4. The commutability equations for the electromagnetic field in empty space (i.e. in the absence of matter, see below):

$$E_k(x)A_l(x') - A_l(x')E_k(x) = -\frac{hc}{2\pi i}\delta_{kl}\delta(x-x'), \qquad (453)$$

$$\left.\begin{array}{l} A_k(x)A_l(x') - A_l(x')A_k(x) = 0 \\ E_k(x)E_l(x') - E_l(x')E_k(x) = 0 \end{array}\right\}. \qquad (453\,\mathrm{a})$$

The equations (450) and (451) along with the quantum conditions (452) can be considered as a generalization of the equations (410) and (410 b) which have been established in § 46 as the exact equivalent of the Schrödinger theory of a system of electrons described by unquantized ψ-waves in the configuration space, and acting on each other according to Coulomb's law. This generalization consists in the introduction of the finite velocity of propagation c of electromagnetic actions, both in an indirect way—by substituting the relativistic equation of motion (450) for the non-relativistic one (410), and in a direct way—by substituting the equations (451) expressing the law of the retarded action for the Poisson equation (410 b).

The differential equations (451) can be replaced by the explicit expressions for the 'retarded' potentials

$$\left.\begin{array}{l} \phi(\mathbf{r},t) = e\int \dfrac{\psi^{\dagger}(\mathbf{r}',t')\psi(\mathbf{r}',t')}{|\mathbf{r}-\mathbf{r}'|}\,dV' + \phi^0(\mathbf{r},t) \\[2ex] \mathbf{A}(\mathbf{r},t) = e\int \dfrac{\psi^{\dagger}(\mathbf{r}',t')\boldsymbol{\gamma}\psi(\mathbf{r}',t')}{|\mathbf{r}-\mathbf{r}'|}\,dV' + \mathbf{A}^0(\mathbf{r},t) \end{array}\right\}, \qquad (454)$$

where $t' = t - |\mathbf{r}-\mathbf{r}'|/c$; ϕ^0 and $\mathbf{A}^0$ are arbitrary solutions of the homogeneous d'Alembert equations

$$\nabla^2\phi^0 - \frac{1}{c^2}\frac{\partial^2\phi^0}{\partial t^2} = 0, \quad \nabla^2\mathbf{A}^0 - \frac{1}{c^2}\frac{\partial^2\mathbf{A}^0}{\partial t^2} = 0, \qquad (454\,\mathrm{a})$$

satisfying the relation

$$\operatorname{div} \mathbf{A}^0 + \frac{1}{c} \frac{\partial \phi^0}{\partial t} = 0. \tag{454 b}$$

If we put $\phi^0 = 0$, $\mathbf{A}^0 = 0$, that is, confine ourselves to the retarded potentials produced by the motion of the electrons which is described by the operator-function ψ, the action of an electron on itself which may seem to follow from these equations is actually eliminated automatically owing to the commutation relations (452). The equations (452), (450), and (454) (with $\phi^0 = 0$, $\mathbf{A}^0 = 0$) must thus give the adequate description of the mutual action of the electrons allowing for the relativity and retardation effects.

The weak point of the Heisenberg-Pauli theory consists, as it seems, in the introduction of additional quantization rules for the electromagnetic field expressed by the equations (453). These equations do not follow from the equations (451) in conjunction with (452), but are postulated on the basis of the analogy between the light waves and the mechanical waves which describe the motion of particles conforming to the Einstein-Bose statistics. In order to obtain the commutability relations for the electromagnetic field, Heisenberg and Pauli (following an earlier paper by Pauli and Jordan) actually come back to the old mechanical theory of light, considered as vibrations of an elastic ether, and give the quantum-mechanical theory of these vibrations, based on the classical wave equations (454 a). It is indeed possible to write down the latter in a form corresponding to the ordinary Hamiltonian equations of motion of a system of material points for the limiting case when these points constitute a continuous medium. Replacing the classical Hamiltonian equations of the motion of such a continuous medium by the corresponding matrix or wave-mechanical equations, one obtains the equations for the quantized elastic or electromagnetic waves. The photons corresponding to these waves are thus introduced in exactly the same way as the phonons, corresponding to ordinary sound waves (Part I). The energy of electromagnetic (or 'elastic') oscillations of a given frequency ν is thus quantized according to the usual formula $(n+\frac{1}{2})h\nu$ for the ordinary harmonic oscillator. In order to get rid of the $\frac{1}{2}$ it is necessary to modify the definition of the energy in the way shown in § 49 and § 50.

It should be remembered that the above theory refers to the 'free ether', i.e. to empty space, without electric charges. This corresponds to the electromagnetic field which has been denoted above as ϕ^0, $\mathbf{A}^0$. Now such a field can be described, as is well known, without loss of generality by putting $\phi^0 = 0$. Treating the components of the vector $\mathbf{A}^0$ as the coordinates of the particles of an elastic ether described by the Lagrangian function $L = \frac{1}{2} \int (\mathbf{E}^2 - \mathbf{H}^2)\, dV$, one can define the electric field $\mathbf{E}^0 = -\frac{1}{c} \frac{\partial \mathbf{A}^0}{\partial t}$ as the quantity corresponding to the mechanical momentum of these particles. Hence we obtain the commutation relations (453), (453 a) which are merely the ordinary commutation relations

$$P_{kn}\, Q_{ln'} - Q_{ln}\, P_{kn'} = \frac{h}{2\pi i}\, \delta_{kl} \delta_{nn'} \qquad (k, l = 1, 2, 3),$$

etc., for a system of particles 1, 2,..., n,..., n',... in the limiting case when these particles form a continuum.

It should be mentioned that this field can be represented as a superposition of plane harmonic waves—as has already been done in § 49. The commutation relations (453), (453 a) can be replaced accordingly by the relations

$$A_m^\dagger(\mathbf{k}) A_n(\mathbf{k}') - A_n(\mathbf{k}') A_m^\dagger(\mathbf{k}) = -\frac{ch}{4\pi k}\, \delta_{mn} \delta(\mathbf{k} - \mathbf{k}'), \qquad (455)$$

to which we must add the relation

$$\phi^\dagger(\mathbf{k})\phi(\mathbf{k}') - \phi(\mathbf{k}')\phi^\dagger(\mathbf{k}) = +\frac{ch}{4\pi k}\, \delta(\mathbf{k} - \mathbf{k}'), \qquad (455\,\text{a})$$

all other combinations being mutually commutable. These relations can be derived directly from the relations of § 49 for the operators $b^\dagger$, b representing the amplitudes of the harmonic terms with positive and negative frequencies respectively for the limiting case of an enclosure with an infinite volume.

In order to preserve the above commutation relations for the electromagnetic field in the presence of electric charges (electrons) it is necessary to modify Maxwell's equations by the addition of small terms proportional to the expression $P_4 = \operatorname{div} \mathbf{A} + \frac{1}{c} \frac{\partial \phi}{\partial t}$ or to its derivatives, replacing the condition (454 b) by the additional commutation relation

$$\epsilon[P_4(x)\phi(x') - \phi(x')P_4(x)] = \frac{hc}{2\pi}\, \delta(\mathbf{r} - \mathbf{r}'), \qquad (455\,\text{b})$$

where ϵ is the above-mentioned proportionality coefficient which in the final result is set equal to zero.

It has been recently shown by Dirac that it is possible to give a somewhat different (relativistically invariant) formulation of the Heisenberg-Pauli theory for a system consisting of a given number of electrons or indeed of electrified particles of any kind. In Dirac's theory the particles are described by the method of the configuration space, and their mutual action is defined implicitly through their coupling with the quantized electromagnetic field in empty space in conjunction with a certain restrictive condition imposed on the wave function.

Let $\psi(x_1, t_1; x_2, t_2; \ldots x_N, t_N)$ be the wave function of the particles (electrons) *each considered with its own individual time*, and let further $\phi(x, t)$, $\mathbf{A}(x, t)$ be the potentials of the quantized electromagnetic field, satisfying the equations (454 a), (454 b) and the commutation conditions (455). Dirac's equations can then be written as follows:

$$\left(H_k + \frac{h}{2\pi i} \frac{\partial}{\partial t_k} \right) \psi = 0, \tag{456}$$

where

$$H_k = e_k \phi(x_k, t_k) + c\boldsymbol{\gamma}_k \left[\frac{h}{2\pi i} \nabla_k - \frac{e_k}{c} \mathbf{A}(x_k, t_k) \right] + \gamma_{0k} m_0 c^2 \tag{456 a}$$

is the Hamiltonian for the kth particle.

The function ψ must be actually treated as a *matrix* with respect to the stationary states of the field taken alone. These states correspond to the different plane harmonic waves specified by the wave-number vector $\mathbf{k}$ and the polarization quantum number ξ. Associating these with photons, we can regard the above treatment as a particular case of the general method of treating incomplete systems, explained in Chap. VII, § 39, the ignored part (B) of the complete system being the 'photon gas'.

It could be argued that it must be possible in this way to give an adequate description of the mutual action between the particles, inasmuch as their mutual action with the photons [ignored in the equations (454 a)] is represented by the energy operators

$$M_k = e_k[\phi(x_k, t_k) - \boldsymbol{\gamma}_k \cdot \mathbf{A}(x_k, t_k)] \tag{456 b}$$

(the operator $c\boldsymbol{\gamma}_k \mathbf{p}_k + \gamma_{k0} m_{k0} c^2$ corresponding to the energy of the kth particle taken alone).

This is, however, *not* so, for the relation between matter and field is expressed not only by this operator M, describing the effect of the latter on the former, but also by the terms $e\psi^\dagger\psi$ and $e\psi^\dagger\boldsymbol{\gamma}\psi$ on the right side of the equations (451) *which describe the effect of the matter on the field*. It is obviously impossible to get rid of this side of their mutual relationship, and it must be introduced somehow, explicitly or implicitly, into the preceding theory in order to transform it into a theory not only of the motion but also of the *mutual action* between all the particles concerned. This is done by Dirac in the following manner:

Let us come back to the complete system: electrons + photons (electromagnetic field), and let us consider ψ as a function both of the x_k, t_k of the former, and of the x, t of the latter, it being understood that the system is doubly quantized with respect to the photons [which corresponds to the commutation relations (455)]. The equations (454 a), (454 b) will then be rewritten in the form

$$\left[\nabla^2\phi-\frac{1}{c^2}\frac{\partial^2\phi}{\partial t^2}\right]\psi = 0, \qquad \left[\nabla^2\mathbf{A}-\frac{1}{c^2}\frac{\partial^2\mathbf{A}}{\partial t^2}\right]\psi = 0, \qquad (457)$$

$$\left[\operatorname{div}\mathbf{A}+\frac{1}{c}\frac{\partial\phi}{\partial t}\right]\psi = 0, \qquad (457\,\text{a})$$

ϕ and $\mathbf{A}$ being defined as certain operators acting on ψ. The latter equation can be considered as a *constraint* to which the function ψ is subject Now in order to describe the influence of matter on the electromagnetic field this equation must be replaced by the following generalized equation:

$$\left[\operatorname{div}\mathbf{A}+\frac{1}{c}\frac{\partial\phi}{\partial t}\right]\psi = \sum_{k=1}^{N} e_k \Delta(X-X_s). \qquad (458)$$

$X_s = x_s, y_s, z_s, t_s$ and $\Delta(X)$ is the so-called 'invariant delta-function' (introduced by Jordan and Pauli)

$$\Delta(X) = \frac{1}{r}[\delta(r+ct)-\delta(r-ct)] \qquad (458\,\text{a})$$

(it represents a spherical wave concentrated in an infinitely thin layer and travelling with the velocity of light from infinity so as to converge at the point $r = 0$ at $t = 0$ and then diverging again to infinity). Using the relations $\mathbf{E} = -\nabla\phi-\frac{1}{c}\frac{\partial\mathbf{A}}{\partial t}$, $\mathbf{H} = \operatorname{curl}\mathbf{A}$, one obtains accordingly, besides the equations

$$\operatorname{curl}\mathbf{E}+\frac{1}{c}\frac{\partial\mathbf{H}}{\partial t} = 0, \qquad \operatorname{div}\mathbf{H} = 0,$$

which can be considered as identities, the equations

$$\left(\operatorname{curl}\mathbf{H}-\frac{1}{c}\frac{\partial\mathbf{E}}{\partial t}\right)\psi = \left[\nabla\sum_{k=1}^{N} e_k\Delta(X-X_k)\right]\psi,$$
$$(\operatorname{div}\mathbf{E})\psi = -\frac{1}{c}\left[\frac{\partial}{\partial t}\sum_{k=1}^{N} e_k\Delta(X-X_s)\right]\psi. \qquad (458\,\text{b})$$

Let us now put $t_1 = t_2 = \dots = t_N = t = T$, i.e. introduce a common time for all the particles and for the field, and denote the corresponding complete derivative for any quantity f by $\partial f/\partial T$, so that

$$\frac{\partial}{\partial T}[f(t, t_1, t_2, \dots, t_N)]_{t_k = t = T} = \left[\frac{\partial f}{\partial t}+\sum_{k=1}^{N}\frac{\partial f}{\partial t_k}\right]_{t_k = t = T}.$$

Then remembering the relations

$$\frac{\partial A}{\partial t} = \frac{\partial A}{\partial T}, \qquad \frac{\partial \phi}{\partial t} = \frac{\partial \phi}{\partial T}, \quad \text{and} \quad \frac{\partial f}{\partial t_k} = [H_k, f],$$

and with the help of the formula

$$\frac{1}{c}\left[\frac{\partial}{\partial t}\Delta(X)\right]_{t=0} = -4\pi\delta(\mathbf{r}),$$

we easily get, along with the trivial expressions

$$\mathbf{E} = -\nabla\phi - \frac{1}{c}\frac{\partial}{\partial T}\mathbf{A}, \qquad \mathbf{H} = \text{curl}\,\mathbf{A},$$

the equations

$$\text{div}\,\mathbf{A} + \frac{1}{c}\frac{\partial\phi}{\partial T} = 0, \tag{459}$$

and

$$\left.\begin{aligned}\left(\text{curl}\,\mathbf{H} - \frac{1}{c}\frac{\partial\mathbf{E}}{\partial T}\right)\psi = 4\pi\Big[\sum_{k=1}^{N} e_k\boldsymbol{\gamma}_k\delta(\mathbf{r}-\mathbf{r}_k)\Big]\psi \\ (\text{div}\,\mathbf{E})\psi = 4\pi\sum_{k=1}^{N} e_k\delta(\mathbf{r}-\mathbf{r}_k)\end{aligned}\right\}, \tag{459 a}$$

which are equivalent to

$$\left(\nabla^2\phi - \frac{1}{c^2}\frac{\partial^2\phi}{\partial T^2}\right)\psi = -\Big[4\pi\sum_{k=1}^{N} e_k\delta(\mathbf{r}-\mathbf{r}_k)\Big]\psi,$$

and

$$\left(\nabla^2\mathbf{A} - \frac{1}{c^2}\frac{\partial^2\mathbf{A}}{\partial T^2}\right)\psi = -\Big[4\pi\sum_{k=1}^{N} e_k\boldsymbol{\gamma}_k\delta(\mathbf{r}-\mathbf{r}_k)\Big]\psi. \tag{459 b}$$

In the limit $c = \infty$ these equations, together with the equations of motion (456), reduce to the ordinary Schrödinger equation for the N particles in the configuration space *with the mutual potential energy*

$$U = \sum_{k<k'}\sum \frac{e_k e_{k'}}{|\mathbf{r}_k - \mathbf{r}_{k'}|} \quad \text{corresponding to the Coulomb forces.}$$

53. Breit's Formula. Concluding Remarks

The theories of Heisenberg and Pauli and of Dirac have been hitherto in practice rather fruitless, that is, they have not led to any marked progress in the theory of the interaction of electrons. The only improvement over the simple interaction theory based on Coulomb's law is represented by a formula originally derived by Breit from the general equations of Heisenberg and Pauli's theory. Breit's results amount to the following approximate expression for the mutual energy of two electrons

$$W = \frac{e^2}{r} - \frac{e^2}{2}\Big[\frac{\boldsymbol{\gamma}^{\mathrm{I}}\!\cdot\boldsymbol{\gamma}^{\mathrm{II}}}{r} + \frac{(\boldsymbol{\gamma}^{\mathrm{I}}\!\cdot\mathbf{r})(\boldsymbol{\gamma}^{\mathrm{II}}\!\cdot\mathbf{r})}{r^3}\Big] \tag{460}$$

where $c\boldsymbol{\gamma}^{\mathrm{I}}$ and $c\boldsymbol{\gamma}^{\mathrm{II}}$ are the respective velocity matrices of Dirac's theory.

This expression takes account of the electromagnetic (spin-orbit) and magnetic (spin-spin) interaction and also to some extent of the retardation effects. It can be derived in a much simpler way without any use of the Heisenberg-Pauli-Dirac electrodynamics. The simplest and most straightforward of these derivations is the following one due to K. Nikolsky.†

The energy of an electron in an external electromagnetic field specified by the potentials ϕ, $\mathbf{A}$ is given by the formula

$$W = e\phi - e\boldsymbol{\gamma}\cdot\mathbf{A}. \tag{461}$$

Let us imagine that these potentials are due to the retarded action of a second electron *moving classically*. Their values at a given point and instant τ can be expanded in Lagrange's series in the form‡

$$\left.\begin{array}{l} \phi = e \displaystyle\sum_{\mu=0}^{\infty} \frac{(-1)^{\mu}}{\mu! c^{\mu}} \frac{\partial^{\mu}}{\partial \tau^{\mu}}(r^{\mu-1}) \\[3mm] \mathbf{A} = e \displaystyle\sum_{\mu=0}^{\infty} \frac{(-1)^{\mu}}{\mu! c^{\mu}} \frac{\partial^{\mu}}{\partial \tau^{\mu}}\left(r^{\mu-1}\frac{\mathbf{v}}{c}\right) \end{array}\right\} \tag{462}$$

where $\mathbf{v}$ is the velocity of the electron producing the field and r its distance from the other electron at the instant τ. It is natural to think that the quantum theory of the interaction can be obtained from the classical one by replacing the classical time derivatives $\partial \phi / \partial \tau$ by the quantum Poisson bracket expression $[H, \phi] = (2\pi i/h)(H\phi - \phi H)$, where H is the Hamiltonian of the system formed by the two electrons without the interaction term W. The velocity vector $\mathbf{v}$ must naturally also be replaced by the matrix vector $c\boldsymbol{\gamma}$. We thus get

$$\frac{\partial^{n}\phi}{\partial \tau^{n}} = \left(\frac{2\pi i}{h}\right)^{n} \sum_{\nu=0}^{n} (-1)^{n-\nu} C_{n}^{\nu} H^{\nu}\phi H^{(n-\nu)}, \tag{463}$$

where
$$C_{n}^{\nu} = \frac{n!}{\nu!(n-\nu)!}.$$

Here τ corresponds to the common time T of the whole system, that is, of the two electrons (the electromagnetic field being no longer considered as a dynamical system and playing an auxiliary role only). It is natural to define the corresponding energy H as the sum

$$H = H^{\mathrm{I}} + H^{\mathrm{II}}, \tag{464}$$

where H^{I} and H^{II} are the Hamiltonians of the two electrons taken separately, i.e.

$$H^{\mathrm{I}} = c\boldsymbol{\gamma}^{\mathrm{I}}\cdot\mathbf{p}^{\mathrm{I}} + \gamma_{0}^{\mathrm{I}} m_{0} c^{2}, \qquad H^{\mathrm{II}} = c\boldsymbol{\gamma}^{\mathrm{II}}\cdot\mathbf{p}^{\mathrm{II}} + \gamma_{0}^{\mathrm{II}} m_{0} c^{2}. \tag{464 a}$$

† Not yet published. The other derivations are due to Möller, Rosenfeld, and Scherzer.
‡ Cf. my *Lehrbuch der Elektrodynamik*, i, p. 184.

It must not be supposed that this expression for H omits completely the mutual action of the electrons. In fact the operators $\mathbf{p}^{\mathrm{I}}$ and $\mathbf{p}^{\mathrm{II}}$ must be considered as representing the *total* momentum of the respective electrons, including the 'potential momentum' due to its partner, i.e.

$$\mathbf{p}^{\mathrm{I}} = \frac{m_0}{\sqrt{\{1-(v^{\mathrm{I}}/c)^2\}}}\mathbf{v}^{\mathrm{I}} + \frac{e^2}{c^2 r}\mathbf{v}^{\mathrm{II}}, \qquad \mathbf{p}^{\mathrm{II}} = \frac{m_0}{\sqrt{\{1-(v^{\mathrm{II}}/c)^2\}}}\mathbf{v}^{\mathrm{II}} + \frac{e^2}{c^2 r}\mathbf{v}^{\mathrm{I}},$$

$$(464\,\mathrm{b})$$

in agreement with the approximate theory of § 38. This will become more apparent when we compare Breit's formula with the result of the above theory. With the help of (461), (462), and (463) we get:

$$W = W^{\mathrm{I, II}} = e^2 \sum_{\mu=0}^{\infty} \sum_{\nu=0}^{\mu} \frac{(-1)^{2\mu-\nu}}{\mu!} C_{\mu}^{\nu}\left(\frac{2\pi i}{h}\right)^{\mu} [H^{\nu}r^{\mu-1}H^{\mu-\nu} +$$
$$+ \gamma^{\mathrm{I}}H^{\nu}\gamma^{\mathrm{II}}r^{\mu-1}H^{\mu-\nu}], \qquad (465)$$

where
$$H^{\nu} = \sum_{\lambda=0}^{\nu} C_{\nu}^{\lambda} H_1^{\lambda} H_2^{\nu-\lambda}. \qquad (465\,\mathrm{a})$$

Dropping terms of the third and higher orders with respect to v/c (i.e. γ), we have

$$W^{\mathrm{I, II}} = e^2\left(\frac{1}{r} - \frac{\gamma^{\mathrm{I}}\cdot\gamma^{\mathrm{II}}}{r}\right) - \frac{2\pi^2 e^2}{h^2 c^2}(rH^2 - HrH + H^2 r)$$

whence, according to (465 a),

$$W^{\mathrm{I, II}} = e^2\left(\frac{1}{r} - \frac{\gamma^{\mathrm{I}}\cdot\gamma^{\mathrm{II}}}{r}\right) - \frac{2\pi^2 e^2}{h^2 c^2}[rH^{\mathrm{I}}H^{\mathrm{II}} - H^{\mathrm{II}}rH^{\mathrm{I}} - H^{\mathrm{I}}rH^{\mathrm{II}} + H^{\mathrm{I}}H^{\mathrm{II}}r]$$

together with terms which are proportional to the square of H^{I} or H^{II}, which we shall neglect as having no physical meaning (they represent the action of a point-like electron on itself)†.

Now the expression in the brackets [ ] can be put in the form

$$H^{\mathrm{II}}(H^{\mathrm{I}}r - rH^{\mathrm{I}}) - (H^{\mathrm{I}}r - rH^{\mathrm{I}})H^{\mathrm{II}}.$$

Using the formulae (464 a) for H^{I} and H^{II} we get

$$H^{\mathrm{I}}r - rH^{\mathrm{I}} = \frac{h}{2\pi i}\frac{dr}{dt^{\mathrm{I}}} = \frac{h}{2\pi i}\frac{c\gamma^{\mathrm{I}}\cdot\mathbf{r}}{r}$$

and

$$H^{\mathrm{II}}(H^{\mathrm{I}}r - rH^{\mathrm{I}}) - (H^{\mathrm{I}}r - rH^{\mathrm{I}})H^{\mathrm{II}} = \left(\frac{ch}{2\pi i}\right)^2\left[\frac{\gamma^{\mathrm{I}}\cdot\gamma^{\mathrm{II}}}{r} - \frac{(\gamma^{\mathrm{I}}\cdot\mathbf{r})(\gamma^{\mathrm{II}}\cdot\mathbf{r})}{r^3}\right],$$

† These terms are physically irrelevant also for another reason, namely, because the squares of the matrices γ^{I} and γ^{II} are equal to 1 (or rather to 3), whereas they must represent small quantities of the second order with respect to v^{I}/c and v^{II}/c. This difficulty has, however, an origin entirely different from the preceding one, being connected with the existence of states of negative proper energy.

which leads to Breit's formula for $W^{I, II}$, this expression being actually symmetrical with regard to the two electrons.

The classical expression for W corresponding to Breit's formula is

$$W = \frac{e^2}{r} - \frac{e^2}{2c^2}\left[\frac{1}{r}\mathbf{v}^I\cdot\mathbf{v}^{II} + \frac{1}{r^3}(\mathbf{r}\cdot\mathbf{v}^I)(\mathbf{r}\cdot\mathbf{v}^{II})\right]. \tag{466}$$

The second term must obviously represent the effect of the *electromagnetic* interaction between the two electrons with due account of the retardation. Now in the non-relativistic theory of § 38 where this retardation was left out of account, the electromagnetic interaction was shown to correspond to a mutual kinetic energy

$$T = \frac{e^2}{c^2 r}\mathbf{v}^I\cdot\mathbf{v}^{II}, \tag{466a}$$

which is quite different from the second term of (466).

This difference is, however, greatly attenuated if we consider the *total* energy of the two electrons $H + W = H^I + H^{II} + W$, or more exactly the classical expression which corresponds to it and which is obtained if $c\gamma$ is replaced by $\mathbf{v}$, γ_0 by $\sqrt{\{1-(v/c)^2\}}$, and the $\mathbf{p}$'s by the expressions (464 b). We thus get

$$H = \mathbf{v}^I\cdot\left(\frac{m_0}{\sqrt{\{1-(v^I/c)^2\}}}\mathbf{v}^I + \frac{e^2}{c^2 r}\mathbf{v}^{II}\right) + m_0 c^2\sqrt{\{1-(v^I/c)^2\}} +$$

$$+ \mathbf{v}^{II}\cdot\left(\frac{m_0}{\sqrt{\{1-(v^{II}/c)^2\}}}\mathbf{v}^{II} + \frac{e^2}{c^2 r}\mathbf{v}^I\right) + m_0 c^2\sqrt{\{1-(v^{II}/c)^2\}}$$

$$= \frac{m_0 c^2}{\sqrt{\{1-(v^I/c)^2\}}} + \frac{m_0 c^2}{\sqrt{\{1-(v^{II}/c)^2\}}} + \frac{2e^2}{c^2 r}\mathbf{v}^I\cdot\mathbf{v}^{II},$$

and consequently

$$H + W = \frac{m_0 c^2}{\sqrt{\{1-(v^I/c)^2\}}} + \frac{m_0 c^2}{\sqrt{\{1-(v^{II}/c)^2\}}} + \frac{e^2}{r} +$$

$$+ \frac{e^2}{2c^2}\left[\frac{3}{r}\mathbf{v}^I\cdot\mathbf{v}^{II} - \frac{1}{r^3}(\mathbf{r}\cdot\mathbf{v}^I)(\mathbf{r}\cdot\mathbf{v}^{II})\right]. \tag{466b}$$

The first three terms in this expression represent the proper energy of the two electrons and their mutual potential energy, whereas the last one gives the energy of the electromagnetic interaction. Although still somewhat different from (466 a), it is, however, much more similar to it than the corresponding term of W. We obtain a still closer similarity if we average over all the directions of the vector $\mathbf{r}$, considering them as equally probable. We thus get

$$\overline{(\mathbf{r}\cdot\mathbf{v}^I)(\mathbf{r}\cdot\mathbf{v}^{II})} = \tfrac{1}{3}\mathbf{v}^I\cdot\mathbf{v}^{II}r^2,$$

which gives

$$\overline{H+W} = \frac{m_0 c^2}{\sqrt{\{1-(v^{\mathrm{I}}/c)^2\}}} + \frac{m_0 c^2}{\sqrt{\{1-(v^{\mathrm{II}}/c)^2\}}} + \frac{e^2}{r} + \frac{4}{3}\frac{e^2}{c^2 r}\mathbf{v}^{\mathrm{I}}\cdot\mathbf{v}^{\mathrm{II}}. \quad (466\,\mathrm{c})$$

The factor $\frac{4}{3}$ appearing in the last (electromagnetic) term is the same as that which is met with in the calculation of the electron's mass as due to the electromagnetic mutual action of the elements of its charge (supposed to be distributed in a spherically symmetrical way in a finite volume).

The above derivation of Breit's formula is not free from objection, especially with regard to the definition (464) of the energy H. It could be slightly modified by adding W to the expression used before (this would not alter the results to the approximation considered). The important point is that any symmetrization of the expression for H leads to cancelling terms of odd degree in the products of γ^{I} and γ^{II}. The same result is obtained if in the derivation of Lagrange's series for the potentials ϕ and A we replace the *retarded* potentials by the mean value of the *retarded* and the *accelerated* ones. This symmetrization with respect to the time (which has been actually used for a similar purpose by Fokker) is equivalent to the symmetrization of the energy H with respect to the two electrons. This is natural since the time and the energy are dynamically conjugate quantities.

We thus see incidentally that so long as we are using a symmetrical energy operator for two electrons, it is impossible to describe that part of their mutual action which is antisymmetrical in the two particles or in the time and which corresponds to the dissipation of energy by radiation.

This reproach may not be applicable to the accurate form of the Heisenberg-Pauli-Dirac theory. This theory cannot be considered, however, as a satisfactory system of quantum electrodynamics for many other reasons. In the first place it is based on a fundamentally wrong interpretation of the relationship between matter (electrons) and electromagnetic field (photons) as a *formal analogy*, the quantum theory of the electromagnetic field being developed accordingly as a wave-mechanical theory of the 'ether' in a somewhat disguised form adjusted to Maxwell's equations.

A second, more important, reason lies in the fact that material particles are visualized as the primary things in Nature and are dealt with as unextended points with dynamical properties independent of those of the electromagnetic field, while the electromagnetic field is treated as but an auxiliary agent introduced for the description of their mutual action and serving to determine their motion. It seems, however, more reasonable to think that the electromagnetic field is the primary and fundamental thing in Nature, the material particles (electrons and protons) being derivable from it, and possessing no independent mechanical properties. This point of view corresponds to the latest development of the classical electrodynamics, culminating in the *electromagnetic theory of mass*. The mechanical momentum and energy—potential and kinetic —must be interpreted from this point of view as the approximate form of electromagnetic momentum and energy, directly connected not with the particles but with the electromagnetic field. The laws of motion can be derived accordingly from the principle of conservation of electromagnetic momentum and energy, applied to separate electrons, if the latter are considered not as points but as extended bodies (spheres) and if the external force acting on them is supposed to be balanced by the 'inner' force, due to their own motion.

This classical theory which means the complete reduction of mechanics to electrodynamics has met with one serious difficulty, connected with the problem of the spatial extension or 'structure' of the electron. It is responsible for the fact that the electromagnetic theory of mass, or, in other words, the electromagnetic derivation of mechanics, has remained without further development until now. The advent of the quantum theory did not in the least alter the situation, the modern wave or quantum mechanics being simply a modified form of the old mechanics of a point-like particle with a given mass.

Now it seems quite certain that this new theory is in principle just as wrong as the old one, and that the next task in the development of our theory of the physical universe will consist in the application of the quantum ideas to the electromagnetic field in such a way as to obtain the mechanical laws as a corollary from the laws of conservation of electromagnetic energy and momentum. It is to be hoped that the main difficulty of the classical theory connected with the problem of the electron's spatial extension will be eliminated by considering the electron as the *product* (and not the source) of the electromagnetic field, described in a consistent quantum way. One might, for example, define the electromagnetic field as a matrix from the point of view of the space-time manifold, i.e. as a matrix with the elements $(x'|F|x'')$, where x is an abbreviation for x, y, z, t, the diagonal elements representing the probable values of the field at different points $x' = x''$. The electron could be described accordingly with the help of a function $D(|x'-x''|/a)$, similar to a Gaussian function, with a finite parameter a playing the role of the electron's radius, $|x'-x''|$ being the four-dimensional distance between the points x' and x''. We are thus entitled to think that Dirac's equation of motion will be replaced by an equation containing the electromagnetic momentum-energy tensor; the mass of the electron, instead of being introduced *a priori* as a parameter, being derivable from the quantum equivalent for its radius. A closer discussion of this question is, however, hardly possible at the present time.

REFERENCES

§ 4

1. Approximate solution of Schrödinger's equation based on the equation of Hamilton-Jacobi:
   G. WENTZEL, *Zs. f. Phys.* **38**, 518 (1926).
   L. BRILLOUIN, *C. R.* **183**, 24 (1926).
   H. A. KRAMERS, *Zs. f. Phys*, **39**, 828 (1926).
   H. A. KRAMERS u. G. P. ITTMANN, *Zs. f. Phys.* **58**, 217 (1929).
2. The Virial Theorem:
   B. FINKELSTEIN, *Zs. f. Phys.* **50**, 293 (1927).
   A. SOMMERFELD, *Wellenmechanischer Ergänzungsband*, Kap. II, § 9.
3. The motion of a wave packet:
   P. EHRENFEST, *Zs. f. Phys.* **45**, 455 (1927).

§ 5

1. Theory of canonical transformations and of conditionally periodic motion:
   M. BORN, *Atommechanik*, I, ch. ii.
2. Connexion between classical and wave-mechanical average values:
   J. H. VAN VLECK, *Proc. Nat. Ac. Sci.* **14**, 179 (1928).

§ 7

BORN, HEISENBERG, u. JORDAN, *Zs. f. Phys.* **35**, 557 (1926).
P. A. M. DIRAC, *The Principles of Quantum Mechanics*, ch. iii.

§ 9

E. SCHRÖDINGER, *Ann. d. Phys.* **79**, 361 (1926).
W. GORDON, *Zs. f. Phys.* **40**, 117 (1926).

§ 10

On the normalization of wave functions in the case of continuous spectra:
E. FUES, *Ann. d. Phys.* **81**, 281 (1926).
P. A. M. DIRAC, *The Principles of Q. M.*, ch. iv.

§ 11

M. BORN, W. HEISENBERG, u. P. JORDAN, *Zs. f. Phys.* **35**, 557 (1926).
E. SCHRÖDINGER, *Ann. d. Phys.* **79**, 734 (1926).

§ 12

W. HEISENBERG, *Zs. f. Phys.* **33**, 879 (1925).
N. BOHR, *Über die Quantentheorie der Linienspektra*, Braunschweig, 1923.

§ 13

M. BORN u. P. JORDAN, *Elementare Quantenmechanik*.
P. A. M. DIRAC, *The Principles of Q. M.*, §§ 29 and 30.

CHAPTER IV (Transformation Theory)

P. A. M. DIRAC, *The Principles of Q. M.*, ch. v.
M. BORN u. P. JORDAN, *Elementare Quantenmechanik.*
J. v. NEUMANN, *Mathematische Grundlagen der Quantenmechanik* (1932); *Gött. Nachr.* 1927, p. 245.

§ 19

E. SCHRÖDINGER, *Abhandlungen zur Wellenmechanik*, III, S. 85.
BORN, HEISENBERG, u. JORDAN, *Zs. f. Phys.* **35**, 557 (1926).
H. WEYL, *Gruppentheorie und Quantenmechanik*, § 16.

§ 21

P. A. M. DIRAC, *Proc. Roy. Soc.* **112**, 661 (1926).

§ 25

W. GORDON, *Zs. f. Phys.* **40**, 117 (1926).
O. KLEIN, *Zs. f. Phys.* **37**, 895 (1926).

§ 28

P. A. M. DIRAC, *Proc. Roy. Soc.* **117**, 610 and **118**, 351 (1928).
C. G. DARWIN, *Proc. Roy. Soc.* **118**, 654 (1928).
J. FRENKEL, *Zs. f. Phys.* **52**, 356 (1928).

§§ 29, 30

W. PAULI, *Zs. f. Phys.* **43**, 601 (1927).
J. FRENKEL, *Lehrbuch der Elektrodynamik*, i. 294 and 353.
L. H. THOMAS, *Phil. Mag.*, June, 1927, and *Nature*, **107**, 514 (1926).

§ 31

P. A. M. DIRAC, *The Principles of Q. M.*, §§ 74 and 76.
G. BREIT, *Proc. Nat. Ac. Sci.* **14**, 553 (1928).
D. IVANENKO, *C. R.*, 25 Feb. 1929.
V. FOCK, *Zs. f. Phys.* **55**, 127 (1929); **57**, 261 (1929).
W. GORDON, *Zs. f. Phys.* **50**, 630 (1927).

§§ 32, 33

P. A. M. DIRAC, *The Principles of Q. M.*, §§ 76, 77, 78.
A. SOMMERFELD, *Wellenmechanischer Ergänzungsband.*

§ 35

P. A. M. DIRAC, *The Principles of Q. M.*, § 75.
O. LAPORTE and G. UHLENBECK, *Phys. Rev.* **37**, 1380 (1931).
H. WEYL, *Gruppentheorie und Quantenmechanik*, § 39.

§ 36

V. FOCK, *Zs. f. Phys.* **55**, 127 (1929).

§ 37

E. Schrödinger, *Abhandlungen zur Wellenmechanik*, II.
V. Fock, *Zs. f. Phys.* **63**, 855 (1930).
H. Weyl, *Gruppentheorie und Quantenmechanik.*
B. L. van der Waerden, *Die gruppentheoretische Methode in der Quantenmechanik.*

§ 38

W. Pauli, *Zs. f. Phys.* **43**, 601 (1927).

§ 41

P. A. M. Dirac, *Proc. Roy. Soc.* **112**, 661 (1926).
—— *The Principles of Q. M.*, ch. xi.
E. Wigner, *Zs. f. Phys.* **40**, 883 (1927).

§ 42

J. C. Slater, *Phys. Rev.* **34**, 1293 (1929); **36**, 57 (1930).
W. Pauli, *Rapport du Congrès Solvay de 1930*, i, § 4.
P. A. M. Dirac, *The Principles of Q. M.*, § 66.

§ 43

D. R. Hartree, *Proc. Cam. Phil. Soc.* **26**, 85 (1928).

§ 44

V. Fock, *Zs. f. Phys.* **61**, 126 (1930).
P. A. M. Dirac, *Proc. Cam. Phil. Soc.* **26**, 376 (1930).

§ 45

V. Fock, *Zs. f. Phys.* **81**, 195 (1933).
L. H. Thomas, *Proc. Cam. Phil. Soc.* **23**, 542 (1927).
E. Fermi, *Zs. f. Phys.* **48**, 73 (1928).

§ 46

P. Jordan u. E. Wigner, *Zs. f. Phys.* **47**, 631 (1928).
V. Fock, *Zs. f. Phys.* **75**, 622 (1932).

§ 47

P. A. M. Dirac, *Proc. Roy. Soc.* **114**, 243 and 710 (1927).
P. Jordan u. O. Klein, *Zs. f. Phys.* **45**, 751 (1927).
V. Fock, *Zs. f. Phys.* **75**, 622 (1932).

§ 48

P. A. M. Dirac, *The Principles of Q. M.*, ch. xii.

§§ 49, 50

W. Heisenberg, *Ann. d. Phys.* **9**, 338 (1931).
V. Weisskopf u. E. Wigner, *Zs. f. Phys.* **63**, 54 (1930); **65**, 18 (1930).
E. Fermi, *Reviews of Modern Physics*, **4**, 87 (1932).
G. Breit, *Reviews of Modern Physics*, **4**, 504 (1932).

§ 52

P. JORDAN u. W. PAULI, *Zs. f. Phys.* **47**, 151 (1927).
W. HEISENBERG u. W. PAULI, *Zs. f. Phys.* **56**, 1 (1927); **59**, 168 (1930).
L. LANDAU u. R. PEIERLS, *Zs. f. Phys.* **62**, 188 (1930).
P. A. M. DIRAC, *Proc. Roy. Soc.* **136**, 453 (1932).
V. FOCK and B. PODOLSKY, *Sow. Phys.* **1**, 801 (1932).
DIRAC, FOCK, and PODOLSKY, *Sow. Phys.* **2**, 468 (1932).

§ 53

G. BREIT, *Phys. Rev.* **34**, 553 (1929); **36**, 383 (1930); **39**, 616 (1932).
CHR. MØLLER, *Zs. f. Phys.* **70**, 786 (1931).
L. ROSENFELD, *Zs. f. Phys.* **73**, 253 (1932).

INDEX TO PART I

INDEX TO PART II*

* This index does not make any claims at completeness, its purpose being simply to
help the reader in locating the definitions of the main terms and some of the authors
quoted in the text.

PURE MATHEMATICS

ANSCHAULICHE GEOMETRIE by D. Hilbert and S. Cohn-Vossen. Yellow
(Grundlehren) Series. Text in German. English translation of table of
contents. German-English glossary-index. 5-1/2 x 8-1/2. x + 314
pages. 330 illustrations. (Originally published at $10.00). $3.95

AUFGABEN UND LEHRSÄTZE AUS DER ANALYSIS by G. Pólya and G.
Szegö. Two volume set. Text in German. English translation of table
of contents. German-English glossary-index. 5-1/2 x 8-1/2. Volume
I: xxvi + 342 pages. Volume II: xx + 412 pages. (Originally published
at $14.40 for both volumes. Each Volume--$3.95, The Set--$7.90

A CONCISE HISTORY OF MATHEMATICS by Dirk J. Struik. Emphasizes
ideas and continuity of mathematics rather than anecdotal aspects
from Oriental beginnings through 19th century. "... rich in content,
thoughtful in interpretation..."--U. S. Quarterly Book List. Two
volume set. Dover Series in Mathematics and Physics. Bibliography.
Index. 4-1/2 x 6-3/4. Volume I: xviii + 123 pages. Volume II: vi + 175
pages. 47 illustrations.   The Set--$3.00

COURS D'ANALYSE INFINITESIMALE by Ch. J. de la Valle Poussin.
Eighth revised edition. "The handling throughout is clear, elegant and
concise..."--Bulletin of the American Mathematical Society. Two volume set. Text in French. 5-1/2 x 8-1/2. Volume I: xxi + 524 pages. Volume
II: xii + 460 pages.   Each Volume--$4.50, The Set--$8.75

EINFUHRUNG IN DIE ALGEBRAISCHE GEOMETRIE by B. L. van der
Waerden. "Clear, systematic exposition of an important new mathematical development."--Bulletin of the American Mathematical Society. Yellow (Grundlehren) Series. Text in German. 5-1/2 x 8-1/2. ix +
247 pages. 15 illustrations. (Originally published at $7.80). $3.95

EINLEITUNG IN DIE MENGENLEHRE by Adolf Fraenkel. Third revised
edition. "The treatise by Fraenkel on the theory of aggregates is now
one of the finest."--Bulletin of the American Mathematical Society.
Yellow (Grundlehren) Series. Text in German. Bibliography. Index.
5-1/2 x 8-1/2. xiii + 424 pages. 13 figures. $4.00

ELEMENTARY MATHEMATICS FROM AN ADVANCED STANDPOINT by
Felix Klein. Volume I: Arithmetic, Algebra, Analysis. Translated from
the third German edition by E. R. Hedrick and C. A. Noble. "A very at-
tractive introduction into some of the most modern developments of the
theory of groups of finite order, with emphasis on its applications."--
American Mathematical Monthly. Yellow (Grundlehren) Series. Index.
5-1/2 x 8-1/2. xiv + 274 pages. 125 illustrations. $3.75

ELEMENTARY MATHEMATICS FROM AN ADVANCED STANDPOINT by
Felix Klein. Volume II: Geometry. Translated from the third German
edition by E. R. Hedrick and C. A. Noble. "Required reading for any-
one planning to teach high school geometry and... interesting and valuable to the experienced teacher."--School Science and Mathematics.
Yellow (Grundlehren) Series. 5-1/2 x 8-1/2. ix + 214 pages. 141 illustrations. $2.95

DOVER BOOKS ON SCIENCE

GRUNDZÜGE DER THEORETISCHEN LOGIK by D Hilbert and W. Ackerman. Second revised edition. Yellow (Grundlehren) Series. Text in German. Bibliography. Index. 5-1/2 x 8-1/2. xi + 133 pages. (Originally published at $4.50). **$3.00**

MENGENLEHRE by F. Hausdorff. Third revised edition. Text in German. Bibliography. Index. 5-1/2 x 8-1/2. v + 307 pages. 12 illustrations. (Originally published at $10.00). **$3.95**

ORDINARY DIFFERENTIAL EQUATIONS by E. L. Ince. Fourth revised edition. "Notable addition to the mathematical literature in English." --Bulletin of the American Mathematical Society. 4 appendices. Index. 5-1/2 x 9. viii + 558 pages. 18 illustrations. (Originally published at $12.00). **$4.95**

THEORIE DER DIFFERENTIALGLEICHUNGEN by Ludwig Bieberbach. Third revised edition. Yellow (Grundlehren) Series. Text in German. Index. 5-1/2 x 8-1/2. xvii + 399 pages. 22 illustrations. (Originally published at $10.00). **$3.95**

DIE THEORIE DER GRUPPEN VON ENDLICHER ORDNUNG by Andreas Speiser. Third revised edition. Yellow (Grundlehren) Series. Text in German. Index. 5-1/2 x 8-1/2. x + 262 pages. 41 illustrations. (Originally published at $9.00). **$3.95**

THEORY OF FUNCTIONS by Konrad Knopp. Part I: Elements of the General Theory of Analytic Functions. Translated from the fifth German edition by Frederick Bagemihl. "There is little doubt but that this is the best monograph on functions of a complex variable yet written." --American Mathematical Monthly. Bibliography. Index. 4-1/4 x 6-1/2. xii + 146 pages. 4 illustrations. **$1.50**

THEORY OF FUNCTIONS by Konrad Knopp. Part II: Applications and Further Development of the General Theory. Translated from the fourth German edition by Frederick Bagemihl. Bibliography. Index. 4-1/4 x 6-1/2. x + 150 pages. 8 illustrations. **$1.50**

PROBLEM BOOK IN THE THEORY OF FUNCTIONS by Konrad Knopp. Volume I: Problems in the Elementary Theory of Functions. Translated by Lipman Bers. "The difficult task of selecting from the immense material of the modern theory of functions the problems just within the reach of the beginner is here masterfully accomplished."--Bulletin of the American Mathematical Society. Dover Series in Mathematics and Physics. 4-1/4 x 6-3/8. viii + 126 pages. **$1.85**

VORLESUNGEN UBER DIFFERENTIALGEOMETRIE by Wilhelm Blaschke. Volume I: Elementare Differentialgeometrie. Third revised edition. Yellow (Grundlehren) Series. Text in German. English translation of table of contents. German-English glossary-index. 5-1/2 x 8-1/2. xiv + 322 pages. 35 figures. (Originally published at $9.00). **$3.95**

APPLIED MATHEMATICS
AND MATHEMATICAL PHYSICS

APPLIED ELASTICITY by John Prescott. "... important contribution... old material presented in new and refreshing form... many original investigations."--Nature. 3 appendices. Index. 5-1/2 x 8-1/2. vi + 666 pages. (Originally published at $9.50). $3.95

BESSEL FUNCTIONS, Eleven and Fifteen-Place Tables of Bessel Functions of the First Kind to All Significant Orders by Enzo Cambi. The main tables give Jn (x) for x = 0 (0.01) 10.5 and n = 0 (1) 29 to 11 places. A supplementary table gives Jn (x) for x = 0 (0.001) 0.5 and n = 0 (1) 11 to 15 places. Bibliography. 8-1/2 x 10-3/4. Hard binding. vi + 160 pages. 2 graphs. $3.95

FOUNDATIONS OF NUCLEAR PHYSICS. Compiled by Robert T. Beyer. Facsimile reproductions with text in the original language of French, German or English of the 13 most important papers in atomic research by Chadwick, Cockcroft, Yukawa, Fermi, etc. 122 page bibliography with over 5,000 classified entries. 6-1/8 x 9-1/4. x = 272 pages. Illustrated. $2.95

HIGHER MATHEMATICS FOR STUDENTS OF CHEMISTRY AND PHYSICS by J. W. Mellor. Fourth revised edition. "... an eminently readable and thoroughly practical treatise."--Nature. 2 appendices. Index. 5-1/2 x 8-1/2. xxix + 641 pages. 189 figures. 18 tables. (Originally published at $7.00). $4.50

HYDRODYNAMICS by Sir Horace Lamb. Sixth revised edition. "Standard work... important theories (of the dynamics of liquids and gases), which underlie many present-day practical applications, are dealt with thoroughly and with mathematical rigour."--Engineering Societies Library. Index. 6 x 9. xviii + 738 pages. 83 illustrations. (Originally published at $13.75). $5.95

INTRODUCTION TO THE DIFFERENTIAL EQUATIONS OF PHYSICS by L. Hopf. Translated by Walter Nef. "There is a surprising amount of valuable material packed into this small book."--School Science and Mathematics. Dover Series in Mathematics and Physics. Index. 4-1/4 x 6-3/8. vi + 154 pages. 48 illustrations. $1.95

INTRODUCTION TO THE THEORY OF FOURIER'S SERIES AND INTE-GRALS by H. S. Carslaw. Third revised edition. "... needs little introduction... much new material has been introduced (in the present edition)... clearly and attractively written."--Nature. 2 appendices. Index. 5-3/8 x 8. xiii + 368 pages. 39 illustrations. $3.95

DIE MATHEMATISCHEN HILFSMITTEL DES PHYSIKERS by Erwin Madelung. Third revised edition. "Standard... collection of mathematical definitions and formulas and of laws and equations used in theoretical and applied physics."--Electronics Industries.Yellow (Grundlehren) Series. Text in German. German-English glossary. Bibliography. Index. 6 x 9. xvi + 384 pages. 25 illustrations. (Originally published at $12.00). $3.95

DOVER BOOKS ON SCIENCE

MICRO-WAVES AND WAVE GUIDES by H. M. Barlow. Up-to-date exposition which describes both the accomplishments and future possibilities in this increasingly important field. Glossary of symbols used. Bibliography. Index. 5-1/2 x 8-1/2. x + 122 pages. 70 illustrations. **$1.95**

PARTIAL DIFFERENTIAL EQUATIONS OF MATHEMATICAL PHYSICS by H. Bateman. First American edition with corrections. "The book must be in the hands of everyone who is interested in the boundary value problems of mathematical physics."--Bulletin of the American Mathematical Society. Appendix. Index. 6 x 9. xxii + 522 pages. 29 illustrations. (Originally published at $10.00). **$4.95**

PRACTICAL ANALYSIS (GRAPHICAL AND NUMERICAL METHODS) by Fr. A. Willers. Translated by Robert T. Beyer. Section on calculating machines rewritten by Tracy W. Simpson to reflect current methods with American-made calculators. "... is to be recommended as a convenient reference book."--Bulletin of the American Mathematical Society. Index. 6-1/8 x 9-1/4. x + 422 pages. 132 illustrations. **$6.00**

SPHERICAL HARMONICS, An Elementary Treatise on Harmonic Functions with Applications by T. M. MacRobert. Second revised edition. "... scholarly treatment of the type of problems arising in a great many branches of theoretical physics and the tools whereby such problems may be attacked."--Bulletin of the American Mathematical Society. Index. 5-1/2 x 8-1/2. vi + 372 pages. **$4.50**

THEORIE UND ANWENDUNG DER LAPLACE-TRANSFORMATION by Gustav Doetsch. Second revised edition. Yellow (Grundlehren) Series. Text in German. German-English glossary. Bibliography. Index. 6 x 9. xiv + 439 pages. 18 illustrations. Tables of Laplace transformations. (Originally published at $14.50). **$3.95**

THE THEORY OF SOUND by Lord Rayleigh. With an Historical Introduction by Robert Bruce Lindsay. Second revised edition. "... makes this outstanding treatise available again, and furthermore, at a popular price."--Review of Scientific Instruments. Appendix. Index. 5-1/2 x 8-1/2. Volume I: xlii + 408 pages. Volume II: xvi + 504 pages. (Originally published in two volumes at $8.00).
Unabridged One Volume Edition-- **$5.95**

A TREATISE ON THE ANALYTICAL DYNAMICS OF PARTICLES AND RIGID BODIES by E. T. Whittaker. Fourth revised edition. "... exhibits great mathematical power and attainments..."--Bulletin of the American Mathematical Society. Index. 6 x 9. xiv + 456 pages. (Originally published at $6.00). **$4.50**

A TREATISE ON THE MATHEMATICAL THEORY OF ELASTICITY by A. E. H. Love. Fourth revised edition. "... has been for years the standard treatise on elasticity... presents a picture of this extensive field in all its aspects in a single volume..."--American Mathematical Monthly. Index. 6 x 9. xxi + 643 pages. 76 illustrations. (Originally published at $10.50). **$5.95**

PHYSICS AND CHEMISTRY

ATOMIC SPECTRA AND ATOMIC STRUCTURE by Gerhard Herzberg. Translated with the cooperation of the author by J. W T. Spinks. Second revised edition. "...the vector model and the quantum mechanical view are skillfully blended together into a unified description of atomic processes..."--Nature. Bibliography. Index. 5-1/4 x 8-1/4. xv + 257 pages. 80 illustrations. 21 tables. (Originally published at $5.70). $3.95

BIOMETRICAL GENETICS, THE STUDY OF CONTINUOUS VARIATION by K. Mather. Based on the use of measurements, this work examines the pheno-type classes for which older methods of discontinuous variation are useless. 5-1/2 x 8-1/2. x + 158 pages. 16 diagrams. $3.50

COSMIC RADIATION. Edited by W Heisenberg. Translated from the German by T. H. Johnson. 15 articles on recent accomplishments in the field written by eminent German physicists during World War II. Material well integrated with numerous cross references and consistent notation. Bibliography. Index. 6 x 9. xvi + 192 pages. 36 illustrations. 13 tables. $3.95

DESIGN OF CRYSTAL VIBRATING SYSTEMS by William J. Fry, John M. Taylor and Bertha W. Henvis. Second revised edition. Procedures for design of projectors involving a general set of curves based on fundamental piezoelectric relations. "Contains much valuable material released for the first time for general publication."--Electronic Engineering. 4 appendices. 6-1/8 x 9-1/4. viii + 182 pages. 126 graphs. $3.50

THE EVOLUTION OF SCIENTIFIC THOUGHT FROM NEWTON TO EINSTEIN by A. d'Abro. "...covers many more topics than any other popular book in English of which I know, and there are many admirable features in the presentation..."--Physical Review. 4 appendices. 5-3/8 x 8. 544 pages. $5.00

GAS DYNAMICS TABLES FOR AIR by Howard W. Emmons. "The precision of the computations makes the tables adequate for many special uses."--Review of Scientific Instruments. 6-1/8 x 9-1/4. Semi-stiff binding. 46 pages. 3 illustrations. 4 tables. 10 graphs. $1.75

HYDROLOGY. Edited by Oscar E. Meinzer. Chapters by 24 experts on precipitation, glaciers, soil moistures, runoff, droughts, hydrology of limestone and lava-rock terranes, etc. "Most up-to-date and most complete treatment of the subject..."--Bulletin of the American Association of Petroleum Geologists. Physics of the Earth Series. Bibliography. Index. 6-1/8 x 9-1/4. xi + 712 pages. 165 illustrations. 23 tables. (Originally published at $8.00). $4.95

MATHEMATICAL FOUNDATIONS OF STATISTICAL MECHANICS by A. I. Khinchin. Translated by G. Gamow. The most rigorous mathematical discussion available. Dover Series in Mathematics and Physics. Appendix. Notations. Index. 5 x 7-3/8. viii + 179 pages. $2.95

MATHEMATISCHE GRUNDLAGEN DER QUANTENMECHANIK by J. Mann von Neumann. Yellow (Grundlehren) Series. Text in German. German-English glossary. Index. 6 x 9. vi + 266 pages. 4 illustrations. (Originally published at $7.85). $3.95

MATTER AND LIGHT, THE NEW PHYSICS by Louis de Broglie. Translated by W. H. Johnston. 21 essays on present day physics, matter and electricity, light and radiation, wave mechanics and the philosophical implications of scientific achievement. 4-7/8 x 7-3/4. iv + 300 pages. (Originally published at $3.50). $2.75

THE NATURE OF PHYSICAL THEORY by P. W. Bridgman. "It can easily be read in about three hours, but it will then demand to be reread, parts of it several times over."--Review of Scientific Instruments. Index. 5-3/8 x 8. xi + 138 pages. $2.25

THE PHASE RULE AND ITS APPLICATIONS by Alexander Findlay. Eighth revised edition. "It has established itself as the standard work on the subject..."--Nature. Index. 5-1/2 x 8-1/2. xxxi + 313 pages: 163 illustrations. $3.95

POLAR MOLECULES by P. Debye. "This book not only brings together for the first time the accumulated information on electric dipoles, but also points out the gaps which still exist in theory and experiment." --Nature. Index. 5-1/2 x 8-1/2. iv + 172 pages. 33 illustrations. (Originally published at $8.00). $3.50

TABLES OF FUNCTIONS WITH FORMULAE AND CURVES (FUNKTION-ENTAFELN) by Eugene Jahnke and Fritz Emde. Fourth revised edition containing 400 corrections of errors and a supplementary bibliography of 43 titles. Text in German and English. Bibliography. Index. 5-1/2 x 8-1/2. xvi + 382 pages. 212 illustrations. (Originally published at $6.00). $4.95

LES TENSEURS EN MECANIQUE ET EN ELASTICITE by Leon Brillouin. "...first comprehensive treatise in any language on which the main emphasis is laid on the tensorial formulation of the classical (non-relativistic) laws of physics..."--Review of Scientific Instruments. Text in French. Index. 6 x 9. xx + 364 pages. 114 figures. $3.95

TERRESTRIAL MAGNETISM AND ELECTRICITY. Edited by J. A. Fleming. Chapters by 14 leading geophysicists. "An important and authoritative production...making available...the present state and fascinating and difficult problems of this branch of earth science."--Proceedings, Physical Society of London. Physics of the Earth Series. Bibliography with 1,523 entries. Index. 6-1/8 x 9-1/4. xii + 794 pages. 296 illustrations. (Originally published at $8.00). $4.95

TIME, KNOWLEDGE, AND THE NEBULAE by Martin Johnson. Foreword by Professor E. A. Milne. "...succinct and lucid summary of the new cosmology involved in Professor Milne's theory of relativity, of its physical background and of its possible philosophical significance." --London Times. Bibliography. Index. 5-1/2 x 8-1/2. iii + 189 pages. $2.75